The Awakening Interest in Science
during the
First Century of Printing
1450–1550

MARGARET BINGHAM STILLWELL

The Awakening Interest in Science during the First Century of Printing

1450–1550

An annotated Checklist of First Editions viewed from the Angle of their Subject Content

ASTRONOMY · MATHEMATICS · MEDICINE
NATURAL SCIENCE · PHYSICS · TECHNOLOGY

The Bibliographical Society of America
New York
1970

Titlepage vignette from the *De ortu et causis subterraneorum libri V* of Agricola, Basel, 1546; courtesy of The Grolier Club. Initial letter, p. ix, from the *Epytoma in Almagestum Ptolemaei* of Regiomontanus, Venice, 1496; courtesy of The Pierpont Morgan Library, PML 366.

PUBLICATION OF
THE LATHROP COLGATE HARPER LITT.D.
TRUST FUND

Dedicated
with Gratitude and Affection to
DOROTHY CARTER ALLAN
and
DOROTHY MAY SCHULLIAN
in Appreciation of their
Spontaneous and Scholarly Aid
in helping to ready
this Book for the Press

CONTENTS

Part I

Part II

INTRODUCTION

T FIRST THOUGHT, it may seem strange that a person steeped for years in the bibliographical aspects of incunabula should, upon retirement, turn to the study of the history of science. The reason, however, is very simple. It might even be described as circumstance bringing about an inevitable result. It happened that I had the good fortune to become acquainted with Dr. George Sarton, the progenitor of the current interest in the history of science, not long after he came to this country from Belgium during World War I. Drawn by his intensity of interest in his chosen field, I was among the earliest American subscribers to *Isis*, the international journal which he had founded in 1912 as an organ devoted to the history of science and its cultural effects. And in later years, it was with deep appreciation that I learned he had listed me as a recipient for complimentary copies of the forthcoming volumes of his massive *Introduction to the History of Science*, in order that each volume might reach me directly it came from the press.

It also happened that I became acquainted with Dr. Arnold Klebs of Switzerland in the days when his work on scientific incunabula was still a matter of unassimilated notes. Because of our common interests in early printing and in early science, he made it a point to come to see me each year during his annual trips to this country. Thus I shared in his enthusiasm as he discussed his plans and as his checklist of *Incunabula Scientifica et Medica* took form and was finally published.

As the result of all this, there came the realization that there is much more to the study and understanding of incunabula than considerations of rarity, typographical collation, the meticulous identification of undated and unsigned editions, the chronological output of a given press, provenance, or the precise edition in which such innovations as the title-page, and woodcut or metal-engraved illustrations or maps, were introduced. These factors are of interest to us today. To fifteenth-century readers, they mattered not at all. To them, the duplicating of texts through the new mechanical process meant the sudden availability of knowledge. It meant privilege of selection in an ever-increasing supply of printed texts, covering in their authorship a span of nearly two thousand years. It meant the opportunity to have books at hand, to read and ponder.

The texts chosen for printing during the incunabula period, a selection controlled largely by the demands of the market, stood in general for the old order. Thus, they made available the backlog of information and the time-honored concepts of the past. Yet perspective shows that the years following the invention of mechanical printing were a transitional period, a link in the gradual interchange of thought that was to weld together two distinct types of civilization. The books representative of that transition, therefore, warrant special study. And the date when the first printing of each text brought it into general circulation has special relevance.

Dr. Klebs felt this keenly. In his introduction, he presented a strong case for the need of studying "the newly evolving science, so to say, *in statu nascendi*, in the more precise and hence comparable form of textual multiplication and wide dissemination which the printer's art not only permitted but fairly forced upon authors or publishers . . ." To this end, he undertook and achieved the difficult task of separating incunabula of scientific interest from the great mass of fifteenth-century books that treat of theology, literature, philosophy, history, rhetoric, and a host of other subjects. It is unfortunate that, having isolated the scientific books, his work stopped there. In his *Incunabula Scientifica et Medica*, issued as a short-title list preliminary to the comprehensive work he had in mind, the titles are entered in an alphabetical author-list with no indication of the various scientific disciplines to which the books belong. Although of great value, this obviously is only a beginning.

The next step, so it seemed to me, was the assignment of texts to the main scientific categories to which they relate and, so far as possible, to the subdivisions within each category. And my interest in this endeavor has lured me on to the end of the first century of printing, and even beyond the artificial barrier—the Berlin Wall between the fifteenth and the sixteenth centuries—which in bibliographical study has long separated incunabula from later books. In reality, except perhaps for a rousing night as the New Year began, the year 1500 merged into 1501 unnoted. Life flowed on in uninterrupted course. So also did the production of books. So also did the awakening interest in science, as—from the continued printing of manuscripts and newly found texts—the scholars of that time absorbed and discussed the wisdom of the past, now made more and more available through the printing of the early texts and the commentaries of their peers. Step by step they worked toward new scientific knowledge and new concepts of their own.

The present volume on *The Awakening Interest in Science, 1450–1550*, consists of a selection of texts important in themselves or as handbooks typical of the period. It emphasizes their first printing, whether issued separately or with other works. And it is in part the result of a quiet accumulation of notes in an abiding interest over the years. Now that time and the tranquility of country living permit me, I have utilized the opportunity to develop this data further and to assemble it, as recently revised, in compact and usable form. It is not, however, a continuation or development of Klebs, for the approach is quite different. It is intended as another step toward the ultimate and common goal.

ACKNOWLEDGMENTS

In addition to the initial interest aroused by Dr. Sarton and Dr. Klebs and the aid given me by their works, I am indebted for the courtesy and help accorded me by several modern scholars, who have generously given of their time to look through sections of my text with a firm and critical eye. The sections on astronomy and mathematics, for instance, have been read by Professor O. Neugebauer of Brown University, and that on physics by Professor Marshall Clagett of the Institute of Advanced Study at Princeton. I greatly appreciate the suggestions they made and several new titles and monographs which they called to my attention—as also have Professor Lynn Townsend White, Jr. of the University of California, and Curt F. Bühler and Richard Priest of the Pierpont Morgan Library, in their reading of the sections on medicine and technology. And as always, queries sent to Frederick Richmond Goff, Chief of the Rare Book Division at the Library of Congress, have been answered with promptness and efficiency, a special boon to an investigator submerged in a welter of detail. I am indebted also to Albert E. Lownes, a member of The Grolier Club and an avid collector of early scientific works, who from time to time put various rare books of natural science at my disposal, or with personal interest searched the pages of his books for elusive answers to my questions. My best thanks are due all those who have so courteously helped me in my rather complicated task, but none of them is in any way responsible for such errors as I may have made.

The same, of course, holds true in my indebtedness to Dorothy May Schullian, Curator of the History of Science Collections at Cornell University, who put at my command her broad knowledge of the subject and, in various instances in reading the transcript of the text, supplied data not available here. Rare titles listed in her *Catalogue of Incunabula . . . in the Army Medical Library* and in R. J. Durling's 1967 *Catalogue of Sixteenth Century Books in the National Library of Medicine* have greatly enriched the section on medicine.

And it is a pleasure to have this opportunity to thank my friend, Nicea Howard of Providence; David A. Jonah, Director of Libraries at Brown University; Thomas R. Adams, Librarian of the John Carter Brown Library, and Stuart C. Sherman, Librarian of the John Hay Library, at Brown University; the late William A. Jackson, Librarian of the Houghton Library at Harvard University; Gabriel Austin, Chairman of the Publications Committee of The Bibliographical Society of America, and Bert Clarke of the printing-firm of Clarke and Way, Inc., of New York, for their interest and aid in my efforts to make typography the handmaid of bibliography, and bibliography the handmaid of the history of science.

Most of all, I would thank my housemate, Dorothy Carter Allan, who for the last four years has graciously put aside her own interest in writing, in order to help in the prosaic tasks of typing and indexing. Without her aid in a hundred-and-one ways, the present volume could not have been brought out.

METHODOLOGY

The present volume treats of the awakening interest in science in the first century of printing as indicated by texts chosen for duplication through the new mechanical art. It rests on the general premise that, since the early printers were craftsmen intent on selling their wares, as were the heads of the publishing-houses of later date, the books printed were for the most part what they thought would sell; thus the texts chosen reflect the demand, or the interests, of the town or distributing center in which they were issued.

The volume has two main parts. The first records important and typical texts arranged alphabetically by authors under each of the six disciplines with which the volume is concerned—Astronomy, Mathematics, Medicine, Natural Science, Physics, and Technology. The second part undertakes to list the same texts in a single chronology, under the dates of their first printing as found in the present survey. It lists also the authors by periods, the places of printing, the printers and publishers, the commentators, editors, and translators.

The book is a contribution, not an exhaustive work. Nor could it be. It lies beyond the powers of anyone who works alone to treat exhaustively the complete subject-analysis and the bibliographical factors of the books pertaining to six scientific disciplines, issued during a century of book-production. Such a task would take a dozen men a dozen years, if indeed it could be done in so short a time by so small a team—and each man a specialist in his given field.

During recent years, interest in the history of the early sciences has grown rapidly and in some instances deeply. In certain areas of the field the study is far advanced. In others, hardly at all. It is my hope that in its presentation of organized data the present volume may serve as a tool in aiding and hastening this study. Its basic purpose is to classify the books listed and to indicate where further information may be found regarding their bibliographical factors and their subject-content. Throughout its compilation I have been conscious that I was preparing it for the use of two distinct groups, whose tools are altogether different. For this reason, the references I cite may seem verbose to the group already familiar with them, and yet be welcomed by the opposing group.

With the exception of Galen, whose multiplicity of texts called for special treatment, the data assembled in each of the sections relating to the six disciplines follows a given pattern. Each group is introduced by a table of subject-analysis, listing authors under sub-divisions of the main category. Each in its listing of first editions—that is, in the first printing of scientific texts—presents an expansion of the methodology introduced in my 1940 census of *Incunabula in American Libraries* and re-established in the 1964 edition edited by Dr. Frederick R. Goff—both being official publications of the Bibliographical Society of America. The present volume, however, is not a census of copies, although a few instances of location are cited for editions that are of extreme rarity or have some special feature. Many of the bibliographies that are cited under *Ref*, however, provide a key to the location of early editions. For instance, Goff registers American-owned incunabula in 1964. The British Museum catalogue of 15th-century books, *BMC*, is supplemented by the more recently published, specialized, short-title lists—*BM-Ger, BM-Ital, etc.*—which also record later editions up to the year 1600. The *Gesamtkatalog der Wiegendrucke, GW*, gives the location of all incunabula known to be extant today; *i.e.*, up to the point of its publication of authors alphabetically listed. And many other bibliographies listed under *Ref* note the location of copies. Thus, in many instances, if a given edition is desired, the location of a copy may be learned without difficulty.

The similarity of method between this volume and the *Census* consists in the noting of variant author-forms in current use; in the method of incorporating the names of translators, editors, and authors of included commentaries, as an integral part of the title-entry; in the brevity of statement in citing title, imprint, and size; and in the inclusion of a block of notes formally arranged, one beneath the other and comprising (1) bibliographical references, *Ref*, in which technical data regarding title, imprint, and so forth, may be found; (2) on occasion, the listing of additional works, *Add*, which appear in the edition cited; (4) a section of notes, *N.B.*, pertinent to the entry; (4) the listing of monographs, *Mon*, or important articles discussing the given edition, text, or author; and (5) the listing of published facsimiles, *Fac*, or of some portion of the edition cited.

In the matter of the authors' name-forms, it is noteworthy that widely variant usage is often evident among the different disciplines and even within them. Since the present volume is primarily for convenient use, the form seeming to be most generally employed has been accepted for the entry; other forms in current usage are given in parenthesis. The latter, however, are cited as an aid to identification and are not to be mistaken for an exercise in philology or nomenclature.

As an expansion of the original scheme, author-dates have been incorporated, as also have dates for the translator and others whose names appear as part of the entered title—the purpose being that the entry for each edition shall as far as possible present a record of the periods when its text was written, translated, revised, edited, commented upon, and finally printed. In many instances, this is not a matter of years or decades but covers a span of many centuries.

Following the title there frequently appears the laconic phrase [LEK], *later editions known*, indicating a continued interest in the text and its increased availability within the first century of printing. As an aid to clarity and quick identification, dashes are used in PART II and in the INDICES, in order to separate the main categories and their references from one another.

In the block of notes beneath each main entry, the section entitled *Ref* includes bibliographical references relative to the edition cited, and references to works on the history of science consulted regarding the author or given title. The latter are printed in italics, in order to differentiate them from those of a purely bibliographic nature. References to the 1940 and 1964 editions of the census of *Incunabula in American Libraries* are cited under Stillwell and Goff, respectively. However, in notes included under *N.B.*, for the sake of economy in space, their common denominator is employed under the term *Cen*, since the 1940 notations appear in a secondary position in the 1964 edition and can be located without great difficulty. In instances where a work is cited in one but not in the other, the name, Stillwell or Goff, is specified. In Hebrew titles, where the usage is different, both references are given. A list of *Symbols*, *Terms*, and *Abbreviations* is given at the front of the book.

Although other matters are sometimes included, the aims of the *N.B.*

section are (1) to state the basis for judgment in the assignment of dates to such editions as were published without stating their date in colophon or imprint; and to indicate in some measure the continued interest in the work, by citing such subsequent editions within the first century of printing as were noted in the course of the present survey; and (2) to indicate the reason for the assignment of a text to a given category. The full subject-analysis of the texts listed, however, must await the monographs and checklists of a wide range of scholars, as the study of the history of science progresses and develops during the coming years. Controversial discussion has been avoided in the notes, but the fact that controversy exists is frequently indicated by such phrases as *Authenticity questioned, Variously assigned to . . .*, and so forth.

Momentary confusion between the italicized references cited under *Ref* and titles entered under *Mon* may be dispelled by recognition of the fact that the former indicate specific pages or bibliographical notations consulted during the compilation of the present volume, whereas the entries under *Mon* are intended to bring to the attention of the reader various monographs or articles in which he may find data suited to his purpose. The two sections supplement one another and should be so used. It will be noted, however, that under this system there are certain instances in which a specific reference as stated under *Ref* duplicates in part the general reference cited below.

The entries are numbered consecutively in order that, for general purposes, reference to them may be in a single notation. Within the volume itself, however, in the CHRONOLOGICAL TABLE the reference numbers to the main text are given in parallel columns designated for the respective categories, thus making it possible to consider the listed publications either as a whole or as related to a single discipline. Similarly in the Index, the categories, as symbolized by Roman numerals, accompany the references—thus again making it possible either to follow those relating to a given discipline without regard to the others, or to consider the author's works in general. Since some of the early texts treated more than one subject, in about 80 instances it happens that a given work is entered in more than one category, a point made evident in the parallel columns of the CHRONOLOGICAL TABLE. It will be noted that, in the interests of space, only the opening phrase or enough of the title for identification is given in the titles cited.

Instead of entering Galenic titles individually according to the usual pattern, the 150 entries for Galen's works which relate to medicine and natural science have been compressed. Since nearly half of these titles saw their first printing in the Opera of 1490, these are entered under the Opera, thus requiring only a single entry in the CHRONOLOGICAL TABLE and relieving the latter of the burden of citing 73 Galenic titles under the year 1490. The remaining

titles, as listed under medicine and natural science, appear as single-line
entries and have subsidiary numbers under group-headings for fifteenth- and
sixteenth-century imprints. In the INDEX all Galenic titles cited in the present
volume are combined in a single alphabet.

MARGARET BINGHAM STILLWELL

Librarian Emerita of the Annmary Brown Memorial
Professor Emerita of Bibliography, Brown University

"Elfendale"
Greenville, Rhode Island
October 30, 1968

LIST OF ABBREVIATIONS

Reference Works

The references cited below, when appearing under "*Ref:*" in the entries of Sections I–VI in the main text, indicate works quoted as specific sources relative to the edition cited. Reference works and monographs listed under "*Mon:*" in Sections I–VI indicate general sources in which further data may be found.

Afnan	AFNAN, S. M. Avicenna: His life and works. London, 1958.
AmBCat	Catalogue of books . . . from the presses of the first printers. Collected by Rush C. Hawkins and deposited in the Annmary Brown Memorial . . . Catalogued by Alfred W. Pollard. Oxford, 1910.
Arber (1938)	ARBER, A. Herbals: Their origin and evolution. A chapter in the history of botany, 1470–1670. A new edition, rewritten and enlarged. Cambridge, 1938.
Armstrong	ARMSTRONG, C. E. Copies of Ptolemy's geography in American libraries (p. 104–114 in New York Public Library. Bulletin. Vol. 66, no. 2. Feb. 1962).
Artz (MMA)	ARTZ, F. B. The mind of the Middle Ages, A.D. 200–1500. 3rd ed., rev., New York, 1959.
Ascarelli	ASCARELLI, F. La tipografia cinquecentina italiana. Firenze, 1953.
Besterman	BESTERMAN, Th. Early printed books to the end of the sixteenth century. A bibliography of bibliographies. 2nd ed., revised . . . Genève, 1961.
BMC	BRITISH MUSEUM. Catalogue of books printed in the XVth century now in the British Museum. London, 1908–1962. [9 parts to date]. (Lithographed reprint, pts. I–IX, London, 1963.)
BM-Fr	—— Short-title catalogue of books printed in France from 1470 to 1600 now in the British Museum. London, 1924.
BM-Ger	—— Short-title catalogue of books printed in the German-speaking countries and German books printed in other countries from 1455 to 1600 now in the British Museum. London, 1962.
BM-Ital	—— Short-title catalogue of books printed in Italy from 1465 to 1600 now in the British Museum, London, 1958.
BM-Port	—— Short-title catalogue of Portuguese books—printed before 1601 now in the British Museum, London, 1926.
BM-Sp	—— Short-title catalogue of books printed in Spain . . . before 1601 now in the British Museum, London, 1921.

Browne (AM)	BROWNE, E. G. Arabian medicine. Cambridge, 1921.
Bühler	BÜHLER, C. F. Fifteenth century books and the twentieth century. New York, 1952.
Bühler (SI)	—— The statistics of scientific incunabula (*Isis*, 1948, vol. 39, pt. 3).
Burckh (CRI)	BURCKHARDT, J. The civilization of the Renaissance in Italy. Vienna, "Copyright edition" [n.d.].
Burndy (Dibner)	BURNDY LIBRARY, Norwalk, Conn. Agricola on metals [by] Bern Dibner. Norwalk, 1958.
C	COPINGER, W. A. Supplement to Hain's *Reportorium bibliographicum*. 2 parts in 3 vols. London, 1895, 1898, 1902.
Camp	CAMPBELL, M. F. A. G. Annales de la typographie Néerlandaise au XVe siècle. La Haye, 1874. Supplements I–IV, 1878–1890. [For a recent supplement, see below, under Kron.]
Campbell (AM)	CAMPBELL, D. Arabian medicine and its influence on the Middle Ages. London, 1926. 2 vols.
Car	CARMODY, Francis J. Arabic astronomical . . . sciences in Latin translation. Un. of Cal. Press, 1956.
Castiglioni (1947)	CASTIGLIONI, A. A history of medicine. Translated . . . by E. B. Krumbhaar. 2nd ed. New York, 1947.
Castiglioni (Ren)	—— The Renaissance of medicine in Italy. Baltimore, 1934.
Cen	The SECOND CENSUS of incunabula in North American libraries. [For title, see below under STILLWELL.] Its notation, however, appears in a secondary position in the THIRD CENSUS whenever applicable to the latter's entries—as in all instances where the term *Cen* is cited in the *N.B.* notes. Thus the term *Cen* serves as a common denominator for both editions, and is so used in the interests of economy in space.
Choulant (Anat)	CHOULANT, L. History and bibliography of anatomic illustration. Translated . . . by Mortimer Frank. New York, 1952 (Leipzig, 1828; New York, 1920).
Choulant (H)	—— Handbuch der Bücherkunde für die ältere Medicin. Graz, 1956 (Leipzig, 1828).
C&J	CRUMP, C. G. and E. F. JACOBS. The legacy of the Middle Ages. Oxford, 1926.
Clagett (Arch)	CLAGETT, M. Archimedes in the Middle Ages. vol. I. Madison, 1964.
Clagett (GSA)	—— Greek science in antiquity. New York, 1955.
Clagett (Marliani)	—— Giovanni Marliani and late Medieval physics. New York, 1941.
Clagett (SM)	—— The science of mechanics in the Middle Ages. Madison, 1959.
CR	A combined reference to bibliographical works already listed as C and R [*q.v.*].
Crombie (A–G)	CROMBIE, A. C. Augustine to Galileo. London, 1952.

Crombie (A–G) 1961 —— Augustine to Galileo. 2 vols. London, 1961.

Cushing CUSHING, H. Bio-bibliography of Andreas Vesalius. New York, 1943. (reprint, Hamden, Conn., 1962)

De Koning DE KONING, P., *tr.* Trois traites d'anatomie arabes par . . . al-Rāzī . . . [Rhasis; Haly Abbas; Avicenna]. Leide, 1903.

DeR (M) RICCI, Seymour de. Catalogue raisonné des premières impressions de Mayence (1455–67). Mainz, 1911 (Gutenberg-Gesellschaft. Veröffentlichungen VIII–IX).

Destombes DESTOMBES, M. Catalogue des cartes gravées au XVe siècle. Paris, Union géographique internationale, 1952. (Rapport de la Commission pour la bibliographie des cartes anciennes. Fascicule II.)

v. Dommer VON DOMMER, A. Die aeltesten Drucke aus Marburg in Hessen, 1527–1566. Marburg, 1892.

Dreyer (HA) DREYER, J.L.E. A history of astronomy. 2nd ed. New York, 1953.

Duhem (Études) DUHEM, P. Études sur Léonard de Vinci. Paris, 1906–1913 (reprint, Paris, 1955). 3 vols.

Durling DURLING, R. J. A chronological census of Renaissance editions and translations of Galen (p. 230–305 in the *Journal of the Warburg and Courtauld Institutes*. Vol. XXIV, nos. 3–4, 1961). [See also under NLMCat.]

Eames (Sabin) SABIN, J. A dictionary of books relating to America, from its discovery to the present time. New York, 1868–1936. [Cited with reference to entries made during the period when Wilberforce Eames was compiler and editor of the series.]

Einbl Einblattdrucke des XV. Jahrhunderts. Ed: Konrad Haebler . . . hrsg. von der Kommission für den Gesamtkatalog der Wiegendrucke. Halle, 1914 (Sammlung bibliothekswissenschaftlicher Arbeiten. H. 35–36).

First edition The term as used in the present volume denotes the *first printing* of a given text.

Fisch (Pol) FISCH, Max H. Nicolaus Pol Doctor 1494. With a critical text of his guaiac tract edited with a translation by Dorothy M. Schullian. New York, 1947.

Garrison (1929) GARRISON, F. H. An introduction to the history of medicine . . . 4th ed., revised and enlarged. Philadelphia, 1929.

Gft GESELLSCHAFT FÜR TYPENKUNDE des XV. Jahrhunderts. Veröffentlichungen. Leipzig, 1907–.

Goff GOFF, Frederick R. Incunabula in American libraries: A third census . . . New York, 1964. [Includes both the Stillwell and the Goff notations, the latter being distinguishable by the fact that Goff employs a dash between the initial and number, as H-7 (*vs.* H7 as in Stillwell).]

Goff (DGI)	—— The dates in certain German incunabula (p. 17–67 in Bibliographical Society of America. *Papers*. XXXIV 1940).
GPB	GESAMTKATALOG DER PREUSSISCHEN BIBLIOTHEKEN. Berlin, 1935, vol. VII.
Greene (LBH)	GREENE, Edward L. Landmarks of botanical history (p. 13–329 in vol. 54 of Smithsonian Miscellaneous Collections. Washington, 1909/10).
Gutenb-Gesell	GUTENBERG-GESELLSCHAFT.
GW	GESAMTKATALOG DER WIEGENDRUCKE [A-Fa]. Vols. I–VIII, pt. 1. Leipzig, 1925–1940. A detailed catalogue of all known incunabula, with location of copies. [See also under *Einblattdrucke* and under *Nachträge*.]
H	HAIN, L. Repertorium bibliographicum . . . ad annum MD . . . Stuttgart, 1826–38.
Haeb (BI)	HAEBLER, K. Bibliografia ibérica del siglo XV. La Haya, 1903–1917. 2 vols.
Hall (SR)	HALL, A. R. The scientific revolution 1500–1800. London, 1954.
Haraszti (MB)	HARASZTI, Z. Fifteenth-century books (in *More Books*, the Bulletin of the Boston Public Library, Boston).
Harrisse (BAV)	HARRISSE, H. Bibliotheca Americana vetustissima. A description of works relating to America, published between the years 1492 and 1551. New York, 1866. (A supplementary volume of *Additions* bearing the same title was printed at Paris in 1872.)
HC	COPINGER, W. A. Supplement to Hain's *Repertorium bibliographicum* . . . In two parts. London, 1895, 1898, 1902. 2 vols. in 3.
HCR	REICHLING, D. Appendices ad Hainii-Copingeri *Repertorium bibliographicum* . . . Additiones et emendationes. Monachii, 1905–11. 6 vols.; index. (Supplement, 1914.)
Heath (AS)	HEATH, *Sir* Thomas. Aristarchus of Samos, the ancient Copernicus. Oxford, 1913.
Heath (HGM)	—— History of Greek mathematics. 2 vols. Oxford, 1921.
HEHCat	Incunabula in the Huntington Library (Ed: Herman R. Mead). San Marino, California, 1937.
Heitz-Haebler	HEITZ, Paul. Hundert Kalender-Inkunabeln. Mit begleitendem Text von Konrad Haebler. Strassburg, 1905.
Holmy (Alch)	HOLMYARD, E. J. Alchemy. Middlesex, 1957.
Holmy (Chem)	—— Chemistry to the time of Dalton. London, 1925.
Hoover (Agricola)	HOOVER, Herbert C. and Lou Henry Hoover. Georgius Agricola: De re metallica. Translated from the first Latin edition of 1556. New York, 1950 (1st publ., 1912).

List of Abbreviations

Horblit	HORBLIT, H. D. One hundred books famous in science. Based on an exhibition held at the Grolier Club. New York, 1964. (Illustrated with facsimiles.)
HR	REICHLING, D. Appendices ad Hainii-Copingerii *Repertorium bibliographicum*. [See under HCR.]
HTech	A history of technology. Ed: Charles Singer [and others]. 5 vols. Oxford, 1954, 1956, 1957, 1958.
Hunt (Quinby)	HUNT BOTANICAL LIBRARY, Pittsburgh. A catalogue of botanical books in the collection of Rachel McMasters Miller Hunt. Volume I. Printed books 1477–1700 . . . Compiled by Jane Quinby. Pittsburgh, 1958.
IGI	Indice generale degli incunaboli delle biblioteche d'Italia. Compilato da T. M. Guarnaschelli e E. Valenziani. Vols. I–IV, A–R. [Rome] 1943, 1948, 1954, 1965–.
Karp (T)	KARPINSKI, L. C. Trigonometrical works to 1700 (p. 269–283 in *Scripta mathematica*. XII. 1946).
Kennedy (IAT)	KENNEDY, E. S. A survey of Islamic astronomical tables. (American Philosophical Society. Transactions. New series, vol. 46, pt. 2. Philadelphia, May 1956.)
Klebs	KLEBS, A. C. Incunabula scientifica et medica: Short title list. Bruges, 1938; Hildesheim, 1963.
Klebs (Gart)	—— Herbals of the 15th century; Gart der Gesundheit (p. 42–48 in Bibliographical Society of America. Papers. XII 1918).
Klebs (Hortus)	—— Herbals of the 15th century: Hortus sanitatis (p. 48–51 in Bibliographical Society of America. Papers. XII 1918).
Klebs (P)	—— and K. Sudhoff. Die ersten gedruckten Pestschriften. München, 1926.
Klebs-Droz (P)	—— and E. Droz. Remèdes contre la peste. Paris, 1925.
Kron	KRONENBERG, M. E. Campbell's Annales de la typographie néerlandaise aux XVe siècle. Contributions to a new edition. The Hague, 1956.
Kühn	KÜHN, C. G. Medicorum Graecorum opera quae extant. Leipzig, 1821. 26 vols.
LC (LJRCat)	ROSENWALD, Lessing J.: The Rosenwald Collection of illustrated books and manuscripts, of books from celebrated presses, and of bindings and maps, 1150–1950. A gift of Lessing J. Rosenwald to the Library of Congress. [Ed: Frederick R. Goff.] Washington, 1954.
LC (Thach)	LIBRARY OF CONGRESS: Catalogue of the John Boyd Thacher collection of incunabula. Washington, 1915.
L-H	LEHMANN-HAUPT, H. Peter Schoeffer. Rochester, 1950.
Lewes	LEWES, G. H. Aristotle: A chapter from the history of science including analyses of Aristotle's scientific writings. London, 1864.

Lindsay (JC)	LINDSAY, R. B. Jerome Cardan, 1501–1576 (p. 311–317 in *American Journal of Physics*. XVI. 1948).
LJR	Lessing J. Rosenwald, *collector.* [See above under LC (LJRCat).]
Lockw (Benzi)	LOCKWOOD, D. P. Ugo Benzi, Medieval philosopher and physician, 1376–1439. Chicago, 1951.
Maier (AG)	MAIER, A. An der Grenze von Scholastik und Naturwissenschaft, 2nd ed., Rome, 1952.
Maier (VG)	—— Die Vorläufer Galileis im 14. Jahrhundert, Rome, 1949.
Maier (ZG)	—— Zwei Grundprobleme der scholastischen Naturphilosophie, 2nd ed., Rome, 1951.
Manoel II (Cat)	MANOEL II, *King of Portugal*. Livros antigos portuguezes, 1489–1600. Cambridge, 1929.
Mayer (1941)	MAYER, C. F. Bio-bibliography of XVI-century medical authors, Washington, 1941 (*Supplement in* Index Catalogue of the Library of the Surgeon-General's Office, 4th Series, G-volume [VI]).
McGill (VZ)	WOOD, Casey A. *ed.* An introduction to the literature of vertebrate zoology . . . in the libraries of McGill University. Montreal, 1931.
Mich	MICHELITSCH, Anton. Thomasschriften. Graz & Wien, 1913.
Moody-Clagett (MSW)	MOODY, E. A. and M. Clagett. The Medieval science of weights. Madison, 1952.
Mottelay	MOTTELAY, P. F. Bibliographical history of electricity and magnetism chronologically arranged. London, 1922.
Nachträge	Nachträge zu Hain's *Repertorium bibliographicum* und seinen Fortsetzungen. Als Probe des Gesamtkatalogs der Wiegendrucke. Leipzig, 1910.
Neugebauer (ESA)	NEUGEBAUER, O. The exact sciences in antiquity. 2nd ed. Providence, 1957.
Nissen	NISSEN, C. Die botanische Buchillustration, ihre Geschichte und Bibliographie. Stuttgart, 1951. 2 vols. in 1.
Nissen (Herb)	—— Herbals of five centuries. Munich [and Zurich], 1958. (*First issued as:* Kräuterbücher aus fünf Jahrhunderten. Munich, 1956.)
NLMCat	NATIONAL LIBRARY OF MEDICINE. A catalogue of sixteenth-century printed books in the National Library of Medicine. Compiled by Richard J. Durling. Bethesda, Md. [Washington, Supt. of Doc.], 1967. [For *A catalogue of incunabula*, see SCHULLIAN (ArMed).]
Nordenskiöld	NORDENSKIÖLD, E. The history of biology. Tr: Leonard Bucknall Eyre. New York, 1928.
Oates	OATES, J. C. T. A catalogue of the fifteenth-century printed books in the University Library. Cambridge, 1954.

O'Leary	O'LEARY, De Lacy. How Greek science passed to the Arabs. London, 1951 (1st ed., 1948).
Ore (Card)	ORE, Oystein. Cardano, the gambling scholar. Princeton, 1953.
Osler (BO)	OSLER, *Sir* William. Bibliotheca Osleriana: a catalogue of books illustrating the history of medicine and science . . . bequeathed to McGill University. Oxford, 1929.
Osler (IM)	—— Incunabula medica: A study of the earliest printed medical books, 1467–1480. Ed: J. V. Scholderer. Oxford, 1923. (Bibliographical Society. Illus. mon., XIX.)
Palter	PALTER, Robert M., *ed.* Toward modern science. New York, 1961. 2 vols. (Studies in Ancient and Medieval Science.)
Pell	PELLECHET, Marie. Catalogue général des incunables des bibliothèques publiques de France. Paris, 1897–1909. 3 vols. [Abano—Gregorius Magnus.] Posthumous section edited by M.-Louis Polain.
Pennink	PENNINK, R. Catalogue der Niet-Nederlandse Drukken: 1500–1540 . . . in de Koninklijke Bibliotheek 's-Gravenhage. 's-Gravenhage, 1955.
Polain	POLAIN, M.-Louis. Catalogue des livres imprimés au quinzième siècle des bibliothèques de Belgique. Bruxelles, 1932. 4 vols.
Poynter	POYNTER, F. N. L. A catalogue of incunabula in the Wellcome Historical Medical Library. London, 1954.
Pr	PROCTOR, R. An index to the early printed books in the British Museum . . . to the year MD. With notes of those in the Bodleian Library. 2 vols. London, 1898 [nos. 1–9841]. Part II, MDI–MDXX. Section I: Germany. London, 1903 [nos. 9842–12004; BM, only].
Pr-Isaac	——Part II, MDI–MDXX. Section II: Italy, Switzerland, and Eastern Europe. London, 1938. [A supplement to Proctor, by Frank Isaac.]
Price (Equatorie)	PRICE, Derek P. The equatorie of the planetis. Cambridge, 1955.
R	REICHLING, D. Appendices ad Hainii *Repertorium bibliographicum* . . . Additiones et emendationes. [See under HCR.]
RA	SMITH, David Eugene. Rara arithmetica: a catalogue of the arithmetics written before the year MDCI, with a description of those in the library of George Arthur Plimpton. Boston, 1908.
Renouard (Alde)	RENOUARD, A. A. Annales de l'imprimerie des Alde . . . 2me édition. Paris, 1825.
Renouard (Colines)	RENOUARD, Ph. Bibliographie des Éditions de Simon de Colines, 1520–1546. Paris, 1894.
Renouard (Estienne)	RENOUARD, A. A. Annales de l'imprimerie des Estienne . . . Première partie. Paris, 1837.
Riccardi	RICCARDI, P. Biblioteca matematica italiana. Bologna, 1887–93 (reprint, Milano, 1952).

Rosenwald	ROSENWALD, Lessing J., *collector* [See under LC (LJRCat).]
Ruppel (JG)	RUPPEL, A. Johannes Gutenberg, sein Leben und sein Werk. Berlin, 1939; second edition, Berlin, 1947.
Sart	SARTON, George. Introduction to the history of science. 3 vols. in 5. [Washington:] Vol. I, 1953 [reprint of 1927]; II, 1931, 1931; III, 1947, 1948.
Sart (Appr)	—— Appreciation of Ancient and Medieval science during the Renaissance (1450–1600). 2nd ed. Philadelphia [1955].
Sart (GP)	—— Galen of Pergamon. Lawrence, Kansas, 1954.
Sart (HS)	—— A history of science (Ed: Dorothy Stimson). Cambridge [Mass.], 1959. 2 vols.
Sart (SW)	—— Six wings: Men of science in the Renaissance. Bloomington, 1957.
Schullian (ArMed)	SCHULLIAN, D. M. A catalogue of incunabula . . . in the Army Medical Library . . . New York [1950]. [A collection now at the National Library of Medicine, Bethesda, Maryland.]
Schullian (Benedetti)	—— *ed* and *tr.* Alessandro Benedetti: Diaria de Bello Carolino. New York, 1967.
Shaaber	SHAABER, M. A., *ed.* Check list of sixteenth-century editions of Latin authors. Trial edition: A. New York, 1963.
Sigerist (GD)	SIGERIST, H. E. The great doctors, a biographical history of medicine. Translated by Eden and Cedar Paul. New York, 1933.
Singer (SHA)	SINGER, Ch. A short history of anatomy and physiology from the Greeks to Harvey. New York: Dover, 1957. [Originally issued as *The evolution of anatomy.*]
Skelton	SKELTON, R. A. Explorers' maps: Chapters in the cartographic record of geographical discovery. London, 1958.
Smith (HM)	SMITH, David Eugene. History of mathematics. 2 vols. New York, 1923, 1925 (rev., New York, 1929, 1931). See also under: RA.
STC	BIBLIOGRAPHICAL SOCIETY. A short-title catalogue of books printed in England, Scotland, and Ireland . . . 1475–1640. London, 1926.
Stillwell	STILLWELL, M. B. Incunabula in American libraries: a second census of fifteenth-century books owned in the United States, Mexico, and Canada. New York, 1940. [A reference-initial *printed tight against a numeral* (as N108) signifies a second-census entry, both in the *Second census* itself and in the *Third census*, edited by Frederick R. Goff. New York, 1964.] [See also above under Cen and under GOFF.]
Stillwell (I&A)	—— Incunabula and Americana, 1450–1800: A key to bibliographical study. New York, 1931 (reprinted, New York, 1961).
Sudhoff (GES)	SUDHOFF, K. Graphische und typographische Erstlinge der Syphilisliteratur . . . 1495–1496. München, 1912.

Sudhoff-Singer	—— and Ch. Singer. The earliest printed literature on syphilis, 1495–1498. In facsimile. Florence, 1925.
Taton (A&MS)	TATON, René, *ed.* Ancient and Medieval science from the beginnings to 1450. Tr. by A. J. Pomerans. New York, 1963. (History of science, vol. I.) The original edition, in French, was reviewed, p. 445–446 in *Isis* 49 1958.
Taton (BMS)	—— *ed.* The beginnings of modern science, from 1450 to 1800. Tr. by A. J. Pomerans. New York, 1964. (History of science, vol. II.)
Taylor (T&E)	TAYLOR, H. O. Thought and expression in the sixteenth century. 2nd ed., rev. New York, 1930.
Thompson (ML)	THOMPSON, J. W. The Medieval library. Chicago, 1939.
Thornd (HM)	THORNDIKE, L. A history of magic and experimental science. 6 vols. New York, 1923–1941. Vols. 7–8: New York, 1958.
Thornd (MS)	—— Michael Scot. London, 1965.
Thornd (SB)	—— The sphere of Sacrobosco and its commentaries. Chicago, 1949.
Thornd (S&T)	—— Science and thought in the fifteenth century. New York, 1929.
Th-Stan	THOMAS-STANFORD, C. Early editions of Euclid's Elements. London, 1926. (Bibliographical Society: Illustrated monographs, XX.)
Van Ortroy (Apian)	VAN ORTROY, F. Bibliographie de l'œuvre de Pierre Apian (*La Bibliographe moderne*, Mars–Oct., 1901; Besançon, 1902).
Vespasiano	VESPASIANO, da Bisticci, 1421–1498. The Vespasiano memoirs (Tr: William George and Emily Waters). London, 1926.
Voull (B)	VOULLIÉME, E. Die Inkunabeln der Königlichen Bibliothek und der anderen Berliner Sammlungen. Leipzig, 1906.
Voull (DD)	—— Die deutschen Drucker des fünfzehnten Jahrhunderts. Berlin, 1916.
Voull (K)	—— Der Buchdruck Kölns bis zum Ende des fünfzehnten Jahrhunderts. Bonn, 1903.
WellHMed (1962)	WELLCOME HISTORICAL MEDICAL LIBRARY. A catalogue of printed books in the Wellcome Historical Medical Library. I. Books printed before 1641. London, 1962. [See also under POYNTER.]
Wightman (1962)	WIGHTMAN, W. P. D. Science and the Renaissance. An introduction to the emergence of the sciences in the sixteenth century. Edinburgh, 1962. 2 vols.
Wilson (WH)	WILSON, C. William Heytesbury: Medieval logic and the rise of mathematical physics. Madison, 1956.
YULCat	YALE UNIVERSITY LIBRARY. Incunabula in the Yale University libraries by Thomas E. Marston with the collaboration of Leon Nemoy. New Haven, 1955.

Zinner (ALD)	ZINNER, E. Bibliographie der astronomischen Literatur in Deutschland . . . (1448–1629). Leipzig, 1941.

Terms, Names, and Symbols

*	An asterisk or star accompanying a Hain number or that of one of the Hain supplements—designated in the references as H, HC, HCR, or HR—indicates that the work so designated was seen by Hain.
°	A small 'o' placed as a superscript is used to signify the Latin ending of terms describing format, as—f°, folio; 4°, quarto; 8°, octavo; 12°, duodecimo.
[]	In the imprint, the use of square brackets to enclose the date of imprint, place, or printer indicates that the data so enclosed is supplied from some source other than the colophon, imprint, or printer's device.
——	A dash at the beginning of an entry serves to avoid repetition of a phrase having a corresponding position in the preceding title or edition.
	When followed by a colon and title, a dash refers to the preceding author. In other instances, a dash is used to separate categories and references, in the interests of clarity.
36-line Bible type	The type used in the so-called 36-line Bible, an early Bible so designated because the fact that it has 36 lines to the type-page is a means of identification. The type in its use during a period of years reveals certain variations or stages of development known as 'states,' which aid in determining the period or chronological sequence of various undated imprints employing the same type.
Add:	Additional texts which are an integral part of a given volume; usually by other authors than that of the entry cited.
AmBM	Annmary Brown Memorial, Brown University, Providence, Rhode Island.
ArMedL	Army Medical Library [now at the National Library of Medicine, Bethesda, Maryland].
Bdsde	Broadside, a single sheet printed on one side only.
BiblNat	Bibliothèque Nationale, Paris.
BiblR	Bibliothèque Royale, Bruxelles.
BM	British Museum, London. BMC, British Museum *Catalogue*. (See ABBREVIATIONS: Reference Works.)
BMC—Zel group	[See below under Zel.]
BPubL	Boston Public Library, Boston, Massachusetts.
B.S.A.	The Bibliographical Society of America, New York.
c.	*circa*, about.

List of Abbreviations

Cen	The Second Census. Its notations, however, appear also in a secondary position in the Third Census, whenever applicable to the latter's entries—as in all instances where the term *Cen* is cited in the notes in the present volume. Thus the term *Cen* and its accompanying number apply to both the editions of 1940 and 1964, and save essential space in the notes. [For titles, see under STILLWELL and GOFF.]
ChL	Chapin Library, Williams College, Williamstown, Mass.
CHP	Carl H. Pforzheimer, *collector*, New York.
Col.	Column.
Comm.	Commentator or commentators.
Con:	Complete or partial contents of a given work.
Cop:	A note listing registered copies of the edition cited.
Corr:	Corrector or correctors.
CPh	College of Physicians, Philadelphia, Pennsylvania.
d.	Deceased.
Ed:	Editor or editors.
Epon. press	Eponymous press, *i.e.*, a term applied in bibliographical usage to a book issued by an unidentifiable press and made to serve as a center around which other unsigned editions of similar typography are grouped as a means of tentative identification or classification; applicable only to the imprint of the title serving as the focal center.
Fac:	A partial reproduction, unless the citing of the full title of the work indicates a complete facsimile.
ff	Folios or leaves. When used after a page reference, however, the term indicates that discussion of the given subject continues on following pages.
fig.	figure, illustration.
First edition	The term as used in the present volume denotes the *first printing* of a given text.
fl.	Flourished; known or believed to have been living during certain years; preferably the creative years.
f°	Folio, indicating the format of the volume, *i.e.* its original size as indicated by the make-up of the volume.
frag	A fragment, an incomplete copy.
G	Gothic type.
ghost	An edition listed but not known to have been extant; frequently the result of loose statements or repeated error.
GrolC	Grolier Club, New York.
GTSL	General Theological Seminary Library, New York.

List of Abbreviations

HarvCL	Harvard College Library, Cambridge, Massachusetts.
HEHL	Henry E. Huntington Library, San Marino, California.
incunabula	A term used to designate the books issued during the first fifty years after the invention of printing, 1450 through 1500.
ind	Index. Consult index in the work or works cited.
JCBL	John Carter Brown Library, Brown University, Providence, R.I.
Label-title	A caption printed on a preliminary leaf or page, without other text and without printer's signature.
LC	Library of Congress, Washington, D.C.
[LEK]	Later edition[s] known; not necessarily, however, by the same editor, translator, or printer as that of the edition listed. Noted merely as an indication of further interest in the text during the period of the present survey.
LJR	Lessing J. Rosenwald, *collector*. [See also ABBREVIATIONS: Reference works, under LC(LJRCat).]
ll	Lines, the number of lines to the page.
Mon:	Monograph, or a special section or article treating of a given subject.
n.a.	Not after.
n.b.	Not before.
N.B.	A note giving miscellaneous data pertinent to the work or the edition cited.
NewL	Newberry Library, Chicago, Illinois.
[n.d.]	No date given or assigned.
[n. pr.]	No printer known.
NYAcMed	New York Academy of Medicine, New York.
NYPL	New York Public Library, New York.
PML	Pierpont Morgan Library, New York.
Pont. Max.	Pontifex Maximus, the Pope.
PrinUL	Princeton University Library, Princeton, New Jersey.
Pseudo-	Authenticity of authorship questioned or repudiated; spurious.
recast	A term applied to a font of type that has been cast on a new body or base—usually on a smaller base, to permit the printing of more text per page.
Ref:	A note citing bibliographical or literary references [the latter, in italics]. The abbreviations used are listed alphabetically in the section on ABBREVIATIONS: Reference works.
	In general, the numbers accompanying them refer to *pages*—that is, unless in a bibliography the entries are found to be numbered *consecu-*

tively throughout, in which case our numbers refer to its numbered entries. If, however, as is sometimes the case, a bibliography has a *repetitive* or only a *partial* notation, or none at all, both the page and an entry-number are cited, whether actual or supplied—as, respectively, 427:21 meaning "page 427, no. 21"; or 652:[6] meaning "page 652, the sixth item." Roman numerals refer to volumes, except in the rare instances where such a numeral is an integral part of a bibliography's notation system.

Rev:	Reviser; revised in or by.
separate	A term used to indicate a work issued individually, which is also known as a part of a compilation.
[Sine nota]	Without statement of place, printer, or date; without a colophon; defying assignment.
state	A term used to designate a type-font which, although ostensibly the same as the original, shows by slight variations that it has been recast.
Tr:	Translator or translators.
UMichL	University of Michigan Library, Ann Arbor.
unique	The only copy on record.
UTorL	University of Toronto Library, Toronto, Canada.
var, variant	A copy which, although ostensibly the same as an edition described, is slightly different in its type-setting or composition.
Zel	Ulrich Zel, the first printer at Cologne, whose printing career began about 1465.

As the majority of his books are undated, their sequence presents a special problem. This has been elegantly solved, however, in the Proctor *Index* and the British Museum *Catalogue*, with the result that —by taking note of the progressive replacing of letters "h" and "T," the gradual introduction of type recast on a smaller base, and improvement in the method of holding the paper in place (as shown by so-called "pinholes")—it proved possible to group the books in an acceptable and more or less chronological system, as: A) Quartos wholly or mainly in type 96, with the *earlier h and T*, and *four pinholes*; B) Quartos wholly or mainly in *type 96 recast* (96/99), with earlier h and T, and four pinholes; C:1) Quartos showing the earlier T and earlier or *later h*, wholly or mainly in type 96 recast, but with *two pinholes*; C:2) later imprints, *with no pinholes*. As an instance of use, the identification of Gerson—no. 388 in our text—as "Zel group A, no. 3 (BMC)" refers to this system and places the book as no. 3 among Zel's earliest imprints. [*It is on the basis of this system in establishing a chronological sequence, that Zel's undated groups are described herein, as Zel groups A, B, C:1, or C:2.*]

PART I

SUBJECT ANALYSIS FOR ASTRONOMY

[1] ASTRONOMY: Al-Battānī; Al-Farghānī; Alfonso X; Al-Zarqālī; Apianus, *Astronomicum, Declaratio, Isagoge*; Aratos; Aristarchos; Autolycos; Bianchini; Brant; Brudzewo; Campano; Cato; Cleomedes; *De cometis*; Copernicus; Danck; Fracastoro; Gemma; Geminos; Gherardo da Sabbioneta; Jābir ibn Aflah; Leopoldus; Māshā'Allah; Paracelsus; Peurbach; Ptolemy; Regiomontanus; Rheticus; Schöner; Stöffler; Thābit ibn Qurra; Theōn; Torres; Willem Gilliszoon (Aegidii); Ziegler.

[2] ALMANACS and CALENDARS: *Almanach*; Arnaldo de Villa Nova; *Calendarium*; *Cisioianus*; *Computus*; Eck; Engel; Faber von Budweis; Hernsheimer; Honiger; Joannes de Sacro Bosco; Lichtenberger; *Manung* (Turkenkalender); Perlach; Pflaum; *Practica*; *Prognosticatio* (?); Regiomontanus; Stöffler; Zacuto. [For the so-called "Calendar for 1448," see *Planetentafel*.]

[3] ASTROLOGY: 'Abd-al-'Azīz (Alchabitius); Abrāhām ben-'Ezrā; Abu Bakr (Albubather); Abū-l-Hasan (Albohazen); Abū-Ma'Shar (Albumasar); Al-Kindi; Biondo; Bonatti; Ciruelo; Engel; Estwood; Faber von Budweis; Firmicus Maternus; Gaurico; Gerson; Granollachs; Lichtenberger; Manilius; Pico della Mirandola; *Planetentafel*; Ptolemy; Savonarola; Schöner; Servetus; Thomas Aquinas; Torrella. [See also above, under ALMANACS AND CALENDARS. For other writers and their works in this field, see THORNDIKE, Lynn. *A history of magic and experimental science*, 6 vols., New York, 1923–1941; and his paper on *The true place of astrology in the history of science* (p. 273–278 in Isis 46 1955).]

[4] COSMOLOGY: Albertus de Saxonia; Al-Bitrūjī; Amici; Aristotle, *De caelo et mundo, Metaphysica*; Calcagnini; François de Meyronnes; Joannes de Sacro Bosco; Macrobius; Martianus Capella; Maurolico; Melanchthon; Nicolaus de Cusa; Pierre d'Ailly; Plato. [See also above, under ASTRONOMY.]

[5] INSTRUMENTS: [See under TECHNOLOGY.]

I. ASTRONOMY

and Allied Subjects

'ABD-al-'AZĪZ ibn 'Uthmān ibn 'Alī al-Qabīsī (*called* Alchabitius), *d.* 967.

1 Introductorium ad scientiam judicialem astronomiae, sive Libellus ysagogicus (Tr: Joannes Hispalensis, *fl.* 1135–1153). [Mantua: Johann Vurster, 1473] 4°. [LEK]

> *Ref*: GW 842; H 615; Klebs 41.1; *Sart* I 669; Car p. 145.
> *N.B*: Issued by Erhard Ratdolt at Venice in 1482 and again in 1485 (Goff A-362, A-363). Also issued at Venice by Joannes and Gregorius de Gregoriis in 1491 (Goff A-364) and again in 1502 (NLMCat 15). A Venetian edition of 1521, printed by Melchior Sessa and Petrus de Ravanis, contains the author's *Libellus de planetarum conjunctionibus* (BM-Ital 1; NLMCat 16). The commentary of Joannes [Danck] de Saxonia appeared in the 1485 edition and thereafter.

ABRĀHĀM ben-'Ezrā (Aben Ezra; Abraham Avenezra; Abrāhām ben Mē'ēr ibn 'Ezrā), *c.* 1092–1167.

2 In re iudiciali opera (Tr: Pietro d'Abano, *c.* 1255–1315). Venice: Peter Liechtenstein, 1507. 4°.

> *Ref*: NLMCat 2523; BM-Ital 2; *Sart* III 439.
> *Mon*: LEVY, Raphael. *The astrological works of Abraham ibn Ezra.* Baltimore, 1927. THORNDIKE, Lynn. *The Latin translations of the astrological tracts of Abraham Avenezra* (p. 293–302 in *Isis* 35 1944).

3 De luminaribus et diebus criticis. [Padua: Matthaeus Cerdonis] 7 Feb. 1482/83. 4°.

> *Ref*: GW 112; HR 22; Klebs 3.1; *Sart* I 187; *Thornd (HM)* IV 139; Stillwell A5; Goff A-6.

4 De nativitatibus. Venice: Erhard Ratdolt, 24 Dec. 1484 ("M.cccc. lxxxv. nonas Kalendas Ianuarij"). 4°.

> *Add*: BATE, Henri, *c.* 1246–1310. Magistralis compositio astrolabii. Descriptio instrumenti pro equatione planetarum.
> *Ref*: GW 113 (1484); HC *21; BMC V 291; BM-Ital 2; Schullian (ArMed) 2; Klebs 4.1; Stillwell A6; Goff A-7.

Abrāhām ben-'Ezrā (continued)

N.B: Ascribed in the volume to Abraham Judaeus; variously identified with Abrāhām ben 'Ezra, but identity also questioned. Schullian notes that the present work is not to be confused with the latter's *De nativitatibus et revolutionibus earum* (Tr: Pietro d'Abano), or his *Liber de nativitatibus* (Tr: Loys de Langle).

ABŪ BAKR al-ḤASAN ibn al-Khasīb (*called* Albubather; Alhasan), *fl.* 900.

5 De nativitatibus.   Venice: Alovisius de Sancta Lucia, 1 June 1492.   f°.
[LEK]

Ref: GW 835; H *607; BMC V 509; BM-Ital 3; IGI 261; Klebs 36.1; *Sart* I 603; Stillwell A322; Goff A-355.

N.B: According to its text this was translated from the Arabic in 1218.

ABŪ-'l-ḤASAN 'Alī ibn Abī-l-Rijāl (*called* Albohazen; Haly, *filius Abenragel*), *fl.* 1020–1040.

6 Liber in iudiciis astrorum (Tr: Aegidius de Tebaldis, *fl.* 1256. Ed: Bartholomaeus de Alten).   Venice: Erhard Ratdolt, 4 July 1485.   f°.
[LEK]

Ref: HC *8349; BMC V 290; Oates 1763; IGI 4643; Car p. 151; Klebs 35.1; *Sart* I 715; Stillwell H3; Goff H-4.

ABŪ-MA'SHAR GĀ'FAR ibn Muḥammad (*called* Albumasar), *c.* 810–886.

7 Flores astrologiae.   Augsburg: Erhard Ratdolt, 18 Nov. 1488.   4°.
[LEK]

Ref: GW 837; HC *609; BMC II 382; Oates 956; IGI 262; Klebs 37.1; Car p. 92; *Sart* I 568, II 170; Stillwell A323; Goff A-356.

N.B: A brief treatise on prognostications, followed in 1489 by the Ratdolt edition of Abū-Ma'shar's *Introductorium in astronomiam* and of his *De magnis coniunctionibus*, of which the *Flores astrologiae* is possibly an abridgment (LC(LJRCat) 113, 124). For discussion of Abū-Ma'shar as a source in tracing the transmission of Hellenistic science, see p. 171–172 in NEUGEBAUER, O. *The exact sciences in antiquity.* 2nd ed., 1957. The *Flores astrologiae* re-issued by Ratdolt in 1495 was printed again at Venice about 1500 (Cen A324, A325).

Fac: *Deutscher Verein für Buchwesen, Leipzig, 1928 [complete reproduction].*

8 Introductorium in astronomiam (Tr: Hermann Dalmata, *12th century*). Augsburg: Erhard Ratdolt, 7 Feb. 1489.   4°. [LEK]

Ref: GW 840; HC *612; BMC II 382; Oates 959; IGI 264; Klebs 38.1; Car. p. 89; Stillwell A326; Goff A-359.

I. *Astronomy*

9 De magnis conjunctionibus (Ed: Joannes Angelus [Johann Engel, 1463–
   1512]). Augsburg: Erhard Ratdolt, 31 Mar. 1489. 4°. [LEK]

   Ref: GW 836; HC *611; BMC II 383; Oates 960; IGI 265; Klebs 39.1; Schullian
   (ArMed) 29; Stillwell A327; Goff A-360.
   N.B: Published at the expense of Melchior Sessa at Venice in 1515 (NLMCat 19).

AL-BATTĀNĪ (*called* Abategnius; Albetegnius), *d.* 929.

10 De motu stellarum ex observationibus tum propriis tum Ptolemaei,
   omnia cum demonstrationibus geometricis et additionibus Ioannis de
   Regiomonte (Tr: Plato Tiburtinus [Plato of Tivoli], *fl.* 1140). (*Issued
   with* AL-FARGHĀNĪ. Compilatio astronomica. Nuremberg: Joannes
   Petreius, 1537).

   Ref: Kennedy (IAT) 55; BM-Ger 11; *Sart* I 602, II 177–179; *Palter* II 143.
   N.B: Based on the *Planetary Hypotheses* controversially assigned to Ptolemy; with new
   observational data by Al-Battānī. The present edition, in fact, includes the works
   of Al-Battānī and Al-Farghānī, the leading Arabic transmitters of these so-called
   Ptolemaic theories, together with data by Regiomontanus, *d.* 1476. The Al-
   Farghānī, however, had already been published at Ferrara in 1493 [*q.v.*].
   Mon: NALLINO, C. A. *Al-Battāni sive Albatenii opus astronomicum*, Milan, 1899–1907.
   3v. [For an abstract of Al-Battānī's text see Kennedy (IAT) p. 154–156.]

ALBERTUS de Saxonia (Albertus de Ricmestorp), *c.* 1330–1390.

11 Quaestiones in Aristotelis libros De caelo et mundo. Pavia: Antonius
   Carcanus, 11 May 1481. f°. [LEK]

   Ref: GW 795; H 575; IGI 250; Klebs 30.1; *Sart* III 1428; Stillwell A316; Goff A-346.
   N.B: Includes discussion of the diurnal rotation of the earth. Its author and François
   de Meyronnes are said to have been responsible for the report that one or more
   contemporary scholars had presented the theory favorably at the University of
   Paris during the fourteenth century.

AL-BIṬRŪJĪ (*called* Alpetragius), *fl.* 1200.

12 Alpetragii arabi planetarum theorica physicis rationibus probata
   nuperrime latinis litteris mandata a Calo Calonymos hebreo neapolitano
   (Tr: Qalonymos ben David, *fl.* 1528). (*Issued with* JOANNES de
   Sacrobosco. Sphera mundi. Venice: Lucantonio Giunta, March 1531.)

   Ref: BM-Ital 597; Car p. 166; *Sart* II 399, 579; *Dreyer* (HA) 264–267; *Clagett* (SM) 515.
   N.B: A work which introduced Alpetragian cosmology, a theory of spiral motion.
   The present translation of 1528, made from a Hebrew version, is claimed in Dr.
   Carmody's collation to be closer to the Arabic than that made in 1217 by Michael
   Scotus.

I. *Astronomy*

Al-Biṭrūgī (continued)

Mon: CARMODY, Francis J. *Regiomontanus' notes on al-Biṭrūjī's astronomy* (p. 121–130 in *Isis* 42 1951); and *Al-Biṭrūjī de motibus caelorum. Critical edition of the Latin translation of Michael Scot.* Berkeley, 1952 (reviewed in *Isis* 44 1953, p. 280). MAIER, A. *Zwei Grundprobleme der scholastischen Naturphilosophie.* 2nd ed. Rome, 1951, p. 127–129.

AL-FARGHĀNĪ (*called* Alfraganus), *fl.* 863.

13 Compilatio astronomica sive De scientia astrorum (Tr: Joannes Hispalensis, *fl.* 1140). Ferrara: Andreas Belfortis, 3 Sept. 1493. 4°. [LEK]

Ref: GW 1268; HC *822; BMC VI 605; IGI 351; Klebs 51.1; *Sart* I 567, 603; *Palter* II 143; *Crombie (A–G)* 1961 I 48; Stillwell A414; Goff A-460.

N.B: A work which—together with the *De motu stellarum* of al-Battānī—was largely responsible for the transmission of the *Planetary hypotheses* sometimes called "the second Ptolemaic system," a transmission brought about through the translation of their Arabic texts into twelfth-century Latin. Known also as *Elementa astronomica*.

Mon: THORNDIKE, L. *John of Seville* [a discussion of identity] (p. 20–38 in *Speculum* 34 1959).

Fac: *Osiris* 5 1938, *fig.* 17.

ALFONSO X, *King of Castile and Leon*, 1221–1284.

14 Tabulae astronomicae. [Venice:] Erhard Ratdolt, 4 July 1483. 4°. [LEK]

Add: JOHANN [Danck] de Saxonia. Canones in tabulas Alphonsi.

Ref: GW 1257; H *868; BMC V 287; Klebs 50.1; *Sart* III 650; *Crombie (A–G)* 1961 I 48; *Taton (A&MS)* 485; Stillwell A473; Goff A-534.

N.B: Wightman (1962) II 115 discusses the transition through which the theory of the tenth sphere as the *primum mobile* was presented in the Alfonsine Tables of 1252. The present modification of the tables was made at Paris by Jean de Linières, *c.* 1320–1350, and his pupil, Johann [Danck] de Saxonia, *c.* 1327–1355. The 1492 Venice edition of the *Tabulae* contains additions by Augustinus Moravus, and the *Canones in tabulae Alphonsi* of Johann Lucilius Santritter, *fl.* 1480 (GW 1258; Cen A474). According to Taton, the Alfonsine Tables were improvements of the Toledan Tables of Al-Zarqālī, *c.* 1029–1100 [*q.v.*].

Mon: DREYER, J. L. E. *On the original form of the Alfonsine Tables* (p. 243–262 in ROYAL ASTRONOMICAL SOCIETY. *Monthly notices*, LXXX).

AL-KINDĪ (Ya 'qūb ibn Isḥāq ibn aṣ-Ṣabbaḥ al-Kindī), *fl.* 870.

15 De iudiciis astrorum. Venice: Petrus Liechtenstein, 1507.

Ref: BM-Ital 739; Car p. 78; *Sart* I 559.

N.B: Written by a Muslim philosopher, whose texts included many aspects of science.

Mon: ROSENTHAL, Franz. *Al-Kindi and Ptolemy* (p. 436–456 in *Studi orientalistici in onore di Giorgio Levi della Vida*. II. 1956).

ALMANACH.

16 Almanach für Wien auf das Jahr 1462 [*German*]. [Germany: Anonymous printer, 1461.] Bdsde. 52 11.

Ref: GW 1287; Einbl 115.

Cop: Donaueschingen.

N.B: Considering the ephemeral character of almanacs, a surprising number of fragments and specimens are extant, their survival due in some instances to the fact that they were used as padding in early bindings. The *Gesamtkatalog der Wiegendrucke*, for instance, has 284 entries under *Almanach* in its text and addenda, and in addition gives cross-references to 66 astronomers whose almanacs were printed before 1501.

Fac: HEITZ-HAEBLER. *100 Kalender-Inkunabeln*, no. 2.

AL-ZARQĀLĪ (*called* Arzachel), *c.* 1029–1100.

17 Canones sive Regule super tabulas astronomie. Canones in tabulas tholetanas [*i.e., the Toledo Tables*]. (Ed: Johann Schöner, 1477–1547). Nuremberg, 1534.

Ref: Car p. 157; *Taton (A&MS) 484–485.*

AMICO, Giovanni Battista, 1512–1538.

18 De motibus corporum coelestium iuxta principia peripatetica sine excentricis & epicyclis. Venice: Joannes Patavinus and Venturinus Ruffinellus, 1536. 4°. [LEK]

Ref: BM-Ital 25; *Dreyer (HA)* 301–303; *Thornd (HM)* V 489; *Taton (BMS)* 56.

N.B: The author reviews the theories of Eudoxos and of Aristotle and adds some cosmological theories of his own to the ancient homocentric system.

APIANUS, Petrus (Peter Bienewitz, *called* Apian), 1495–1552.

19 Astronomicum Caesareum. Ingolstadt: In aedibus nostris, 1540. f°.

Ref: BM-Ger 8; Van Ortroy (Apian) 112; *Price (Equatorie)* 132.

N.B: A handsome volume, with thirty-seven full-page volvelles or revolving discs, in accord with Apian's belief that diagrams with movable parts are of greater aid than mathematical tables in solving astronomical problems. In fact, his volvelles are so constructed that each may function as an equatorium without the need of employing planetary tables. Those in the present volume relate to the calculation

Apianus (continued)

of the longitude of Mars. Published with a privilege for thirty years granted by Charles V on 3 July 1532. Part II contains *Observationes cometarum quinque*, including an account of the comet of 1531. The final section on the torquetum had been issued in Apian's *Introductio geographica*, Ingolstadt, 1533.

Mon: IONIDES, S. A. *Caesar's astronomy (Astronomicum Caesareum) by Peter Apian* (p. 356–389 in *Osiris* 1, 1936). [For a brief description and account of the relation of this work to the times, see PRICE (Equatorie). Of Apian himself a rather devastating appraisal was given by Kepler—see vol. III, p. 142 of the Caspar edition of his works, Munich, 1937.]

20 Declaratio et usus typi cosmographici. Regensburg: Paulus Khol [1522]. 4°.

Ref: Van Ortroy (Apian) 12; Shaaber, p. 99.
N.B: Variant known.

21 Instrumentum primi mobilis. Nuremberg: Joannes Petreius, 1534. f°. [LEK]

Add: JĀBIR ibn Aflah (Geber ibn Aphlas), *fl.* 1140. De astronomia libri IX (Tr: Gherardo da Cremona, 1114–1187).
Ref: BM-Ger 37; Van Ortroy (Apian) 107; Car p. 163.
N.B: With "Tabula sinuum rectorum." According to van Ortroy (Apian) 108, Apian's *Instrumentum sinuum, seu Primi mobilis*, Nuremberg: Joannes Petreius, 1541, is a second edition of the first part of the *Instrumentum primi mobilis* of 1534.

Introductio geographica. Ingolstadt: [In aedibus Apiani], 533. *See under* MATHEMATICS.

22 Isagoge in typum cosmographicum seu mappam mundi. Landshut: Joannes Weissenburger [*c.* 1521]. 12°.

Ref: Van Ortroy (Apian) 10.
N.B: One of the earliest of Apian's printed texts. Its preliminary section was re-issued in part in his *Declaratio et usus typi cosmographici* at Regensburg about 1522.

ARATOS of Soli, *fl.* 275 B.C.

23 Phaenomena (Tr: Germanicus Caesar). (*Issued with* MANILIUS, M. Astronomicon. Bologna: Ugo Rugerius and Doninus Bertochus, '20 Mar.' 1474) f°. [LEK]

Ref: HCR 10707; BMC VI 805; Klebs 661.2; *Sart* I 157; Stillwell M175; Goff M-203.
N.B: A scientific poem treating of the risings and settings of the stars, and the weather signs; based largely on Eudoxos and Theophrastos or, as suggested by Sarton,

on an earlier common source. Issued with the *Arati phaenomena* of Rufus Festus
Avienus at Venice in 1488 (Cen A1277; Schullian (ArMed) 82). A compilation
in which Greek-Latin versions of the *Phaenomena* appeared—printed at Venice
by Aldus Manutius in 1499 and sometimes known as the *Scriptores astronomici
veteres*—contains also the commentary on Aratos ascribed to Theōn of Alexandria
(Cen F169).

ARISTARCHOS, *c.* 310–230 B.C.

24 De magnitudinibus et distantiis solis et lunae. (*In* VALLA, Giorgio,
1447–1499, *ed.* Collectio. Venice: Antonius de Strata, 1488?) f°.

> *Ref*: Heath (AS) 301–310; O'Leary 30; Taton (A&MS) 306–308.
> *N.B*: An edition cited by Heath (AS) 321 and Sart (HS) II 60, but otherwise apparently
> unlisted. Valla's *Collectio*, printed at Venice by Simon Bevilaqua in 1498 (Cen
> N33) contains this title, however. It is possible, therefore, that confusion may
> have been caused by the fact that Valla's translation of *Aratos* was published in a
> compilation printed at Venice in 1488 (Cen A1277). In other words, the Aris-
> tarchos of 1488 may be a 'ghost'; and inclusion in Valla's 1498 compilation may
> be the first time the text was printed.
>
> Written by one of the earliest astronomers known to have recognized the sun
> as the center of the universe. Although the text in which Aristarchos presented
> his heliocentric hypothesis is lost, his theory is known through quotations by his
> successors, the earliest statement occurring in the *Psammites*, the so-called "Sand-
> Reckoner" of Archimedes, *c.* 287–212 B.C.
> *Mon*: HEATH, *Sir* Thomas. *Aristarchus of Samos, the ancient Copernicus. A history of Greek
> astronomy to Aristarchus, together with Aristarchus' treatise on the sizes and distances of
> the sun and moon* [Greek text, with translation]. Oxford, 1913.

ARISTOTLE (Aristoteles), *c.* 384–322 B.C.

25 De caelo et mundo (Comm: Averroës, 1126–1198). Padua: Laurentius
Canozius for Johannes Philippus Aurelianus et fratres, 5 March 1473.
f°. [LEK]

> *Ref*: GW 2357; HCR 1688; Oates 2544; IGI 807; Pell 1201; Klebs 87.1; *Crombie*
> (A–G) 1961 I 58, 75–78; *Taton* (A&MS) 228; *Lewes* 136–140; Stillwell A874;
> Goff A-977.
> *N.B*: Books I and II of the *De caelo* treat of astronomical theories; III and IV, of the
> elements. Drawing upon theories advanced by his predecessors, Aristotle's
> theories in general may be summarized as representing the earth as fixed at the
> center of a spherical universe, with the spheres of the moon, Mercury, Venus,
> the sun, Mars, Jupiter, and Saturn in orbit around the earth, and beyond them
> the sphere of the fixed stars and the realm of the *primum movens* or force which,
> every twenty-four hours, caused the planetary spheres to complete their revo-
> lutions, while each planet with an individual motion moved at times slightly

Aristotle (continued)

retrograde. [For a diagram illustrating the Aristotelian system by means of concentric circles, see p. 80–81 in Crombie, as cited above.]

Also issued by this firm in a compilation of Aristotelian titles individually dated, or assigned to, the years 1472–1474 (Horblit 6). [A Latin Opera, containing the *De caelo*, cited in Copinger 615 as printed at Lyon about 1468, is not known today.] Issued without the commentary at Leipzig about 1492 and at Venice in August and October 1495 (GW 2354; Cen A875, A876), the two Venice editions edited by Hermannus de Virsen and containing the commentaries of Thomas Aquinas and Petrus de Alvernia. The text appeared in volume II of the Greek *Opera* published at Venice by Aldus Manutius, in February 1497 (*see no. 570, below*). Latin versions are included in compilations brought out by five Venetian presses in 1482, 1483, 1489, 1495/96, and 1496 and at the Cologne press of Heinrich Quentell in 1497, an issue subsequently reprinted (Cen A860, A861, A863–A866; Goff A-968).

26 Metaphysica libri XIV (Comm: Averroës, 1126–1198). Padua: Laurentius Canozius, de Lendenaria, for Johannes Philippus Aurelianus et fratres, 30 Jan. 1473. f°. [LEK]

Ref: GW 2419; BMC VII 907; Oates 2543; IGI 828; Pell 1229; Klebs 90.1; Stillwell A898; Goff A-1005.

N.B: In the *Metaphysica* Aristotle increased the theoretical number of orbiting spheres to fifty-four; retained the sphere of the fixed stars; invested the *primum mobile* with "intelligences" to rotate the spheres; and described the world as composed of earth and water having a downward pull, of air and fire having an upward pull, plus an unknown fifth quality or quintessence.

Also issued by this firm in a compilation of Aristotelian titles individually dated, or assigned to, the years 1472–1474 (Horblit 6). Printed by Martin Landsberg at Leipzig in 1499 (Cen A899). Included in compilations printed at Venice in 1482, 1483, 1489, 1495/96, 1496; and in volume IV of the Greek *Opera* published by Aldus Manutius at Venice, 1 June 1497 (*no. 570, below*).

ARNALDO de Villa Nova (Arnoldus de Villa Nova; Arnold de Ville Neuve), *c.* 1235–1311, *ed.*

27 Computus ecclesiasticus et astronomicus. Venice: Bernardino dei Vitali, 17 Feb. 1501. 4°.

Ref: RA 73, *fac.*

AUTOLYCOS of Pitane, *fl.* 300 B.C.

28 De sphaera quae movetur liber. De ortibus et occasibus libri duo. (Book XVI of VALLA, Giorgio, 1447–1499. De expetendis et fugiendis rebus. Venice: In aedibus Aldi Romani [Aldus Manutius], Dec. 1501.)

Ref: BM-Ital 709; *RA* 71; *Heath (HGM)* I 348–353; *Sart (Appr)* 149, 217:53.

N.B: According to Dr. O. Schmidt (p. 202–209 in *Transactions* of the 11th Scandinavian mathematical congress at Trondheim, published at Oslo in 1952 and noted in Neugebauer (ESA) 1957, 226), the *De ortibus et occasibus libri duo* are in reality two versions of one work.

Mon: MOGENET, Joseph. *Autolycus*. Louvain, 1950. HEIBERG, Johann Ludwig. *Beiträge zur Geschichte Georg Vallas und seiner Bibliothek*. Leipzig, 1896 (Beihefte zum Centralblatt für Bibliothekswesen, XVI).

BIANCHINI, Giovanni (Johannes Blanchinus), *fl.* 1450.

29   Tabulae celestium motuum eorumque canones.   Venice: Simon Bevilaqua, 10 June 1495.   4°.

> *Ref*: GW 4410; H *3233; BMC V 520; BM-Ital 106; IGI 1755; Klebs 188.1; Stillwell B627; Goff B-697.
> *N.B*: With additions by Giovanni Basilio Augustone, *fl.* 1490–1500.

BIONDO, Michel-Angelo (Michaeleangelus Blondus), 1497–1565.

30   Tabulae annuae de anticipatione stellarum fixarum cum suis significationibus in disponendis vel constituendis operibus humanis.   Rome: Hieronymus de Cartulariis, 1544.   8°.

> *Ref*: BM-Ital 106; *Thornd (HM)* V 263.

BONATTI, Guido, 1230—*c.* 1296.

31   Decem tractatus astronomiae (Ed: Joannes Angelus [Johann Engel, 1463–1512]).   Augsburg: Erhard Ratdolt, 26 Mar. 1491.   4°.   [LEK]

> *Ref*: GW 4643; HC *3461; BMC II 384; IGI 1879; Klebs 195.1; *Sart* II 988; Stillwell B757; Goff B-845.
> *N.B*: Written by the leading astrologer of the time, the foremost defender. With caption on f.16a reading: Incipit liber introductorius ad iudicia stellarum.

BRANT, Sebastian, 1458–1521.

32   Von dem donnerstein gefallen im xcii. iar: vor Ensishein [*German and Latin*].   [Basel: Michael Furter for] J[ohann] B[ergmann], [after 7 November] 1492. Bdsde. [LEK]

> *Ref*: GW 5020; Einbl 458.
> *N.B*: An early news-sheet. The first printed account of a meteorite. Signed and dated 1492, J.B. Also issued by Michael Greyff at [Reutlingen] in 1492 (GW 5021; Einbl 460); and by Johann Prüss at [Strasbourg] in 1492 (GW 5022; Einbl 461). Reprinted for Johann Bergmann at Basel (GW 5023; Einbl 459).
> *Fac*: *Osiris* 5 1938, *fig.* 49.

I. *Astronomy*

BRUDZEWO, Albertus de (Albertus Blar de Brudzewo; Brudzewski), 1445–1497.

33 Commentum in theoricas planetarum. Milan: Uldericus Scinzenzeler, 8 Nov. 1494. 4°. [LEK]

Ref: GW 5576; *Wightman* (1962) I 109.
N.B: A commentary on the *Novae theoricae planetarum* of Georg von PEURBACH by one of the advanced thinkers of the day. A work which is believed to have influenced Copernicus. Known also in an edition from this press with additions by Johannes Otto de Valle Vracensi, issued 30 March 1495 (GW 5577; HC *3999; BMC VI 769—Stillwell B1080; Goff B-1218).

CALCAGNINI, Celio, of Ferrara, 1479–1541.

34 Quod caelum stet, terra moveatur, vel de perenni motu terrae. (*In his* Opera aliquot. Basel: Hieronymus Froben and Nicolaus Episcopius, 1544).

Ref: BM-Ger 173; *Dreyer* (*HA*) 292–294.
N.B: Presents the thesis that the earth, having been given an impetus by nature, continues to revolve upon its own axis but inclines from side to side. Possibly written before 1525. According to Dreyer, it is printed in Dr. Hipler's paper on Calcagnini, p. 69–78 in COPERNICUS VEREIN. *Mittheilungen*. IV, 1882.

CALENDARIUM.

35 Calendarium, 1457. [Mainz(?): 36-line Bible type, *1st state*, 1456.] Bdsde.

Ref: GW 1286; Einbl 114; DeR (M) 21.
Cop: Bibliothèque Nationale, Paris.
N.B: A calendar giving auspicious days for purging during the year 1457. The first medical piece known to have been printed.
Fac: GUTENBERG-GESELLSCHAFT. *Veröffentlichungen*. I. Taf. V.

——, 1475 *and later. See* REGIOMONTANUS.

36 —— 1479–1578. Geneva: Henricus Wirczburg and Adam Steynschaber, 17 Oct. 1479.

Ref: Klebs 239.1; Polain 2407 *var*.

37 —— 1486–1504. Venice: Conrad Zeninger, 26 July 1486. Bdsde.

Ref: BMC V xxxvii; HEHCat 2954; Stillwell C48; Goff C-53.
N.B: An unassigned calendar for 1490–1508 is known at Munich (H *4263).

38 —— perpetuum. [Trent: Albrecht Kunne, *c.* 1475.] 12°.

> *Ref*: Klebs 237.1—Stillwell C48; Goff C-52.
> *N.B*: A *calendarium perpetuum*, in Dutch and assigned to Louvain about 1476, is listed in Klebs 238.1.

CAMPANO, Giovanni, da Novara, *c.* 1260–1292.

39 Tractatus de sphaera. (*Issued with* JOANNES de Sacro Bosco. Sphaera. Venice: Heredes Octaviani Scoti, 19 Jan. 1518.)

> *Ref*: *Thornd (SB)* 23, 26–28, *etc.*; *Taton (A&MS)* 497–498.
> *N.B*: Opposes the theory of the diurnal rotation of the central earth. An independent treatise rather than a commentary on Sacro Bosco. Riccardi I 449 lists also an edition of 30 June 1518 and discusses the relationship of the two editions, citing Boncompagni on the translations of Platone Tiburtino.

CATO, Angelus (Angelo Catone de Sepino?), *fl.* 1450–1495.

40 De cometa anni 1472. [Naples: Sixtus Riessinger, after 1 Mar. 1472.] 4°.

> *Ref*: GW 6385; H 4706; Klebs 256.1.

CIRUELO, Pedro Sánchez, *c.* 1470—*c.* 1550.

41 Apotelesmata astrologiae Christianae. Alcalá: Arnaldus Guillelmus Brocarius, 12 Oct. 1521.

> *Ref*: *Thornd (HM)* V 276–278.
> *N.B*: A treatise on definitions and sound astrological judgments written by a theologian and astronomer in opposition to the practices of illicit astrology. Includes also his *Centiloquium* and his *Responses* to the attack of Pico della Mirandola on astrology.

CISIOIANUS.

42 Cisioianus (*from* Cisio Janus; *also called* Cisianus) [*German*]. [Mainz: 36-line Bible type, *2nd state* (?), *c.* 1457.] Bdse.

> *Ref*: GW 7054; Einbl 494; DeR (M) 22.
> *Cop*: University of Cambridge (Oates 18).
> *N.B*: A calendar listing days of the year, applicable to every year. Without symbols pertaining to the solar and lunar cycles, and therefore not a perpetual calendar in the full technical meaning of the term. In rhymed couplets as an aid to memory. Text begins: Das is der Cisianus zu dutsche . . . Because of its reference to Saint Bilhilt of Mainz, the calendar is presumed to have been printed there. Goff C-699 [addenda] lists a Low-German version of the *Cisioianus* printed by Ludwig von Reuchen at Cologne [about 1485] (GW 7056; Einbl 496).

Cisioianus (continued)

> *Mon*: HAEBLER Konrad. *Le soi-disant Cisianus* . . . (in *La Bibliographe Moderne*, VI, 1902, p. 1 *ff.*, 188).
>
> *Fac*: GUTENBERG-GESELLSCHAFT. *Veröffentlichungen*. II, 1903. Taf. II.

CLEOMEDES, *variously placed from the first century B.C. to the 2nd century A.D.*

43 De contemplatione orbium excelsorum disputatio, sive De motu circulari corporum caelestium libri II (Tr: Carolus Valgulius) [*and other works*]. Brescia: Bernardinus Misintis for Angelus Britannicus, 3 April 1497. 4°.

> *Ref*: GW 7122; HC *5450; BMC VII 991; BM-Ital 187; Pell 3847; Klebs 280.1; Sart I 211; Sart (HS) II 304; Taton (A&MS) 316, 319; Stillwell C676; Goff C-741.
>
> *N.B*: According to Taton (A&MS), p. 301, Cleomedes discusses the laws of refraction set forth by Ptolemy, *fl.* 150. The present work provides also a guide to the geographical methods of Erastosthenes and of Posidonios, upon whom Cleomedes is believed to have based much of his study of atmospheric refraction. Although Sarton cites a first edition as Venice, 1488, it has not been identified in the present survey. Included in Valla's compilation printed at Venice by Simon Bevilaqua in 1498 (Cen N33). The Greek princeps was issued at Paris by Conradus Neobarius in 1539 (BM-Fr 117). An edition printed at Paris in 1547 bears the title *Circularis inspectionis meteororum libri duo* (BM-Fr 117). Also known as *De mundo*.
>
> *Mon*: ZIEGLER, Hermann. *Cleomedis de motu circulari corporum caelestium libri duo*. Leipzig, 1891. NEUGEBAUER, O. *Cleomedes and the meridian of Lysimachia* (p. 344–347 in *American Journal of Philology* 62 1941).
>
> *Fac*: Sart (HS) II, p. 306.

De COMETIS.

44 De cometis tractatus. [Beromünster: Helias Heliae, after April 1472.] f°. [LEK]

> *Ref*: GW 7252; H *15512; BMC III 799; Klebs 972.1; Stillwell C713; Goff C-784.
>
> *N.B*: According to references quoted in GW 7252, the *Thurecensis physicus* mentioned in the text as author of this tract might be either Eberhard Schleusinger or Konrad Heingarter.

COMPUTUS.

45 Computus Cracoviensis. [Leipzig: Printer of Capotius, *c.* 1487/88.] 8°. [LEK]

> *Ref*: GW 7274; Klebs 295.1.

——manualis. *See* ANIANUS, II 134.

46 —— Nurembergensis. [Leipzig: Gregor Boettiger, not after 1494.]
4°. [LEK]

> *Ref*: GW 7277; H *5597; Voull (B) 1379; Klebs 296.1; Goff C-798.

COPERNICUS, Nicolaus (Niklas Koppernigk), 1473–1543.

47 De revolutionibus erbium coelestium libri VI. Nuremberg: Joannes
Petreius, 1543.

> *Ref*: Horblit 18b; *Sart (Appr)* 161; *Dreyer (HA)* 305–344; *Taton (A&MS)* 57–66.
>
> *N.B*: Advances the heliocentric hypothesis presenting the sun as the center of the uni-
> verse, and with amendments re-states the theory of Ptolemy. Copernicus failed
> to realize, however, that the orbits of the planets are not circular in their course,
> but elliptical. He cited the diurnal rotation of the earth (known to Anaximander
> in the sixth century B.C.) as having a sidewise motion; he encroached upon the
> realm that theology has assigned to Heaven; and by presenting the sun as the
> focal point of the planetary system, he contradicted the theological belief that the
> earth was the center of God's universe. See HEATH, Sir Thomas, *The heliocentric
> hypothesis* (p. 301–310 in his *Aristarchus of Samos, the ancient Copernicus*. Oxford,
> 1913).
>
> *Mon*: BARANOWSKI, Henryk. *Bibliografia kopernikowska*, 1509–1955 (POLISH ACADEMY
> OF SCIENCES, Section of the History of Science. Warsaw, 1958). KUHN, Thomas
> S. *The Copernican revolution* . . . Cambridge [Mass.], 1957 (reviewed, p. 366–367
> in *Isis* 49 1958). [For a discussion of the formal relationships between hypotheses
> set forth by Ptolemy, Copernicus, and Tycho Brahe, see HANSON, Norwood
> Russell. *Contra-equivalence: A defense of the originality of Copernicus* (p. 308–325 in
> *Isis* 55 1964).]
>
> *Fac*: Horblit 18c, recto.

DANCK, Johann, de Saxonia (*called* Johann de Saxonia), *fl.* 1325–1355.

48 Canones in tabulas Alphonsi. (*Issued with* ALFONSO X, *King of Castile
and Leon*. Tabulae astronomicae. [Venice:] Erhard Ratdolt, 4 July 1483).

> *Ref*: GW 1257; H *868; BMC V 287; Klebs 50.1; Stillwell A473; Goff A-534.
>
> *N.B*: His commentary on Alchabitius was issued at Venice by Erhard Ratdolt in 1485
> (Cen A330).

ECK, Paulus, *fl.* 1479.

49 Almanac, 1486. [Leipzig: Anonymous printer, 1485.] Bdse.

> *Ref*: GW 9229; Einbl 525.
>
> *N.B*: GW 9229–9234 record editions for the years 1486, 1487 [for Leipzig], and for the
> year 1489. GW 9235–9236 record editions of his *Practica* for 1488.

ENGEL, Johann (Joannes Angelus; Johannes Angeli), 1463–1512.

50 Almanach auf das Jahr 1484 [*German*]. [Bamberg: Johann Sensen-schmidt, 1483?] Bdsde.

> *Ref*: GW 1892; Einbl 546; Stillwell A623; Goff A-710.
> *N.B*: GW 1892–1899 record eight editions for the years 1484, 1488, 1489, and 1490, in Latin and in German.
> *Fac*: HEITZ-HAEBLER 43.

51 Astrolabium planum. Augsburg: Erhard Ratdolt, [6(?) October] 1488. 4°. [LEK]

> *Ref*: GW 1900; BMC II 382; IGI 3674; Klebs 375.1; Schullian (ArMed) 172; *Thornd (HM)* V 345; Stillwell A624; Goff A-711.
> *N.B*: An important astrological work containing tables of the sign and degree of the ascendent for each hour and minute (*in tabulis ascendens continens qualibet hora atque minuto*); equations of the astrological houses (*equationes domorum celi*); and nearly 400 illustrations showing the potential occupations and types of persons born under given auspices. Subsequently condemned in part, in the report of the Faculty of Theology at the University of Paris.

ESTWOOD, John (Eschuid; John of Eschenden), *fl.* 1340–1370.

52 Summa astrologiae judicialis de accidentibus mundi. Venice: Johannes Lucilius Santritter, for Franciscus Bolanus, 7 July 1489. f°.

> *Ref*: GW 9392; HC *6685; BMC V 462; IGI 3711; Klebs 381.1; *Sart* III 672; Car p. 171; Stillwell E84; Goff E-109.
> *N.B*: Written by a professional astrologer who believed that the universe was integrated according to divine plan.
> *Mon*: THORNDIKE, Lynn. *John of Eschenden: specialist in conjunctions* (Chap. XXI in vol. III of his *A history of magic and experimental science.* New York, 1934).

FABER von Budweis, Wenzel, *fl.* 1475–1495.

53 Almanach für Leipzig auf das Jahr 1487. [Leipzig: Martin Landsberg, 1486.] Bdsde.

> *Ref*: Einbl 568.
> *N.B*: According to the *Gesamtkatalog der Wiegendrucke*, twenty-eight editions of Faber's *Almanach für Leipzig*, for various years through 1501, are known to have been issued in Latin or German. Issues for 1492 and 1497 in Latin, and for 1492 and 1496 in German, are listed in Goff F-1, F-2, F-3, F-4.

54 Prognostikon für Leipzig auf das Jahr 1482 [*German*]. [Leipzig: Marcus Brandis, *c.* 1481.] 4°.

> *Ref*: H 6862; Klebs 387.01.

N.B: Recorded by Panzer but no copy now known. Specimens of over 30 editions before 1501, however, are extant, the earliest being a fragment of the issue for 1484, at Helmstedt. Fragments at Yale University Library for 1492 and 1494, in Latin and German, are registered in Goff F-6, F-7, F-8.

55 Tabulae solis et lunae coniunctionum [for Leipzig]. [Leipzig: Martin Landsberg, *c.* 1494/95.] 4°.

Ref: HC 6860; BMC II 469, 660; Klebs 338.1; Goff F-9.

N.B: Another issue printed by Martin Landsberg and assigned to Leipzig, not before 1499, is listed as Goff F-10.

FIRMICUS MATERNUS, Julius, *fl.* 340.

56 De nativitatibus. Venice: Simon Bevilaqua, 13 June 1497. f°. [LEK]

Ref: H *7121; BMC V 522; Oates 2095; IGI 3975; Klebs 404.1; Schullian (ArMed) 192; Sart I 354; Stillwell F168; Goff F-190.

N.B: The *Matheseos* (identified by Klebs with the *De nativitatibus*) ranks as the most comprehensive text-book of astrology of ancient times. It relates to judicial and psychological astrology and discusses ethical rules for its practice. It mentions a solar eclipse of 334 A.D. as a recent event. In the Aldine compilation of 1499, it appears as the first item in a compilation sometimes entitled *Scriptores astronomici veteres* (Cen F169; *see also* NLMCat 1582).

FRACASTORO, Girolamo (Hieronymus Fracastorius), 1483-1553.

57 Homocentrica. Venice, 1538. 4°.

Ref: BM-Ital 275; *Dreyer (HA)* 296-300; *Crombie (A-G)* 1961, II 167; *Thornd (HM)* V 489-490; *Taton (BMS)* 55-56.

N.B: An attempt to revive the theory of concentric spheres without epicycles. Based upon the early theories of Eudoxos of Cnidos, *c.* 408-355 B.C. and of his pupil, Kallippos, *fl.* 330 B.C.; and upon those of Fracastoro's contemporary, Giovanni Battista della Torre. Possibly first printed in 1535. Contains also Fracastoro's *De causis criticorum dierum.*

FRANÇOIS de Meyronnes (Franciscus de Mayronis), *d.* 1325.

58 Scripta in quator libros Sententiarum. Venice: Bonetus Locatellus, 1520. f°.

Ref: BM-Ital 279; *Thornd (S&T)* 141; Sart III 529.

N.B: In contrast to his predominant scholasticism, in his commentary on Book II of the *Libri sententiarum* of Petrus Lombardus, François shows a certain independence of thought in mentioning the theory of the rotation of the earth as being more credible than the rotation of the heavens. [For text (fol. 150) see Sarton III 530*n.*] Possibly first printed in a Venetian edition of 1504-1507.

Mon: DUHEM, P. *François de Meyronnes et la question de la rotation de la terre* (p. 23-25 in *Archivum franciscanum historicum*, VI, 1913).

GAURICO, Luca, 1476–1558.

59   Tractatus astrologiae iudiciariae de nativitatibus virorum & mulierum.

Nuremberg: Joannes Petreius, 1540.

> *Ref*: *Thornd (HM)* V 165–168, *etc.*; *Sart (Appr)* 215:23.
>
> *N.B*: BM-Ital 292 lists a copy of his *Trattato d'astrologia*, printed at Rome by Valerio and Luigi Dorici in 1539, possibly an earlier edition of this work. Gaurico was astrological adviser to several popes and to Henri II of France. He was also a mathematician and astronomer and a promoter of the calendar reform. His oration in praise of astrology and its founders, delivered before the Academy of Ferrara, appeared in the 1531 edition of Joannes de Sacro Bosco, printed at Venice by Lucantonio Giunta.

GEMINOS of Rhodes, *fl.* 70 B.C.

60   Elementa astronomiae [*Greek*]. (*Issued with* FIRMICUS MATERNUS, *4th century*. Astronomicon. Venice: Aldus Manutius, 1499). f °. [LEK]

> *Ref*: *Sart (HS)* II 305–307; Stillwell F169; Goff F-191.
>
> *N.B*: According to Sarton, at the end of this compilation sometimes known as the *Scriptores astronomici veteres* of 1499, a section entitled *Proclu sphaera* [see under MATHEMATICS, no. 211] is derived from the *Elementa* of Geminos, comprising extracts from his text. Nearly a century later the full text in Greek and Latin, edited by Edo Hildericus, was printed at Altdorf in 1590 by Christophor Lochner and Johann Hofmann.

GEMMA (Gemma Regnier, of Frisia; Gemma *Frisius*), 1508–1555.

61   De principiis astronomiae et cosmographiae. Antwerp: Joannes Grapheus, Oct. 1530. [LEK]

> *Ref*: Harrisse (BAV) 156, *add.* 92.
>
> *N.B*: For a note on the importance of this work, see its entry under MATHEMATICS, no. 173. The author was the teacher of Mercator and one of the leading astronomers of his time.

GERSON, Jean Charlier de (*called* Johannes Gerson), *Chancellor of the University of Paris*, 1363–1429.

62   Trigilogium astrologiae theologisatae. (*Issued with his* De simplificatione cum aliis tractatibus. [Cologne: Ulrich Zel, about 1472.]) 4°. [LEK]

> *Ref*: HC *7681; BMC I 190; Oates 374; Polain 1639; *Thornd (HM)* IV 114–119; Stillwell G250; Goff G-270.
>
> *N.B*: In order to avoid quackery, Gerson advocates a cautious weighing of astrological findings and recommends that astrologers should be trained in astronomy and

adequately examined by trained astronomers. An edition of this treatise as a separate is assigned to the press of Sensenschmidt and Frisner at Nuremberg about 1475 (Cen G255). Also included in an edition of Pierre d'Ailly of about 1483 (Cen A426). Written to warn the Dauphin against uncritical reliance on the predictions of pseudo-astrologists.

Mon: THORNDIKE, Lynn. *Jean Gerson: A Pre-Reformation Puritan* (chap. 43 in vol. IV of his *A history of magic and experimental science*. New York, 1934—particularly p. 115-119).

GHERARDO da Sabbioneta (*called* Cremonese), *fl.* 1250.

63   Theorica planetarum.   Ferrara: Andreas Belfortis, 1472.   4°.   [LEK]

Ref: Klebs 874.1; Sart II 987.

N.B: Also issued with an edition of Joannes de Sacro Bosco assigned to [Venice: Florentinus de Argentina, not after 15 May 1472]—Cen J359. The present treatise was disputed by Regiomontanus in his *Disputationes contra Cremonensia deliramenta, see no.* 101. As Gherardo da Sabbioneta is often called Cremonese— doubtless because of the nearness of Sabbioneta to Cremona—he is sometimes confused with the famous translator, Gherardo da Cremona, 1114-1187.

Mon: CARMODY, F. J. *Theorica planetarum Gerardi*. Berkeley, 1942.

GRANOLLACHS, Bernat de (Bernadus de Granollachs).

64   Sommario dell' arte di astrologia (Lunarium, 1485–1550) [*Italian*]. [Naples: Francesco del Tuppo, 1485].   4°.

Ref: C 2772; BMC VI 871; Klebs 470.1.

N.B: According to Klebs 470.2, an edition in Catalan is assignable to the same year. Twenty-eight editions covering various periods before 1501 are known. Thirteen, including one in Italian and one in Spanish, are listed in Goff G-337—G-348, D-137.

HERNSHEIMER, Peter.

65   Almanach für Mainz, 1492 [*German*].   [Mainz: Peter von Friedberg, 1491.]   Bdsde (f°).

Ref: Einbl 686; Stillwell H77; Goff H-84.

HONIGER, Jakob, von Grussen, *fl.* 1493.

66   Almanach für Erfurt auf das Jahr 1494 [*German*].   [Nuremberg: Caspar Hochfeder, 1493.]   Bdsde (f°).

Ref: Einbl 690; BM-Ger 414 (?).

N.B: A Latin edition was issued simultaneously (Einbl 691; BMC II 474;Cen H289).

HYGINUS, Caius Julius, *fl.* 25 B.C.

67   Poeticon astronomicon.   [Ferrara:] Augustinus Carnerius, 1475.   4°.
     [LEK]

> *Ref*: HR 9061; Pr 5736; IGI 4958; Klebs 527.1; *Sart* I 226; Stillwell H486; Goff H-
> 559.
> *N.B*: An elementary description of the constellations, based on Aratos. Not in verse.
> Issued in several Latin editions within our period and in a German translation
> (Cen H490). An example of plagiarism occurs in two Venetian editions, that of
> Erhard Ratdolt issued on 22 Jan. 1485 being reproduced—not only in the text,
> but in the traced-off illustrations shown in reverse—and issued by Thomas de
> Blavis on 7 June 1488.

JĀBIR ibn Aflah (Geber ibn Aphlas), *fl.* 1145.

68   De astronomia libri IX in quibus Ptolemaeum . . . emendavit (Tr:
     Gherardo da Cremona, 1114–1187). (*Issued with* APIANUS, Petrus.
     Instrumentum primi mobilis. Nuremberg: Joannes Petreius, 1534).

> *Ref*: BM-Ger 37; Van Ortroy (Apian) 107; Car p. 163; *Sart* II 206.
> *N.B*: The author is not to be confused with the alchemist, Jābir ibn Ḥaiyān, who is
> frequently called Geber.

JOANNES de Sacro Bosco (John of Holywood; *called* Sacrobosco; Sacrobusto), *fl.* 1200–1250.

69   De anni ratione, seu De computo ecclesiastico. (*Issued with his* Sphaera
     mundi. Wittenberg, 1540.)   8°.   [LEK]

> *Ref*: *Sart* II 618.
> *N.B*: Edited by Philipp Melanchthon, 1497–1560. According to Sarton, translated
> into Icelandic within the century.

70   Sphaera mundi.   [Venice: Florentius de Argentina, not after 8 May
     1472.]   4°.   [LEK]

> *Add*: GHERARDO da Sabbioneta, *fl.* 1250. Theorica planetarum.
> *Ref*: HC 14106; Oates 1686; IGI 5338; Klebs 874.2; *Palter* II 143, 153; *Haraszti* (MB)
> XVI.2, p. 67–70; *Taton* (BMS) 53; Stillwell J359; Goff J-400.
> *N.B*: An elementary discourse on the theoretical mechanism of the universe; popular
> for more than two centuries in spite of the writings of Peurbach, Regiomontanus,
> and other astronomers which refuted it. Based on al-Battānī and al-Farghānī but
> not, as sometimes said, on use of Ptolemy's *Almagest*.
>
> A dated edition, known through a copy at Florence, was printed at Ferrara by
> Andreas Belfortis in 1472 (Klebs 874.1) and may possibly have been issued
> earlier in 1472 than that cited above. A contemporary note in a copy of the latter
> at the Library of Congress bears the date 8 May 1472. [For a Portuguese trans-

lation by Pedro Nunes, printed at Lisbon in 1537, see LC(LJRCat) 782. For an
Italian version by Antonio Brucioli printed at Venice in 1543, see NLMCat 4044.]
An *Introductorium cōpendiosum in Tractatum spere material' mḡri Ioānis de Sacrobusto*
is assigned to the press of Jan Haller (?) at Cracow in 1506—LC(LJRCat) 781.

Mon: THORNDIKE, Lynn. *The sphere of Sacrobosco and its commentators*. Chicago, 1949.
[Although this relates primarily to manuscript commentaries, early printed
editions are occasionally mentioned.]

LEOPOLDUS, *ducatus Austriae, 13th century*.

71 Compilatio de astrorum scientia. Augsburg: Erhard Ratdolt, 9 Jan.
1489. 4°.

> *Ref*: HC *10042; BMC II 382; Oates 958; IGI 5747; Klebs 601.1; Car p. 171; *Sart*
> II 996; Stillwell L161; Goff L-185.

LICHTENBERGER, Johannes, d. 1503.

72 Conjunctio Saturni et Martis 1473. [Lübeck: Lucas Brandis, after 3
Dec. 1474; before 28 June 1475.]

> *Ref*: Klebs 605.1; *Thornd (HM)* IV 473-480; Stillwell L177; Goff L-203.

73 Prognosticatio, 1488–1567. [Ulm: Johann Zainer (?), after 1 April
1488.] f°.

> *Ref*: HC *10080; BMC II 532; Klebs 606.1; Stillwell L178; Goff L-204.

> *N.B*: Klebs lists twelve editions and a variant, issued in 1488, 1492, 1497, 1499, and
> 1500—In Latin, German, or Italian. Two German versions, 1492–1567, printed
> about 1500? and in 1534, are listed in Goff L-208 and NLMCat 2816.

MACROBIUS, Ambrosius Theodosius, *fl.* 400.

74 In somnium Scipionis expositio. Saturnalia. Venice: Nicolaus Jenson,
1472. f°. [LEK]

> *Ref*: HCR 10426; BMC V 172; IGI 5923; Klebs 638.1; Stillwell M4; Goff M-8.

> *N.B*: A commentary on Cicero's *Somnium Scipionis* [bk. VI of his *De republica*]. The
> *Exposito* of Macrobius contains references to the theory that Venus and Mercury
> rotate around the sun.
>
> With regard to Macrobius's description of an armillary sphere and his possible
> use of a planetarium such as Archimedes constructed, see LATTIN, Harriet P.
> *Use of a sphere by Macrobius* (p. 168–169 in Isis 39 1948). For discussion of Macro-
> bius's text see STAHL, Wm. H. *Traditions in early medieval Latin science* (p. 111–121
> in Isis 50 1959). A translation by Stahl was issued by Columbia University Press
> in 1952 (reviewed, p. 267–268 in Isis 43 1952).

MANILIUS, Marcus, *fl.* 14 A.D.(?).

75   Astronomicorum libri quinque. Nuremberg: Johann Müller of
      Königsberg (Regiomontanus), *private press* [1473/74].   4°.   [LEK]

> *Ref*: H *10703; BMC II 456; IGI 6125; Klebs 661.1; *Sart* I 237; Stillwell M174; Goff
> M-202.
> *N.B*: An astrological poem. Later re-issued in the compilation known as *Scriptores
> astronomici veteres*, Venice, 1499 (Cen F169; *see also* NLMCat 1582). A dated
> edition was issued at Bologna in 1474 (IGI 6126).

MANUNG.

76   Ein Manung der Christenheit widder die Durken (*the so-called* Turkish
      calendar for 1455) [*German; dialect of Mainz*]. [Mainz: Eponymous
      press, in 36-line Bible type, *1st state*, December 1454.]   6 ff.

> *Ref*: H *10741; DeR (M) 19.
> *Cop*: Munich, *unique*.
> *N.B*: Not strictly a calendar, although often so called. A propaganda pamphlet in
> verse, in which the section for each month is addressed to some high potentate of
> Christendom, warning him of the peril of invasion by the Turks. The fact that
> news is mentioned of a repulse of the infidels at the Hungarian border, which
> reached Frankfurt on December 6, 1454, occasions the assignment of this tract
> to the latter portion of the month. Having found common characteristics in his
> typographical analyses, Dr. Carl Wehmer in his re-assignment of pieces in the
> early 36-line Bible type uses this "Türkenkalender für 1455" as a focal point in
> assembling the group of fragments of unknown date hitherto assigned to the
> 1440s.
>   The tract is described by Dr. Aloys Ruppel, with reproductions, in his book
> on *Johannes Gutenberg, sein Leben und sein Werk*, 1939, p. 127–131. As Dr. Ruppel
> indicates, the characteristics of a calendar are subordinated to the purposes of
> propaganda; the monthly divisions are used as a device for addressing the heads
> of church and state. The watermark in the paper is of a Turkish head and turban.
> *Fac*: RUPPEL, *ibid*, p. 128, 129. NEUHAUS, J. *Das erste gedruckte Buch Gutenbergs in
> deutscher Sprache*. Copenhagen, 1902 (*complete facsimile*).

MARTIANUS CAPELLA, *fl.* 470.

77   Satyricon, sive De nuptiis Philologiae et Mercurii (Ed: Franciscus
      Vitalis Bodianus).   Vicenza: Henricus de Sancto Ursio, 16 Dec. 1499.
      f°.   [LEK]

> *Ref*: H *4370; BMC VII 1048; IGI 2426; Klebs 668.1; *RA* 66; *Sart* I 407; *Taton*
> (*A&MS*) 367; Stillwell C105; Goff C-117.
> *N.B*: An encyclopedia in prose and verse relating to the seven liberal arts, in which,
> according to Sarton, Book VIII relates to astronomy.

I. *Astronomy*

Mon: STAHL, William H. *Dominant traditions in early medieval Latin science* (Martianus Capella, p. 98–111 in *Isis* 50 1959).

MĀSHĀ 'ALLĀH (Mīshā; *called* Messahalla, Messahalah), *d.* 815.

78   De scientia motus orbis.   Nuremberg: Johannes Weissenburger, 3 Apr. 1504.   4°.   [LEK]

Ref: Pr 11041; *Sart* I 531.

N.B: The translation from the Arabic usually attributed to Gherardo da Cremona, 1114–1187, is questioned in Carmody, p. 32. According to Sarton, a 1549 edition was printed at Nuremberg under the title *De elementis et orbibus coelestibus*. Texts entitled *De receptionibus planetarum* and *De revolutionibus annorum mundi* are included in an edition of Ptolemy's *Quadripartitum* brought out at Venice by Erhard Ratdolt, 15 Jan. 1484/85, and *De ratione circuli & stellarum . . . liber I* in a compilation issued by Johann Herwagen at Basel in 1533 (NLMCat 1582).

MAUROLICO, Francesco, 1494–1575.

79   Cosmographia.   Venice: Heirs of Lucantonio Giunta, 1543.   4°. [LEK]

Ref: BM-Ital 428; *Dreyer* (*HA*) 295.

N.B: A re-statement of the medieval concept of the universe, to which Maurolico clung as an opponent of the Copernican theory.

MELANCHTHON, Philipp, 1497–1560.

80   Initia doctrinae physicae.   Wittenberg: Johann Lufft, 1549.   8°.   [LEK]

Ref: Zinner (ALD) 1961.

N.B: Re-issued at Wittenberg by Johann Lufft in 1550 (NLMCat 1550). Melanchthon was among the first of the opponents to the theories of Copernicus. For a brief account of these opponents and their comments, see ROSEN, Edward. *Galileo's misstatements against Copernicus* (p. 323–330 in *Isis* 49 1958).

Mon: MÜLLER, Konrad. *Ph. Melanchthon und das kopernikanische Weltsystem* (p. 16–28 in *Centaurus* 9 1963).

NICOLAUS de Cusa (Nicolaus Khrypffs of Cues; *called* Nicholas Krebs, Cusa, Cusanus), *Cardinal*, 1401–1464.

81   De docta ignorantia. (*In volume I of his* Opuscula. [Strasbourg: Martin Flach, *c.* 1500.]   f°.   [LEK]

Ref: H 5893; BMC I 157, 158; IGI 6803, 6804; *RA* 43; *Thornd* (*HM*) V 344n; *Sart* (*SW*) 263:1; *Taton* (*BMS*) 52; Stillwell N80; Goff N-97.

N.B: The earliest edition found in the present survey. *RA* 43 mentions a printing in 1511 and in 1514; and Sarton mentions editions of the *Opera* printed at Stras-

Nicolaus de Cusa (continued)

bourg before 1502 [possibly Cen N80] and at Milan during that year. Issued in a translation by *Fr.* Germain Heron, New Haven, 1954 (cited, p. 373 in *Isis* 46 1955).

In a section of the *De docta ignorantia* designated as "Correlaria de motu" Cusa makes a rather vague statement—more mystical than scientific—suggesting that the earth rotates upon its axis, the gist of his thought, as given here and in other comments, seeming to be that the sun and planets, following an initial impetus, revolve perpetually about the earth but in an unbounded universe comprising other worlds having no focal center. Thorndike (S&T) 133–141, in discussing these comments, emphasizes their mystical quality and the over-importance attributed to them. Dreyer (HA) 1953, 282–288, on the other hand, gives them a more astronomical interpretation. Crombie (A–G) 255–266 gives an analysis of the theories of rotation as presented by Cusa and by Nicole Oresme [the latter's important *Traité du Ciel et du Monde* not being known, however, in an early printed edition]. Still other views of Cusa's status are presented by William H. Hay in *Nicolaus Cusanus: The structure of his philosophy* (p. 14–25 in *Philosophical Review*, 61, 1952); and by Alexandre Koyré in his volume *From the closed world to the infinite universe*, Baltimore [1957]. [See also under PHYSICS.]

Mon: HOFFMANN, E. *Cusanus Studien. I. Das Universum des Nikolaus von Cues*. (HEIDELBERGER AKADEMIE DER WISSENSCHAFTEN. *Sitzungsberichte*. Kl. XX, 1930, no. 3) HEINZ-MOHR, G. and W. P. ECKERT. *Das Werk des Nicolaus Cusanus, eine bibliophile Einführung*. Cologne, 1963 (*Zeugnisse der Buchkunst*, III).

PARACELSUS (Philippus Aureolus Theophrastus Bombastus Paracelsus von Hohenheim; *variously called* Paracelsus, Theophrastus, *or* Bombast), 1493–1541.

82 [A] usslegung des Commeten erschynen im hochbirg zu mitlem Augusten, Anno 1531 [*German*]. [Zurich: Anonymous printer, 1531.] 4°.

Ref: Sudhoff (BiblP) 10.
N.B: An early comet-tract, possibly the second to appear in German. Similar tracts by Paracelsus relate to comets of 1532 and 1534—Sudhoff (BiblP) 10*n*, 11.
Mon: *See under* MEDICINE: Paracelsus, *no.* 467.

PERLACH, Andreas, *fl.* 1500–1550.

83 Ephemerides ... pro anno domini ... M.D.XXXI cum configurationibus & habitudinibus planetarum inter se & cum stellis fixis. [Vienna: Hieronymus Vietor, after 12 Dec. 1530.] 4°.

Ref: *Thornd* (HM) V 348, 382.
N.B: Compiled by a pupil of Georg Tannstetter (*called* Collimitius), and his successor at the University of Vienna, whose *Usus almanach ... ex commentariis Georgii Tannstetter ... decerpti* had been issued by the same press at Vienna in 1518.

PEURBACH, Georg von (*also called* Purbach), 1423–1461.

84 Tabulae eclypsium magistri Georgii Peurbachii. Vienna: Joannes Winterburg, idibus Apr. 1514. f°.

> *Add*: REGIOMONTANUS. Tabula primi mobilis [*q.v.*]
> *Ref*: Thornd (*HM*) V 348.
> *N.B*: A handsome folio, comprising tables and *Problemata*, with an introduction relative to astronomical instruments.

85 Theoricae novae planetarum. [Nuremberg: Johann Müller of Königsberg (Regiomontanus), *private press, c.* 1473.] f°. [LEK]

> *Ref*: HC *13595; BMC II 456; Klebs 752.1; Taton (*BMS*) 54; Stillwell P1029; Goff P-1134.
> *N.B*: A textbook combining the planetary theory of Ptolemy with factors derived from Arabic sources, for discussion of which see Dreyer (HA) 288. Said to have been written to introduce the epitome of Ptolemy's *Almagest*. [For the *Epytoma in Almagestum Ptolemaei*, for which Peurbach was in part responsible, see REGIOMONTANUS. *Epytoma*. Venice, 1496.] According to Taton, as cited above, Peurbach following the Arabs added trepidation to Ptolemy's six motions of the celestial spheres and substituted solid crystal spheres for the hypothetical circles employed in Ptolemy's *Almagest*.

PFLAUM, Jakob, *fl.* 1450–1500.

86 Calendarium, 1477–1554 [*German*]. [Ulm: Johann Zainer, *c.* 1477.] f°.

> *Ref*: Klebs 757.1; Schullian (ArMed) 352, 353; Stillwell P497; Goff P-543.
> *N.B*: In another issue, Ulm and Johann Zainer are named as the place of printing and the printer (Cen P498). Klebs lists two editions and two variants under Pflaum. [See also under STÖFFLER, Johann.]

PICO della Mirandola, Giovanni, *c.* 1463–1494.

87 Disputationes contra astrologos. (*In Pt. II of his* Opera. [Ed: Giovanni Francesco Pico della Mirandola, 1470–1533, *nephew of the author*.] Bologna: Benedictus Hectoris, 16 July 1495 [1496?]. f°. [LEK]

> *Ref*: HC (Add) *12992; BMC VI 843; BM-Ital 514; IGI 7731; Klebs 764.1; Thornd (*HM*) VI 107, 170; Stillwell P579; Goff P-632.
> *N.B*: Re-issued as a separate in 1498, but with the original date unchanged (Cen P587). Included in the *Opera* edited by Jakob Wimpheling and printed in 1504; and issued as a separate at Deventer in 1502 (NLMCat 3627 and 3629, respectively.). The *Opera* itself was re-issued at [Lyon, 1498–1500] and Venice, 1498 (Cen P580, P581; Schullian (ArMed) 355). The story is that Pico, the great opponent of astrology, was enraged because the astrologers had foretold the time of his death—yet his death occurred on the day, month, and year predicted.

Pico della Mirandola (continued)

> *Mon*: THORNDIKE, Lynn. *Astrology at bay, I: Pico della Mirandola* (Chap. LXI in vol. IV
> of his *A history of magic and experimental science*, New York, 1934).

PIERRE d'Ailly (Alliaco, Petrus de), *Cardinal*, 1350–1420.

88 Concordantia astronomie cum theologia. Augsburg: Erhard Ratdolt,
2 Jan. 1490. 4°.

> *Ref*: H *834; BMC II 383; BM-Ger 21; Klebs 768.1; *RA* 41; Stillwell A422; Goff
> A-471.

89 Imago mundi [*and other works*]. [Louvain: Johann of Paderborn, *c.*
1483.] f°.

> *Ref*: HC *836; BMC IX 146; Oates 3737; IGI 387; Klebs 766.1; *Sart* III 1148—Still-
> well A426; Goff A-477.
>
> *N.B*: A summary of cosmographical and geographical knowledge written about 1410
> and referring (cap. 19) to the theory that India lay not far to the west of Spain.
> The copy at the Biblioteca Colombina in Sevilla belonged to Columbus and is
> annotated in his hand. Sarton notes that, although the recently discovered (1406)
> manuscript of Ptolemy's *Geographia* was not known to the writer at the time
> when this summary of geographical knowledge was composed, mention is made
> of it in this edition of 1483.

PLANETENTAFEL.

90 Planetentafel für Laienstrologen; *formerly called the* "Calendar for 1448"
[*German*]. [Mainz: 36-line Bible type, *2nd state, c.* 1458.] Bdsde.

> *Ref*: GW 1285; Einbl 113; DeR (M) 5.
>
> *N.B*: A controversial item, which until the relatively recent studies of Dr. Carl Weh-
> mer and Dr. Viktor Stegemann was believed to be an "astronomical almanac
> for 1448," printed in 1447. Dr. Stegemann has shown it to be a planet-table for
> simple astrological usage, based on the positions of 1448 but capable of use during
> a period of years; and Dr. Wehmer's type-analysis shows its type to be in a slight-
> ly earlier state than that in which the greater part of the so-called "36-line Bible"
> [*c.* 1460/61] was printed, and in a later state than that used in the *Kalender für 1457*
> —hence the present assignment of the *Planetentafel* to about 1458. In spite of the
> change in its date assignment, it still ranks as one of the earliest printed pieces of
> scientific interest. Only variant fragments at Wiesbaden and Cracow are known;
> probably separate editions.
>
> *Mon*: WEHMER, Carl. *Mainzer Probedrucke in der Type des sogenannten Astronomischen
> Kalenders für 1448, ein Beitrag zur Gutenbergforschung. Mit einer Untersuchung: Der
> Astronomische Kalender, eine Planetentafel für Laienastrologen von Viktor Stegemann.*
> München: Leibniz Verlag, Bisher R. Oldenbourg Verlag, 1948. [For review,
> see C. F. BÜHLER in BIBLIOGRAPHICAL SOCIETY OF AMERICA. *Papers.* 1949, p. 85–
> 86. See also RUPPEL, A. *Johannes Gutenberg*, 2nd ed., 1947, p. 122.]

I. *Astronomy*

Fac: Gutenberg Gesellschaft I. Taf. I [Wiesbaden fragments]. Wehmer, C. *Mainzer Probedrucke.* Taf. I–IV [Cracow and portions of Wiesbaden fragments]. Reproductions of the Wesbaden fragment in its several sections appear in Burger and Voulliéme, *Deutsche und italienische Incunabeln in getreuen Nachbildungen,* p. 184; and on p. 17 in McMurtrie, D.C. *Some facts concerning the invention of printing,* Chicago, 1939.

PLATO, *c.* 423–347 B.C.

91 Opera [*Latin*] (Tr: Marsilio Ficino, 1433–1499). Florence: Laurentius de Alopa [May 1484; before Apr. 1485.] f°. [LEK]

> *Ref:* HC *13062; BMC VI 666; Oates 2436; Klebs 785.1; Sart I 113; Dreyer (*HA*) 1953 51–86; Taton (*A&MS*) 225–226; Stillwell P702; Goff P-771.
>
> *N.B:* The date assignment of this edition rests upon evidence in the 1483/84 day-book of the Ripoli Press of Florence, and upon letters written by Marsilio Ficino, the translator. The first Greek edition was issued by the Aldine press at Venice in 1513 (BM-Ital 524). Dr. P. H. Michel (Taton), in summarizing Plato's cosmology as stated in the *Republic,* the *Timaeus,* and the *Laws,* finds a consistent belief in the sphericity of the universe, the sphericity of all celestial bodies including the earth, the central position and immobility of the earth, and the circular motion of celestial bodies at various distances from the earth, the sphere of the fixed stars being the most distant. Variant views, however, are stated in the controversial *Epinomis,* among them the hypothesis that the sun is much larger than the earth.
>
> *Mon:* Martin, T. H. *Études sur le Timée de Platon,* Paris, 1841. Boeckh, A. *Untersuchungen über das kosmische System des Platon,* Berlin, 1852. Cornford, F. M. *Plato's cosmology: The Timaeus of Plato translated with a running commentary.* London, 1937.

PRACTICA.

92 Practica auf das Jahr 1482 [*German*]. [Mainz: Anonymous printer, 1481.] Bdsde.

> *Ref:* Einbl 1204.
>
> *N.B:* Klebs 808.01–.02 lists 2 fragments of possibly earlier date, followed by 11 entries for 1485–1500. Two of these, for the years 1494 and 1500, are registered as Cen P865, P866.

PROGNOSTICATIO.

93 Prognosticatio, for 1479. [Lübeck: Lucas Brandis, *c.* 1478.]

> *Ref:* Klebs 808.3.
>
> *N.B:* The earliest known fragment with assignable date; at Leipzig. Possibly antedated by fragments at Berlin and London (Klebs 808.1 and 808.2). [For Prognostications and Practica before 1501—see Klebs p. 262–265; and Cen P920 note.]

PTOLEMY (Ptolemaios; *called* Claudius Ptolemaeus), *fl.* 150.

94 Inerrantium stellarum significationes [*and other works*] (Tr: Nicolaus Leonicenus, 1428–1524). Venice: In aedibus Aldi et Andreae soceri, Jan. 1516.

> *Ref*: Renouard (Alde) I 176.
> *N.B*: An entry for this work and with similar imprint is listed in BM-Ital 479 and 542 with the date 1515, which may either indicate an earlier printing or a difference in date interpretation. Included in a compilation issued at Basel in 1533 (NLMCat 1582). [See also below: no. 97*n*, paragraph 3.]

95 De iudiciis ad Aristonem. Venice: Petrus Liechtenstein, 1509.

> *Ref*: Car p. 17; p. 13 [6].
> *N.B*: According to Carmody, it would seem that the volume also contains works by Al-Kindi, Māshā Allāh, and Sahl. Attribution to Ptolemy questioned.

96 Quadripartitum, sive Tetrabiblon. Centiloquium. Venice: Erhard Ratdolt, 15 Jan. 1484/85. 4°. [LEK]

> *Ref*: HC *13543; BMC V 288; Klebs 814.1; Car p. 13[1]; Stillwell P994; Goff P-1088.
> *N.B*: Ptolemy's *Quadripartitum* ranks as the Bible of Astrology, but the attribution of the *Centiloquium* is considered spurious. The volume contains also half a dozen other works of astrological interest, *i.e.* HERMES. *Centiloquium. De stellis beibeniis* [the 'desert stars'] (Car p. 53–55); BETHEM. *Centiloquium* (Car p. 74); MĀSHĀ 'ALLAH [Messahalah], *d.* 815. *In revolutionibus annorum mundi* [prognostications regarding royalty]; *De receptione planetarum* [Tr: Joannes Hispalensis, *fl.* 1150] (Car p. 26–27); SAHL IBN BISHR, *fl.* 822. *Liber temporum* [prognostications on times to travel, *etc.*], *Liber introductorius* (Car p. 41, 43). The *Quadripartitum* is included in compilations printed at Venice in 1493 (Cen P995) and at Basel in 1533 (NLMCat 1582).

97 Syntaxis mathematika (*usually called the* Almagest, *a corruption of its Arabic title*). (Tr: *from Arabic:* Gherardo da Cremona, 1114–1187) Venice: Petrus Liechtenstein, 10 Jan. 1515. f°. [LEK]

> *Ref*: Dreyer (*HA*) 1953, 160–170, 191–206; Palter II 148; Neugebauer (*ESA*) 1957, 191–207; O'Leary 31–33; HTech III 586–592; Taton (*A&MS*) 319–322.
> *N.B*: The first edition. An epitome, however, prepared by Regiomontanus and Peurbach, had been printed at Venice in 1496 [no. 103].
> Ptolemy here presents the earth as the center of the universe but not of the planetary orbits, and rejects the theory of the earth's free suspension said by Eudemos to have been advanced by Anaximander in the sixth century B.C. He charts the orbits of the planets by means of eccentrics and epicycles and combines the geometry of Apollōnios and the actual observations of Hipparchos. It has been said that the *Almagest* was as wide-reaching in its influence as the *Elements*

of Euclid. For analysis and discussion, see NEUGEBAUER and TATON, as noted above. See also PRICE, Derek J. de S. *The Ptolemaic planetary system* (93–118 in his monograph on *The equatorie of the planetis*, Cambridge, 1955), and his article *Contra-Copernicus* (p. 197–218 in *Critical problems in the history of science*. Ed: Marshall Clagett. Madison, 1959).

Although a mathematical treatise, the *Almagest* relates to astronomy in its applications. Books VII and VIII comprise a catalogue of stars, for discussion of which see PETERS, C. H. F. and E. B. KNOBEL. *Ptolemy's catalogue of stars*. Washington, 1915 [cited in *Isis* 2 401]; DREYER, J. L. E. *On the origin of Ptolemy's catalogue* (in vols. 77 and 78, ROYAL ASTRONOMICAL SOCIETY. *Monthly Notices*, 1917–1918) [cited in *Isis* 4 131].

Among the instruments mentioned or described in the *Almagest* are the *equatorial armillary* for determining the equinoxes at Alexandria; the *plinth* and the *meridional armillary* for determining the midday and meridian altitude of the sun; the *triquetrum* for measuring meridian transits of the moon or fixed stars; and the *armillary astrolabon* [described and illustrated by Dr. Price, p. 586–592 in vol. III of *A history of technology*. Ed: Charles Singer and others. Oxford, 1957].

The present edition, as noted above, is a Latin translation made in 1175 from the Arabic—presumably from the Arabic translation made about 829 by Al-Hajjāj from a Greek text. [For a long lost Sicilian translation known in four manuscripts and made from the Greek about 1160, see HASKINS, Charles H. and Dean P. LOCKWOOD. *The Sicilian translators of the twelfth century* (Harvard Studies in Classical Philology. XXI. 1910, p. 75–102); and HASKINS, Charles H. *Studies in Medieval science*. 2nd ed. Cambridge [Mass.], 1927, p. 157–168.] The first printed Latin translation was made directly from the Greek in 1451 by George "of Trebizond," who was born in Crete in 1396 [see Thornd (HM) IV 697–698]; issued at Venice in 1528. The first Greek text (Ed: vol. I, Simon Grynaeus, 1493–1541; vol. II, Joachim Camerarius, 1500–1574, containing the commentary of Theōn) was brought out at Basel in 1538. A compilation of three minor works by Ptolemy, issued at Basel by Petri in March 1541, contains also the *Almagest* and the fifth-century commentary of Proclos.

Mon: TANNERY, Paul. *Recherches sur l'histoire de l'astronomie ancienne*, Paris, 1893. ROME, Adolphe. *Commentaires de Pappus et de Théon d'Alexandrie sur l'Almageste*. Rome: Biblioteca Apostolica Vaticana (Studi e Testi). 3 vols.—54 (1931); 72 (1936); 106 (1943)—the commentaries of Pappos, *3rd century*, and Theōn, *4th century*, as edited by Joachim Camerarius, 1500–1574 (reviewed by O. Neugebauer, p. 347–358 in *Quellen und Studien zur Geschichte der Mathematik Astronomie und Physik* . . . Abteilung B: Studien. Band 4. Berlin, 1938). For a controversial discussion of the formal relationships between hypotheses of Ptolemy, Copernicus, and Tycho Brahe, see HANSON, Norwood Russell. *Contra-equivalence: A defense of the originality of Copernicus* (p. 308–325 in *Isis* 55 1964).

The "SECOND PTOLEMAIC SYSTEM" *so-called, although its attribution to Ptolemy is a matter of controversy.*

N.B: Also called the "Planetary hypotheses." No printed edition is known within our period. Its context was known, however, through the texts of Moslem scholars

Ptolemy (continued)

and, as derived from them, through the *Sphaera mundi* of Joannes de Sacro Bosco. Book I summarizes the *Almagest*. Book II, in geometric terms, combines the planetary orbits into an integrated system encompassing the cosmos—solid orbs, two eccentrics and an epicycle, revolving together with machine-like precision. The Greek text is lost. An Arabic version in German translation is given in Heiberg's *Claudii Ptolemaei Opera*, 1907. [For discussion of the *Hypotheses*, see the essay on *Medieval astronomy*, by J. L. E. DREYER (p. 102–120 in vol. II of *Studies in the history and method of science*. Charles Singer, *ed.* Oxford, 1921); p. 93 in E. S. KENNEDY. *A survey of Islamic astronomical tables* (American Philosophical Society. *Transactions*. New series, vol. 46, pt. 2. Philadelphia, May 1956); and p. 138–144 in vol. II of *Toward modern science*. R. M. Palter, *ed.* New York, 1961. For a comparison of the hypotheses with those of Hipparchos, see p. 320–322 in *Ancient and Medieval science*. René Taton, *ed.* A. J. Pomerans, *tr.* New York: Basic Books Inc., 1963; see also p. 54 in the 1964 volume—the second in this Taton History of Science series—entitled *The beginnings of modern science*.]

REGIOMONTANUS (Johann Müller of Königsberg; Joannes de Monteregio), 1436–1476.

98 Bücheranzeige. [Nuremberg: Johann Müller of Königsberg (Regiomontanus), *private press*, 1474.] 62 ll. Bdsde.

Ref: HC *13775; BMC II 457; Einbl 805; Klebs 835.1.

N.B: A list of about forty items printed or slated for publication by Regiomontanus and related to astronomy, astrology, music, arithmetic, mechanics, and allied topics—as found in the works of Ptolemy, Euclid, Apollōnios, Theōn, Hyginus, Witelo, and others. Many of these remained unpublished because of his early death, or were printed posthumously. Only two copies of the booklist are known—at the British Museum and at Munich.

Mon: THORNDIKE, Lynn. *Aftermath of Regiomontanus* (p. 332–377 in vol. V of his *History of magic and experimental science*, New York, 1941). KOYRÉ, Alexandre. *The revival of mathematical studies* (p. 12–51 in TATON, René, *ed. The beginnings of modern science from 1450 to 1800*, New York, Basic Books, Inc., 1964).

Fac: Osiris 5 1938, p. 163. BURGER, C. *Buchhändleranzeigen des XV. Jahrhunderts*, Leipzig, 1907, no. 15.

99 Calendarium [*Latin*]. [Nuremberg:] Johann Müller of Königsberg (Regiomontanus), *private press* [1474]. 4°. [LEK]

Ref: HC *13775; BMC II 456; BM-Ger 631; Klebs 836.1; LC(LJRCat) 43; *Taton (BMS)* 71; Stillwell R87; Goff R-92.

N.B: Issued also by Regiomontanus in a German version in [1474] (H 13784; BMC II 456; Klebs 837.1). With diagrams of eclipses and *instrumenta* including a volvelle. During the years 1474–1500 nine Latin editions of a *Calendarium* based upon the computations of Regiomontanus were issued at Nuremberg (1), Venice (4), and

Augsburg (4) (Cen R87—R95). Four are known in German versions issued at Nuremberg (1), Venice (1), and Augsburg (2) (Klebs 837.1, .3–.5; Goff R-101, R-102); and one in Italian—the *Calendario* printed by Erhard Ratdolt and his associates at Venice in 1476 presenting in this, and in the firm's Latin and German versions, prototypes of the modern titlepage (*no.* 100*n*). Among astronomical almanacs issued for specified periods, the computations of Regiomontanus are the earliest known to have been printed (*see* Klebs 839.1–.12; Goff R-105–R-110).

Mon: ZINNER, Ernst. *Leben und Werke des Johann Müller von Königsberg.* Munich, 1938.

Fac: (German issue:) GESELLSCHAFT FÜR TYPENKUNDE. *Veröffent.* Reihe B, no. 1, Leipzig, 1937, *with introduction by E. Zinner.*

100 ——[*Latin*]. Venice: Bernhard Maler (Pictor), Erhard Ratdolt, Peter Löslein, 1476. 4°. [LEK]

Ref: HC *13776; BMC V 243; BM-Ital 234; Oates 1737; IGI 5310; Klebs 836.2; Stillwell R88; Goff R-93.

N.B: Of bibliographical importance in that in this edition—together with the Italian version issued by this firm in 1476 (Cen R99; Klebs 838.1) and their German version (Klebs 837.3)—Ratdolt and his associates introduce the idea of the modern title-page. That is, instead of signing the books in a colophon on the final page in accord with manuscript tradition, they placed their names and that of the place and date of printing at the bottom of the opening page. [The text of the titlepage is quoted in LC (LJRCat) 199.] It was not, however, until close to the end of the century that the use of a titlepage gradually became established.

Fac: POLLARD, A. W. *Last words on the history of the title-page*, London, 1891, *fig.* 3.

101 Disputationes contra Cremonensia deliramenta. [Nuremberg: Johann Müller of Königsberg (Regiomontanus), *private press, c.* 1475.] f°.

Ref: H *13805; BMC II 457; Klebs 840.1; Stillwell R100; Goff R-104.

N.B: A controversial attack upon the *Theorica planetarum* of Gherardo da Sabbioneta, *fl.* 1250.

102 Ephemerides, 1475–1506. [Nuremberg:] Johann Müller of Königsberg (Regiomontanus), *private press*, 1474. 4°. [LEK]

Ref: HC *13790; BMC II 457; BM-Ger 631; Klebs 839.1.

N.B: Klebs notes fourteen fifteenth-century issues, five of which are registered as Goff R-105–R-109. [See also BM-Ital 234.] The computations in the *Ephemerides sive Almanach perpetuum*, edited by Johannes Lucilius Santritter and printed at Venice in 1498 (Goff R-110) are attributed to Regiomontanus.

103 Epytoma in Almagestum Ptolemaei. Venice: Johannes Hamman, 31 Aug. 1496. f°. [LEK]

Ref: HC *13806; BMC V 427; Klebs 841.1; Horblit 89; *Thornd (HM)* V 341; *Wightman* (1962) II 558; Stillwell R106; Goff R-111.

Regiomontanus (continued)

N.B. A summary of Ptolemy's *Syntaxis mathematika*, the so-called *Almagest*. Begun by Georg von Peurbach, 1423–1461, at the request of Cardinal Bessarion, and completed by Regiomontanus before the end of 1472. Re-issued at Basel in 1543 and at Nuremberg in 1550. Analysis has shown that the text was used by Copernicus. The complete text was first printed in Latin at Venice in 1515 [no. 97]. The first edition in Greek, Basel, 1538 was based on the Greek manuscript used by Regiomontanus.

Fac: *Osiris* 5 1938, p. 162; Horblit 89 [b–d].

104 In ephemerides commentarium. (*Issued with* STÖFFLER and PFLAUM. Almanach nova, 1499–1531. Ulm: Johann Reger, 13 Feb. 1499.) 4°.

Ref: HC*15085; BMC II 542; BM-Ger 834; Klebs 934.1; Stillwell S703; Goff S-791.

105 Tabula primi mobilis Joannis de Monteregio (Ed: Georg Tannstetter [*called* Collimitius], *c.* 1482–1530). (*Issued with* PEURBACH, Georg von, 1423–1461. Tabulae eclypsium. Vienna: Johann Winterburger, idibus Apr. 1514.)

Ref: *Thornd (HM)* V 324; Karp (T) 268.
N.B: The earliest edition found in the present survey.

REGNIER, Gemma. *See* GEMMA.

RHETICUS, Georg Joachim (Rhäticus), 1514–1576.

106 De libris revolutionum... Nicolai Copernici... narratio prima. Danzig: F. Rhode, 1540. [LEK]

Ref: Horblit 18 a; Zinner (ALD) 1758; Dreyer (HA) 1953, 318.
N.B: A preliminary view of the theories of Copernicus as set forth in the latter's *De revolutionibus orbum caelestium*, which was printed three years later. Reprinted at Basel in 1541.
Mon: Translated, with introduction, in ROSEN, Edward N. *Three Copernican treatises.* New York, 1939 [2nd ed., New York, Dover, 1950, with bibliography].
Fac: Horblit 18 b, recto.

RINGELBERG, Joachim, *c.* 1499 – *c.* 1536.

107 Institutiones astronomicae. Basel: Apud Valentinum Curionem, 1528. 12°.

Ref: BM-Ger 741.

I. *Astronomy*

SAVONAROLA, Girolamo Maria Francesco Matteo, 1452–1498.

108 Contro gli astrologi [*Italian*]. [Florence: Bartolommeo di Libri, about 1497.] 4°.

> *Ref*: HC *14378; BMC VI 661; Oates 2387; Klebs 881.1; Stillwell S163; Goff S-175.

SCHÖNER, Johann, 1477–1547.

109 Opusculum astrologicum ex diversorum libris. Nuremberg: Joannes Petreius, 1539.

> *Ref*: *Thornd (HM)* V 361–362.
> *N.B*: An astrological primer with quotations from various authors and instructions for the use of the author's *Ephemerides* and *Tables*. For his *In lunae observationem collectanea*, included in a compilation printed at Nuremberg in 1530, see NLMCat 2924.

110 Tabulae astronomicae. Nuremberg: Joannes Petreius, 1536. 4°.

> *Add*: REGIOMONTANUS, 1436–1476. De aequationibus duodecim domorum coeli.
> *Ref*: Zinner (ALD) 1647.
> *N.B*: With preface by Philipp Melanchthon. Schöner's *Aequatorii astronomici omnium ferme uranicorum theorematum explanatorum canones* was issued at Bamberg in 1521 and re-issued at Nuremberg in 1524 and 1534.

SCRIPTORES ASTRONOMICI VETERES. *See under* FIRMICUS MATERNUS.

SERVETUS, Michael (Miguel Servet y Reves of Villanueva de Sigena; Michel Villeneuve), 1511–1553.

111 Apologetica disceptatio pro astrologia. [Paris: Anonymous printer, not before 12 Feb. 1538.]

> *Ref*: *Thornd (HM)* V 288–291.
> *N.B*: Servetus, a beloved physician who saw deeply into medicine and religion, had the misfortune to live in a viciously controversial time. Much that he taught or wrote became controversial. The present tract was no exception. Its sale was prohibited. The edition was ordered to be destroyed. Only copies at the Bibliothèque Nationale and the Sorbonne in Paris are known today. The assigned date is derived from a reference in the text.
> *Mon*: FULTON, John F. *Michael Servetus, humanist and martyr*, New York, 1953 (with bibliography by Madeline E. Stanton, in which the present work is listed as no. 23). O'MALLEY, Charles D. *Michael Servetus: A translation of his geographical, medical and astrological writings with introduction and notes*, Philadelphia, 1953. OSLER, Sir William. *Michael Servetus* (p. 100–124 in his *A way of life*. New York, Dover, 1958).

I. *Astronomy*

STÖFFLER, Johann, 1452–1531.

112 Calendarium Romanum, 1518–1579. Oppenheim: Jacob Köbel, 24 March 1518. f°.

Ref: AmBMCat 194.
N.B: With four diagrams of *Instrumenta*.

113 Ephimeridum reliquiae . . . ad annum Christi 1556 (Ed: Petrus Pitatus). [Tübingen:] Ulricus Morhardus, 1548. 4°.

Ref: Zinner (ALD) 1947.
N.B: With tables of the risings of the sun, moon, and planets. The *Ephemeris* covers the years 1544 through 1556 and contains a woodcut portrait of the author in his 79th year.

114 Tabulae astronomicae. Tübingen: Thomas Anshelm, [after 3 Feb.] 1514. f°.

Ref: Pr 11741.

STÖFFLER, Johann, 1452–1531, and Jacob PFLAUM, *fl.* 1450–1500, *joint authors.*

115 Almanach nova, 1499–1531. Erklärung des neuen Almanach [*German*]. Canon de domibus fabricandis. Ulm: Johann Reger, 13 Feb. 1499. 4°.

Add: Regiomontanus. In ephemerides commentarium.
Ref: BMC II 542; BM-Ger 834; Klebs 934.1; Stillwell S703; Goff S-791.

116 Almanach nova plurimis annis venturis inservientia, 1504–1531. Venice: Petrus Liechtenstein, 2 Jan. 1504. 4°.

Ref: AmBMCat 283.
N.B: Includes almanacs for the years 1504–1531, each with a separate titlepage; various tables; and a *Canon de dominibus celi fabricādis*—also five almanacs, 1499–1503, and a *Tabula correctoria in Ephimerides*, 1499–1531.

THĀBIT ibn Qurra (Abū-'l-Ḥasan Thābit ibn Qurra), *c.* 835–901.

117 De figura sectore (Tr: Gherardo da Cremona, 1114–1187). (*Issued with* JOANNES de Sacro Bosco. Sphaera mundi. Venice, 1518).

Ref: *Sart* I 599; *O'Leary* 171–174; *Kennedy* (*IAT*) 93; *Taton* (*A&MS*) 322, 496.
N.B: Relates to spherical trigonometry, as applied to geometric representation of the universe. According to Kennedy, Thābit's version of Ptolemy's (?) *Planetary hypotheses*, not known to have been printed before 1550, is given in German

translation in *Ptolemaei Opera* II, Leipzig, 1907, p. 71–145. [See also under
MATHEMATICS.]

Mon: CARMODY, Francis J. *Notes on the astronomical works of Thabit b. Qurra* (p. 235–242
in *Isis* 46 1955); *The astronomical works of Thabit b. Qurra*. Berkeley, 1960 [1961]
(reviewed by O. Neugebauer in *Speculum* 37, no. 1, Jan. 1962, and by Heinrich
Hermelink in *Isis* 54 1963).

THEŌN of Alexandria, *4th century.*

118 In Claudii Ptolemaei magnam constructionem commentariorum lib.
XI [*Greek and Latin*]. Basel: Johann Walder, 1538. sm. f °.

Ref: Pennink 1890; Sart I 367.

N.B: Although called for on the titlepage of the 1538 edition of Ptolemy's *Almagest*,
the Theōn has individual signaturing and thus it would seem that, as here, it was
intended to be issued also as a separate. [The Greek commentary on Aratos sometimes ascribed to Theōn appeared in a compilation issued at Venice by Aldus
Manutius in 1499 and sometimes known as the *Scriptores astronomici veteres—*
Cen F168.]

Mon: ROME, Adolphe. *Commentaires de Pappus et de Théon d'Alexandrie sur l'Almageste.*
Roma: Biblioteca Apostolica Vaticana [Studi e Testi. 3 vols., 54 (1931); 72
(1936); 106 (1943)] (reviewed by O. Neugebauer, p. 347–358 in *Quellen und
Studien zur Geschichte der Mathematik Astronomie und Physik . . .* Abteilung B:
Studien. Band 4. Berlin, 1938).

THOMAS AQUINAS, *Saint, c.* 1225–1274.

119 De judiciis astrorum. (*Issued with* AUGUSTINUS, *St., spurious.* Solilo-
quium: Verbum mihi est ad te . . . [Cologne: Printer of 'Dictys,' about
1470]) 4°.

Ref: GW 3021; H 1533; Pr 982; Voull (K) 211; Stillwell A1186; Goff A-1334.

N.B: Although not an advocate of astrology, St. Thomas ascribed to it an important
place in natural science and is said to have believed judicial astrology possible.

Mon: THORNDIKE, Lynn. *Thomas Aquinas* (Chap. LX in vol. II of his *History of magic
and experimental science*, New York, 1933).

TORRELLA, Girolamo (Hieronymus Torella), *c.* 1460–1496.

120 Opus de imaginibus astrologicis, 1 Dec. 1496. ['Valencia: Alfonso de
Orta,' after 1 Dec. 1496]. 4°.

Ref: H 15560; BM-Sp 94; Klebs 981.1; Schullian (ArMed) 469; NLMCat 4391;
Stillwell T357; Goff T-392.

N.B: Among other things, Torrella believed that the aptitudes of persons differed according to their nativities, the position of the stars at birth. Place of printing
uncertain. Assigned by Klebs to [Barcelona, after 1500].

Mon: THORNDIKE, Lynn. *Jerome Torrella on astrological images* (p. 574–585 in vol. IV of
his *History of magic and experimental science*, New York, 1934).

TORRES, Didaco de.

121 Eclipse del sol [*Spanish*]. Salamanca: [Printer of Nebrissensis, *Introductiones*] 1 Mar. 1485. 4°.

Ref: H 15561; Klebs 982.1; Stillwell T358; Goff T-393.

WILLEM GILLISZOON (Guillermus Aegidii; *called* Aegidii), of Wissekerke, *fl.* 1494.

122 Super coelestium motuum indagatione sine calculo (Tr: Boninus de Boninis). Cremona: Carolus Darlerius, 14 Feb. 1494/95. 4°. [LEK]

Ref: GW 264; BMC VII 958; Oates 2609; IGI 54; Stillwell A52; Goff A-61.
N.B: Variants known. Another edition, assigned to Antoine Lambillon and Marinus Saracenus at Lyon, has the date 1494 at the end of the text—GW 263; Klebs 1050.1; Cen A51.

ZACUTO, Abraham Ben-Ṣemū'ēl, *Rabbi, c.* 1450–1510.

123 Almanach perpetuum . . . Radix est 1473 (Tr: Josephus Vizinus). Leiria: Abraham Dortas, 1496. 4°.

Ref: GW 115; Klebs 1054.1; AmBCat 542n; *Thornd*(*S&T*) 148; *Kennedy*(*IAT*) X215; Stillwell Z14; Goff Z-14.
N.B: Known at Evora in a Spanish version, Leiria, 1496 (GW 116) and cited in editions printed at Venice in 1496 and 1499 (GW 116a, 116b). The work had been used in manuscript by Columbus and other early navigators, and it long continued to be consulted.

ZIEGLER, Jakob, *fl.* 1530?, *ed.*

124 Sphaerae atque astrorum coelestium ratio, natura, & motus [*Greek and Latin*]. Basel: Johann Walder, 1536. 4°.

Ref: Zinner (ALD) 1653; *Wightman* (1962) II 752.
N.B: A compilation including among its various tracts Ziegler's *De solidae sphaerae constructione*; Proclos's *De sphaera scholiis Ziegleri*; the *Planisphaerium* of Ptolemy; the *De siderum natura & motu* of Aratos [*spurious?*], with the commentary of Theōn; and the *Hemicyclium* [*sundial*] erroneously ascribed to Berosos.

SUBJECT ANALYSIS FOR
MATHEMATICS

[1] ALGEBRA: Cardano; Ghaligai; Pacioli; Roche; Rudolff; Scheubel; Schreiber; Stifel; Tartaglia; Van der Hoecke.

[2] ALGORISMS: *Algorithmus*; Beldamandis; Ciruelo; Huswirt; Jean de Linières; Joannes de Sacro Bosco; Licht; Peurbach; Widmann. [*The term* ALGORISM *denotes a simple arithmetic intended for practical use and generally employing Hindu-Arabic numerals.*]

[3] APPLIED MATHEMATICS—MATHEMATICAL GEOGRAPHY: Apianus; Berlinghieri; Fernel; Gemma; Glareanus; Joannes de Stobnicza; Oresme; Ptolemy, *Geographia, Planisphaerium*; Rojas Sarmiento; Stöffler; Waldseemüller; Werner.—NAVIGATION, see under TECHNOLOGY.—OPTICS (*i.e.*, Reflection and Refraction) Abū Alī al-Ḥasan [Alhazen]; Euclid; Grosseteste; Peckham; Ptolemy; Witelo.—PROPORTION (as applied in art, architecture, and anatomy) Dürer; Pacioli [*see also* TECHNOLOGY: Architecture].—SURVEYING, *see under* TECHNOLOGY.

[4] ARITHMETIC: Anianus; Apianus; *Arsmetrike*; *Arte dell'abbaco*; Boethius; Bonini; Borghi; Bradwardine; Calandri; Cardano; Chiarini; Chuquet; *Die maniere om te leeren cyffren . . .*; Feliciano; Gemma; *Introduction for to lerne . . .*; Isidorus Hispalensis; Jean de Meurs; Joannes de Gmunden; Johannes de Cusa; Jordanus de Nemore; Juan de Ortega; Köbel; Le Fèvre d'Étaples; Nicolas; Nicolaus de Cusa; Nicomachos; Pellos; Recorde; Reisch; Riese; Roche; Rudolff; Sanct Climent; Scheubel; Sfortunati; Stifel; Tagliente; Tunstall; Ventallol; Wagner; Widmann. [*Regional differences in the spelling of the word "arithmetic" will be noted in the various editions cited.*]

[5] GEOMETRY: Apollōnios; Archimedes; Autolycos; Boethius; Bradwardine; Dürer; Euclid; Eutocios; Gaurico; Hypsicles; Juan de Ortega; Proclos; Theodosios; Theōn; Vögelin; Werner.

[6] TRIGONOMETRY: Al-Battānī [Abategnius]; Apianus; Copernicus; Fine; Jābir ibn Aflah [Geber ibn Aphlas]; Menelaos; Peurbach; Ptolemy; Regiomontanus; Thābit ibn Qurra [Abū-l-Ḥasan Thābit ibn Qurra].

II. MATHEMATICS

and Allied Subjects

ABŪ ALĪ al-ḤASAN ibn al-Haitham (Alhazen; Allacen; Ibn al-Haitham), *c.* 965–1038.

125 De speculis comburentibus. (*Issued with* PTOLEMY, *fl.* 150. Quadripartitum. Louvain, 1545).

> *Ref*: Car p. 141.
> *N.B*: Relates to the reflection of light. Variously attributed also to Archimedes or to Ptolemy. [For discussion see J. Folge, p. 218–231 in *Bibliotheca Mathematica* 10 1929–31.] Alhazen's great work on optics appeared with that of Witelo, in an edition edited by Friedrich Risner and issued at Basel in 1572. His work on the cause of twilight was issued with the treatise *De crepusculis* of Pedro Nunes at Lisbon in 1542 (*no.* 717).

AL-BATTĀNĪ (*called* Abategnius; Albetegnius), *d.* 929.

126 De motu stellarum (Tr: Plato Tiburtinus [Plato of Tivoli], *fl.* 1140). (*Issued with* AL-FARGHĀNĪ. Compilatio astronomica. Nuremberg: Joannes Petreius, 1537.)

> *Ref*: BM-Ger 11; *Sart* I 602, II 177–179.
> *N.B*: The third chapter relates to trigonometry and makes use of sines, tangents, and cotangents. One of the earliest Arabic treatises on trigonometry known. [See also THĀBIT ibn Qurra.]

ALGORITHMUS.

127 Algorithmus [*German*]. [Trent: Albrecht Kunne, *c.* 1475.] 4°.

> *Ref*: GW 1279; Klebs 53.1.
> *N.B*: Known only in a copy at the Fürst-Georgs Bibliothek at Dessau.

128 —— [*Italian*]. Venice: Adam von Rottweil, *c.* 1476/78.] f°.

> *Ref*: GW 1280; Klebs 52.1.
> *N.B*: Known only in a copy at the Staatsbibliothek at Vienna.

129 Algorithmus integrorum cum probis annexis. [Leipzig: Martin Landsberg, *c.* 1490/95.] 4°. [LEK]

Algorithmus integrorum (continued)

> *Ref:* a) GW 1272; Klebs 55.1; Stillwell A415; Goff A-461. b) GW 1273; Klebs 55.2; Pr 2959 A; BMC III 638; BM-Ger 21.
>
> *N.B:* Sometimes attributed to Johannes Widmann, 1440–1524. Two variants known, as noted above.

130   Algorithmus linealis.   [Leipzig: Martin Landsberg, *c.* 1495.]   4°.

> *Ref:* a) GW 1269; Klebs 54.1; Stillwell A416; Goff A-462. b) GW 1270; Pr 2961; Klebs 54.2; BMC III 638. c) GW 1271; H *828; BMC III 638; BM-Ger 21; Klebs 54.3; Stillwell A417; Goff A-463.
>
> *N.B:* According to *RA* 30, this is the first printed work on calculating with the aid of counters. Sometimes attributed to Johannes Widmann, 1440–1524. Three variants known, as noted above.

131   Algorithmus minutiarum physicarum.   [Leipzig: Martin Landsberg, *c.* 1490/95.]   4°.

> *Ref:* GW 1275; Klebs 57.1; Stillwell A418; Goff A-464.
>
> *N.B:* Sometimes attributed to Johannes Widmann, 1440–1524. Relates to sexagesimal fractions.

132   Algorithmus minutiarum vulgarium.   [Leipzig: Martin Landsberg, *c.* 1490/95.]   4°.

> *Ref:* GW 1274; Pr 2962; BMC III 638; BM-Ger 21; Klebs 56.1; Stillwell A419; Goff A-465.
>
> *N.B:* Relates to common fractions.

133   Algorithmus novus de integris, de minutiis vulgaribus et de physicalibus.   [Cologne: Cornelis de Zierikzee, *c.* 1500.]   4°.

> *Ref:* *a)* GW 1278; H *826; Voull (K) 98; Klebs 58.3. *b)* GW 1276; HC *825; Klebs 58.1; BMC I 308; Goff A-466. *b, var)* GW 1277; H *827; Voull (K) 99; Pell 514; Klebs 58.2; Stillwell A420; Goff A-467.
>
> *N.B:* Sometimes assigned to as early as about 1491. Known in two editions and a variant, as noted above.
>
> *Fac:* RA 45 (*b, var*).

ANIANUS, *variously assigned to the 13th and 15th centuries.*

134   Computus manualis cum commento.   Strasbourg: Johann Prüss, 14 Nov. 1488.   4°.   [LEK]

> *Add:* JOANNES de Sacro Bosco. De arte numerandi seu Algorismus vulgaris.
>
> *Ref:* GW 1951; H *1109; BMC I 121; BM-Ger 34; Oates 209; IGI 573; Klebs 71.3; Sart II 992; Stillwell A644; Goff A-732.
>
> *N.B:* The first *dated* edition of a computus. Based on finger reckoning. (For two undated editions, listed by Klebs as earlier, see GW 1983 and 1984.) An edition

printed by Matthias Huss is assigned to Lyon about 1492 (Schullian (ArMed) 41, with reproduction of F. 18a). GW 1951–1984 records 34 editions before 1501; Klebs lists 37 in 3 series. Also known as *Computus metricus*.

Mon: SMITH, David Eugene. *Le comput manuel de Magister Anianus*. Paris, 1928.

APIANUS, Petrus (Peter Bienewitz; *called* Apian), 1495–1552.

135 Cosmographiae introductio cum quibusdam geometriae ac astronomiae principiis ad eam rem necessariis. Ingolstadt: [In aedibus Apiani] 1529/31. 12°. [LEK]

Ref: Van Ortroy (Apian) 81.

N.B: One of three editions having a 1529 titlepage but a variant date in the colophon. With running-title: *Rudimenta cosmographiae*. According to Van Ortroy, an abridgement of Apian's *Cosmographicus liber* of 1524. Heawood's monograph on *Glareanus: his geography and maps* (The Geographical Journal, June 1905), calls attention to the fact that Apian here appropriated considerable of the text from his *De geographia liber I* printed at Basel in 1527.

136 Cosmographicus liber. Landshut: Johannes Weyssenburger, Jan. 1524. 4°. [LEK]

Ref: BM-Ger 37; Van Ortroy (Apian) 22; *Crombie (A–G)* 1961, II 246.

N.B: Relates to longitude and latitude and the position of important towns. The name of Gemma *Frisius* (Gemma Regnier) as editor appears in the Antwerp edition of February 1529 and thereafter [see under TECHNOLOGY].

137 Eyn Newe Vnnd wolgegründte vnderweysung aller Kauffmanns Rechnung [*German*]. Ingolstadt: Georg Apian, 9 Aug. 1527. 8°. [LEK]

Ref: RA 155; Smith (HM) I 333, II 508–510; *Taton (BMS)* 32–33.

N.B: With titlepage showing a so-called 'Pascal triangle,' a century before Pascal investigated its properties. Important also because the author, like Chuquet, began arithmetical progressions with zero.

Fac: RA 156, showing the triangle and a cut of a line counter. Also reproduced in Smith (HM) II 508.

138 Introductio Geographica. Ingolstadt: [In aedibus Apiani] 1533. f°.

Ref: BM-Ger 37; Van Ortroy (Apian) 101.

N.B: An influential work containing Johann Werner's correction of the meridians in Ptolemy's second projection, with an introduction by Apian. The appended translation of the first Book of Ptolemy's *Geographia* is not only that of Johann Werner, published in 1514, but it seems literally to comprise sheets from that volume.

[For his *Astronomicum Caesareum*, 1540, and various other works, see under ASTRONOMY.]

II. *Mathematics*

APOLLŌNIOS of Perga (Apollonius), *c.* 262–190 B.C.

139 Opera, libri I–IV (Tr: Giovanni Battista Memo). Venice: Bernardino Bindoni, 1537. f°.

> *Ref*: BM-Ital 34; *Sart (Appr)* 142–144; *O'Leary* 30, 31.
> *N.B*: Contains Books I–IV of his theory of conics, one of the greatest scientific books of antiquity. The Greek text of Books V–VIII is lost. Books V–VII are known in Arabic text; Book VIII lost. Dreyer (HA) 152, in stating that the known writings of Apollōnios relate solely to pure mathematics, also notes that, according to Ptolemy's *Almagest*, Apollōnios played an important part in the development of planetary theory.
> *Mon*: HEATH, *Sir* T. L. *Apollonius of Perga: Treatise on conic sections.* Cambridge, 1896. NEUGEBAUER, O. *Apollonius-Studien* (p. 215–254 in *Quellen und Studien zur Geschichte der Mathematik.* Abt. B, II, 1932).

ARCHIMEDES of Syracuse (Archimenides), *c.* 287–212 B.C.

140 Opera [*Greek and Latin*]. (Comm: Eutocios, *fl.* 500. Tr: Jacopo da Cremona, *fl.* 1450. Corr: Regiomontanus [Johann Müller of Königsberg], 1436–1476. Ed: Thomas Geschauff [*called* Ventorius], *fl.* 1540.) Basel: Johann Herwagen, 1544. f°. [LEK]

> *Ref*: Horblit 5; BM-Ger 39; *Sart (HS)* II 72–84.
> *N.B*: The first edition of Archimedean texts in Greek and a more important edition than the Latin *Opera* of 1543. In four parts: I–II, Archimedes in Greek and Latin; III–IV, the commentaries of Eutocios of Ascalon, *fl.* 500, in Greek and Latin—an inclusion which, although having a separate titlepage and registration, is listed in the general table of contents. The Eutocios is thus an integral part of the volume, although apparently issued also as a separate.
> The table of contents lists the following works: De sphaera et cylindro. Circuli dimensio. De conoidibus et sphaerodibus. De lineis spiralibus. Planorum aequeponderantium inventa. De harenae numero. Quadratura parabolae. Eutocii ... commentarius ... de sphaera et cylindro. In circuli dimensionem. In primum et secundum aequeponderantium. (The *Circuli dimensio* and the *Quadratura parabolae*, however, had been issued in 1503, and the *Planorum aequeponderantium inventa* in the Latin *Opera* of 1543 as noted under PHYSICS.)
> The Latin *Opera* of 1543 and particularly this Greek edition of Archimedes's works mark the beginning of the so-called Archimedean renaissance, which gained further impetus from Commandino's rendering published by Paulus Manutius at Venice in 1558.
> *Mon*: See below under the *Opera* of 1543.
> *Fac*: Horblit 5 [b].

141 Opera (Tr: William of Moerbeke, *c.* 1215–1286. Ed: Nicolò Fontana, *called* Tartaglia, *c.* 1506–1557). Venice: Venturino Ruffinelli, 1543. 4°. [LEK]

II. *Mathematics*

Ref: BM-Ital 36; *Sart* (*HS*) II 68–86; *Heath* (*HGM*) II 26; *Clagett* (*Arch*) I 13.

N.B: The first printing of some of Archimedes's works. The *Measurement of the circle* (*Circuli dimensio*) and the *Quadrature of the parabola* (*Quadratura parabolae*), which are included in this edition, had already been published, however, by Luca Gaurico at Venice in 1503, and according to Heath, portions of Archimedes's texts appeared in Valla's *De expetendis et fugiendis rebus*, Venice, 1501 (BM-Ital 709). [For notes on Archimedes's works on statics and hydrostatics, see under PHYSICS.]

Mon: HEIBERG, J. L., *ed. Archimedis opera omnia cum commentarii Eutocii*, 3 vols. Leipzig, 1910–1915. HEATH, *Sir* Thomas. *The works of Archimedes*, Cambridge, 1897; Suppl., 1912; *also* New York, Dover, 1953. DIJKSTERHUIS, E. J. *Archimedes* (Acta Historica Scientiarum Naturalium et Medicinalium, XII, Copenhagen, 1956), *in English translation*. CLAGETT, Marshall. *The impact of Archimedes on Medieval science* (p. 419–429 in *Isis* 50, 1959); *Archimedes in the Middle Ages*, vol. I. Madison, 1964. [See also monographs cited under no. 731.]

142   Circuli dimensio. Quadratura parabolae. (*Issued in* GAURICO, Luca, 1475–1558, *ed*. Tetragonismus. Venice: Giovanni Battista Sessa, 1503.) 4°.

Ref: BM-Ital 292.

N.B: The first printing of any of Archimedes's works.

Mon: CLAGETT, Marshall. *Archimedes in the Middle Ages, the* "*De mensura circuli*" (p. 587–618 in *Osiris* 10 1952, with translations).

Fac: *Sart* (*HS*) II 84.

ARSMETRIKE.

143   Arsmetrike and whereof it proceedeth. (*Bk. X in* MYRROUR of the worlde. [Westminster: William Caxton, 1481.]) f °. [LEK]

Ref: HC 11656; Pr 9638; Klebs 531.1; LC(LJRCat) 401; *RA* 10 *note*; Stillwell M758; Goff M-883.

N.B: The earliest printed reference to arithmetic in English.

ARTE DELL' ABBACO.

144   Arte dell' abbaco [*Italian*]. Treviso: [Michele Manzolo] 10 December 1478. 8°.

Ref: GW 2674; HCR 1863; BMC VI 833 *note*; Oates 2456; IGI 906; Klebs 115.1; *RA* 3; Stillwell A1009; Goff A-1141.

N.B: The first *dated* arithmetic printed. Variously assigned also to the press of Gerardus de Lisa, de Flandria. With diagrams showing multiplication and the "galley form" of division employed before the introduction and acceptance of long division (*RA* 4–7, *fac*.). [For arithmetics of possibly earlier date, see under ALGORISMS.]

II. *Mathematics*

AUTOLYCOS of Pitane, *fl.* 300 B.C.

145 De sphaera quae movetur. De ortibus et occasibus libri duo. (*In* VALLA, Giorgio, 1447–1499, *ed*. De expetendis et fugiendis rebus. Venice: In aedibus Aldi [Aldus Manutius], Dec. 1501.) f°.

> *Ref*: BMC-Ital 709; *RA* 71; *Heath (HGM)* I 348–352; *Sart* I 141; *Sart (Appr)* 149, 217:53.
>
> *N.B*: According to Dr. Sarton, who had access to the copy of Valla at Harvard University, these two treatises on spherical geometry—the handmaiden to astronomy before the introduction of trigonometry—are included in Book XVI of Valla's encyclopaedia of 1501. The two books *On the risings and settings* have been found to be two versions of the same work—see note in Neugebauer (ESA) 1957, 226.
>
> *Mon*: MOGENET, Joseph. *Autolycus*. Louvain, 1950.

BELDAMANDIS, Prosdocimus de, *c*. 1380–1428.

146 Algorithmus de integris. Padua: [Matthaeus Cerdonis] 22 Feb. 1483. 4°. [LEK]

> *Add*: JOHANNES de Liveriis [Jean de Linières]. De minutiis physicis.
>
> *Ref*: GW 3799; HCR 2753; BMC VII 920; BM-Ital 78; IGI 1442; Klebs 167.1; *Smith (HM)* II 502; *RA* 13; Stillwell B262; Goff B-299.
>
> *Fac*: *RA* 14; *Osiris* 5 1938, *fig.* 36.

BERLINGHIERI, Francesco, 1440–1501.

147 Geographia in terza rima et lingua toscana [*Italian*]. (*With additions by* Marsilio Ficino, 1433–1499). [Florence: Nicolaus Laurentii, not after 1480]. f°. [LEK]

> *Ref*: GW 3870; H *2825; BMC VI 629; IGI 1491–92; Klebs 812.4; Stillwell B298; Goff B-342.
>
> *N.B*: An adaptation of Ptolemy's *Geographia*. Known in two issues: the first, unsigned and undated as noted above; the second, undated and apparently in later type, with an added final leaf stating in its colophon that the book was printed at Florence by Nicolò Todescho. A copy of the unsigned issue, at Constantinople, bears the presentation date 1480. Maps metal-engraved; with the world map on a conical projection with curved meridians as in Ptolemy's projection B; and regional maps in the early concept of parallels and meridians intercepting at right angles, a form introduced by Marinos of Tyre, *fl.* 120, and Ptolemy, *fl.* 150.

BOETHIUS, Anicius Manlius Severinus, *c*. 480–524.

148 Arithmetica. Augsburg: Erhard Ratdolt, 20 May 1488. 4°. [LEK]

> *Ref*: GW 4586; HC *3426; BMC II 381; BM-Ger 134; Klebs 191.1; *RA* 25–28; Stillwell B743; Goff B-828.
>
> *Fac*: *Osiris* 5 1938, *fig.* 14.

149 De geometria libri duo (*in vol. I of his* Opera. Venice: Joannes and Gregorius de Gregoriis, 1491/92).

> *Ref*: GW 4511; H*3351; BMC V 341; Oates 1803; IGI 1816; *RA* 28, 29 *fac*; Stillwell B683; Goff B-767.
> *N.B*: The authenticity of these two books on geometry frequently attributed to Boethius has been questioned, as possibly a redaction of Euclid dating from a later period, the ninth or tenth century.

BONINI, Pietro Maria, *early 16th century.*

150 Lucidario darithmetica. Florence: Gianstephano di Carlo, 7 Jan. 1517. 8°.

> *Ref*: *RA* 122.
> *N.B*: Relates to commercial problems of exchange and to mensuration.
> *Fac*: *RA* 123.

BORGHI, Pietro (Borgo), *d. after 1494.*

151 Arithmetica [*Italian*]. Venice: Erhard Ratdolt, 2 August 1484. 4°. [LEK]

> *Ref*: GW 4936; HCR 3660; BMC V 289; IGI 2009; Klebs 205.1; *RA* 16–18; Stillwell B919; Goff B-1034.
> *N.B*: Relates to operations with integers, fractions, compound numbers, mercantile rules, currency, commercial problems, barter, and matters relative to partnership. The second commercial arithmetic printed in Italy.
> *Mon*: SMITH, David Eugene. *The first great commercial arithmetic* (p. 41–49 in *Isis* 8 1926).
> *Fac*: BORGHI, P. *Arithmetica, 1484.* Munich: Graphos-Verlag, 1964 (with foreword and bibliography by Kurt Elfering).

BRADWARDINE, Thomas, 1290?–1349.

152 Arithmetica speculativa (Corr: Pedro Sánchez Ciruelo, *c.* 1470 – *c.* 1550). Paris: Gui Marchand, Feb. 1495/96. 4°. [LEK]

> *Ref*: GW 5003; Pr 7998; BMC VIII 61; Oates 2960; LC(LJRCat) 360; Klebs 209.1; *Sart* III 668; *RA* 61 *note*; Goff B-1071.

153 Geometria speculativa (Corr: Pedro Sánchez Ciruelo, *c.* 1470–*c.* 1550). Paris, Gui Marchand, 20 May 1495. f°. [LEK]

> *Ref*: GW 5002; HCR 3712; BMC VIII 61; BM-Fr 80; Oates 2959; Klebs 208.1; *Sart* III 668; Stillwell B954; Goff B-1072.
> *N.B*: Divided into four parts, for an analysis of which see Sart III 669.

CALANDRI, Filippo, *late 15th century*.

154 Pictagoras arithmetrice introductor [*Italian*]. Florence: Lorenzo de Morgianis and Johannes Petri, 1 Jan. 1491/92. 8°. [LEK]

> *Ref*: GW 5884; HCR 4234; BMC VI 681; BM-Ital 136; Oates 2423; IGI 2352; Klebs 236.1; LC(LJRCat) 233; Stillwell C30; Goff C-34.
> *N.B*: The first printed Italian arithmetic. Employs a system of long division (*RA* 47, *fac.*). Contains tables of money exchange and calculations of money and weight. With illustrated problems. Variant known, with colophon giving the printers as Lorenzo de Morgiani and Giovanni Thedesco da Maganza.

CAMPANO, Giovanni, da Novara. *See no. 163 note*.

CARDANO, Girolamo (*called* Cardan), 1501–1576.

155 Artis magnae sive De regulis algebraicis liber I... Nuremberg: Johann Petreius, 1545. f°.

> *Ref*: BM-Ger 182; Smith (*HM*) I 295; Ore (*Card*) 48; Lindsay (*JC*) 314; Taton (*BMS*) 38.
> *N.B*: According to Dr. Oystein Ore, a book as important to mathematics as were those of Copernicus and Vesalius to astronomy and anatomy. Although not the earliest printed, this is the first important treatise devoted solely to algebra to be published. A second treatise in the volume relates to mathematics, in 10 Books. In addition, the *Ars magna* contains the solution to the cubic equation by Nicolò [Fontana] Tartaglia, *c.* 1506–1557, and the equation of the 4th degree by Ludovico Ferrari, 1522–1565. In a subsequent dispute between Tartaglia and Cardano regarding this publication, Ferrari defended the latter in a volume addressed to Tartaglia and printed at Milan about 1547 (BM-Ital 247). Tartaglia's *Risposta* is listed in BM-Ital 658. For accounts of the dispute, see ARCHIBALD, R. C. *Outline History of Mathematics*, 4th ed., 1939, p. 28; LINDSAY, R. B. *Jerome Cardan, 1501–1576* (p. 314–315 in *American Journal of Physics*, vol. 16, May 1948); ORE, O. *The battles of the scholars* (p. 53–107 in his *Cardano, the gambling scholar*, Princeton, 1953).

156 Practica arithmetice et mensurandi singularis. Milan: Giovanni Antonino de Castiglione, 1539. 8°. [LEK]

> *Ref*: BM-Ital 149, 805; *RA* 193, 194 *fac.*; Smith (*HM*) I 295; Ore (*Card*) 11, 65; Lindsay (*JC*) 314.
> *N.B*: A theoretical work for advanced students and for the use of scholars. One of the most influential arithmetics produced in Italy.

CHIARINI, Giorgio, *15th century*.

157 Libro che tratta di mercanzie et vsanze paesi [*Italian*]. Florence: Francesco di Dino, 10 Dec. 1481. 4°. [LEK]

Ref: HR 4956; BMC VI 633; IGI 2747; Klebs 271.1; *RA* 10; Stillwell C404; Goff C-449.

N.B: Relates to rates of exchange employed by Florentine merchants. Re-issued at Florence about 1497 (Cen C405), and included in part in Pacioli's general treatise, *Somma di aritmetica*, Venice, 14[9]4 (Cen L282).

CHUQUET, Nicolas, *fl.* 1484. *See under* ROCHE, Estienne de la—*no. 224 note*.

CIRUELO, Pedro Sánchez (Petrus Cirvellus), *c.* 1470 – *c.* 1550.

158 Algorismus. Paris: Gui Marchand, 22 Feb. 1495/96. 4°. [LEK]

Ref: GW 7052, 7053; BMC VIII 69; BM-Fr 115; Klebs 277.1 and .1 *var*.
N.B: *Text begins*: Tractatus arithmethice pratice qui dicitur Algorismus.

CLICHTOVE, Josse (Jodocus Clichtovus), 1472–1543.

159 De mystica numerorum significatione opusculum. Paris: Henricus Stephanus (Henri Estienne), 16 Dec. 1513. 4°.

Ref: BM-Fr 117; Renouard (Estienne) 15:5; *RA* 94-95.
N.B: Relates to the mystery of numbers and contains a section on finger reckoning.

COPERNICUS, Nicolaus (Niklas Koppernigk), 1473–1543.

160 De lateribus et angulis triangulorum. Wittenberg: Johann Lufft, 1542. 4°.

Ref: BM-Ger 221.
N.B: Edited by Georg Joachim Rheticus, 1514–1576. L. C. Karpinski in his checklist of books on trigonometry (*Scripta Math.* 12 1946) notes copies at the British Museum and Cornell University.

DÜRER, Albrecht, 1471–1528.

161 Vnderweyssung der Messung mit dem Zirckel vñ Richtscheyt, in Linien, Ebnen, vnnd gantzen Corporen [*German*]. [Nuremberg: Hieronymus (Andreae), *Formschneider*] 1525. f°. [LEK]

Ref: BM-Ger 256; LC(LJRCat) 464; *Smith* (HM) I 326; II 296, 328; *Taton* (BMS) 29-30.
N.B: Relates to polyhedrons and the epicycloid, with some treatment of perspective and descriptive geometry. Diagrams show the use of a geometric base in the designing of initial letters and in charting the human figure. Re-issued at [Nuremberg] in 1538—LC(LJRCat) 477. [For his work on anatomical proportion, see NATURAL SCIENCE.]
Mon: CROUS, Ernst. *Dürer und die Schrift mit einer Wiedergabe von Dürers Abhandlung aus seiner "Unterweisung der Messung."* Berlin, 1933, with diagrams showing the

Dürer (continued)

mathematical proportions of his initials. GROLIER CLUB, The. (New York) *Of the just shaping of letters from the Applied Geometry of Albrecht Dürer, book III.* New York [London], 1917. GÜNTHER, S. *Die geometrischen Näherungskonstruktionen Albrecht Dürers.* Ansbach, 1886. PANOFSKY, Erwin. *Dürer as a mathematician* [with "*Commentary on Dürer and the mathematics of painting*"] (p. 600–621 in *The world of mathematics.* James R. Newman, *ed.* Vol. I. New York, 1956).

EUCLID (Eucleidēs), *fl.* 300 B.C.

162   Catoptrica. (*Issued in* VALLA, Giorgio, 1447–1499, *ed.* De expetendis et fugiendis rebus opus. Venice: Impensa I.P. Vallae in aedibus Aldi, Dec. 1501.) f°. [LEK]

Ref: BM-Ital 709; Renouard (Alde) 72.
N.B: Relates to mirrors and the law of reflection. Authorship questioned. Included also in Euclid's *Opera*, in Zamberti's translation issued at Venice by Joannes Tacuinus in 1505—BM-Ital 238; Th-Stan p. 3; *Heath (HGM)* I 444.
Mon: LEJEUNE, Albert. *Recherches sur la catoptrique grecque.* Bruxelles, 1957.

163   Elementa geometriae (Tr: Adelhard of Bath?, *c.* 1110–1142) (Ed: Giovanni Campano, da Novara, *c.* 1260–1292). Venice: Erhard Ratdolt, 25 May 1482. f°. [LEK]

Ref: GW 9428; HC *6693; Oates 1748; IGI 3722; Klebs 383.1; Horblit 27; Stillwell E86; Goff E-113. a) BMC V 285, IB 20514; Pell 4630A. b) BMC V 286, IB 20513; Pell 4630; AmBCat 254.
N.B: The first edition of a work that has held its place as a basic text for more than two thousand years. In the version of Campano, a translation from Arabic into Latin presumably derived from the 12th-century translation of Abelhard of Bath, together with notes by Campano. A sumptuous and decorative volume. The first dated book with diagrams, which are set in a wide margin close to the theorems to which they relate and are notable for their clearcut delineation.

In two issues, in which the first nine leaves are differently set and other variations occur. These may be roughly identified by the fact that in issue a) the first line ends with "impres," whereas in issue b) the line ends with the word "Serenissimo." At least four vellum copies of issue a) are known in which the dedication to the Doge of Venice is printed in gold. Presumably this is the earlier of the two issues, a theory further substantiated by the fact that in issue b) certain errors are corrected.

Books I–III are accepted as genuine. Book XIV is accepted as the work of Hypsicles, *fl. 2nd century* B.C. (O'Leary 31), and Book XV, according to GW (as noted above) is the work of "eines römischen Feldmessers des 6. Jhs.," variously believed to be a sixth-century pupil of Isidoros of Miletos. The first printing of a translation of Euclid from a Greek text (made by Bartolommeo Zamberti, *fl.* 1480) was issued by Joannes Tacuinus at Venice in 1505. The first printing of the Greek text itself was produced by Johann Herwagen at Basel in 1533, under the editorship of Simon Grynaeus, *d.* 1541. At least forty editions, in whole or in part, were issued before the end of 1550.

Mon: WEISSENBORN, H. *Die Uebersetzungen des Euklid durch Campano und Zamberti*, Halle, 1882. THOMAS-STANFORD, Charles. *Early editions of Euclid's Elements*, London, 1926. HEATH, *Sir* Thomas. *Euclid's Elements in English*, 3 v., Cambridge, 1926; *The thirteen books of Euclid's Elements*, Dover, 1956. CLAGETT, Marshall. *The Medieval Latin translations from the Arabic of the Elements of Euclid, with special emphasis on the versions of Abelard of Bath* (p. 16–42 in *Isis* 44 1953). SARTON, George. *Euclid of Alexandria* (p. 136–140 in his *Appreciation of Ancient and Medieval science*, Philadelphia, 1955; and also p. 35–52 in his *History of science*, II, Cambridge [Mass.], 1959.

Fac: Th-Stan *fig.* Ia, Ib, II; *Osiris* 5 1938, *fig.* 6; Horblit 27 [c–f].

164　Perspectiva seu Optica. (*Issued in* VALLA, Giorgio, 1447–1499, *ed.* De expetendis et fugiendis rebus opus. Venice: In aedibus Aldi [Aldus Manutius], Dec. 1501.)　f°.　[LEK]

Ref: BM-Ital 709; Renouard (Alde) 72.

N.B: In the recension of Theōn. Issued also by Joannes Tacuinus in Euclid's *Opera*, in Zamberti's translation, Venice, 1505—BM-Ital 238; Th-Stan p. 3; *Heath* (*HGM*) I 441.

Mon: LEJEUNE, Albert. *Euclide et Ptolémée, deux stades de l'optique géométrique grecque.* Louvain, 1948. HEIBERG, Johann Ludwig. *Beiträge zur Geschichte Georg Vallas und seiner Bibliothek.* Leipzig, 1896 (Beihefte zum Centralblatt für Bibliothekswesen, XVI).

EUTOCIOS of Ascalon, *fl.* 500.

165　In eosdem Archimedis libros commentaria [*Greek and Latin*]. (In ARCHIMEDES, *c.* 287–212 B.C. Opera [*Greek and Latin*]. Basel: Johann Herwagen, 1544.)　f°.

Ref: BM-Ger 39; *Sart* (*HS*) II 81, 84, *fac.*

N.B: Comprises commentaries on the treatises *De sphaera et cylindro*, *De circuli dimensione*, and *Planorum aequeponderantium inventa*.

FABER Stapulensis, Jacobus. *See* LE FÈVRE d'Étaples, Jacques.

FELICIANO, Francesco, da Lazisio, *c.* 1500–1563.

166　Libro de abaco [*Italian*].　Venice: Nicolò Zoppino, 1517/18.　[LEK]

Ref.: *Sart* (*Appr*) 153; *RA* 146 *note.*

N.B: One of the most popular Italian arithmetics of the period.

Feliciano (continued)

167 Libro di arithmetica et geometria . . . intitulato Scala gramaldelli [*Italian*]. Venice: Francesco di Alessandro Bindoni and Mapheo Pasini, *compagni*, 1526/27. 4°. [LEK]

> Ref: *RA* 146, 147 *fac*; Sart (*Appr*) 153.
> N.B: A widely used textbook and revision of the author's *Libro de abaco* published in 1517/18. Influenced by the writings of Borghi and of Pacioli. The titlepage has a cut of a ladder and a skeleton key.

FERNEL, Jean, 1497–1558.

168 Cosmotheoria. Paris: Simon de Colines, 1528. f°.

> Ref: Renouard (Colines) 116; Sart (*SW*) 194; *Wightman* (1962) II 247.
> N.B: On the size and shape of the earth. According to Dr. Sarton, the text contains the measurement of a meridian based upon the distance between Paris and Amiens, which have nearly the same longitude; a measurement repeated by Jean Picard with greater precision in his *Mesure de la terre*, Paris, 1671.
> Mon: SHERRINGTON, Charles, Sir. *The endeavor of Jean Fernel, with a list of the editions of his writings*. Cambridge, University Press, 1946.

FINE, Oronce, 1494–1555.

169 De mundi sphaera, sive cosmographia, primave astronomiae parte lib. V . . . Rectarum in circuli quadrante subtensarum (quos sinus vocant) demonstratio . . . Organum universale . . . quo tum geometrici, tum omnes astronomici canones ex quatuor sinuum proportione pendentes mira facilitate practicantur. Paris: Simon de Colines, 1542. 8°.

> Ref: BM-Fr 166; Karp(T) 268; Renouard (Colines) 358; *Taton* (*A&MS*) 44.
> N.B: Colines had already published the author's *Arithmetica practica* in 1535.

GAURICO, Luca, 1475–1558, *ed.*

170 Tetragonismus, idest circuli quadratura per Campanum, Archimedem Syracusanum atque Boetium, adinventa. Venice: Giovanni Battista Sessa, 1503. 4°.

> Ref: BM-Ital 292.
> Fac: Sart (*HS*) II 84.

GEMMA, (Gemma Regnier of Frisia; Gemma *Frisius*), 1508–1555.

171 Arithmeticae practicae methodus facilis. Antwerp: Georgius Bontius, 1540. 8°. [LEK]

Ref: Sart (*Appr*) 157; Smith (*HM*) I 341; *RA* 200 *note.*

N.B: A popular textbook comprising ancient arithmetical theories with commercial practices. More than fifty editions were published before the end of the century.

172 Libellus de locorum describendorum ratione & de eorum distantiis inveniendis. (*Issued with his edition of* APIANUS, Petrus, 1495–1552. Cosmographicus liber. Antwerp: Joannes Grapheus, Feb. 1533.) [LEK]

Ref: Van Ortroy (Apian) 26, 27 (*var*); Smith (*HM*) I 342.

N.B: The first treatise on topographical triangulation. Variant imprints known. Gemma's method proved applicable and valuable to surveying, as well as to mapping. [For his work on mathematical navigation, see under TECHNOLOGY: Navigation. See also note under APIANUS. *Cosmographicus liber.* Landshut, 1524.]

Mon: VAN ORTROY, F. *Bio-bibliographie de Gemma Frisius fondateur de l'école belge de géographie* (ACADÉMIE ROYALE DE BELGIQUE. Mémoires. Classe des lettres, collection in-8°. 2me série, tome XI. Bruxelles, Dec. 1920). POGO, Alexander. *Gemma Frisius, his method of determining differences of longitude by transporting time-pieces (1530), and his treatise on triangulation (1533), with 4 plates and a facsimile reproduction of Gemma's* Libellus . . . (p. 469–504 in *Isis* 22 1934–35).

Fac: *Isis* 22 1934–35, pl. 18.

173 De principiis astronomiae & cosmographiae. Antwerp: Joannes Grapheus, Oct. 1530. [LEK]

Ref: Harrisse (BAV) 156, *Add* 92.

N.B: A work that marks the beginning of mathematical navigation. Chapter XVIII in the section *De usu globi,* under the heading *De novo modo inveniendi longitudinem,* introduces the method of employing differences in time for obtaining longitude, a principle still used today. Variant imprints known.

Mon: [See Van Ortroy and Pogo as noted in the preceding entry.]

Fac: *Isis* 22 1934–35, pl. 17, 19.

GHALIGAI, Francesco, *d.* 1536.

174 Summa de arithmetica [*Italian*]. Florence, 1521. [LEK]

Ref: *RA* 132, *note.*

N.B: Books X–XIII relate to algebra.

GLAREANUS (Heinrich Loritz, *or* Loriti; *called* Glareanus) 1488–1563.

175 De geographia liber I. Basel: Joannes Faber, 1527. sm. 4°. [LEK]

Ref: Harrisse (BAV) 142; BM-Ger 527.

N.B: In the course of this brief treatise on mathematical geography, a method is described for constructing gore-maps for use in the making of globes. [A manuscript at the John Carter Brown Library, upon which this 1527 edition was ap-

Glareanus (continued)

> parently based, shows a few minor variations from the printed text, which, how-
> ever, includes marginal corrections appearing in the manuscript. Included in the
> latter—which formerly belonged to Maj. Gen. E. Renouard James, R. E.—are
> handsome manuscript maps, similar to those at Bonn which date from about
> 1510. Among them are two hemispheric maps displaying for the first time
> equidistant polar projection, the North and South Hemispheres showing por-
> tions of the Americas and being in each case encompassed within a circle denoting
> the equator.]

Mon: Heawood, Edward. *Glareanus: His geography and maps* (*The Geographical Journal*, June 1905) with a reproduction in color of the North Polar map.

GROSSETESTE, Robert (Robertus Lincolniensis; *sometimes called* Lincoln), *c.* 1175–1253.

176 De physicis lineis angulis et figuris seu De fractionibus et reflexionibus radiorum (Ed: Andreas Stiborius Boius).   Nuremberg, [Johann Weissenberger] 1503.

> *Ref*: BM-Ger 372; Sart II 583; Wightman (1962) II 319.
>
> *Mon*: Crombie, A. C. *Robert Grosseteste and the origins of experimental science*, Oxford, 1953.   Turbayne, Colin M. *Grosseteste and an ancient optical principle* (p. 467–472 in *Isis* 50 1959).

HERODIANOS, Ailios, *fl.* 175.

177 De numeris [*Greek*]. (*Issued with* Gaza, Theodoros. Grammatica introductiva [*Greek*]. Venice: Aldus Manutius, 25 Dec. 1495.)   f°.

> *Ref*: HC *7500; BMC V 553; BM-Ital 293; Oates 2165; IGI 4181; Klebs 438.1; *Heath* (HGM) 1921, I 30; Sart I 312;   Stillwell G100; Goff G-110.
>
> *N.B*: Relates to the so-called Herodianic signs, the first letters of number words.

HUSWIRT, Johann, *late 15th century*.

178 Enchiridion novus algorismi de integris.   Cologne: In officina felicis memorie honesti viri Heinrich Quentell, 1501.   4°.   [LEK]

> *Ref*: BM-Ger 425; Pr 10359; *RA* 75 *fac.*

HYPSICLES of Alexandria, *c. 2nd century B.C.*

Interpretatio libri Euclidis. [The so-called 14th book of Euclid attributed to Hypsicles; included in the Campano rendering printed at Venice in 1482, and in various other early editions of Euclid—see no. 163 *note*.]

II. *Mathematics*

AN INTRODUCTION FOR TO LERNE TO RECKEN.

179 An introduction for to lerne to recken with the pen or with the counters. St. Albans: John Herford, 1537. [LEK]

> *N.B*: The origin of the text is discussed by Bockstaele, especially in its relation to the Dutch arithmetic entitled *Die maniere om te leeren cyffren na die rechte consten Algorismi int gheheele ende int ghebroken*. Brussels: Thomas van der Noot, 9 Sept. 1508. STC 14118 lists a London edition brought out by N. Bourman in 1539, and STC 14119 an edition printed at London by J. Herford in 1546.
>
> *Mon*: RICHESON, A. W. *The first arithmetic printed in English* (p. 47–56 in *Isis* 37 1947). BOCKSTAELE, P. *Notes on the first arithmetics printed in Dutch and English* (p. 315–321 in *Isis* 51 1960).

ISIDORUS Hispalensis (Isidore, *Bp. of Sevilla*), *St., c.* 570–636.

180 De vocabulario arithmetice discipline. (*In Bk. III of his* Etymologiae. [Augsburg:] Günther Zainer, 19 Nov. 1472.) [LEK]

> *Ref*: H *9273; BMC II 317; BM-Ger 432; IGI 5404; Klebs 536.2; Schullian (ArMed) 250; *RA* 8; Stillwell I153; Goff I-181.
>
> *N.B*: The first printed reference to arithmetic (5 ff.).

JĀBIR ibn Aflah (Geber ibn Aphlas), *fl.* 1145.

181 De astronomia libri IX in quibus Ptolemaeum . . . emendavit (Tr: Gherardo da Cremona, 1114–1187). (*Issued with* APIANUS, Petrus. Instrumentum primi mobilis. Nuremberg: Joannes Petreius, 1534.) f °.

> *Ref*: BM-Ger 37; Van Ortroy (Apian) 107; *Car* p. 163; *Sart* II 206.
>
> *N.B*: With a section on spherical trigonometry. [The author is not to be confused with the early chemist, Jābir ibn Ḥaiyān, called Geber.]

JEAN de Linières (Joannes Liverius; Jean de Lignières *or* Lineriis), *fl.* 1320–1350.

182 Algorithmus de minutiis physicis. (*Issued with* BELDAMONDIS. Algorithmus de integris. Padua: [Matthaeus Cerdonis], 22 Feb. 1483.)

> *Ref*: GW 3799; HCR 2753; BMC VII 920; BM-Ital 78; IGI 1442; *RA* 13, 14; *Sart* III 651; Stillwell B262; Goff B-299.
>
> *N.B*: Relates to common and sexagesimal fractions.

JEAN de Meurs (Jan de Meurs; Joannes de Muris), *fl.* 1300–1350.

183 Arithmetica communis ex . . . Boetij Arithmetice . . . compendiose excerpta. Vienna: Joannes Singrenius, 10 May 1515.

#I.*Mathematics*

II. *Mathematics*

Jean de Meurs *(continued)*

Ref: RA 117; Sart III 656.

N.B: Based on Boethius but more as a point of departure than as an actual commentary. Issued together with works by Bradwardine, Oresme, Peurbach, and Joannes de Gmunden, possibly as lectures for university use.

JOANNES de Gmunden, *c.* 1380–1442.

184 Tractatus de minucijs phisicis. (*Issued with* JEAN de Meurs. Arithmetica communis. Vienna: Joannes Singrenius, 10 May 1515.)

Ref: RA 117.
N.B: A treatise on sexagesimal fractions.

JOANNES de Sacro Bosco (*variously called* John of Holywood; Sacrobosco; Sacrobusto), *fl.* 1200–1250.

185 De arte numerandi seu Algorismus vulgaris. (*Issued with* ANIANUS. Compotus manualis. Strasbourg: Johann Prüss, 14 Nov. 1488.) [LEK]

Ref: GW 1951; H *1109; BMC I 121; BM-Ger 34; Oates 209; IGI 573; Sart II 618; Stillwell A644; Goff A-732.
N.B: The popularity of this simple and practical book of arithmetic is said to have influenced the acceptance of Hindu-Arabic numerals in the West.

JOANNES de Stobnicza (*called* Stobnicza; Johannes Stobniciensis), *fl.* 1510.

186 Introductio in Ptholomei cosmographiā. Cracow: Florianus Unglerius, 1512. 4°.

Ref: Harrisse (BAV) 69 + *Add.*
N.B: An abridgement of Ptolemy's *Cosmographia* [see no. 212], *cum longitudinibus et latitudinibus regionum et civitatum celebriorum.* With two medallions, the hemispheric projections, with minor changes, which were first printed in 1507 as ornaments at the top of Waldseemüller's great wall-map of the world. Although not named on the medallion showing the New World, "America" is mentioned in the text, on signature Ci verso.

JOHANNES de Cusa.

186b Algorismus proiectilium de integris novus. Zwolle: Arnoldus Kempen, 1502.

N.B: The first arithmetic printed in The Netherlands.
Mon: SMEUR, A. J. E. M. *De Zestiende-eeuwse Nederlandse Rekenboeken.* 's Gravenhage, 1960. [Pt. I, a bibliography of arithmetics printed in The Netherlands before 1601; Pt. II, a systematic discussion of the contents of the books listed in its Pt. I.]

II. *Mathematics*

JORDANUS de Nemore (Jordanus *Nemorarius*), *fl.* 1246(?).

187   Arithmetica decem libris (Comm: Le Fèvre d'Étaples, Jacques, 1455–1536).   Paris: Johann Higman and Wolfgang Hopyl, 22 July 1496.   f °.

> *Ref*: HC 9436; BMC VIII 137; BM-Fr 246; Oates 3032; Klebs 563.1; *RA* 62–64; Stillwell J425; Goff J-472.
> *N.B*: Relates to the theory of numbers.   The volume as a whole, however, is a compilation of works centering about Le Fèvre and containing his treatise on music, his epitome of Boethius's arithmetic, and an anonymous tract, *Rithmimachiae ludus*, variously attributed to him.
> *Fac*: *RA* 63.

JUAN de Ortega, *c.* 1495–1567.

188   Tratado subtilissimo de arismética y de geometria [*Spanish*].   Sevilla: Jacob Cromberger, 1512.   [LEK]

> *Ref*: *Sart (Appr)* 156.
> *N.B*: Professor Frick (p. 333 in *Scripta Mathematica* XI 1945) mentions an edition of Barcelona, 1512; and J. Rey Pastor (p. 155 in his *Los matemáticos espanoles del siglo XVI* [Madrid? 1926]) cites a 1512 edition printed at Lyon.   Its translation by Claude Platin—*Oeuvre très subtile . . . de l'art de science arisméticque . . .* Lyon: Estienne Balard, 1515 (BM-Fr 331)—rates as the first commercial arithmetic published both in France and in French.

KÖBEL, Jacob, 1470–1533.

189   Ein neu geordnetes Visierbuch [*German*].   Oppenheim: [Jacob Köbel, *private press*, after 22 March 1515].   4°.

> *Ref*: BM-Ger 475; Pr 11928; *RA* 113 *fac*.
> *N.B*: A book on gauging by a mathematician who operated his own press from about 1502 to 1518.

190   Ein new geordnet Rechenbiechlin auf den linien mit Rechenfeningen [*German*].   Augsburg: Erhart Öglin, 1514.   4°.   [LEK]

> *Ref*: BM-Ger 475; Pr 10717; *RA* 100, 103–5 *fac*.
> *N.B*: A popular book, often reprinted.

191   Mit der Kryden od' Schriebfedern durch die zeiferzal zu rechnen [*German*].   Oppenheim: [Jacob Köbel] 1520.   4°.   [LEK]

> *Ref*: BM-Ger 475; *Sart (Appr)* 154.
> *N.B*: Describes the solving of problems without using counters.   Subsequently reprinted with his *Rechenbiechlin*.

LE FÈVRE d'Étaples, Jacques (Jacobus Faber Stapulensis), *c.* 1455–1536.

192 Epitoma in duos libros arithmeticos Boetii. (*Issued with* JORDANUS de Nemore. Arithmetica. Paris: Johann Higman and Wolfgang Hopyl, 22 July 1496.) f°.

> *Ref:* HC 9436; BMC VIII 137; BM-Fr 246; Oates 3032; Klebs 563.1; *RA* 62–63; Stillwell J425; Goff J-472.
>
> *N.B:* See note under JORDANUS regarding Le Fèvre's editorship.

193 De ludo arithmomachiae, sive Rithmimachiae ludus. (*Issued with* JORDANUS de Nemore. Arithmetica. Paris: Johann Higman and Wolfgang Hopyl, 22 July 1496.) f°.

> *Ref:* HC 9436; BMC VIII 137; BM-Fr 246; Oates 3032; Klebs 563.1; *RA* 62; Stillwell J425; Goff J-472.
>
> *N.B:* Authenticity sometimes questioned. For the rules of the game, see RICHARDS, J. F. C. *Bossiere's Pythagorean game* (p. 213–214 in *Scripta Mathematica* XII. 1946). With reference to mathematical literature relative to games, see *Commentary on games and puzzles* (p. 2414–2415 in *The world of mathematics*. J. R. Newman, *ed.* vol. IV. New York, 1956).

LICHT, Balthasar, *late 15th century.*

194 Algorithmus linealis, cum conditionibus regulae de tri. Leipzig: Melchior Lotter [1500]. 4°.

> *Ref:* H *829; BMC III 652; BM-Ger 497; Klebs 604.1; *RA* 69, 70 *fac.*; Stillwell L176; Goff L-202.
>
> *N.B:* Variants known.

MARIANI, Giovanni, *16th century.*

195 Tariffa perpetua [*Italian*]. Venice: 1535. [LEK]

> *Ref:* Sart (*Appr*) 153; *RA* 180 *note.*
>
> *N.B:* Tables of interest and rates of exchange for Venetian usage and the towns of northern Italy.

MENELAOS of Alexandria, *1st century.*

196 Sphaericorum libri III. Messina, 1550(?).

> *Ref:* Karp (T) 268; Sart I 253; O'Leary 32.
>
> *N.B:* A treatise on spherical triangles and trigonometry. Karpinski lists a copy of this edition as at the Bibliothèque Nationale in Paris. The date, however, may possibly be a misprint for that of the 1558 Messina edition, which is usually accepted as the earliest known.

Mon: Krause, Max. *Die Sphärik von Menelaos aus Alexandrien in der Verbesserung von Abū Naṣr Manṣūr B. 'Alī B. 'Irāq* (Gesell. Wissensch. zu Göttingen. *Abhandlungen.* Philolog.-Hist. Klasse. Dritte Folge, no. 17. Berlin, 1936).

NICOLAS, Gaspar, *fl.* 1500.

197 Tratado da practica darismetyca. [Lisbon:] Germão Galharde, 1519. [LEK]

> *Ref*: *Sart* (*Appr*) 156.
> *N.B*: A practical arithmetic written for the use of Portuguese merchants in their "transactions with the merchants of India, Persia, Arabia, Ethiopia, and other places discovered by us."
> *Mon*: Frick, Bertha M. *The first Portuguese arithmetic* (p. 327–339 in *Scripta Mathematica.* XI 1945, with list of editions).

NICOLAUS de Cusa (Nicolaus Khrypffs of Cues; *called* Nicholas Krebs, Cusa, Cusanus), *Cardinal*, 1401–1464.

198 Opuscula theologica et mathematica. [Strasbourg: Martin Flach, about 1500.] f°. [LEK]

> *Ref*: HC *5893; BMC I 157, 158; Oates 262, 263; Polain 2814; IGI 6803, 6804; Klebs 700.1; *RA* 42; *Taton* (*BMS*) 13, 71; Stillwell N80; Goff N-97.
> *N.B*: A collection including tracts on arithmetic, mensuration, geometry, and reform of the calendar. Another undated edition (Goff N-96) is assigned in IGI, IV p. 129 to [Carpi: B. Dolcibelli, about 1502]. Cusa's treatise *De quadratura circuli* was issued at Nuremberg in 1533, with the *De triangulis omnimodis libri V* of Regiomontanus [*q.v.*].

NICOMACHOS of Gerasa (Nicomachus), *fl.* 100.

199 Nicomachi Gerasini arithmeticae libri duo [*Greek*]. Paris: In officina Christieni Wecheli, 1538. 4°.

> *Ref*: *RA* 186; *Sart* I 253, 425.
> *N.B*: The source from which the arithmetic of Boethius was derived. The text of Nicomachos presents the Pythagorean theory of numbers and contains the earliest mention of the so-called "mense Pythagorica," a multiplication table of Greek origin.
> *Mon*: Robbins, F. E. and L. C. Karpinski. *Nicomachus of Gerasa: Introduction to arithmetic* (Tr: M. L. D'Ooge). New York, 1926.
> *Fac*: *RA* 187.

NIDER, Johann, *d.* 1438.

200 De contractibus mercatorum. [Cologne: Ulrich Zel, *c.* 1470, or earlier] 4°. [LEK]

Nider (continued)

> *Ref:* HC *11822; BMC I 185; BM-Ger 653; Oates 328; Voull (K) 863; *Smith (HM)*
> II 563; Stillwell N149; Goff N-170.
>
> *N.B:* Discusses the payment of interest. Zel group C:2 (BMC). BMC II 513 and IGI
> 6888 list an edition assigned to Esslingen, 1474/75 (?).

ORESME, Nicole (*called* Orem; Nicolaus Horen), *c.* 1323–1382.

201   Traicté de l'espère [*French*].   Paris: Simon Dubois [*c.* 1505].   [LEK]

> *Ref:* Sart III 1490, 1496; *Taton (A&MS)* 503, 505–507; *Taton (BMS)* 19, 57.
>
> *N.B:* Re-issued by the same press in 1508. In this work relative to mathematical
> geography, written in French about 1361, Oresme was forced to coin many new
> scientific terms. The glossary thus developed is said to be responsible for much
> of the French scientific vocabulary of today. His important *Traité du ciel et du
> monde* has not been found in an early printed edition. For evaluation of his
> theories, see DURAND, D. B. *Nicole Oresme and the medieval origins of modern
> science* (p. 167–185 in *Speculum* 16 1941). His treatise *De moneta* appeared with
> Gerson's *Opera* in an edition issued at Cologne in 1483–1484 (Cen G168). [See
> Oresme also under PHYSICS.]

PACIOLI (Luca da Pacioli; Lucas de Burgo San Sepulchri), *c.* 1450–1509.

202   De divina proportione.   Venice: Paganinus de Paganinis, 1 June 1509.
f°.

> *Ref:* LC(LJRCat) 530; BM-Ital 482; RA 87; Sart (Appr) 135.
>
> *N.B:* Variant known. Relates to the division of a line into extreme and mean ratio
> and applies this so-called divine proportion to architecture, the arts including
> letter design, and the laws determining beauty in the human body. With mar-
> ginal drawings variously ascribed to Leonardo da Vinci.

203   Somma di aritmetica, geometria, proporzioni e proporzionalità [*Italian*].
Venice: Paganinus de Paganinis, 10-20 Nov. 14[9]4.   f°.   [LEK]

> *Ref:* HC 4105; Pr 5168; BMC V 457; BM-Ital 482; IGI 7132; Klebs 718.1; LC
> (LJRCat) 256; Sart II 611; Sart (Appr) 163; RA 54–57, fac; Taton (A&MS) 482–
> 484; Taton (BMS) 21–27; Stillwell L282; Goff L-315.
>
> *N.B:* The earliest printed book to treat algebra comprehensively. An important
> volume in that it contains the theories of Leonardo Fibonacci of Pisa (*c.* 1170–
> 1250), whose works transmitted Hindu-Arabic numerals and theories to the
> West and thus marked the beginning of the mathematical renaissance. It dis-
> cusses double-entry bookkeeping and presents methods of accountancy that have
> stood the test of centuries. It includes part of the text of the *Libro che tratta di
> mercanzie* of Chiarini, first printed at Florence in 1481; and the influential theories
> of perspective advanced by Pacioli's former teacher, Piero della Francesca (*c.*
> 1416–1492). [With regard to Pacioli's references to Piero della Francesca, see

II. *Mathematics*

GOLDSCHREIBER, Ludwig. *Leonardo da Vinci*, London, 1943, p. 16. A manuscript of Piero's *De prospectiva pingendi* is registered as at the Palatina at Parma (Cod. Cart. no. 1576).]

Fac: *Osiris* 5 1938, *fig. 40.*

PASI, Bartolommeo di, *late 15th century.*

204   Tariffa de pesi e mesure [*Italian*]. Venice: Albertino de Lissona (Vercellensis), 1503. 4°. [LEK]

Ref: BM-Ital 491; *RA* 77, 78 *fac.*; *Sart (Appr)* 156.
N.B: A manual for use in Venetian trade with various cities and countries.

PECKHAM, John de, *Abp. of Canterbury, c.* 1240–1292.

205   Prospectiva communis (Ed: Facio Cardano, 1444–1524). [Milan:] Petrus de Corneno [1482?]. f°. [LEK]

Ref: H *9425; BMC VI 759; BM-Ital 496; IGI 7385; Klebs 738.1; Stillwell J355; Goff J-394.
N.B: Contains propositions on reflection and refraction; with 77 diagrams. An undated edition which possibly shares with the 1482 Euclid in the honor of having the first printed diagrams. Also known as the *Perspectiva communis*. For editions printed at Venice and Leipzig about 1504 and at Nuremberg in 1542, see NLMCat 3579–3581.

PELLOS, Frances (Pellus, Franciscus), *late 15th century.*

206   De la art arithmeticha. Cōpendiō de lo abaco. Turin: Nicolaus de Benedictis and Jacobinus Suigus, 28 Sept. 1492. 4°.

Ref: R 1835; BMC VII 1057; Klebs 740.1; *RA* 50, 51–52 *fac.*; Stillwell P226; Goff P-260.
N.B: Employs a decimal point in dividing by a power of ten. In *Osiris* 5 1938, p. 114, Dr. Sarton calls attention to the book's curious dialect—"Provençal, Italian, or Nicois." IGI 7393 describes it as "in dialetto nizzardo."

PEURBACH, Georg von (*also called* Purbach), 1423–1461.

207   Algorithmus. [Vienna: Johann Winterburger, 1495.] [LEK]

Ref: Klebs 753.1.
N.B: Possibly issued as early as 1492. A textbook frequently reprinted. An undated edition, assigned in BMC III 813 to about 1499–1500, bears the imprint of Johann Winterburger at Vienna (Cen P1028).

208   Tractatus super propositiones Ptolemaei de sinibus et chordis. Nuremberg: Johann Petreius, 1541.

61

Peurbach (continued)

> *Ref*: Smith (*HM*) I 259; *Wightman* (1962) II 514; *Taton* (*BMS*) 14.
>
> *N.B*: Two *Tabulae* by Regiomontanus, a supplement to Peurbach's treatise, which are included in the volume, are called for on the title-page.

PLATEA, Francesco de, *d.* 1460.

209   Opus restitutionum, usurarum, excommunicationum.   [Italy: Anonymous printer, not after 1472.]   f °.   [LEK]

> *Ref*: H *13034; BMC VII 1124; IGI 7839; Stillwell P682; Goff P-751.
>
> *N.B*: Relates to the laws regarding usury. According to BMC, a copy is known with a rubricator's note dated 'anno domini 1472' . . . An edition was printed by Bartolomeo da Cremona [at Venice] in 1472 (Cen P683). Seven other editions are known by 1490 (Cen P684–P690).

PROCLOS (Proklos; Proclus), *c.* 412–485.

210   In primum Euclidis elementorum librum commentarii [*Greek*]. (*Issued with* EUCLID. Elementa geometriae [*Greek*]. Basel: Johann Herwagen, 1533.)

> *Ref*: BM-Ger 288; *Sart* I 212, 402; Th-Stan 7; Van der Waerden 291; *Taton* (*A&MS*) 209–210.
>
> *N.B*: The first Greek edition of Euclid's text as well as that of the commentary of Proclos, who was one of the last of the neo-Platonists to head the School of Athens. The commentary contains historical information on ancient Greek geometry; derived in part from Eudemos, *4th century B.C.*, and Geminos of Rhodes, *fl.* 70 B.C. Edited by Simon Gryne (Gryneus), *d.* 1541.
>
> *Mon*: A translation into French by P. Ver Eecke was published at Bruges in 1948.

211   Sphaera [*Greek*] (Tr: Thomas Linacre, 1460–1524). (*Issued with* FIRMICUS MATERNUS, *4th century*. Astronomicorum libri V. Venice: Aldus Manutius, Romanus, June and [17] Oct. 1499.)   f °.   [LEK]

> *Ref*: HC *14559; BMC V 560; Klebs 405.1; *Sart* I 212; *Sart* (*Appr*) 24; Stillwell F169; Goff F-191.
>
> *N.B*: Published repeatedly under the name of Proclos; but long believed to be the text, or excerpts from the text, of Geminos of Rhodes, *fl.* 70 B.C., dealing with spherical geometry. Haraszti (p. 260 in *More Books*, Sept. 1934) notes that Delambre found the text to be that of Geminos, *verbatim*. First issued with Firmicus Maternus in this 1499 compilation which is known as the *Scriptores astronomici veteres*. A possible English version of this work (NLMCat 3765) was printed at London about 1550 under the title, *The description of the sphere or frame of the worlde . . . Englysshed by me Wyllyam Salysbury.*

II. *Mathematics*

PTOLEMY (Ptolemaios; *called* Claudius Ptolemaeus), *fl.* 150.

212 Geographia [*in early editions frequently called* Cosmographia] (Tr: Giacomo d'Angelo, da Scarperia, *fl.* 1409. Ed: Angelus Vadius; Barnabus Picardus). Vicenza: Hermann Liechtenstein, 13 Sept. 1475. f°. [LEK]

Ref: HC *13536; BMC VII 1035; IGI 8180; Klebs 812.1; Eames (Sabin) 66469; Armstr 1; Taton (*A&MS*) 327–329; Stillwell P987; Goff P-1081.

N.B: The first edition of Ptolemy's important and influential treatise on mathematical geography comprises two sections. One treats of the mapping of the known areas of the physical world, which Ptolemy believed to be a sphere, as had Eratosthenes before him (O'Leary 30, 163). The other records the longitude and latitude of some 8,000 places. Issued without maps. (The earliest to include maps was an edition issued at Bologna, dated '1462' but assigned to 1477—BMC VI 814; Horblit 86; Cen P988.)

The *Geographia*, lost to the Western World for many centuries, was recovered in a Greek text, together with 27 maps, found at Constantinople by Giacomo d'Angelo about 1406 and translated by him during the next three years. Known in a unique manuscript at Nancy [for reproduction, see Nordenskiöld, p. 13, 49]. Without the accompanying maps, however, a reconstruction of the Ptolemaic methods of map-making would have been possible from the text.

For small areas Ptolemy utilized the simple rectangular projection for mapping introduced by Marinos of Tyre, *fl.* 120, and using a theoretically fixed point in making astronomical computations, Ptolemy similarly employed the island of Rhodes as a zero meridian. For larger regional maps or for world maps, Ptolemy developed two conical projections. In each, on a sector of a circle representing the equator, he devised a network of parallels and meridians upon which the known world or some area of it could be charted. In one he employed rectilinear meridians (Projection A); in the other, curved meridians (Projection B)— the latter particularly suited to the drafting of world maps.

On the margin of the world maps, in the early editions of the *Geographia*, are listed the so-called "climates" based on the hours in the longest day of the year at each of the parallels indicated [See NEUGEBAUER (ESA), p. 183–185. See also Waldseemüller's discussion of the Ptolemaic "climates" as transcribed and translated into English, in FISCHER and VON WIESER. *The Cosmographie introductio of Martin Waldseemüller*, New York, 1907.] Because new maps were included in succeeding editions of the *Geographia*, it came to have the status of an atlas, especially after 1500, as new regions were constantly discovered. [The first appearance in Ptolemy's *Geographia* of part of the New World occurs in a world map by Johann Ruysch in the Rome edition of 1508, and in certain copies of the 1507 edition of Ptolemy from the same press—possibly implying that the map of 1508 was inserted in such copies of the 1507 edition as were in hand as stock remainders.]

The text of Book I of the *Geographia*, which is accepted as genuine, was translated into Portuguese by Pedro Nunes and printed at Lisbon in 1537 (LC(LJRCat) 782). The authenticity of the remaining seven books has been

II. *Mathematics*

Ptolemy (continued)

questioned, and their origin attributed to Byzantine sources—see Bagrow, L. *The origin of Ptolemy's Geographia* (p. 318–387 in *Geografiska Annaler*, 1943), and his *Geschichte der Kartographie*, Berlin, 1951 [translated into English by D. L. Paisey; revised and enlarged by R. A. Skelton. Cambridge, Mass./London, 1964]; Polaschek, Erich. *Ptolemy's Geography in a new light* (p. 17–37 in *Imago Mundi*, XIV, 1959). See also p. 327 in Taton, René, ed. *Ancient and Medieval science*. Tr: A. J. Pomerans. New York: Basic Books Inc., 1963.

The Ulm edition of 1482 (Cen P990) contains the first use of woodcut maps—those in earlier editions having been metal-engraved—and in addition to the traditional Ptolemaic maps, includes "modern" maps of France, Italy, Spain, the Holy Land and its tribal areas, and a map of Greenland and the North possibly derived from a lost map drawn by Claudius Clavus about 1424 to 1430.* The maps in this 1482 Ptolemy, the so-called "Donis" edition, are without meridians and parallels, in a trapezoidal projection as found in a 1466 manuscript map of Dominus Nicolaus Germanus, but the world map in the "Donis" edition† has curved meridians as in the Ptolemaic projection B. [In the 1514 Nuremberg edition of Ptolemy, Johann Werner, the translator, includes an analysis of Ptolemaic map construction and an emendation of projection B, with curved meridians. Re-issued in 1533—*see* Apian, no. 138. For a commentary and translation of *Ptolemy's Geography, Book VII, chapters 6 and 7*—a section discussed by Werner—see Neugebauer (p. 22–29 in *Isis* 50 1959.)]

Mon: Eames, W. *A list of editions of Ptolemy's Geography, 1475–1730.* New York, 1886 (reprinted from Sabin, J. *A dictionary of books relating to America*, vol. XVI). Nordenskiöld, A. E. *Facsimile-atlas to the early history of cartography* (Tr: J. A. Ekelöf and C. R. Markham), Stockholm, 1889. Berger, H. *Geschichte der wissenschaftlichen Erdkunde der Griechen*, 2nd ed., Leipzig, 1903. Stevenson, E. L., tr. and ed. *Geography of Claudius Ptolemy translated into English . . . based upon Greek and Latin manuscripts and important late fifteenth and early sixteenth century printed editions. Including reproductions of the maps from the Ebner manuscript ca. 1460* [at the New York Public Library]. *With an introduction by Professor Joseph Fischer, S.J.* New York, 1932. Fischer, J., S.J. *Claudii Ptolemaei Geographiae codex Urbinas Graecus 82.* I., Leiden and Leipzig, 1932 (Codices a vaticanis selecti, XIX, 2 v.). Bagrow, L. [as cited earlier in this entry]. Mzik, H. V. and F. Hopfner. *Des Klaudios Ptolemaios Einführung in die darstellende Erdkunde.* Klotho V, 1938. Tooley, R. V. *Maps and map-makers*, 2nd ed., London, 1952. Armstrong, Ch. E. *Copies of Ptolemy's Geography in American libraries* (p. 105–114 in New York Public Library. *Bulletin*, vol. 66, no. 2. New York, Feb. 1962).

213 Planisphaerium (Tr: *Arabic*, Maslama, *d.* 1007; *Latin*, Hermann of Carinthia, *fl.* 1143). (*Issued with* Ptolemy. Geographia. Rome: Bernardino dei Vitali, 8 Sept. 1507.) f°.

---

* For discussion of Clavus's maps, see p. 160, 176–77, 189–191, *etc.* in Skelton, R.A., *jt. ed. The Vinland map and the Tartar relation*, New Haven and London, 1965.

† The term "Donis" is apparently a corruption of the contracted form of "Dominus," which sometimes appears as "Donus," *i.e.* Do[mi]nus. The full form—Dominus Nicolaus Germanus—appears at the end of the main text in the 1486 Ptolemy (Cen P991).

Ref: Car p. 18; *Sart* I 277, III 668; *HTech* III 603–4; *Heath* (*HGM*) II 292–3; *Wightman*
(1962) I 118; *Neugebauer* (*ESA*) 1957, 219–220, 226.

N.B: A theory of stereographic projection. Authenticity questioned. [Ptolemy's
De analemmate liber, on sundials, was not printed until after our period, with the
publication of Commandino's translation at Rome in 1562.]

214   De speculis (*F. 250v–253v in* JOANNES de Sacro Bosco. Sphaera mundi.
Venice: "Impensis . . . Luceantonij de Giūta" 30 June 1518). f° .

Ref: BM-Ital 597; Car p. 21; *Heath* (*HGM*) II 294.

N.B: A work on mirror-reflection. Authenticity questioned. Variously attributed to
Heron of Alexandria. Carmody, p. 21, lists the *De speculis* as appearing in the
Venice edition of 19 Jan. 1518.
    [Ptolemy's *Optica*—publication of which was prevented by the death of
Regiomontanus in 1476—is not known to have been printed during our period.
For its text, see LEJEUNE, Albert. *L'Optique de Claude Ptolémée dans la version latine
d'après l'arabe de l'émir Eugene de Sicile. Edition critique.* Louvain, 1956. For dis-
cussion of Ptolemy's laws of refraction, see Taton (*A&MS*) 301.]

215   Syntaxis mathematika (*the so-called* Almagest—*from a corruption of its
title in Arabic*) (Tr: Gherardo da Cremona, 1114–1187).   Venice: Petrus
Liechtenstein, 10 Jan. 1515. f° . [LEK]

Ref: Car p. 15; *Heath* (*HGM*) II 257–261, 276–286; *Sart* I 273; *O'Leary* 32; *Taton*
(*A&MS*) 296.

N.B: Book I, especially chapters 9 and 11, contains theories of plane and spherical
trigonometry and their astronomical applications. [See under ASTRONOMY.]

RECORDE, Robert, 1510–1558.

216   The grounde of artes, teachyng the worke and practise of arithmetike.
London: Reginalde Wolf, 1542. 8°.

Ref: STC 20798; *Sart* (*Appr*) 153; *RA* 213 *note*.

N.B: The first separately printed arithmetic in the English language (but see note under
Tunstall). At least eighteen editions of this popular work were published during
the 16th century.

Mon: CLARKE, Frances M. *New light on Robert Recorde* (p. 50–70 in *Isis* 8 1926).

REGIOMONTANUS (Johann Müller of Königsberg; Joannes de Monte-regio), 1436–1476.

217   Tabulae directionum et profectionum. Tabella sinus recti (Ed: Johann
Engel, 1463–1512). Augsburg: Erhard Ratdolt, 2 Jan. 1490. 4°.

Ref: HC *13801; BMC II 383; BM-Ger 632; Oates 961; IGI 5328; Klebs 834.1;
Thornd (*S&T*) 148; *Taton* (*BMS*) 15–17; Stillwell R107; Goff R-112.

Regiomontanus (continued)

N.B: The earliest edition found in the present survey. Karpinski, however, in his check-list of books of trigonometry, notes possible editions printed at Nuremberg, 1475, and at Venice, 1485. [A work by Regiomontanus entitled *Compositio tabularum sinuum* was printed at Nuremberg in 1541.]

218 De triangulis omnimodis libri quinque (Ed: Johann Schöner, 1477–1547). Nuremberg: Johann Petreius, 1533. f °.

Ref: BM-Ger 631; *Sart (Appr)* 160–161; *Taton (BMS)* 16.
Add: Nicolaus de Cusa. De quadratura circuli.
N.B: The first *important* work on trigonometry to be printed; written in 1464. The holding in escrow of some of the works of Regiomontanus for a considerable period may account for their relatively late publication.

REGNIER, Gemma, of Frisia. *See* Gemma.

REISCH, Gregor, *d.* 1525.

219 Margarita philosophica. Freiburg [im Breisgau]: Johann Schott, *citra festum Margarethe* [before 13 July] 1503. 4°. [LEK]

Ref: H 13852; BM-Ger 731; Pr 11717; LC(LJRCat) 429; *Sart (Appr)* 163–164; *Taton (BMS)* 31, 54.
N.B: A popular encyclopaedia that treats of arithmetic, geometry, and astronomy, and covers the *trivium* and *quadrivium* as a whole. At least nine editions were issued before 1550. The author's name is revealed in a poem dated 1496, and for a time this was erroneously taken for the date of printing. No fifteenth-century edition is known. Editions printed at Strasbourg in 1504, 1508, and 1512 and at Basel in 1508 are recorded in NLMCat 3847–3850. [See also under Technology.]
Mon: Ferguson, John. *Bibliography of the Margarita philosophica of Gregorius Reisch* (p. 194–216 in *The Library*, 4th Ser., X, no. 2, 1929).

RIESE, Adam, (Ries), *c.* 1489–1559.

220 Ein gerechent Büchlein [*German*]. Leipzig, 1533. [LEK]

Ref: *RA* 139[3], 171; *Sart (Appr)* 155.
N.B: Because of their popularity and helpfulness, Riese's manuals here listed made his name a household word in Germany. Although frequently reprinted as separates or in varied combinations, their constant use destroyed them, with the result that the surviving copies are now among the rare books of their period and their relation to one another has not been satisfactorily established. Sarton ventures the statement that the first edition of each of them appeared in 1518 but gives no proof. The present work is said to present a set of mercantile tables for the multiplication and division of denominate numbers.

221 Rechenung nach der lenge auff den Linihen und Feder [*German*]. Leipzig: Jacob Berwalt, 1550. 4°.

> *Ref*: *RA* 140[4], 250, 251 *fac*; *Taton* (*BMS*) 31, 32.
> *N.B*: Relates to counter reckoning [Linihen] and to reckoning by writing [Feder]. Said also to relate to commercial practice and gauging. According to Koyré (Taton), "this book, the best of its kind in the 16th century, was extremely popular, 38 editions appearing in the course of the century."

222 Rechnung auff der Linien und Federn [*German*]. Erfurt, 1522. [LEK]

> *Ref*: *Sart* (*Appr*) 154; *RA* 139[2].
> *N.B*: Relates to the use of counters and written numerals.

223 Rechnung auff der Linihen [*German*]. Erfurt: Mathes Maler, 1525. 8°.

> *Ref*: BM-Ger 741.
> *N.B*: Relates to the use of counters, the line abacus. Although an edition of 1518 is recorded (*RA* 139[1]), no copy has been found in the present survey. Collation is needed to determine the relation or inter-relation of Riese's various works and editions.

ROCHE, Estienne de la, *fl.* 1500.

224 Larithmetique . . . de la regele de la chose [*French*]. Lyon: Guillaume Huyon, 2 June, 1520. f°. [LEK]

> *Ref*: *RA* 128, 129 *fac*; *Smith* (*HM*) II 84, 519.
> *N.B*: The first French arithmetic printed. A comprehensive work, but largely a printing of *Le triparty en la science des nombres*, written in 1484 by Nicolas Chuquet, a brilliant French mathematician with whom de la Roche had studied and who was one of the first to treat of large numbers [antedated by Jehan Adam, who had written of billions and trillions, in 1475]. For discussion of Chuquet's importance in introducing new mathematical concepts, see p. 19–21 in TATON, René, ed. *The beginnings of modern science*, New York, 1964 (History of science, vol. 2).

ROJAS SARMIENTO, Juan de, *fl.* 1530.

225 Commentariorum in astrolabium quod planisphaerium vocant libri VI. Paris: Apud Vascosanum, 1550. 4°. [LEK]

> *Ref*: BM-Fr 378; *Crombie* (*A–G*) 1961 I 95.
> *N.B*: A treatise on the planisphere, combined with an annotated reprint of the first six chapters of GEMMA's *Libellus*.

II. *Mathematics*

RUDOLFF, Christoff, *early 16th century.*

226 Behend vnnd hübsch Rechnung durch die Kunstreichen regeln Algebre [*German*]. Strasbourg: Wolfgang Koepfel, 1525. 8°. [LEK]

> *Ref*: BM-Ger 759; *RA* (Add) 17, *note*; *Taton* (BMS) 32.
> *N.B*: A forerunner of his *Die Coss* published with a commentary by Michael Stifel, at Königsberg in 1553 (*RA* 259, *fac.*).

227 Die künstliche Rechnung mit der Ziffer [*German*]. Vienna: Joannes Singrenius, 1526. 8°. [LEK]

> *Ref*: BM-Ger 759; *Sart* (Appr) 155; *RA* 151 *note*.
> *N.B*: Relates to the use of ciphers or figures.

228 Exempel Büchlin [*German*]. Augsburg: Heinrich Stayner, 1530.

> *Ref*: *Sart* (Appr) 155; *RA* 159 *fac.*
> *N.B*: A manual of arithmetical problems and examples.

SANCT CLIMENT, Francesch.

229 Suma de la art de arismetica [*Catalan*]. Barcelona: Pedro Posa, 1482 4°.

> *Ref*: Klebs 419.1; *RA* 375 *note* [1582, *by error*]; Haebler (BI) 602.
> *N.B*: The first arithmetic printed in Spain; known only in a copy at Barcelona.
> *Mon*: KARPINSKI, L. A. *The first printed arithmetic of Spain* (p. 411–420 in *Osiris* 5 1936), with reproduction.

SCHEUBEL, Johann, 1494–1570.

230 Algebrae porro regulae. (*Issued with* EUCLID. Elementa, libri I-VI. Basel: Johann Herwagen, Sept. 1550.)

> *Ref*: BM-Ger 288[5]; Th-Stan 12.

231 Compendium arithmeticae artis. Basel: Jacobus Parcus, for Joannes Oporinus, 1549. 8°. [LEK]

> *Ref*: *Sart* (Appr) 155; *RA* 246.

232 De numeris et diversis rationibus computationum. Leipzig: Michael Blum, 1545. 8°.

> *Ref*: BM-Ger 787; *Sart* (Appr) 155; *RA* 233, 235 *fac.*

II. *Mathematics*

SCHREIBER, Heinrich (*called* Grammateus), *fl.* 1490–1510.

233   Ein neues künstliches Buch [*German*].   Nuremberg: Johann Stüchs for Lucas Alantse, Vienna, [after 20 July] 1518.   8°.   [LEK]

> *Ref*: BM-Ger 796; Pr 11105; Smith (*HM*) I 330; RA 123, *note*.
> *N.B*: Schreiber, the master with whom Christoff Rudolff studied, is credited with being the first German mathematician to use plus and minus signs in algebraic equations.

SFORTUNATI, Giovanni (Johannes Infortunatus), *early 16th century*.

234   Nuovo lume. Libro di arithmetica [*Italian*].   Venice: Nicolò di Aristotile detto Zoppino, 1534.   4°.   [LEK]

> *Ref*: BM-Ital 624; RA 174, 176 *fac*.
> *N.B*: Treating of commercial arithmetic and including mercantile tables and reference to interest on loans.

SHERWOOD, John, *Bishop of Durham, d*. 1494.

235   Epitome de ludo arithmomachiae.   [Rome: Stephan Plannck, after 1 April 1482.]   4°.

> *Ref*: BMC IV 101; BM-Ital 625.
> *N.B*: With woodcut diagram. BMC sees "no apparent connexion" between this epitome and the description of the mathematical game which appears in the *Arithmetica* of JORDANUS de Nemore, Paris, 1496, and is attributable to Jacques Le Fèvre d'Étaples, the editor of the latter volume.

STIFEL, Michael, 1487–1567.

236   Arithmetica integra [*with preface by* Philipp Melanchthon].   Nuremberg: Johann Petreius, 1544.   4°.   [LEK]

> *Ref*: BM-Ger 832; Sart (*Appr*) 155; RA 223; Taton (*BMS*) 33–35.
> *N.B*: A scholarly work, comparable to those published in Italy by Cardano and Tartaglia.
> *Fac*: RA 225.

237   Deutsche Arithmetica inhaltend die Hausrechnung, Deutsche Coss, Kirchrechnung [*German*].   Nuremberg: Johann Petreius, 1545.   4°.

Ref: BM-Ger 832; RA 231, 232 *fac*.; Taton (*BMS*) 32.

> *N.B*: A book to assist in domestic accounts, simple algebra [employing plus and minus signs], and the use of the church calendar.
> *Fac*: Smith (*HM*) II 403.

Stifel (continued)

238 Ein Rechenbüchlein vom End Christ. Apocalypsis in Apocalypsim [*German*]. Wittenberg, 1532.

> *Ref*: RA 223 *note*.
> N.B: Works in which Stifel, a religious fanatic and an outstanding arithmetician, mingled his two interests in the theory and mysticism of numbers.

239 Rechenbuch von der Welschen und Deutschen Practick [*German*]. Nuremberg, 1546.

> *Ref*: RA 226[4] *note*.
> N.B: Relates to accounting in foreign and German practice.

STÖFFLER, Johann. *See under* TECHNOLOGY.

TAGLIENTE, Girolamo, and Giovanni Antonio TAGLIENTE [*early 16th century; not brothers*], *jt. au.*

240 Opera che insegna a fare ogni ragione de mercatia [*Italian*]. Venice, 1515. [LEK]

> *Ref*: Sart (*Appr*) 152; RA 114 *note*.
> N.B: A popular commercial arithmetic of which over thirty 16th-century editions are known. The earliest edition cited in BM-Ital 655 is assigned to [Venice: Nicolò Zoppino, 1525].

TARTAGLIA (Nicolò Fontana, *the Stammerer; also called* Tartalea), *c*. 1506–1557.

241 Quesiti e inventioni diverse [*Italian*]. Venice: Venturino Ruffinelli, 1546. 4°. [LEK]

> *Ref*: BM-Ital 658; *HTech* III 539, *illus*; *Wightman* (1962) II 673; *Taton* (BMS) 38–39.
> N.B: Book IX relates to arithmetic, geometry, and algebra. For an evaluation of Tartaglia and an account of the controversies in which he became involved, see ORE, Oystein. *The battles of the scholars* (p. 53–107 in his *Cardano, the gambling scholar*. Princeton University Press, 1953). (See also under PHYSICS; TECHNOLOGY.)

THĀBIT ibn Qurra (Abū-'l-Ḥasan Thābit ibn Qurra), *c*. 835–901.

242 De figura sectore (*Tr. from the Arabic*: Gherardo da Cremona, 1114–1187). (*Issued with* JOANNES de Sacro Bosco. Sphaera mundi. Venice, 1518.)

Ref: Car p. 123; *Kennedy (IAI)* 93; *O'Leary* 171–174; *Taton (A&MS)* 322, 496.

N.B: One of the earliest Arabic treatises on spherical trigonometry. Said to include in its sources the writings of Menelaos, possibly in the lost Arabic version of Al-Māhānī, *fl.* 850. Since BM-Ital 596 and 597 list two Venetian editions of Joannes de Sacro Bosco, (a) Venice: Heirs of Octavianus Scotus, 19 Jan. 1518; b) Venice: Lucantonio de Giunta, 30 June 1518), collation is needed to determine which edition includes the Thābit ibn Qurra—and also the *Sphaera* of Theodosios, for which see below. [See also under ASTRONOMY.]

THEODOSIOS of Bithynia, *1st century B.C.*

243 Sphaera, libri II. (*Issued with* JOANNES de Sacro Bosco. Sphaera. Venice, 1518.)

Ref: BM-Ital 596; *Sart (Appr)* 149.

N.B: Spherical geometry without reference to trigonometry. The first separate, edited by Johann Vögelin, was printed at Vienna in 1529 by Joannes Singrenius. [With regard to the 1518 printing of the Theodosios, see note under THĀBIT ibn Qurra.]

THEŌN of Alexandria, *4th century*.

244 Interpretatio libri Euclidis. (*In* EUCLID. Elementa geometriae. Tr: Bartolommeo Zamberti. Venice: Joannes Tacuinus, 25 Oct. 1505.)

Ref: Th-Stan 3.

TUNSTALL, Cuthbert (Tonstallius), *Bp. of Durham, 1474–1559*.

245 De arte supputandi. London: Richard Pynson, 1522. 4°. [LEK]

Ref: *Sart (Appr)* 153, 163; *RA* 132–135.

N.B: The first separate arithmetic printed in England, although a section on arithmetic had appeared in the *Myrrour of the worlde* printed by William Caxton at Westminster about 1481 (Cen M758). The engraved titlepage is signed HH, the signature of Hans Holbein. The text is said to be derived in part from Pacioli's *Somma*, Venice, 1494. Relates to method in calculation.

Fac: *RA* 133.

VAN DER HOECKE, Giel, *early 16th century*.

246 Een sonderlinghe boeck in dye edel conste arithmetica [*local dialect*]. Antwerp: Symon Cock, 9 Feb. 1537. 8°. [LEK]

Ref: *RA* 183–185, *fac.*

N.B: An arithmetic containing a section on algebra.

II. *Mathematics*

VENTALLOL, Joan.

247   Practica mercantivol [*Spanish dialect*].   Lyon: Jean de la Place, 23 April
2[1]521.   f°.

> *N.B*: A commercial arithmetic treating also of geometry. Relates also to rates of
> exchange at Barcelona, Mallorca, Valencia, Perpignan, Aragon, Navarre, and
> Castille. Written by a citizen of Mallorca and bearing on its frontispiece the
> arms of Spain and of Mallorca.
> *Mon*: BORDONA, Jesús Dominguez. *La practica mercantivol de Joan Ventallol* (p. 118–121
> in *Gutenberg Jahrbuch* 1961); with three reproductions.

VÖGELIN, Joannes, *fl.* 1520.

248   Elementale geometricum ex Euclidis geometria decerptum.   Strasbourg: Christian Egenolff, 1529.   8°.

> *Ref*: Th-Stan p. 50:III.
> *N.B*: A textbook frequently reprinted. Probably first issued in 1528 by Joannes
> Singrenius at Vienna, where the author was or had been a professor of mathe-
> matics.

WAGNER, Ulrich, *15th century*.

249   Rechenbuch [*German*].   Bamberg: Heinrich Petzensteiner, 17 May
1482.

> *Ref*: Klebs 1045.1; *RA* 12, *note*.

WALDSEEMÜLLER, Martin (*called* Ilacomilus; Hylacomylus), *c.* 1475–
1516.

250   Cosmographiae introductio.   St. Dié: Lud et Ilacomilus, 25 April
1507.   4°.   [LEK]

> *Add*: VESPUCCI, Amerigo (Americus Vespucius). Quattuor navigationes.
> *Ref*: Harrisse (BAV) 44, 45; Church 23.
> *N.B*: A brochure which discusses geometric and astronomical terms applicable to
> cosmography and devotes special sections to the discussion of parallels, and to the
> so-called "climates." Dedicated to the Emperor by Waldseemüller. Re-issued
> on 29 August 1507 and dedicated to the Emperor by the Gymnasium Vosagense,
> a scholarly association to which Waldseemüller belonged. Variant issues known.
> As stated on the titlepage, a map and a globe were issued to accompany the
> brochure. In his map, so he noted in his text, Waldseemüller followed the

Ptolemaic system—*Et ita quidem temporauimus rem | ut in plano circa nouas terras & alia quaepiam Ptholemaeū*; but in his globe he followed the reports of Vespucci, as appended to his text—*in solido vero quod plano additur descriptionē Americi subsequentem sectati fuerimus*, the difference being shown mainly in the locating of the equator. His 1507 wall-map of the world, although a horizontally elongated version of Ptolemy's projection B, employing curved meridians and delineating the traditional landmasses, also displays the full African continent and the eastern coast of the newly found "fourth" continent, which bears the name "America" [*i.e.*, South America].

This world-map, mammoth in size, is more than thirty square feet in area. At its top are two round medallions showing the hemispheres of the East and the West, on a different projection from that of the map itself. The Western hemisphere, although here unnamed, depicts a landmass relatively close in its shape to about seven-eighths of the continent of South America. These medallions were re-issued at Cracow in 1512, in the *Introductio in Ptholomei cosmographia* of Joannes de Stobnicza.

Under the impression that Amerigo Vespucci had been the first to discover land across the sea, Waldseemüller suggested in Chapter IX of his brochure that in Amerigo's honor the newly found fourth continent be named America. As already noted, the name appears on the great wall-map, although not on its medallions. It appears, however, on his [1507] gore-map [*i.e.*, a map made up of gorelike sections, which if cut and pasted onto a sphere, would represent the world as a globe]. Later, Waldseemüller apparently learned of his error in naming the new land and endeavored to correct it. Among the twenty "modern" maps designed by him for the 1513 edition of Ptolemy's *Geographia*, on a map entitled *Tabula Terre Nove* is the following statement boldly printed on a northern portion of South America: *Hec terra cum adiacentibus insulis inuenta est per Columbum ianuensen ex mandato Regis Castello*. The name "America" was here omitted, as also on his world map, *Typus universalis* in the *Margarita philosophica* of 1515 and on his *Carta marina* of 1516. Waldseemüller's efforts at correction, however, were of no avail.

The only known copy of the great wall-map of the world was discovered at the turn of our century at Wolfegg Castle in Württemberg. A copy of the global gore-map (formerly in the Hauslab-Liechtenstein collection at Vienna) was offered for sale at the Parke-Bernet Galleries in New York in 1950, withdrawn, and later acquired for the Bell collection, now at the University of Minnesota. Although undated and unsigned, the maps have been identified as those originally issued with the 1507 brochure, through reference to them which appeared in 1509. In that year Johann Reinhard of Grüningen, a printer at Strasbourg, re-issued Waldseemüller's *Cosmographiae introductio* and with it a booklet describing its maps. The booklet appeared both in Latin and in German, as the *Globus mundi declaratio* (Proctor 9917) and as *Der welt kugel Beschrybung*. It is on the basis of their description, substantiated by data in the edition of Waldseemüller's treatise assigned to Lyon [1517/18], that the identification of the wall-map and the global gore-map rests.

Mon: FISCHER, Joseph, S.J., and Franz von WIESER, ed. *The oldest map with the name America of the year 1507 and the Carta marina of the year 1516 by M. Waldseemüller*

Waldseemüller (continued)

(*Ilacomilus*), Innsbruck, 1903; *The Cosmographiae introductio of Martin Waldsee-müller*, New York, 1907. The latter contains descriptions of variants, translation and facsimiles of text and maps. The Bell copy of the global gore-map was reproduced in the sales brochure, *The Hauslab-Liechtenstein global map of the world* . . . *Public auction sale* . . . *May 24* . . . *Parke-Bernet Galleries, Inc.* . . . New York, 1950. [*See also* SKELTON, R. A. *Bibliographical note* (p. xvii–xx in Theatrum Orbis Terrarum, Second ser., IV 1966; ADAMS, T. R. *A Collection's progress. Two retrospective exhibitions by the John Carter Brown Library*. Providence, 1968, no. 66.]

WERNER, Johann, 1468–1528.

251 Libellus . . . super vigintiduobus elementis conicis.   Nuremberg: Fridericus Peypus, 1522.

Ref: BM-Ger 910; *Sart (Appr)* 144, 216:35; *Sart (HS)* II 97; *Taton (BMS)* 28, 29.
N.B: The first original work on conics written within our period, and the first to be printed. According to Taton, the volume also includes Werner's commentary on the duplication of the cube, which in addition to his own observations includes a free translation of the work of Eutocios.

252 De quatuor terrarum orbis in plano figurationibus. (*Issued with* PTOLEMY, *fl.* 150. Geographia, liber I [Tr: Johann Werner]. Nuremberg: Johann Stüchs, 4 Nov. 1514).

Ref: Eames (Sabin) 66479; Pr 11095; Zinner (ALD) 1019.
N.B: An analysis of Ptolemy's methods of projection, with a correction of the curved meridians in the latter's second conical projection, including meridian lines for the case of the North Pole as center. For a commentary and translation of *Ptolemy's Geography, Book VII, Chapters 6 and 7*, a section discussed by Werner, see NEUGEBAUER (p. 22–29 in Isis 50 1959). [Re-issued with an introduction by Petrus Apianus at Ingolstadt, 1533—see above, under no. 138.]
Mon: SCHOTTENLOHER, Karl. *Der Mathematiker und Astronom. Johann Werner* (p. 147–155 in JANSEN, Max, *ed. Festgabe an Hermann Grauert*, [Freiburg im Breisgau, 1910]).

WIDMANN, Johann (*called* Mechinger), 1440–1524.

253 Rechnung auf allen Kaufmannschaft [*German*]. Leipzig: Conrad Kachelofen, 1489. 8°. [LEK]

Ref: HC *13712; BMC III 624; BM-Ger 913; Klebs 1047.1; LC(LJRCat) 130; *Taton (BMS)* 18, 19; Stillwell W11; Goff W-14.
N.B: *Title begins*: Behēde vnd hubsche Rechenung. According to *RA 39 note*, this was the first notable German textbook on arithmetic. It contains the first plus and minus signs to be printed, here used to indicate excess or deficiency in warehouse measures. [For works sometimes attributed to Widmann, see entries under: Algorithmus.]

II. *Mathematics*

WITELO (Vitelo), *fl.* 1230–1270.

254 Perspectiva, libri X (Ed: Georg Tannstetter [Collimitius] 1482–1530, and Petrus Apianus, 1495–1552). Nuremberg: Joannes Petreius, 1535. f°. [LEK]

> *Ref:* NLMCat 4757; Van Ortroy (Apian) 110; *Sart* II 1027; *Smith (HM)* II 341 (1533?).
>
> *N.B:* Derived from the optics of Abū Alī al-Ḥasan (Alhazen), *c.* 965–1038. Six of the ten books relate to reflection and refraction. Important in transmitting Greco-Arabic theories, and because of the fact that Kepler based his study of optics upon it—see vol. II of his *Gesammelte Werke* (Ed: Max Caspar), München, 1938.
>
> *Mon:* BIRKENMAJER, Aleksander. Studja nad Witelonem. Krakow, 1921 (*Isis* 1923, 5 214). CASPAR, Max. *Bibliographia Kepleriana, ein Führer durch das gedruckte Schrifttum* ... München, 1936.

SUBJECT ANALYSIS FOR
MEDICINE

[1] ASTROLOGY and MEDICINE: *Almanach*, 1462; *Calendar for* 1457 [*Latin*]; *Calendrier des bergiers*; Estwood; Ganivet; Hippocrates, *De medicorum astrologia*; Pietro d'Abano.

[2] AUTOPSIES: Benivieni.

[3] BATHS and HOT SPRINGS: Bonaventura de' Castelli; Casini; Gentile da Foligno; Paracelsus; Savonarola.

[4] BLOODLETTING and LAXATIVES: *Aderlassbüchlein*; *Aderlassregeln*; *Almanach*, 1462; Arnaldo de Villa Nova, *Phlebotomia*; Brissot; *Calendar for* 1457 [*Latin*]; Galen; Gesner; Mesuë *the Younger*.

[5] CLINICAL RECORDS—Case Histories and Notations: Benzi, *Cura cuiusdam hominis*; Savonarola; Valasco de Taranta.—Centuriae: Rodriguez de Castello Branco.—Consilia (*systematic statements of case and treatment*): Bavarii; Benzi; Cermisone; Ferrari; Ficino; Gentile da Foligno; Montagnana; Schelling; Torrella.

[6] COLLECTIONS of MEDICAL TRACTS: *Articella*; Ketham; Thorer [Albanus Torinus]. [For subsequent editions and their added titles, see Choulant (H) 398–408, 415–417 for the *Articella* (14 *eds.*, *c.* 1476–1525) and for Ketham (7 *eds.*, 1491–1522), respectively. Choulant also lists a *Collectio Dietetica* printed at Strasbourg by Heinrich Sybold in 1530 and at Paris by Simon de Colines in 1533; two collections printed in 1534 at Strasbourg and Mainz beginning, respectively, with works by Joannes Caesarius and Christopher Heyll; and a collection of early medical works published in 1547 at Venice by the sons of Aldus Manutius. Various medical collections are discussed in Sart (Appr) 45–49, and in Wightman (1962) II, p. 272–276.]

[7] COMMENTARIES:—Avicenna: Benzi; Dino del Garbo; Ferrari; Gentile da Foligno; Jacopo da Forlì.——Galen: Benzi; Champier; Jacopo da Forlì; Maimonides; Sermoneta; Torrigiani.——Hippocrates: Benzi; Champier; Galen; Jacopo da Forlì; Marsiglio da Santa Sofia; Sermoneta.——Mesuë, *the Younger*: Manardi; Mondino.——Pliny Secundus; Barbaro; Collenuccio; Leonicenus.—— Rhasis: Arcolani; Barzizza; Jean de Tournemire.

77

[8] CONDITION [diagnosis through "complexion"]: Benzi; Galen; Hippocrates.

CONSILIA: [See under CLINICAL RECORDS.]

[9] CRITICAL DAYS: Antonius Cartaginensis; Fracastoro; Galen. [See also ASTROLOGY.]

[10] DENTISTRY and TOOTHACHE: Arcolani; *Artzney Büchlein*; Celsus; Petrarca.

[11] DIET, DIETETICS: Barbantini; Galen; Hippocrates; Isḥāq al Isrā Īlī; Magninus; Maimonides; Montagnana; Oreibasios; Paulos of Aigina; Pietro da Tossignano; Platina; *Regimen sanitatis Salernitanum*; Theodorus Priscianus.—WEIGHT CONTROL: Benzi, *Consiglio*, *Libro de conservare*.

[12] DISEASE and INFIRMITIES—ALCOHOLISM: Arcolani.—APOPLEXY: Pietro da Tossignano.—CATARACTS: [See under OPHTHALMOLOGY].—DEAFNESS: Cardano; Petrarca.—DROPSY: Saliceto.—ELEPHANTIASIS: Augustone; Gregorius I.—EPILEPSY: Pietro da Tossignano.—FEVERS: Antonius Cartaginensis; Arcolani; Arnaldo de Villa Nova; Avicenna; Benzi; Champier; Estwood; Galen; Gentile da Foligno; Guaineri; Paulos of Aigina; Saliceto; Savonarola.—GOUT: Gregorius I.—HEART: Avicenna.—INSANITY AND MELANCHOLIA: Augustone; Galen; Hippocrates, *De insania Democriti*.—INTESTINAL DISORDERS: Guaineri.—MEASLES: Rhasis.—PARALYSIS: Pietro da Tossignano.—RESPIRATORY DISEASES: Galen.—SMALLPOX: Rhasis.—STONES: Avenzohar; Benzi; Guaineri.—TUMORS: Galen. [See also under EPIDEMICS; GERONTOLOGY; GYNECOLOGY; OPHTHALMOLOGY; PATHOLOGICAL WORKS; PEDIATRICS; SYPHILIS; etc.]

DRUGS, Use of: [See PHARMACOLOGY.]

[13] EPIDEMICS and PLAGUES—CONTAGION: Fracastoro; Rhasis.—EPIDEMICS: Hippocrates.—MEASLES: Rhasis.—PESTILENCE: Alcañiz; Antonius Cartaginensis; Bavarii; Benedetti; Brunschwig; Canutus; Capelluti; Cermisone; Conrad von Megenberg; Estwood; Ficino; Fracastoro; Gentile da Foligno; Jasme; Jung; Manfredi; Methodius; Pietro da Tossignano; *Régime de l'épidémie*; *Regimen contra pestilentiam*; Soldi; Steinhöwel; Valasco de Taranta.—SMALLPOX: Rhasis.—SWEATING SICKNESS: Cordus, E.—SYPHILIS: *See below*. [For other works relating to epidemics and plagues, see KLEBS, Arnold C. and E. DROZ. *Remèdes contre la peste. Fac-similés, notes et liste bibliographique des incunables sur la peste. Documents scientifiques du XVᵉ siècle*, Paris, 1925; SUDHOFF, Karl and A. C. KLEBS. *Die ersten gedruckten Pestschriften . . . Geschichtliche und bibliographische Untersuchungen*, München, 1926.]

FEVERS: [See under DISEASE and INFIRMITIES.]

[14] GERONTOLOGY: Arnaldo de Villa Nova, *De conservanda juventute et retardanda senectute*; Zerbis, *Gerontocomia*.

[15] GYNECOLOGY, OBSTETRICS, and topics relative to women—CAESA-REAN SECTION: Methodius.—COSMETICS; DERMATOLOGY: Le Fourniere; Saliceto; *Trotula*.—DISEASES: Arnaldo de Villa Nova; Guaineri; Theodorus.—MIDWIFERY, PREGNANCY, *etc.*: Aëtius; Albertus Magnus; Michael Scotus; Ortolff von Bayrlandt; Paulos; Röslin; Saliceto; Soranos; *Trotula*. [See also under NATURAL SCIENCE: Biology.]

[16] HEALTH, HYGIENE, and SANITATION: Albertus Magnus; Arnaldo de Villa Nova, *Regimen sanitatis*; Benzi, *Trattato*; Cepolla; Crescenzi; Falcucci; Galen; Gerson; Hippocrates; Jasme; Magninus; Maimonides, *De regimine sanitatis*; Paulos of Aigina; Pietro da Tossignano, *De regimine sanitatis*; *Regimen sanitatis* [*German: Die Ordnung der Gesundheit*]; *Regimen sanitatis Parisiense*; *Regimen sanitatis parvum*; *Regimen sanitatis Salernitanum*.

HERBALS: [See under MEDICINAL PROPERTIES and VIRTUES: Plants].

[17] MEDICAL ETHICS, CONDUCT, and LAW: Galen; Hippocrates, *Iusiurandum, Medicinae lex*; Soranos, *In artes medendi isagoge*; Zerbis, *De cautelis medicorum tractatus*.

[18] MEDICINAL PROPERTIES and VIRTUES—ALCOHOL: Joannes de Rupescissa.—ANIMALS: Albertus Magnus.—BEZOAR: Pietro d'Abano.—CHINA ROOT: Vesalius.—GUAIAC POWDER: Pol; *Ain recept*; Schmaus; Ulrich von Hutten. —MEDICAL ALCHEMY: Joannes de Rupescissa.—MINERAL WATER: *Eaux artificielles*. —PLANTS, HERBALS: Albertus Magnus, *Liber aggregationis*; Amatus (*see* Rodriguez de Castello Branco); *Arbolaire*; Augustone; Banckes; Barbaro; Brasavola; Champier; Conrad von Megenberg; Crescenzi; Dioskorides; Du Bois; Fuchs; Galen; *Gart der Gesundheit*; Gesner; *Herbarium Apulei*; *Herbarius*; Hildegard; *Hortus sanitatis*; *Macer floridus*; Mattioli; Musa; Orebasios; Rhasis; Rodriguez de Castello Branco; Silvatico; Strabo.—STONES: Albertus Magnus; Conrad von Megenberg.—VERONICA: Musa.—WINE: Arnaldo de Villa Nova, *Von Bewahrung und Bereitung der Weine*. [See also under NATURAL SCIENCE: Botany.]

[19] OPHTHALMOLOGY: Aëtius; Celsus; Grassus; Hippocrates; 'Isā ibn 'Alī [Jesu Haly]; Paulos of Aigina; Soranos. [See also Cardano.]

[20] PATHOLOGY, *general*: Bagellardo; Celsus; Fernel; Galen; Hippocrates; Rhasis; Saliceto; Soranos; Theodorus. [See also DISEASE and INFIRMITIES.]

[21] PEDIATRICS: Bagellardo; Metlinger. [See also Zerbis, *Anatomia infantis* under NATURAL SCIENCE.]

[22] PHARMACOLOGY: Abū al-Kāsim [Abulcasis]; Al-Kindi; Avicenna; Brasavola; Brunschwig; Champier; Cordus, Euricius; Cordus, Valerius; Dino del Garbo; Dioskorides; Estwood; Hippocrates; Mattioli; Mesuë *the Younger*; Mondino; Nicolaus Salernitanus; Paracelsus; Pliny *the Elder*; Serapion *the Younger*; Ulsen.—WEIGHING OF DRUGS: Dino del Garbo.

PHYSIOLOGY: [See under NATURAL SCIENCE.]

PHYSIOGNOMY: [See under NATURAL SCIENCE.]

[23] SURGERY: Abū al-Kāsim [Abulcasis]; Berengario da Carpi; Brunschwig; Gersdorff; Guy de Chauliac; Lanfranchi; Paracelsus; Paré; Paulos of Aigina; Pietro d'Argellata; Saliceto. [See also NATURAL SCIENCE: Anatomy.]

[24] SYPHILIS: Brant; Fracastoro; Gilino; Grünpeck; Hock von Brackenau; Leonicenus; Massa; Montesauro; Paracelsus; Pistor; Pol; *Recept*; Scanaroli; Schellig; Schmaus; Scillacio; Sommariva; Steber; Torrella; Ulrich von Hutten; Ulsen; Vesalius; Widmann. [For monographs on publications relative to this subject, see FUCHS, C. H. *Die ältesten Schriftsteller über die Lustseuche in Deutschland*, Göttingen, 1843; SUDHOFF, Karl. *Aus der Frühgeschichte der Syphilis*, Leipzig, 1912; *Graphische und typographische Erstlinge der Syphilisliteratur*, 1495–1496, München, 1912; *Zehn Syphilis Drücke*, Milan, 1924; SUDHOFF, K. and Charles SINGER. *The earliest literature on syphilis*, Milan, 1925. For other monographs and for notes on theories regarding the origin of the plague, see Garrison (1929) 189–191 and Castiglioni (1947) 1161–1162.]

[25] TERMINOLOGY: Champier; Dondis; Silvatico; Simon of Genoa.

[26] THERAPEUTICS: Medical Theory and Practice—THEORY: Abū al-Kāsim [Abulcasis]; Averroës; Avicenna; Champier; Dino del Garbo; Galen; Haly Abbas; Hippocrates; Ḥunain ibn Ishāq [Johannitius]; Jābir ibn Ḥaiyān; Mesuë, *the Elder*; Mesuë, *the Younger*; Rabanus Maurus; Rhasis; Serapion, *the Elder*; Vincent de Beauvais.—PRACTICE: Arnaldo de Villa Nova; Avenzohar; Avicenna; Barzizza; Celsus; Champier; Dino del Garbo; Ferrari; Galen; Gentile da Foligno; Haly Abbas; Hippocrates; Jean de Tournemire; Mesuë, *the Younger*; Ortolff von Bayrlandt; Paulos of Aigina; Pietro da Tossignano; Pliny; Rhasis; Saliceto; Savonarola; Valasco de Taranta.—BIBLIOGRAPHICAL LISTS: Champier; Galen. [See also DISEASE and INFIRMITIES; EPIDEMICS; PATHOLOGICAL WORKS.]

[27] TOXICOLOGY—POISONS and ANTIDOTES: Arnaldo de Villa Nova, *De arte cognoscendi venena*; Averroës, *De venenis*; Benzi, *Cura cuiusdam hominis morsi a serpente venenoso*; Nicander, *Theriaca*; Pietro d'Abano, *De venenis eorumque remediis*; Ponzetti, *Libellus de venenis*; Saliceto, *Summa conservationis*.—BEZOAR STONES: Pietro d'Abano, *De lapide bezoar ex Pandectis*.

[28] UROSCOPY: Cermisone; Ferrari; Gilles of Corbeil [Aegidius Corboliensis]; Michael Scotus.

[29] VETERINARY PRACTICE: Albrecht, *Meister*; Constantinos VII; Crescenzi; *Hippiatrica*; *Pferdearznei-Büchlein*; Ruffo; Rusio.

[30] WOUNDS, Treatment of: Abū al-Kāsim [Abulcasis]; Berengario da Carpi; Biondo; Brunschwig; Gersdorff; Guy de Chauliac; Paracelsus (?); Paré; Vigo. [See also under SURGERY.]

[For related subjects see NATURAL SCIENCE: Anatomy, Biology, Husbandry, Physiology, *etc.* For bibliographies and monographs arranged under subjects, see p. 1146–1163 in CASTIGLIONI, Arturo. *A history of medicine. Translated from the Italian and edited by E. B. Krumbhaar.* 2nd ed., revised and enlarged. New York, 1947. See also KEYS, T. E. *Medical works in facsimile, a bibliography* (p. 133–176 in *Bulletin of the History of Medicine*, XXVII, 1953.]

III. MEDICINE

ABŪ al-KĀSIM (Abū-l-Qasim al-Zahrāwī; *called* Abulcasis, Abulkasim, Albucasis, Alsaharavius), *fl.* 1000.

255 Cyrurgia Albucasis cum cauteriis & aliis instrumentis (*Issued with* Guy de Chauliac. Cyrurgia parva.   Venice: Bonetus Locatellus, for the heirs of Octavianus Scotus, 27 Jan. 1500/01).   f°.

> *Ref*: NLMCat 2251; HCR 4813; BMC V 453; BM-Ital 321; IGI 4561; Klebs 497.1; *Sart* I 681; *Browne (AM)* 97; *Garrison* (1929) 131; *Castiglioni* (1947) 274; Stillwell G512; Goff G-564.
>
> *N.B*: The leading text on surgery up to the time of Guglielmo da Saliceto, 1210–1277. The author ranks as one of the greatest physicians of the Arab race. Originally part of his encyclopaedic work, *al-Tasrif.* Based largely on Paulos of Aigina and Galen, but with some account of contemporary practice and the instruments used. Relates also to cautery and the treatment of abdominal wounds.

256 Liber servitoris de praeparatione medicinarum simplicium (Tr: Abraham *Judaeus* of Tortosa and Simon of Genoa, *d.* 1330).   Venice: Nicolaus Jenson, 1471.   4°.   [LEK]

> *Ref*: GW 130; BMC V 169; BM-Ital 365:16; IGI 11; Klebs 5.1; *Sart* I 681; Stillwell A13; Goff A-14.
>
> *N.B*: Treats of the preparation of drugs. Garrison (1929) 133 identifies Abraham *Judaeus* of Tortosa as Abraham ben Shemtob, *fl.* 1290.
>
> *Mon*: CORDONNIER, Ernest. *Le liber servitoris d'Aboulcasis* (p. 425–432, 481–487 in *Janus*, IX, 1904).

257 Liber theoriae necnon practicae.   Augsburg: For Sigismund Grimm and Marcus Wirsung, 24 Mar. 1519.   f°.

> *Ref*: NLMCat 21; Pr 10896; *Garrison* (1929) 131.
> *N.B*: Originally the medical section of his encyclopaedia, the *al-Taṣrif.*

ADERLASSBÜCHLEIN.

258 Aderlassbüchlein [*German*].   [Alost(?): Johann de Paderborn and Thierry Martens, about 1473–74.]   4°.

Aderlassbüchlein (continued)

    Ref: GW 220; H *86; Camp-Kron 5a; Klebs 9.1; Stillwell A42; Goff A-51.

    N.B: A manual for blood-letting, an important factor in astrological medicine. Also assigned to the press of Johann de Paderborn at Strasbourg.

ADERLASSKALENDER. *See* Calendarium, 1457, *no.* 324.

ADERLASSREGELN.

259   Aderlassregeln [*German*]. [Basel: Berthold Ruppel, about 1471/72.] Bdsde.

    Ref: GW 221; Einbl 86.

    N.B: Rules for blood-letting set forth in verse. Another edition is assigned to Alost or Strasbourg about 1473 (GW 220; Camp-Kron 5a; Stillwell A42; Goff A-51).

AETIUS of Amida, *fl.* 550.

260   Librorum medicinalium tomus primus, libri I-VIII [*Greek*]. Venice: In aedibus haeredum Aldi Manutii et Andreae Asulanis, 1534. f°.

    Ref: NLMCat 43; BM-Ital 9; Renouard (Alde) 267; *Sart* I 434; *Garrison* (1929) 123; *Castiglioni* (1947) 251; *O'Leary* 35.

    N.B: According to NLMCat only the first volume was published. The author, physician to Justinian I, is known as one of the leading physicians of the pre-Islamic period and an important writer on ophthalmology, gynecology, obstetrics, and various diseases as known to Galen and the physicians of antiquity. Various Latin editions of his writings published during the years 1533–1549 at Basel (4), Venice (1), Lyon (1), and Antwerp (1) are listed in NLMCat p. 7–8.

ALBERTUS MAGNUS (Albrecht von Bollstädt), *Saint, c.* 1200–1280.

261   Liber aggregationis, seu Liber secretorum de virtutibus herbarum, lapidum, et animalium quorundam. [Ferrara: Severinus Ferrariensis, *c.* 1477] 4°. [LEK]

    Ref: GW 630; BMC VI 609; BM-Ital 13; BM-Fr 7; Osler (IM) 126; Klebs 18.14; *Sart* II 934; *Castiglioni* (1947) 349.

    N.B: Issued in more than fifty Latin editions during the fifteenth century, many of them containing his *De mirabilibus mundi* and the *Parvum regimen sanitatis* (Klebs 18.1–.53); also issued in Italian, Catalan, and French translations (Klebs 18.01–.09). Authenticity questioned. The first dated edition was printed by Johann Schriber of Bologna in 1478 (GW 631; Goff A-249). For undated, 16th-century editions, see NLMCat 83, 84, and 91.

262 Secreta mulierum et virorum, cum commento. [Cologne: Nicolaus Götz, *c.* 1475.] 4°. [LEK]

> *Ref:* GW 719; BMC I 239; Voull (K) 44; Klebs 26.1; *Sart* II 941; *Castiglioni* (1947) 349.
>
> *N.B:* Relates to gynecology, hygiene, and astrology. The authenticity, which is sometimes questioned, is discussed in Lynn Thorndike's *Treatises ascribed to Albert* (p. 739–742 in vol. II of his *History of magic and experimental science*, New York, 1923). Fifty-four editions are listed in Kleb's *Incunabula scientifica et medica*, Bruges, 1938. In the sixteenth century, the popularity apparently waned. NLMCat 91 lists a German version included in a compilation issued at Frankfort a.M., about 1550. [See also the works of Albertus Magnus as listed under NATURAL SCIENCE.]

ALBRECHT, *Meister.*

263 Arzneibuch der Rosse [*German*]. [Augsburg: Anton Sorg, 1485.] 4°. [LEK]

> *Ref:* GW 820; Klebs 28.2; *Sart* III 1238; Goff A-353.
>
> *N.B:* A veterinary treatise on the care of horses; attributed to Meister Albrecht and believed to date from the fourteenth century. Known in two editions of 32 and 24 leaves, respectively. Printed in at least eight German editions during the fifteenth century.

ALCAÑIZ, Luis, *fl.* 1475.

264 Regiment de la pestilencia [*Spanish*]. [Valencia: Nicolaus Spindeler, about 1490.] 4°.

> *Ref:* GW 841; Klebs 40.1; Schullian (ArMed) 30; Stillwell A328; Goff A-361.

ALEXANDER of Tralles (*called* Trallianus), 525–*c.* 605.

265 Practica Alexandri yatros Greci cum expositione glose interlinearis Jacobi de Partibus et Januensis in margine posite. [Lyon: François Fradin, 1504.] 4°. [LEK]

> *Ref:* NLMCat 145; BM-Fr 10; *Sart* I 453; *Sart* (*Appr*) 37; *Taton* (*A&MS*) 449, 451.
>
> *N.B:* A revised edition was issued at Pavia, *c.* 1520. Written by a Byzantine physician whose clinical work caused him to question various theories advanced by Hippocrates and Galen. Sarton describes him as the first original practitioner since Galen. Brunet cites him as the first clinical writer on psycho-therapy. One of four Byzantine physicians of the pre-Islamic period—*i.e.*, Oreibasios, Aetius of Amida, Alexander of Tralles, and Paulos of Aigina.
>
> A Greek version of his *Biblia iatrica*, an encyclopedia in eleven books translated from a Syriac text, was issued at Paris by Robert Estienne in 1548. Its main topics include diseases of the nervous system and of the respiratory and digestive tracts, with a section on fever sometimes counted as a twelfth book. A Latin translation by Johann Günther—*Omnes nunc primum de Graeco accuratissime con-*

Alexander of Tralles (continued)

> *versi, multisque in locis restituti & emendati*—was issued at Strasbourg in 1549. *Paraphrases in libros omneis Alexandri Tralliani* in the translation of Alban Thorer, a revision of his version published by Henricus Petrus at Basel, *c.* 1533, was issued by that firm in 1541. [For these and other editions, see NLMCat p. 19–20.]

Mon: BRUNET, F. *Œuvres médicales d'Alexander de Tralles*, 4 vols., Paris, 1933–35.

Al-KINDĪ (Ya 'qūb ibn Ishāq ibn as-Sabbāh al-Kindī), *fl.* 870.

266 De medicinarum compositarum gradibus investigandis libellus. Strasbourg: Johann Schott, 1531.

> *Ref*: Sart I 559; *Clagett (Marliani)* 35; *Campbell (AM)* I 64.
>
> *N.B*: A treatise developing Galen's attempt at classifying simples by degrees into a discussion of the calculating of the temperature of medicinal compounds through the temperature of their several parts. Possibly a separate, from a compilation entered in *NLMCat* 2520 under Ibn Butlān.

ALMANACH.

267 Almanach für Wien auf das Jahr 1462 [*German*]. [Germany: Anonymous printer, 1461.] Bdsde. 52 ll.

> *Ref*: GW 1287; Einbl 115; *Garrison* (1929) 198.
>
> *N.B*: Known only in a copy at Donaueschingen. Refers to auspicious times for blood-letting. Knowledge of auspicious and negative days derived through astrological studies was frequently used as a control for medicinal treatments, blood-letting, and administering laxatives. Such days or periods were presumably designated on many early calendars or almanacs for domestic use. [See below under *Calendar for 1457*. See also MATHEMATICS: Almanach.]
>
> *Fac*: HEITZ-HAEBLER. *Hundert Kalender-Inkunabeln*, no. 2; Taf. 2. Strassburg, 1905.

ANTONIUS Cartaginensis, *fl.* 1525.

268 Liber de peste, de signis febrium, et de diebus criticis. Additus est etiam huic operi libellus eiusdem de fascinatione. Alcalà, 1530.

> *Ref*: *Thornd (HM)* V 475.
>
> *N.B*: The addition on fascination is an attempt at an understanding of personal attraction and antagonism.

ARBOLAIRE.

269 Arbolayre . . . [*French*]. [Besançon: Peter Metlinger, about 1486–88.] f°. [LEK]

> *Ref*: GW 2312; C 584; Klebs 508.1; Stillwell A843; Goff A-944.

N.B: A herbal relating to the medicinal properties of plants; subsequently issued under the title, *Le grant herbier en françois* (see NLMCat 2146, 2147). Two Paris editions assigned to 1498 and 1500 are listed under Klebs 508. Hunt (Quinby) 25 lists an English version entitled *The Grete Herball*, printed at London by Peter Treveris, 27 July 1526. A 1529 edition is cited in Arber (1938) 274.

ARCOLANI, Giovanni (Joannes Arculanus), *fl.* 1450.

270 Expositio in primam fen quarti Canonis Avicennae de febribus. Ferrara: Andreas Belfortis, 24 January 1489. f°. [LEK]

Ref: GW 2316; HR 1552; BMC VI 604; IGI 4680; Klebs 80.1; Stillwell A847; Goff A-948.

271 Practica, seu Expositio noni libri Almansoris. [Padua: Petrus Maufer] 1 May 1480. [LEK]

Ref: H 13898; Osler (IM) 200; Klebs 79.1; *Garrison* (1929) 159; *Castiglioni* (1947) 332, 333.

N.B: A commentary on the popular ninth Book of Rhasis's *Liber ad Almansorem*; also issued with the latter text, at Padua, 'circa' 1 May 1480 (Cen R173). It contains a section on dentistry and dental instruments, mentions the filling of teeth with gold, describes surgery of the mouth, and gives an account of the mental symptoms of alcoholism.

ARNALDO de Villa Nova (Arnoldus de Villa Nova; Arnold de Ville Neuve), *c.* 1235–1311.

272 Antidotarium. Valencia: Nicolaus Spindeler, 1495. f°.

Ref: GW 2519; Klebs 105.1; Stillwell A951; Goff A-1065.

N.B: An uncritical list of many works written by or attributed to this prominent Catalan physician is given in Sart II 893–900. An *Opera* edited by Thomas Murchius was printed at Lyon by François Fradin for Baldassare de Gabiano in 1504 (NLMCat 305).

273 De arte cognoscendi venena. Padua: [Leonardus Achates, de Basilea] 1473. 4°. [LEK]

Add: VALASCO de Taranta, 1382–1417. De epidemia et peste. PIETRO d'Abano, *c.* 1255–1316. De venenis eorumque remediis. De lapide bezoar ex Pandectis.

Ref: GW 2521; HCR 8; BMC VII 909; Oates 2549; IGI 862; Klebs 98.2; Osler (IM) 40; Stillwell A952; Goff A-1066.

N.B: Relates to poisons and curative treatments. Also issued at Mantua [by Johann Vurster] in 1473 (GW 2522), but analysis has not yet revealed which of the 1473 editions has priority. Each of the three tracts appearing in these editions was frequently reprinted in combination or as a separate.

Arnaldo de Villa Nova (continued)

274 Breviarium practicae medicinae.   Milan: Christophorus Valdarfer, 26
Apr. 1483.   f°.   [LEK]

> *Ref:* GW 2526; H *1800; IGI 865; Klebs 103.1; *Sart* II 894; *Garrison* (1929) 163;
> Stillwell A955; Goff A-1071.
>
> *N.B:* A manual of practical medicine relating to ills of the head, of the body, women's
> diseases, and fever. Various early Italian printings and an edition issued at Lyon
> in 1532 are known. A possible French version, *Le trésor des pauvres*, printed by
> Antoine Vérard at Paris is assigned to 1503 (GW col. 693).
>
> *Mon:* [See under the following entry.]

275 Liber de conservanda juventute et retardanda senectute.   Leipzig:
Wolfgang Stoeckel, 1511.   4°.

> *Add:* Liber de conferentibus et nocentibus principalibus membris nostri corporis.
> *Ref:* NLMCat 312; GPB VII col. 211; *Sart* II 898.
> *N.B:* Said to be the text of Roger Bacon's *Liber de conservatione juventutis* with some
> alterations and a substitution of prescriptions for prolonging youth. Translated
> into English by Jonas Drummond in 1544; issued in Italian at Venice in 1550—
> *see* NLMCat 3636.
> *Mon:* DANA, Charles L. *The conservation of youth, translated by Jonas Drummond, with ad-
> ditions from the Breviarium.* Woodstock, Vt., 1912.

276 Phlebotomia. (*Issued with other medical tracts in* MAGNINUS MEDIOLANEN-
SIS, *d.* 1368. Regimen sanitatis.   [Lyon: François Fradin?, after 1500.])
4°.

> *Ref:* NLMCat 3041; H *10482; Klebs 640.5; IGI 5954 *sub* [about 1505];   Stillwell
> M45; Goff M-56.
> *N.B:* A treatise on blood-letting; also issued at Paris about 1500 (Cen M46) and at
> Lyon in 1517.

277 Regimen sanitatis ad regem Aragonum.   [France or Italy: Printer of
Valasco de Taranta, 'De epidemia' (Cen V5), about 1474?.]   4°.   [LEK]

> *Ref:* GW 2532; H *1817; BMC VIII 413; Osler (IM) 72; Klebs 99.1;   Stillwell A959;
> Goff A-1075.
> *N.B:* A book on rules of health addressed to the King of Aragon, for Arnaldo was
> frequently consulted by both the throne and the popes. Reprinted far into the
> sixteenth century. His *Regimen senum et seniorum*, printed for Claude Jaumar and
> Thomas Julian, is assigned to the press of Félix Baligault at Paris about 1500 (GW
> 2533).

278 Speculum medicinae.   [Leipzig:] Martin Landsberg [*c.* 1495].   4°.
[LEK]

> *Ref:* GW 2534; HC *1803; BMC III 640; BM-Ger 47; Stillwell A961; Goff A-1077.

279 Von Bewahrung und Bereitung der Weine [*German:*] Von bewarūg
vñ beraitūg der wein (Contributor and translator: Wilhelm von Hirnkofen, *fl.* 1478). [Esslingen: Conrad Fyner, after 2 Oct. 1478.] f °.
[LEK]

> *Ref*: GW 2537; HR 1810; BMC II 516; BM-Ger 46; Pell 1317; Klebs 101.1; Stillwell
> A964; Goff A-1080.
>
> *N.B*: Relates in part to the pharmaceutical value of wines. St. Michael's Day, 1478, is
> mentioned in the text. A dated edition was printed at Augsburg on 27 Aug. 1479
> (Cen A965; GW 2538), and nine others are known with fifteenth-century im-
> prints (GW 2539-47). Latin versions, *De vinis*, appeared about 1500 (Cen A962,
> A963, M45; GW 2535, 2536). For German versions published in 1506 and
> 1530 (?), the latter assigned to the press of Wolffgang Meyerpeck at Zwickaw,
> see NLMCat 313, 314. [See also under TECHNOLOGY.]
>
> *Fac*: SIGERIST, H. E., *tr. and ed. The earliest printed book on wine, by Arnald of Villanova
> … now for the first time rendered into English and with an historical essay by Henry E.
> Sigerist, M.D. With a facsimile of the original edition, 1478. New York, 1943.*

ARTICELLA.

280 Articella.   [Padua: Nicolò Petri, about 1476.] f °. [LEK]

> *Ref*: GW 2678; Osler (IM) 181; Poynter 82; Klebs 116.1; Choulant (H) 398, 139;
> *Sart* I 478.
>
> *N.B*: A compilation of medical tracts of variable contents which, as listed in Choulant,
> was issued in seventeen editions before the end of 1535. The present edition com-
> prises: ḤUNAIN ibn Isḥāq [Johannitius], *Isagoge Tegni Galeni*.—THEOPHILOS
> (known also as Philotheus, or Philaretus), *Liber pulsuum*; *Liber urinarum*.—
> HIPPOCRATES, *Aphorismi* (Comm: Galen. Tr: Constantinus Africanus); *Prog-
> nostica* (Comm: Galen); *De regimine acutorum morborum* (Comm: Galen).—
> GALEN, *Ars medica sive Tegni* (Comm: 'Alī ibn Ridwān).
>
> The first dated edition was printed at Venice by Hermann Liechtenstein, 29
> Mar. 1483—Cen A1011. [For additional works appearing in the 1483 edition,
> see GW 2679.]

ARTZNEY BÜCHLEIN.

281 Artzney Büchlein wider allerlei Kranckeyten und Gebrechen der Zeen
[*German*].   Leipzig, 1530. [LEK]

> *Ref*: *Garrison* (1929) 208.
>
> *N.B*: An early German book on dentistry summarizing the teachings of Galen,
> Mesuë, and various early writers, but antedated in its printing by references to
> dentistry in the texts of both Petrarca and Arcolani. Reprinted as the *Zene
> Artznei*, Mainz, 1532 and known in various editions.

III. *Medicine*

Artzney Büchlein (continued)

> *Mon*: POLETTI, G. B. *De re dentaria apud veteres*, Milan, 1951. BUDJUHN, G. *Quellen-kritische Untersuchung über die Geschichte des ältesten zahnheilkundlichen Druckes, Vorwort von K. Sudhoff*, Berlin, 1921 (Olschki, Choix 9830) [cited in Poletti, p. 16, as containing a facsimile of the *Artzney Büchlein*].

AUGUSTONE, Giovanni Basilio (Augustonus, Johannes Basilius), *fl.* 1490–1500.

282   De curatione elephantiasis. Defensio Cornelii Celsi. De helebori natura. (*Issued with his* Prognosticon de cometa, qui anno 1500 apparuit. [Genève: Jean Bellot, after 1 June 1500].)   4°.

> *Ref*: GW 3075; H 2702; Klebs 126.1.
> *N.B*: Known only in a copy at the Biblioteca Comunale Passerini-Landi at Piacenza. The tract on the properties of *heleborus* relates to a plant believed to cure madness.

AVENZOAR (Abū Marwān ʿAbd al-Malik . . . ibn Zohr [Zuhr]; Avenzohar), *c.* 1092–1162.

283   De curatione lapidis. (*Issued with* RHASIS. Liber ad Almansorem. [Venice:] Bonetus Locatellus, for Octavianus Scotus, 7 Oct. 1497.)   f°. [LEK]

> *Ref*: HC *13893; BMC V 448; BM-Ital 456; Klebs 826.2; *Sart* II 231–234; *Castiglioni* (1947) 270; Stillwell R170; Goff R-176.
> *N.B*: Possibly a part of his *Rectificatio medicationis*. Also issued with the editions of the *Aphorismi* of MAIMONIDES printed at Venice in 1500 by Johannes Hamman— Cen M64 and M65.

284   Rectificatio medicationis et regiminis, sive Liber al-Tasir. Antidotarium.   Venice: Joannes and Gregorius de Gregoriis, de Forlivio, 4 Jan. 1490/91.   f°. [LEK]

> *Add*: AVERROËS. Colliget. [First printed at Ferrara in 1482.]
> *Ref*: GW 3103; H *2186; BMC V 341; BM-Ital 2; IGI 1103; Klebs 127.1; *Campbell (AM)* I 90–92; *Sart* II 231–234; Stillwell A1253; Goff A-1408.
> *N.B*: A practical handbook for the physician. Translated from Arabic into Hebrew by Jacobus *Hebraeus*; translated into Latin by a 'Magister Patavinus.' The attribution of the translation from Hebrew into Latin to Paravicus as cited in the incipit has been shown by Professor Lynn Thorndike to be a probable misreading for Patavinus, who completed a translation in 1281—*Isis* 26, Dec. 1936, 33–36. For inclusion of the text in sixteenth-century compilations, see NLMCat 368–370, 374.

AVERROËS (Abū-l-Walīd Muḥammad ibn Aḥmad ibn Muḥammad ibn Rushd; *variously called* ibn Rushd; Muḥammad ibn Aḥmad; Averroës), 1126–1198.

285   Liber universalis de medicina qui dicitur Colliget.   Ferrara: Laurentius de Rubeis et socii, 5 Oct. 1482.   f°.   [LEK]

> *Ref:* GW 3107 and 3107 note (*var*); HC *2189 (*var*); BMC VI xi; IGI 1107; Klebs 128.1 and 128.1 (*var*); Campbell (*AM*) I 92–96; *Castiglioni* (1947) 277; *Sart* II 360; Stillwell A1256; Goff A-1411.
>
> *N.B:* A book of generalities on medicine; a medical encyclopaedia called *Colliget* from its original Arabic title, *Kitāb al-kullīyāt*. Variants known. Written by a great natural philosopher, whose commentaries on Aristotle gave rise to the school known as Averroism.

286   De tyriaca. De venenis. (*Issued with* MAGNINUS MEDIOLANENSIS, *d.* 1368. Regimen sanitatis. [Lyon: François Fradin?, *c.* 1500.])   4°.

> *Ref:* NLMCat 3041; H *10482; BMC VIII 439 [16th c.]; BM-Fr 296; IGI 5954 *sub* [about 1505]; Klebs 640.5; Stillwell M45; Goff M-56.
>
> *N.B:* Authenticity questioned—GW 3109.

AVICENNA (Abū ʼAlī al-Ḥusain ibn ʼAbdallah ibn Sina; *variously called* Avicenna, Alhossein, Ibn Sina, or Ḥusain), *c.* 985–1037.

287   Canon medicinae [al-Qānūn], libri V (Tr: Gherardo da Cremona, *c.* 1114–1187).   Milan: Philippus de Lavagnia, 12 Feb. 1473.   f°.   [LEK]

> *Ref:* GW 3115; BMC VI 700; BM-Ital 336[7]; IGI 1115; Klebs 131.2; *Sart* I 709–711; *Castiglioni* (1947) 270–273; *Afnan* 60–65, 204–205.
>
> *N.B:* The first *dated* edition of a work that comprises a codification of Aristotelian and Muslim medical knowledge and was the basis for many commentaries. An influential work which saw many editions but through its adherence to Aristotle and its misinterpretations of Galen retarded progress in experiment, although including much matter of its own, especially with regard to drugs. Its five Books treat of I) the human body, theoretical medicine, and hygiene; II) materia medica; III) special or localized diseases, the structure of the head; IV) general diseases affecting the entire body; V) the composition and preparation of drugs, known as Grabadin [Aqrabādhin]. A new translation of the *Canon* was made by Andrea Alpago, *d.* 1520.
>
> An undated edition is variously assigned to Strasbourg before 1473 (Cen A1262; Horblit 7); and its third Book was anonymously printed in an edition dated 23 Dec. 1472. Among later editions is a Hebrew version printed at Naples, 9 Nov. 1491 (Stillwell H493; Goff Heb-4), the first medical book printed in that language. A collection of commentaries by Gentile da Foligno and others was published by Lucantonio Giunta at Venice in 1523, in five folio volumes (BM-Ital 335). Issued in Arabic at Rome in 1593 (NLMCat 376). [For various six-

Avicenna (continued)

teenth-century editions and commentaries, see BM-Ital 335–337, BM-Fr 234, and NLMCat 376–393, *etc.* For the influence of Avicenna on Albertus Magnus, Thomas Aquinas, and other Western scholars, see AFNAN, p. 258–288. For an account of Avicenna's life based on his autobiography, see AFNAN p. 57–82.]

Mon: CHOULANT, L. *Abu ali Alhossein* (Chap. 92 in his *Handbuch der Bücherkunde für die ältere Medicin.* Graz, 1956 (Leipzig, 1841). SIGERIST, H. E. *Rhazes and Avicenna* (p. 78–87 in his *The great doctors, a biographical history of medicine.* Translated by E. and C. Paul. New York, 1933). AFNAN, Soheil M. *Avicenna, his life and works.* London, 1958. [See also NATURAL SCIENCE: Avicenna, *no.* 589.]

288   Canon medicinae, liber III (Tr: Gherardo da Cremona, *c.* 1114–1187). [Italy: Anonymous press] 23 Dec. 1472.   f °.   [LEK]

Ref: GW 3125; HR 2213; IGI 1126; Osler (IM) 21; Klebs 131.1.
N.B: The first edition of a part of the famous *Qānūn*, or *Canon*, a five-Book encyclopaedia of medicine [*see above*], which combines Greek and Muslim knowledge. Book III, in twenty-two sections, relates to special or localized diseases such as pleurisy, accumulation of pus, intestinal diseases, the condition of the urine, venereal diseases, and so forth.

289   Cantica de medicina (Comm: Averroës, 1126–1198).   Venice: Petrus Maufer and Nicolaus de Contugo, 24 Mar. 1483.   f °.   [LEK]

Ref: GW 3128; IGI 1128; Klebs 133.1; Schullian (ArMed) 81; *Afnan* 263; Stillwell A1274; Goff A-1430.
N.B: The translation from Arabic into Latin is credited to Armengandus, son of Blasius, a thirteenth-century physician. Printed at Venice by a rival press in 1484, and also issued with the 1490–95 Venice edition of Avicenna's *Canon medicinae* printed by Baptista de Tortis.

290   De viribus cordis (Tr: Arnaldo de Villa Nova, *c.* 1235–1311). (*Issued with* AVICENNA. Canon medicinae, libri V. Padua: Johannes Herbort, de Seligenstadt, 28 Sept. – 12 Dec. 1476.)   f °.   [LEK]

Ref: GW 3116; Pell 1660; IGI 1116; Klebs 131.4; Stillwell A1263; Goff A-1418.
N.B: A treatise on the heart. Here dated 27 Nov. 1476, but with variable dates in other editions of the *Canon* to which it is appended. It appeared also in the undated edition assigned in GW 3114 to [Strasbourg: Adolph Rusch, before 1473] —Cen A1262.

BAGELLARDO, Paolo (Paulus Bagellardus), *c.* 1425–1492.

291   De aegritudinibus infantium.   [Padua:] Bartholomaeus de Valdezoccho and Martinus de Septem Arboribus, 21 Apr. 1472.   4°.   [LEK]

Ref: GW 3166; H *2244; BMC VII 904; BM-Ital 67; IGI 1146; Klebs 139.1; *Garrison* (1929) 198; *Castiglioni* (1947) 372; Stillwell B10; Goff B-10.

N.B: The first printed book on pediatrics. An Italian translation completed on 16 March 1486 is assigned to the press of Boninus de Boninis at Brescia (GW 3168).

BANCKES, Rycharde, *publisher*.

292 Herball. London: R. Banckes, 1525. [LEK]

> *Ref*: Arber (1938) 274; *Hunt (Quinby)* I App. 19.
> *N,B*: A popular herbal; consequently a rare one today. The first book devoted solely to herbs to be printed in England. Known usually as *Banckes's Herbal* although its full title reads: Here begynneth a new mater, the whiche sheweth and treateth of ye vertues and proprytes of herbes, the whiche is called an Herball. Known in copies at the British Museum and the Henry E. Huntington Library, San Marino.
> *Fac*: *Facsimile of R. Banckes's Herbal of 1525*. [New York:] The New York Botanical Garden, 1941. (Edited by Sanford V. Larkey and Thomas Pyles.)

BARBANTINI de Zantuliete, Giovanni (Jean de Zantuliete; Johannes Barbantinus).

293 De dietis totius anni. (*Issued with* MAGNINUS MEDIOLANENSIS, *d*. 1368. Regimen sanitatis. [Lyon: François Fradin?, after 1500.]) 4°.

> *Ref*: NLMCat 3041; H *10482; BMC VIII 439; BM-Fr 296; IGI 5954 *sub* [about 1505]; Klebs 640.5; Stillwell M45; Goff M-56.

BARBARO, Ermolao (Hermolaus Barbarus; Barbari), 1454–1493.

294 In Dioscoridem corollariorum libri V. Venice: Aloysius et Franciscus Barbarus and Joannes Bartholomaeus, Astensis, 1516. f°. [LEK]

> *Ref*: NLMCat 1140; BM-Ital 71, 218; Choulant (H) 82; *Sart (Appr)* 71; *Castiglioni* (1947) 373.
> *N.B*: A commentary and correction of the text of Dioscorides's treatise on medical botany. With additions by Giovanni Battista Cipelli (Joannes Baptista Egnatius, *pseud.*), 1473–1553. [For Barbaro's *Castigationes Plinianae*, see under NATURAL SCIENCE.]

BARZIZZA, Cristoforo (Christophorus Barzizius; Barzizio), *fl.* 1450.

295 Introductorium ad opus practicum medicinae. Pavia: Antonius Carcanus, for Octavianus Scotus, 20 Aug. 1494. f°. [LEK]

> *Add*: RHASIS. Liber nonus Almansoris, *with commentary of Barzizza*.
> *Ref*: GW 3672; IGI 1406; Klebs 159.1; Schullian (ArMed) 94; *Castiglioni* (1947) 648; Stillwell B224; Goff B-260.
> *N.B*: Written by a fifteenth-century physician, who with Michele Savonarola supported the Hippocratic belief in the value of hydrotherapy.

BAVARII, Bavario de (Baverio Baviera; Baverio Maghinardo de' Bonetti; Baverius de Baveriis), *d.* 1480.

296 Consilia medica [*and other works*]. Bologna: Franciscus (Plato) de Benedictis, for the author's sons, 5 Nov. 1489. f°. [LEK]

> *Ref:* GW 3739; HC 2712; BMC VI 824; IGI 1423; Schullian (ArMed) 95; Klebs 163.1; Garrison (1929) 167—Stillwell B247; Goff B-283.
>
> *N.B:* One of a series of *Consilia*, printed in Italy as early as 1476, which systematically record the patient's condition and the treatment prescribed by the physician. For works entitled *Consilia Baverii* and *Consiliorum de re medica*, printed at Pavia in 1521 and Strasbourg in 1543 respectively, *see* NLMCat 503, 504.
>
> *Mon:* MÜNSTER, Ladislao. *Baverio Maghinardo de' Bonetti, medico imolese del Quattrocento: la vita, il tempo, il pensiero scientifico*. Imola, 1956 (Atti dell' Associazione per Imola storico-artistica, VII).

297 Reggimento della peste [*Italian*]. Bologna: Johannes Schriber, 17 Dec. 1478. 4°. [LEK]

> *Ref:* GW 3740; Klebs 162.1; Klebs (P) 4; Osler (IM) 150.
>
> *N.B:* Issued in Italian at Venice in 1523 as *Trattato mirabile contra peste* (NLMCat 505).

BENEDETTI, Alessandro (Alexander Benedictus), *c.* 1450–1512.

298 De observatione in pestilentia. Venice: Joannes and Gregorius de Gregoriis, 29 July 1493. 4°.

> *Ref:* GW 864; H *807; BMC V 344; BM-Ital 83; IGI 1461; Klebs 172.1; Klebs (P) 6; Schullian (ArMed) 98; *Garrison* (1929) 215; *Castiglioni* (1947) 369; *Schullian (B) 14*; Stillwell A356; Goff A-390.
>
> *N.B:* A work relating to pestilential fever. His *Collectiones medicinae* was issued at [Venice, *c.* 1493] (Cen A354; Schullian (ArMed) 96) and included in Champier's *De medicinae claris scriptoribus* [Lyon, 1506]— *see no.* 340. See also the listing of Benedetti's works in NLMCat 517–524, and p. 240–241 in SCHULLIAN, D. M., *ed.* and *tr. Alessandro Benedetti: Diaria de bello Carolino*, New York, Renaissance Society of America, 1967.

BENIVIENI, Antonio, 1443–1502.

299 De abditis nonnullis ac mirandis morborum et sanationum causis (Ed: G. Benivieni). Florence: Filippo Giunta, 24 Sept. 1507. 4°. [LEK]

> *Ref:* NLMCat 528; BM-Ital 84; *Sart (Appr)* 119; *Castiglioni* (1947) 370.
>
> *N.B:* Contains the record of twenty autopsies. Written by a Florentine physician, a Galenist, who nevertheless used post-mortems as a means of studying disease. He is sometimes called the founder of pathology, in which he was a pioneer, and the forerunner of Morgagni, *d.* 1771. [See also the entry under NATURAL SCIENCE.]

Fac: A facsimile, with translation by Charles Singer and a biographical sketch of the author by Esmond R. Long, was issued at Springfield, Illinois, in 1954.

BENZI, Ugo (Benzo; Hugo Senensis; Ugo da Siena), 1376–1439.

300 Consilia ad diversas aegritudines (Ed: Laurentius de Gozadinis). [Bologna:] Johann de Nördlingen and Henricus de Harlem, 3 Oct. 1482. f°. [LEK]

Ref: HC *9020; BMC VI 819; BM-Ital 85; IGI 4941; Schullian (ArMed) 103; Klebs 1001.1; *Lockw (Benzi)* 238–317, 381, 394–395; *Sart* III 1239; Stillwell H466; Goff H-538.

N.B: Contains 83 *Consilia* by Benzi, plus 2 by other hands. Professor Lockwood, in his exhaustive monograph on Benzi, notes the presence of an additional 27 in the edition of [1496–99], and the omission of one in the edition of 1503—leaving the printed corpus at the fixed number of 111 thereafter, of which more than a hundred are complete in form.

Although Benzi was one of the earliest physicians to compile a record of symptoms in a given case and a comprehensive program for treatment, his *Consilia* were not the first to be printed. The *Consilia* of at least three other physicians were put through the press before his were issued—see below under MONTAGNANA (1476); CERMISONE (1476); FERRARI [1480]. [The earliest *Consilia* on record were written by Taddeo Alderotti, *fl.* 1250. For Benzi's *Consiglio* on weight control, see no. 309 *note*.]

Mon: LOCKWOOD, Dean Putnam. *Ugo Benzi, medieval philosopher and physician, 1376–1439*. Chicago, 1951.

301 Cura cuiusdam hominis morsi a serpente venenoso. (*Issued with his* Consilia ad diversas aegritudines. [Bologna:] Johann de Nördlingen and Henricus de Harlem, 3 Oct. 1482.)

Ref: *Lockw (Benzi)* 79.
N.B: The only case-history, as the term is understood today, among Benzi's *Consilia*. An account of the treatment of a man poisoned by an adder.

302 De cura lapidis renum. (*Issued with his* Consilia ad diversas aegritudines. Pavia: [Leonardus Gerla] for Franciscus de Nebiis, 14 Apr. [1496–99].) f°.

Ref: R 1544; Klebs 1001.2; *Lockw (Benzi)* 79, 344–347; Stillwell H467; Goff H-539.
N.B: A treatise on the kidney-stone, intended perhaps as a medical manual. The date assignment is derived from the statement in the book that it was printed "regnante Ludovico Maria Sfortia."

303 Expositio in primam [et secundam] fen primi Canonis Avicennae (Ed: Antonio Cittadino of Faenza). Ferrara: Andreas Belfortis, Gallus, 13 Aug. 1491. f°. [LEK]

Benzi (continued)

> *Add*: CITTADINO, Antonio. Tractatus de febre.
>
> *Ref*: HCR 9016; BMC VI 604; IGI 4946; Klebs 998.1; *Lockw (Benzi)* 396; Stillwell H472; Goff H-544.
>
> *N.B*: In the Venetian reprint of 1498 (Cen H474) the contents are the same, but the presence of the second *fen* is noted.

304 Expositio in primam fen quarti Canonis Avicennae. Pavia: Joannes Andreas de Boscho, for Franciscus de Nebiis, 29 Oct. 1498. f°.

> *Ref*: R 1766; IGI 4948; Schullian (ArMed) 108; Klebs 999.1; *Lockw (Benzi)* 30, 38, 42, 232, 395; Stillwell H473; Goff H-547.
>
> *N.B*: A commentary on Avicenna which Benzi had planned to read publicly—that is, to "publish"—as a treatise on fevers, but his death prevented its completion. Although his other commentaries on Avicenna were in the nature of textbooks or university lectures, this he had planned as his *magnum opus* after retirement, "aloof from academic bickering." The present edition contains his *Quaestio de modo augmentationis*.

305 Expositio super libros Tegni Galeni. Pavia: Antonius Carcanus for Mauritius Moretus, 29 Feb. 1496. f°. [LEK]

> *Ref*: HR 9014; IGI 4953; Klebs 1003.1; *Lockw (Benzi)* 395; Stillwell H470; Goff H-542.

306 Exposito super quarta fen primi Canonis Avicennae. Pavia: Damianus de Confaloneriis [1478-80?] f°. [LEK]

> *Add*: MARSIGLIO da Santa Sofia, *c.* 1367-1405? Super quarta primi, *in part*.
>
> *Ref*: BM-Ital 85; BMC VII 1000; IGI 4949; Osler (IM) 159; Klebs 997.1; *Lockw (Benzi)* 42, 394 [1], 396.
>
> *N.B*: A controversial treatise in keeping with Benzi's proud place in disputation. Includes chapters 1–16 of Benzi's commentary and chapters 17–31 of that by Marsiglio. The second edition, printed at Venice by Andreas Calabrensis (Cen H475), was issued on 4 Feb. 1485. Others appeared in Siena, 2 Mar. 1485/86 and Pavia, 29 Jan. 1496, the latter with a slight addition to the Benzi text. At least seven sixteenth-century editions are known.

Libro de conservare la persona in sanitate. *See no. 309 note.*

307 Quaestio de malitia complexionis diversae. (*Issued with* JACOPO da Forlì, *c.* 1360–1413. Expositio in primum librum Canonis Avicennae. Pavia: Christophorus de Canibus, for Hieronymus de Durantibus, 7 May 1488.) f°. [LEK]

> *Ref*: HR *7243; IGI 4985; Klebs 548.3; *Lockw (Benzi)* 143, 180, 229, 394[6]; Stillwell J48; Goff J-51.

N.B: A paper read [*i.e.*, "published"] at the University of Florence on 20 January and expounded by its author on 1 March, 1422. With regard to the fact that this work appears in the printed editions of our period solely in conjunction with the Avicenna commentary of Jacopo da Forlì, a statement in the preface of this edition would seem to indicate—as Professor Lockwood notes—that this may have been due to the fact that these two disputants were diametrically opposed to one another.

308 Super Aphorismos Hippocratis et Galeni expositio. Ferrara: Laurentius de Rubeis (Lorenzo de Rossi) and Andreas de Grassis, 15 Nov. 1493. f °. [LEK]

Ref: H *9011; BMC VI 612; BM-Ital 85; Oates 2245; IGI 4944; Klebs 1002.1; *Lockw (Benzi)* 212, 393, 394; Stillwell H468; Goff H-540.
N.B: Issued in Venice for Octavianus Scotus, in 1498—Cen H469.

309 Trattato utilissimo circa la conservazione della sanità [*Italian*]. Milan: Petrus de Corneno, 31 May 1481. 8°.

Ref: HCR 9021; BMC VI 759; IGI 4943; Klebs 1000.1; *Lockw (Benzi)* 77–79, 121, 318, 338–343; Stillwell H476; Goff H-548.
N.B: The earliest treatise on personal hygiene and the conservation of health to be printed in Italian. Contains also Benzi's *Libro de conservare la persona in sanitade*, a treatise on weight control, and his *Consiglio*, a regimen for the prevention of obesity drawn up for Niccolò d'Este and not included in Benzi's *Consilia*.

BERENGARIO da Carpi, Jacopo (Jacobus Berengarius; *called* Carpi), *c.* 1460–1530.

310 Commentaria cum amplissimis additionibus super anatomia Mundini. Bologna: Hieronymus de Benedictis, 1521. 4°. [LEK]

Ref: NLMCat 530; BM-Ital 456; *Garrison* (1929) 226.
N.B: Written by an advocate of a simple treatment for gunshot wounds, one of the controversial subjects of the time. [For an account of the work, see under NATURAL SCIENCE: Anatomy.]
Mon: PUTTI, V. *Berengario da Carpi*. Bologna, 1937.

311 Tractatus de fractura calve sive cranei. Bologna: Hieronymus de Benedictis, 1518. 4°. [LEK]

Ref: NLMCat 531; BM-Ital 86; *Thornd* (*HM*) V 513; *Garrison* (1929) 215; *Castiglioni* (1947) 417.
N.B: A treatise on fractures of the skull.
Mon: PUTTI, V. *Berengario da Carpi. Saggio biografico e bibliografico seguito dalla traduzione del "De fractura calve sive cranei."* Bologna: L. Cappelli, 1937.

BERNARDUS de Gordonio (Bernard Gordon), *fl.* 1300.

312 Practica dicta Lilium medicinae. Naples: Francesco del Tuppo, 20 May 1480. f°. [LEK]

> *Ref*: GW 4080; H *7795; IGI 1568; Pr 6683; Klebs 177.1; *Garrison* (1929) 164; *Castiglioni* (1947) 352; Goff B-447.
>
> *N.B*: Relates to epilepsy, scabies, trachoma, leprosy, and various contagious diseases. Known in five Latin editions and in French and Spanish versions issued before 1500. For discussion of the term *oculo berillino*, which occurs in fourteenth-century manuscripts of this text, see ROSEN, Edward. *The invention of eyeglasses* (Journal of the History of Medicine and Allied Sciences), 1956, 11, 201–203. [Garrison, p. 185, speaks of the earliest spectacles known to be extant as having belonged to Willibald Pirkheimer, 1470–1530.] The author's treatises *De urinis* and *De pulsibus* were issued together at Ferrara by Andreas Belfortis, 4 March 1487 (GW 4087; Cen B392).

BERTUCCIO, Nicolò (Nicolaus Bertucius; Vertuccio), *d.* 1347.

313 Collectorium. Lyon: Claudius Davost, for Barthomeus Trote, 1509. 4°. [LEK]

> *Ref*: NLMCat 563; BM-Fr 51; *Sart* III 847–848.
>
> *N.B*: The author, a professor at Bologna and the writer of several medical works, had studied with Mondino, and in his classes he continued the latter's practice of dissecting cadavers as he lectured. Sometimes called his *Compendium*; comprising the following sections: *De regimine sanitatis*; *De aegritudinibus particularibus*; *De febribus*; *De crisi et de diebus creticis*; *De venenis*; *De decoratione*. According to Sarton, it contains also a chapter on anatomy including a description of the brain.

BIONDO, Michel-Angelo (Michaelangelo Blondo), 1497–1565.

314 Compendiosa de medicamentis, quae apud pharmacopolas comperiuntur. Rome: Domina Hieronyma de Cartulariis, for the author, 1544. 8°.

> *Ref*: NLMCat 584; BM-Ital 105; *Castiglioni* (1947) 471.
>
> *N.B*: An author of many interests, whom Castiglioni cites as advocating treatment of wounds with applications of cold water or non-irritants.

BONAVENTURA de' **CASTELLI** (Tura de' Castelli), *fl.* 1340.

315 Ricetta dell' aqua del bagno de Porretta [*Italian*]. [Padua: Anonymous printer] 1473. [LEK]

> *Ref*: Osler (IM) 44; Klebs 995.1; *Sart* III 857.
>
> *N.B*: On the medicinal value of the sulphur baths at Porretta. A Latin edition of about 1473 is assigned to Padua (Klebs 994.1). Issued also with the tract *De balneis* of Gentile da Foligno [Padua], 24 Mar. 1473 and with the *Chyrurgia* of Guy de

Chauliac, Venice, 21 Nov. 1498 and 23 Dec. 1499 (Schullian (ArMed) 202, 227, 228; Cen G121, G510–511). For early editions of the sixteenth century, see NLMCat 2233–2237.

BRANT, Sebastian, 1458–1521.

316 De pestilentiali scorra eulogium. Basel: Johann Bergmann, von Olpe, Sept. 1496. Bdsde. [LEK]

Ref: GW 5038; *Garrison* (1929) 189.
N.B: A poem on syphilis; also issued with Grünpeck's *De pestilentiali scorra* in five editions before the end of the century (Goff G-517; Klebs 476.1–5), and in German in two editions (Klebs 477.1–2).

BRASAVOLA, Antonio Musa, 1500–1555.

317 Examen omnium simplicium medicamentorum quorum in officinis usus est. Rome: Antonio Blado, de Asula, 1536. f°. [LEK]

Ref: *Thornd* (*HM*) V 445; *Sart* (*Appr*) 32; *Castiglioni* (1947) 442.
N.B: Treats of herbs and medicinal simples; a combination of botany and pharmacy, written in dialogue form. A work which, while it discusses the use of medicinal simples by the writers of antiquity, the Arabs, and more recent pharmacists, states the author's belief in experimentation and tells of collecting and testing specimens for their reputed value. An edition was issued at Lyon by Jean and François Frellon in 1537 (NLMCat 680). Subsequent editions of this and other pharmaceutical works by this author are listed in BM-Fr 81 and BM-Ital 124–125.
Mon: THORNDIKE, Lynn. *Brasavola and pharmacy* (chap. XX in vol. V of his *History of magic and experimental science*, New York, 1941).

318 In libros de ratione victus in morbis acutis Hippocratis & Galeni commentaria. Venice: Hieronymus Scotus, 1546. f°.

Ref: NLMCat 692; BM-Ital 329; *Castiglioni* (1947) 442; *Sart* (*Appr*) 33.
N.B: A commentary on the *De ratione victus* of Hippocrates, and on Galen's commentary, which had been issued by Simon de Colines at Paris in 1531 and again in 1542. With texts. According to Castiglioni, Brasavola was among the first who opposed the authority of Galen. He was the compiler of an index of the latter's works, the *Index refertissimus in omnes Galeni libros*, volume II in the Galen *Opera*, printed by the Giunta press at Venice in 1550–1551, and subsequently re-issued—*see* NLMCat 1754, 1756, 1759.

BRISSOT, Pierre (Petrus Brissotus), 1478–1522.

319 Apologetica disceptatio, qua docetur per quae loca sanguis mitti debeat in viscerum inflammationibus (Ed: Antonius Luceus). Paris: Simon de Colines, 1525. 4°. [LEK]

Brissot (continued)

> *Ref*: NLMCat 709; BM-Fr 82; Renouard (Colines) 70; *Castiglioni* (1947) 443-444; *Garrison* (1929) 232.
>
> *N.B*: A treatise on blood-letting which resulted in a violent controversy, since Brissot reverted to the Hippocratic method of blood-letting near the lesion, whereas contemporary practice, following the teachings of Arabic physicians, advocated a distant location. Re-issued at Basel in 1528, 1529, and 1530; and at Venice in 1539.

BRUNSCHWIG, Hieronymus (Jeronimo Brunschweick; Hieronymus von Braunschweig), *c.* 1450–1512.

320 Chirurgia [*German*]. Strasbourg: Johann (Reinhard) Grüninger, 4 July 1497. f°. [LEK]

> *Ref*: GW 5593; H *4017 = HC *4018; IGI 2182; Klebs 225.1 and 225.1 *var.*; *Castiglioni* (1947) 372; Stillwell B1087; Goff B-1225.
>
> *N.B*: A detailed account of the treatment of gunshot wounds, the first in medical history. An important book on surgery. One of the first medical books to be illustrated. Known also as *Das Buch der Wund-Artzney*. Published also at Augsburg in December 1497, 1534, and 1539. An English edition of 1525 and a Dutch version of 1535 are listed in NLMCat 747, 746. Some copies include the author's *Anathomia*, which is found also as a separate—thus suggesting that the works may have been issued independently and the remainders combined. Variants known.
>
> *Fac*: KLEIN, Gustav, ed. *Das Buch der Cirurgia des Hieronymus Brunschwig, Strassburg, Johann Grüninger, 1497*. München, 1911 (*Alte Meister der Medizin und Naturkunde* 3). SIGERIST, H. E. *Hieronymus Brunschwig and his work*. New York, 1946.

321 Pestbuch [*German*]. [Strasbourg:] Johann (Reinhard) Grüninger, 19 Aug. 1500. f°.

> *Ref*: NLMCat 765; GW 5596; HC *4020; BMC I 115; BM-Ger 149; Schullian (Ar-Med) 130; Klebs 228.1; Stillwell B1090; Goff B-1228.
>
> *N.B*: Text in German but with title, *Liber pestilentialis de venenis epidimie*. Variant known. Based largely on Heinrich Steinhöwel's *Büchlein der Ordnung der Pestilenz*, Ulm, 1473.

322 Thesaurus pauperum [*German*]. (*Issued with his* De arte distillandi de compositis, *the so-called* Grosses Distillierbuch. Strasbourg: Johann (Reinhard) Grüninger, 1512.) f°. [LEK]

> *Ref*: NLMCat 748-757.
>
> *N.B*: A popular handbook. Re-issued as the *HaussApoteck*, which in an English version is described as "A most excellent and perfecte homish apothecarye or homely physick booke, for all the grefes and diseases of the bodye." [For Brunschwig's

so-called *Kleines Distillierbuch*, 1500, and *Grosses Distillierbuch*, 1512, see under
TECHNOLOGY.]

CAIUS, John, 1510–1573.

323 De medendi methodo libri duo ex. Cl. Galeni Pergameni, et Jo. Baptista
Montani Veronensis principum medicorum sententia.   Basel [Heirony-
mus Froben and Nicolaus Episcopius] 1544.   8°.

Ref: NLMCat 795; BM-Ger 173; Sart (*Appr*) 31; *Wightman* (1962) I 222.

N.B: Based upon the texts of Galen and Joannes Baptista Montanus (Giovanni Battista
da Monte), 1498–1551. A selection of Galen's works was included in a volume
edited by Caius and published in Greek by this firm at Basel in 1544 (NLMCat
1763).

CALENDARIUM.

324 Calendarium, 1457.   [Mainz(?): 36-line Bible type, *1st state*, 1456.]
Bdsde.

Ref: GW 1286; Einbl 114; DeR(M) 21.

N.B: The first piece of medical interest known to have been printed. Sometimes cited
as the *Aderlasskalender für 1457*. A broadside listing auspicious days for purging.
Known only in a copy at the Bibliothèque Nationale, Paris.

Fac: GUTENBERG-GESELLSCHAFT. Veröffentlichungen I, Taf. V.

CALENDRIER.

325 Calendrier des bergiers [*French*].   Paris: Guy Marchant, 2 May 1491.
f°.   [LEK]

Ref: GW 5906; Pell 3904; Klebs 291.1.

N.B: A popular manual combining medicinal and astrological lore. First edition;
known only in an imperfect copy at the Bibliothèque Mazarine in Paris. Re-
issued 18 April 1493 (Cen C50). Later called *Le compost et kalendrier des bergiers
nouvellement refait*. Marchant's amplified edition of 18 July 1493 (Cen C51) has
been reproduced in facsimile by Pierre Champion, Paris [1927]. About fifteen
editions, complete or in part, printed in France or at Geneva, are known within
our period.

CAPELLUTI, Rolando (Rolandus Capellutus), *fl.* 1475.

326 De curatione pestiferorum apostematum.   Rome: Ulrich Han [about
1475].   4°.   [LEK]

Ref: GW 6017; H *4373; Osler (IM) 81; Pell 3226; IGI 2428; Klebs 248.1; Klebs (P)
36.

N.B: Variant known (GW 6018; Cen C107).

CARDANO, Girolamo (*often Cardan in English usage*), 1501–1576.

327 Contradicentium medicorum liber continens contradictiones centum octo.   Venice: Hieronymus Scotus, 1545.   [LEK]

> *Ref*: NLMCat 835; *Wightman* (1962) II 127.
> *N.B*: An important, critical work by a man of independent thought and action, colorful and contradictory in his personality but keen-eyed as a physician and a mathematician. Issued in two volumes at Lyon by Sébastien Gryphe in 1548, *Liber secundus* containing the addition of 108 contradictions, two tracts by Cardano, *De sarza parilia* and *De radice cina*, and other matter (NLMCat 836). Cardano's autobiography, *De propria vita liber*, was published by Gabriel Naudé at Paris nearly a century later, in 1643.

> *Mon*: LINDSAY, R. B. *Jerome Cardan, 1501–1576 (American Journal of Physics*, XVI, May 1948).   ORE, Oystein. *Cardano, the gambling scholar*, Princeton, 1953.

328 De malo recentiorum medicorum medendi usu libellus...   De simplicium medicinarum noxa.   Venice: Apud Octavianum Scotum, 1536. 8°.   [LEK]

> *Ref*: NLMCat 841; BM-Ital 149; *Sart (SW)* 187; *Ore (Card)* 12, 13; *Lindsay (JC)* 313
> *N.B*: A criticism of medical practices and an attack upon the pompous postures of medical men. Cardano's first printed book, and although not calculated to increase his standing with the professional medical men of his time, it is said eventually to have won him admission to the College of Physicians and the right to practice medicine in Milan. Re-issued at Venice in 1545.

329 De subtilitate rerum libri XXI.   Paris: Michel Fezandat and Robert Granjon, 1550.   8°.   [LEK]

> *Ref*: BM-Fr 91; *Garrison* (1929) 210; *Ore (Card)* 15; *Lindsay (JC)* 315–317.
> *N.B*: A work written in a popular style and treating a wide range of subjects. Includes a description of a touch-system not unlike Braille, as an aid to the blind, and a suggestion regarding a sign-language for the deaf. According to Garrison, Cardano's biological concepts tended toward evolution. For further comment on this work, see under PHYSICS: Cardano. [One of the few books known to have been printed by Robert Granjon, the famous type-designer.]

CASINI, Francesco (Francesco da Siena).

330 Dicta de balneo Petriolo. (*Issued with* GENTILE da Foligno. Balneae. [Padua:] Joannes de Reno, 24 Mar. 1473.)

> *Ref*: *Sart* III 1684–1686; Stillwell G121; Goff G-133.
> *N.B*: Uncertainty regarding the author's dates is discussed by Sarton, who assigns his birth to about 1345–49 and his death to some time after 1415. His writings relate largely to treatments for poisons and to medicinal baths.

III. *Medicine*

CELSUS, Aulus Cornelius, *early years of the first century.*

331   De medicina libri VIII (Ed: Bartolommeo Fonti, 1445–1513).   Florence: Nicolaus Laurentii, 1478.   sm. f°.   [LEK]

> *Ref:* GW 6456; HC *4835; BMC VI 627; Oates 2333; IGI 2674; Klebs 260.1; *Sart (Appr)* 12–14; *Sart* I 240; *Castiglioni* (1947) 205–213; *Garrison* (1929) 108; *Taton (A&MS)* 352; Stillwell C325; Goff C-364.
>
> *N.B:* The first organized treatise on medicine to be printed. The text, recovered in 1426–1443, describes medicine in the Hellenistic period, treating the Dogmatic, Methodist, and Empiric schools impartially; records practices in Alexandrian surgery; and devotes separate sections to the dietetic, pharmaceutical, and surgical treatment of disease. It describes surgical appliances and treats of the removal of tonsils and cataracts, plastic operations, dental practice, the use of ligatures in surgery, malarial fever, insanity, and so forth. Written in elegant Latin, as part of an encyclopaedic work. According to Beaujeu's analysis (in Taton), Book I discusses the history of medical schools, methodology and dietetics; Books II–IV, prognosis and therapy; Books V–VI, pharmacology; Book VII, surgery; and Book VIII, bone diseases. Its Latin terms, often translations of those used in Greek medicine, make it a valuable source of terminology. [See also NATURAL SCIENCE. For the text, see the edition in the Loeb Classical Library, with English translation by W. G. Spencer, Cambridge, Mass., 1935–1938. 3 vols.]
>
> *Mon:* TEMKIN, O. *Celsus' 'On Medicine' and the ancient medical sects* (p. 249–264 in Institute of the History of Medicine. *Bulletin,* vol. 3, 1935). CASTIGLIONI, A. *Aulus Cornelius Celsus as a historian of medicine* (p. 857–873 in *ibid.,* vol. 8, 1940).

CEPOLLA, Bartolomeo (Bartholomaeus Caepolla), *d.* 1477.

332   Cautelae.   Milan: Christophorus Valdarfer, 15 Sept. 1475.   f°.   [LEK]

> *Ref:* GW 6475; HCR 4855; BMC VI 725; IGI 2686; Pell 3477; Stillwell C339; Goff C-379.
>
> *N.B:* Frequently issued with his *De servitutibus urbanorum et rusticorum praediorum,* a combination which Poynter 163 notes as treating of laws relative to dwellings, with sections on water supply, heating, ventilation, domestic hygiene, and burial. The *De servitutibus* had been issued in an undated edition (Cen C348) assigned to Perugia about 1473–74. The combination is found in the editions of the two works produced by Franciscus de Sancto Pedro at Pavia in 1480 and 1481 (Cen C340 and C352).

CERMISONE, Antonio (Antonius Cermisonus; Cernisone), *d.* 1441.

333   Consiglio per preservar dalla peste [*Italian*].   [Naples: Jodocus Hohenstein, 1475/76.]   4°.

> *Ref:* Klebs 263.1; *Castiglioni* (1947) 366; Stillwell C361; Goff C-401.

Cermisone (continued)

334 Consilia medica. Brescia: Henricus de Colonia, 4 Sept. 1476. f°.
[LEK]

> *Ref*: GW 6514; HC *4885; BMC VII 965; IGI 2708; Osler (IM) 116; Klebs 266.1;
> Stillwell C362; Goff C-402.
> *N.B*: The second account of prescribed treatments to be printed. According to
> Professor Lockwood in his monograph on *Ugo Benzi*, p. 322, six or eight prescrip-
> tions from Cermisone are also included in the *Consilia* of Benzi printed at
> [Bologna] in 1482 and at Pavia in [1496–99], although not in subsequent editions.

335 Recollectae de urinis. [Upper Italy?: Printer of Jacopo da Forlì, 'Expositio,' about 1475.] f°.

> *Ref*: GW 6516; H 4887; IGI 2710; Pell 3501; Klebs 265.1; Stillwell C364; Goff C-
> 404.
> *N.B*: Also found with Jacopo's *Expositio in primum librum Canonis Avicennae—see no.*
> 430.

336 Ricette contro la pestilenza [*Italian*]. [Milan: Philippus de Lavagnia,
1480.] 4°. [LEK]

> *Ref*: GW 6517; R II 147; IGI 2711; Klebs 264.1.
> *N.B*: Re-issued and assigned to the press of Christophorus Valdarfer about 1483–84
> (Cen C365).

CHAMPIER, Symphorien (Symphorianus Champerius), 1472–*c*.1535.

337 Castigationes seu emendationes pharmacopolarum sive apothecariorum
ac Arabum medicorum Mesuae Serapionis Rasis . . . et aliorum junior-
um, Lyon: Joannes Crespin, 1532. 8°.

> *Ref*: NLMCat 930; BM-Fr 98; *Thornd(HM)* V 122, 123, 461.
> *N.B*: A work which criticizes without condemning the works of the Arabic pharma-
> cists and physicians. Instead, Champier commends their good points and adds
> occasional comments based on his own observations. The opening section
> discusses the medicinal use of simples. Although treating the same subject, the
> work apparently did not influence the more advanced text of Brasavola printed
> four years later.
> *Mon*: THORNDIKE, Lynn. *Symphorien Champier* (chap. VII in vol. V of his *History of
> magic and experimental science*, New York, 1941). ALLUT, P. *Etude biographique
> & bibliographique sur Symphorien Champier*. Lyon, 1859.

338 Hortus gallicus. Lyon: Melchior and Gaspar Trechsel, 1533. 8°.

> *Ref*: NLMCat 934; BM-Fr 99; *Garrison* (1929) 196; *Wightman* (1962) II 146.
> *N.B*: Written on the thesis that whatever remedies are needed for the curing of disease
> in France can be produced in the soil of France.

339   Le myrouel des appothiquaires. Les lunectes des cyrurgiens & barbiers [*French*].   Lyon: P. Mareschal [1525?].   8°.   [LEK]

> *Ref*:   BM-Fr 99; *Sart* (*Appr*) 23.
> *N.B*:   A Paris edition of 1532 is also cited by Sarton.

340   De medicinae claris scriptoribus.   [Lyon: Jannot de Campis, 1506.]

> *Ref*:   NLMCat 935; BM-Fr 98; *Sart* (*Appr*) 23; *Garrison* (1929) 196.
> *N.B*:   An important medical bibliography. It consists of two parts: *Primus De medicine claris scriptoribus in quinque partibus tractatus*; *Secundus De legum divinarum conditoribus*. Includes, among other works, the "Opera parva" of Hippocrates and the "Collectiones" of Alessandro Benedetti. Variously assigned to the Lyon press of Claude Davost, Etienne Gueynard, or Jannot de Campis.
> *Mon*:   FULTON, J. R. *The great medical bibliographers, a study in humanism*. Philadelphia, 1951.

341   Practica nova in medicina . . . De omnibus morborum generibus ex traditionibus Grecorum, Latinorum, Arabum . . . Liber de omnibus generibus febrium.   [Lyon: Jean Marion for Simon Vincent, c. 1509–n. a. 1515.]

> *Ref*:   NLMCat 937; HC *4907; GW VI col. 420; BM-Fr 99; Klebs 269.1; Schullian (ArMed) 147; Stillwell C380; Goff C-422.
> *N.B*:   The context of the book shows it could not have been printed before Dec. 10, 1508, and the fact that the edition is mentioned in a letter from Veit Bild to Dr. Nicolaus Pol dated April 11, 1515, indicates that it must have been issued prior to that date. The anonymous press is identified in JOLY and LACASSAGNE. *Médecins & imprimeurs lyonnais au XVI* eme *siècle* (p. 98 in *Revue lyonnaise de Médecine*, vol. 7, 1958).

342   Speculum Galeni. Epithome Galeni, sive Galenus abreviatus.   Lyon: Simon Vincent, 1512.   f °.   [LEK]

> *Ref*:   NLMCat 945.
> *N.B*:   Re-issued, with added matter, at the press of Joannes de Jouvelle at Lyon in 1517. [For other Champier texts printed in the first half of the sixteenth century, see NLMCat p. 114-117.]

343   Symphonia Galeni ad Hippocratem, Cornellii Celsi ad Avicennam: una cum sectis antiquorum medicorum ac recentium . . .   [Lyon? 1528?] 8°.

> *Ref*:   NLMCat 947; BM-Fr 99; *Garrison* (1929) 196.
> *N.B*:   An effort to harmonize various medical theories, by one of the conciliators of Greek and Arabic doctrine. In similar fashion he endeavored to reconcile Plato and Aristotle in his *Symphonia Platonis cum Aristotele*, printed at Paris for Jodocus Badius Ascensius in 1516.

III. *Medicine*

COLLENUCCIO, Pandolfo (Pandulphus Collenucius), *fl.* 1490.

344 Pliniana defensio adversus Nicolai Leoniceni accusationem. Ferrara:
Andreas Belfortis [1493]. f°.

> *Ref:* GW 7164; HC *5483; BMC VI 605; IGI 3055; Pell 3854; Klebs 282.1; *Sart*
> (*Appr*) 82; Stillwell C687; Goff C-754.

CONRAD von Megenberg, *c.* 1309–1374.

345 Buch der Natur [*German*]. Augsburg: Johann Bämler, 30 Oct. [14]75.
f°. [LEK]

> *Ref:* H *4041; BMC II 333; BM-Ger 476; Klebs 300.1; *Sart* III 817–821; *Garrison*
> (1929) 165; Stillwell C759; Goff C-842.
> *N.B:* Among the many subjects treated are sections on anatomy, physiology, plagues,
> and the medicinal value of plants and stones. [For further account of its contents
> and importance, see under NATURAL SCIENCE.]

CONSTANTINOS VII, Porphyrogennetos, *d.* 959.

346 Veterinariae medicinae libri II (Tr: Jean de la Ruelle, 1479–1537).
Paris: Ludovicus Blaubomius for Simon de Colines, 1530. f°. [LEK]

> *Ref:* NLMCat 2310; BM-Fr 387; Choulant (H) 421; *Sart* I 356, 657.
> *N.B:* A veterinary encyclopaedia. Also known as *Hippiatrici scriptores*, or the *Hippiatri-
> ca*. One of a series of compilations on various subjects, compiled by order of the
> Emperor. Based upon a compilation made in the 4th century under Constantine
> I, *the Great*, and in itself of still earlier origin. The contents as given in Choulant's
> entry for the Greek edition indicates a collection dating from remote antiquity.
> Issued in Greek at Basel in 1537 under the editorship of Simon Grynaeus, 1493–
> 1541, with Latin translation by Jean de la Ruelle (NLMCat 2309). French, Ger-
> man, and Italian translations were issued in the sixteenth century. Italian editions
> printed at Venice in 1543 and 1548 are listed in NLMCat 2313, 2314. Ruelle,
> the translator of the Latin version, was famed as a botanist and at one time was
> Court Physician to Francis I.

CORDUS, Euricius, 1484–1535.

347 Botanologicon sive Colloquium de herbis. Cologne: Joannes Gymnicus, 1534. 8°. [LEK]

> *Ref:* NLMCat 1022; Pennink 603; v. Dommer 61; *Greene* (*LBH*) 265–269.
> *N.B:* A dialogue calling for greater care in the identification of medicinal plants and
> berating German pharmacists for the use of incorrect labels on their jars. Written
> by the father of the botanist, Valerius Cordus, 1515–1544. Re-issued at Paris in
> 1551.

348 Ein Regiment: Wie man sich vor der Newen Plage, Der Englisch
schweis genant, bewaren . . . [*German*]. Marburg: [Franciscus Rhode]
1529. 4°. [LEK]

> *Ref*: NLMCat 1024; v. Dommer 23, 23a.
>
> *N.B*: A pest-tract for use in epidemics of the so-called English sweating disease. Known
> in two issues.

CORDUS, Valerius, 1515–1544.

349 Dispensatorium pharmacorum omnium quae in usu potissimum sunt
Nuremberg: Johannes Petreius, 1546. 4°. [LEK]

> *Ref*: NLMCat 1026n; *Garrison* (1929) 229; *Sart* (*Appr*) 74; *Castiglioni* (1947) 486.
>
> *N.B*: Written by a brilliant young botanist, who lost his life in an effort to obtain new
> plant specimens. Described as "the first real pharmacopeia to be published."
> Garrison, in speaking of its popularity, notes 35 editions and 8 translations [but
> gives no terminal dates]. An edition cited as printed at Nuremberg in 1535 has
> not been found in the present survey. Cordus's botanical works were published
> posthumously and after our period.
>
> *Mon*: GREENE, E. L. *Landmarks of botanical history*. Washington, (Smithsonian Miscel-
> laneous Collection, 1909/10, v. 54, p. 270–314).
>
> *Fac*: GESELLSCHAFT FÜR GESCHICHTE DER PHARMAZIE, Mittenbach, 1934 (cited in
> *Isis* 1935 24 215).

CRESCENZI, Pier de' (Petrus de Crescentiis), 1233–1321.

350 Ruralia commoda. [Augsburg:] Johann Schüssler, 'circiter' 16 Feb.
1471. f°. [LEK]

> *Ref*: GW 7820; HC *5828; BMC II 328; Oates 891; Klebs 310.1; *Sart* III 811–815;
> Stillwell C858; Goff C-965.
>
> *N.B*: A popular work, frequently reprinted, which relates to agriculture in general
> and in addition to its account of the medicinal use of various plants discusses
> domestic hygiene and the diseases of cattle and horses. [See also under NATURAL
> SCIENCE.]

DINO del Garbo (Dinus de Florentia; *called* Expositor Avicennae), c. 1260–1327.

351 Expositio super tertia, quarta, et parte quintae fen IV. Canonis Avicennae. Ferrara: Andreas Belfortis, 27 Oct. 1489. f°. [LEK]

> *Ref*: GW 8346; H *6166; IGI 3430; Pell 4250; Klebs 336.1(I); Schullian (ArMed)
> 163; *Sart* III 837–838; Stillwell D153; Goff D-194.
>
> *N.B*: A commentary on Avicenna's treatises on epidemics and surgery. Contains also
> Dino's *De emplastris et unguentis*, dated 28 Oct. 1489 and sometimes found as a
> separate (Cen D152). [*See also* IV 666n.]

Dino (continued)

352   De ponderibus et mensuris. (*Issued with his* Expositio super tertia, quarta, et parte quintae fen IV. Canonis Avicennae.   Venice: Bonetus Locatellus for Octavianus Scotus, 24 Dec. 1496.)   f°.   [LEK]

> *Ref*: GW 8347; HR 6167; BMC V 446; IGI 3431; Klebs 336.1; *Sart* III 712; Stillwell D154; Goff D-195.
>
> *N.B*: Weights and measures as used by doctors in handling drugs. A Ferrara edition printed in 1485 by Andreas Belfortis, cited in Hain 6169 as issued with the author's *Chirurgia*, is listed by GW as not known today.

353   Super IV fen primi Avicennae praeclarissima commentaria, quae dilucidatorium totius practicae generalis medicinalis scientiae nuncupantur.   Venice: Georgius Arrivabenus for the heirs of Octavianus Scotus, 1514.   [LEK]

> *Ref*: NLMCat 394; WellHMed (1962) 1761; *Sart* III 838.

DIOSKORIDES, Pedianos (Dioskurides, Dioscorides), *fl.* 50 A.D.

354   De materia medica (Comm: Pietro d'Abano, *c.* 1250–1316).   Colle: Johannes de Medemblick, July 1478.   f°.   [LEK]

> *Ref*: GW 8436; HC *6258; BMC VII 1078; BM-Ital 218; IGI 3492; Klebs 342.1; Choulant (H) 76–81; *Sart* I 258–260; *Greene (LBH)* 151–154; *Garrison* (1929) 109; *Arber* (1938) 6–12; O'*Leary* 170, 171; Stillwell D217; Goff D-261.
>
> *N.B*: Relates to pharmacy and the medicinal properties of plants. The first book on medical botany as an applied science. The authoritative source of herbal therapy for more than fifteen centuries. In five books. Describes over 600 plants and their medicinal properties. In the translation ascribed to Constantinus Africanus (*d.* 1087).
>
> The first Greek edition—issued by Aldus Manutius at Venice in July 1499 (Cen D216)—includes two poems, *Alexipharmaca* and *Theriaca*, attributed to Nicander and describing 125 medicinal herbs as antidotes for poison and the venom from poisonous animals. Although the *De materia medica* itself comprises only Books 1–5, at least ten editions of the Latin text published during 1516–1550 treat the added titles, *De venenis* and *De venenatis animalibus*, respectively, as Book 6 and Books 7–8 or 7–9, according to the typographical make-up of the edition.
>
> Thirty-two editions of Dioscorides are known to have been issued during the years 1478–1550 at Basel (3), Colle (1), Cologne (3), Florence (3), Frankfurt (2), Lyon (4), Paris (4), Strasbourg (1), Mantua (1), and Venice (10). Of these, three are in Greek, one of them an improved text edited by Girolami Rossi and Francesco Torresani, and published by the Aldine press at Venice in 1518. Three editions have Greek-and-Latin texts. Nineteen are in Latin, ten of which are in the translation of Jean de la Ruelle (*d.* 1537), first published by Henri Estienne at

Paris about 1516. Six are in Italian as translated by Sebastiano Fausto (1); Marc-antonio Montigiano (1); and Pierandrea Mattioli (4), as issued in 1544, 1548, 1549, and 1550 together with his commentary which in successive editions became a classic in its own right. A German version by J. Danz von Ast was issued at Frankfurt in 1546. [For other commentaries and translations, see under NATURAL SCIENCE: Dioskorides, no. 618. See also NLMCat p. 143–146.]

Mon: GUNTHER, Robert T. *The Greek herbal of Dioscorides.* (Illustrated by a Byzantine, A.D. 512; Englished by John Goodyer A.D. 1655; edited and first printed . . . A.D. 1933) New York, 1959 (reviewed, p. 588–590 in *Isis* 51 1960).

DONDIS, Jacobus de (Jacopo de' Dondi), 1298–1359.

355 Aggregator, sive De medicinis simplicibus. [Strasbourg: The R-Printer (Adolf Rusch), about 1470.] f°. [LEK]

Ref: GW 9042; HC *6395; BMC I 64; IGI 3570; Schullian (ArMed) 166; Klebs 349.2; Sart III 1669–1671; Garrison (1929) 166; Stillwell D288; Goff D-358.
N.B: A manual of medical recipes; of interest because of its terminology. The first dated edition was printed in Venice in 1481—Cen D289.

DRYANDER, Johannes (Johann Eichmann), 1500–1560.

356 Ein new Artznei unnd Practicir Büchlein [German]. Marburg: Apud Eucharium Cervicorum, 1537. 8°.

Ref: v. Dommer 88.
N.B: Another 1537 edition, listed as NLMCat 1219, gives the place of printing as Cologne.

DUBOIS, Jacques (Jacobus Sylvius), 1478–1555.

357 De medicamentorum simplicium delectu libri III. Paris: Jacobus Gasellus, 1542. f°. [LEK]

Ref: BM-Fr 141; *Castiglioni* (1947) 420.
N.B: Known also as *Pharmacopoeia seu De medicamentorum simplicium delectu, praeparationibus, mistionis modo libri tres*—*see* NLMCat 1243 ff.

358 Methodus sex librorum Galeni in differentiis et causis morborum et symptomatum. Paris: Christien Wechel, 1539. f°. [LEK]

Ref: NLMCat 1266; BM-Fr 142; *Garrison* (1929) 222.
N.B: Written by an ardent Galenist who, although a former teacher of Vesalius, denounced the latter's anatomical works. Re-issued by same press in 1548. For other editions and for other works by this author, see NLMCat p. 154–157.

EAUX ARTIFICIELLES.

359 Traicte des eaux artificielles [*French*]. Vienne: Peter Schenck, [before 1485]. 4°. [LEK]

> *Ref*: GW 9165; H 6524; Klebs 358.1; *Sart* III 1241.
>
> *N.B*: Relates to the virtues of mineral waters. Preceded by an edition recorded as printed at Lyon by LeRoy about 1483 but not known today. Printed in at least eight editions before the end of 1500, and included in a French version of the *De proprietatibus rerum* of Bartholomew the Englishman, printed at Lyon during that year—Cen B134.

ESTWOOD, John (Eschuid; John of Eschenden), *fl.* 1340–1370.

360 Summa astrologiae judicialis de accidentibus mundi. Venice: Johannes Lucilius Santritter, for Franciscus Bolanus, 7 July 1489. f°.

> *Ref*: GW 9392; HC *6685; BMC V 462; IGI 3711; Klebs 381.1; *Sart* III 672; Stillwell E84; Goff E-109.
>
> *N.B*: Written by a professional astrologer who believed that the universe was integrated according to divine plan; and who, having lived through the Black Death of 1348, took occasion in this treatise to discuss pestilential fever, epidemics, and the dangers inherent during times of air corruption or conjunction. It is, therefore, one of the first contemporary discussions of the Plague, and it includes mention of a powder successfully used by physicians at Oxford—a compound of aloes, myrrh, cinnamon, saffron, mace, cloves, and mastic—which a century later was still regarded as effective for fever.
>
> *Mon*: THORNDIKE, Lynn. *John of Eschenden: specialist in conjunctions* (Chap. XXI in vol. III of his *A history of magic and experimental science*. New York, 1934).

FALCUCCI, Nicolò (Nicolaus Falcutius), *d.* 1411/12.

361 Sermones medicinales, libri VII (Ed: Caesar de Landulfis and Joannes Antonius de Bassinis). Pavia: Damianus de Confaloneriis, I) 24 Dec. 1484; II) 1481; III–VI) [n.d.]; VII) 18 Nov. 1484. f°. [LEK]

> *Ref*: GW 9704; H *11767; BMC VII 1000 (v. II–VII); IGI 3800; Klebs 389.1; *Sart* III 1194; *Castiglioni* (1947) 332; Stillwell F32; Goff F-45.
>
> *N.B*: An encyclopaedic work treating of health, fevers, physiology, *etc.* [For contents see NATURAL SCIENCE.] Derived largely from Arabic compilations, but giving high tribute to Galen. Various sections are known to have been re-issued as separates or in combination with other works.

FASCICULUS MEDICINAE. *See* KETHAM, Johann de.

FERNEL, Jean, *d.* 1558.

362 De vacuandi ratione liber. Paris: Christien Wechel, 1545. 4°. [LEK]

Ref: NLMCat 1482; *Sart (SW)* 191–196, 299:53; *Castiglioni* (1947) 443, 491.

N.B: Fernel, who is rated as the founder of physiology, was a careful observer and a physician of the new school opposed to the doctrines of Galen. His most important medical work, the *Medicina* of 1554 (NLMCat 1459), contained a revision of the present treatise on pathology, the work as a whole relating to his newly created categories of physiology, pathology, and therapeutics.

Mon: SHERRINGTON, *Sir* Charles S. *The endeavour of Jean Fernel.* Cambridge University Press, 1946 (reviewed in *Isis* 37 199; 41 212).

FERRARI, Gianmatteo (Joannes Matthaeus Ferrarius, de Gradibus), *d.* 1472.

363   Expositiones super tractatum de urinis et fen XXII tertii Canonis Avicennae.   Milan: Jacobus de Sancto Nazario, de Ripa, I) 26 July 1494; II) 17 Nov. 1494.   f°.

Ref: H *7840; BMC VI 783; IGI 3843; Klebs 394.1; *Castiglioni* (1947) 366, 368; Stillwell F94; Goff F-118.

N.B: Castiglioni refers to Ferrari as a devoted Arabist.

Mon: FERRARI, Henri Maxime. *Une chaire de médecine au XV*e *siècle. Un professeur a l'université de Paris de 1432 à 1472.* Paris, 1899.

364   Perutilia consilia ad diversas aegritudines.   [Pavia: Damianus de Confaloneriis, about 1480.]   f°.

Ref: IGI 3841; Osler (IM) 157; Klebs 393.1; *Sart* III 1239, 1861.

N.B: The third of the five systematically arranged collections of diagnoses and prescribed treatments published between 1476 and 1489.

365   Practica cum textu noni ad Almansorem.   [Milan: Philippus de Lavagnia, 1472/73.]   f°.   [LEK]

Ref: Osler (IM) 37; IGI 3844 (II); Schullian (ArMed) 184; Klebs 392.1; Stillwell F95; Goff F-119.

N.B: Variously ascribed also to the press of Joannes de Sidriano at Pavia. According to Dr. Klebs's essay, p. 212, this edition contains the first printed "commentary on the great schoolbook of therapeutics, Rhazes's 'ninth book to Almansar' with fragments of its text . . ." Editions of the *Practica* were printed at Venice in 1502 and Lyon in 1527 (NLMCat 1502, 1503).

Mon: KLEBS, Arnold C. *The Practica of Gianmatteo Ferrari da Gradi editio princeps* (in *Essays on the history of medicine presented to Karl Sudhoff.* Zurich, 1924, p. 211–236).

FICINO, Marsilio (Marsilius Ficinus), 1433–1499.

366   Consiglio contro la pestilenza [*Italian*].   Florence: Apud Sanctum Jacobum de Ripoli [not before Aug.] 1481.   4°.   [LEK]

Ref: HR 7082; BMC VI 623; Oates 2331.7; Pell 4790; Klebs 396.1; Klebs (P) 44; Stillwell F137; Goff F-153.

N.B: For various sixteenth-century editions, see NLMCat p. 184–185.

III. *Medicine*

FRACASTORO, Girolamo (Hieronymus Fracastorius), 1483–1553.

367   De causis criticorum dierum. (*Issued with his* Homocentrica. **Venice, 1538.**)   4°.

> *Ref*: NLMCat 1640; BM-Ital 275; *Thornd (HM)* V 491–492; *Crombie (A–G)* 1961 II 167.
> *N.B*: Fracastoro wrote also of astronomy, in an attempt to revive the theory of concentric spheres without epicycles.

368   De contagione et contagiosis morbis et eorum curatione libri III. (*Issued with his* De sympathia et antipathia rerum liber unus.   Venice: Heredes Lucantonii Giuntae, 1546.)   4°.   [LEK]

> *Ref*: NLMCat 1636; BM-Ital 275; *Sart* III 1658; *Crombie (A–G)* 1961 II 284.
> *N.B*: The first scientific definition of contagion known and a competent discussion of causes of infection. Gives a clear account of typhus. [For notes on epidemics and related literature, see *Castiglioni* (1947) 452–467; *Sart* III 1650–1665. For Fracastoro's theories of contagion, see *Wightman* (1962) I 277–281.]
> *Mon*: SIGERIST, H. E. *Girolamo Fracastoro* (chap. XII in his *The great doctors, a biographical history of medicine*. Translated by E. and C. Paul. New York, 1933). THORNDIKE, Lynn. *Fracastoro (1478–1553)* (chap. XXII in vol. V of his *History of magic and experimental science*, New York, 1941). SINGER, Ch. and D. *The scientific position of Girolamo Fracastoro (1478?–1553) with especial reference to the source, character and influence of his theory of infection* (p. 1–34 in vol. I of *Annals of medical history*, 1917). CASTIGLIONI, A. *Gerolamo Fracastoro and the doctrine of "contagium vivum"* (p. 747–759 in vol. I of *Scientia medica italica*, 1950). WRIGHT, W. C., translator. *Hieronymi Fracastorii de contagione, libri III*. New York, 1930 (N.Y. ACAD. MED. History of medicine, Series II). PELLEGRINI, F. *La dottrina Fracastoriana del contagium vivum*, Verona, 1950.

369   Syphilis sive Morbus gallicus, libri III.   Verona [Stefano Nicolini da Sabbio e fratelli], 1530.   4°.   [LEK]

> *Ref*: BM-Ital 275; *Sigerist (GD)* 106; *Castiglioni* (1947) 455–461.
> *N.B*: An educational poem summarizing the therapeutic knowledge of the time, and advising treatment for the disease to which it gave its name.
> *Mon*: BAUMGARTNER, L., and J. F. FULTON. *A Bibliography of the poem Syphilis sive Morbus Gallicus by Girolamo Fracastoro*, New Haven, 1935.

FUCHS, Leonhart, 1501–1566.

370   Annotationes aliquot herbarum et simplicium a medicis hactenus non recte intellectorum (*Issued in vol II of* BRUNFELS, Otto. Herbarum vivae eicones. Strasbourg: Johann Schott, 1531.)

> *Ref*: BM-Ger 155; *Greene (LBH)* 194.

N.B: An early work showing Fuchs's keen interest in the correct identification of medicinal plants for pharmaceutical purposes. It contains 34 chapters dealing mostly with the correcting of errors.

Mon: STÜBLER, E. *Leonhart Fuchs, Leben und Werk*. München, 1928 (Münchener Beiträge zur Geschichte und Literatur der Naturwissenschaften und Medizin, 13–14).

371 Compendiaria ac succincta admodum in medendi artem . . . seu introductio. Hagenau [:Johannes Secerius] 1531.   [LEK]

Ref: NLMCat 1672; *Wightman* (1962) I 213, II 278, *note*.

N.B: A brief and popular introduction to the art of healing. Originally written as a student manual introducing the theories of Hippocrates and Galen, but with some reference to the Arabic knowledge of drugs. Subsequently enlarged, appearing, in a third [or fourth] edition, as *Methodus seu ratio compendiaria cognoscendi veram solidamque medicinam ad Hippocratis & Galeni scripta* . . . Paris, Jacobus Dupuys, 1550; issued that same year at Lyon by Guillaume Roville (NLMCat 1711, 1712).

372 De historia stirpium commentarii.   Basel: In officina Isingriniana (Michel Isengrin), 1542.   f°.   [LEK]

Ref: NLMCat 1675; Horblit 33 b; BM-Ger 326; Nissen 658; *Garrison* (1929) 229; *Greene (LBH)* 192–219; *Arber* (1938) 275; *Hunt (Quinby)* I 48.

N.B: A handsome and well illustrated volume containing 500 or more figures made from actual plants as an aid to identification for medicinal purposes. Of great botanical interest as well. Written by a professor of medicine at Tübingen. [For further comment, see the entry under NATURAL SCIENCE.]

Fac: Horblit 33 [c].

373 De medendis singularum humani corporis partium a summo capite ad imos usque pedes passionibus ac febribus libri quatuor nunquam antea in lucem editi . . .   Basel: Robert Winter, 1539.   4°.   [LEK]

Ref: NLMCat 1686; BM-Ger 326; *Wightman* (1962) II 280.

N.B: Issued that same year at Paris by Conrad Néobar, and in at least five editions at Paris and Lyon before 1550 (NLMCat 1687–1692).

GALEN (Galenos, Galenus), 131 – *c*. 200.

Major Compilations of Galen's Works

374 Opera [*Greek*] (Ed: Andrea Torresani (Asulanus) and Giovanni Battista Opizo).   Venice: Ex aedibus Aldi et Andreae Asulani soceri, 1525. f°.   [LEK]

Ref: NLMCat 1748; BM-Ital 285; Renouard (Alde) 239; Choulant (H) 112–113; *Sart (Appr)* 20–22; *Castiglioni* (1947) 217–226.

Galen (continued)

N.B: In five volumes. Also published in Greek at Basel, by Andreas Cratander in 1538, collated with new manuscripts under the editorship of Joachim Camerarius, 1500–1574, Leonhart Fuchs, 1501–1566, and Hieronymus Gemusaeus, 1505–1543; a Greek compilation edited by Joannes Caius was issued at Basel in 1544—NLMCat 1749 and 1763, respectively.

For the first Galenic texts of medical interest printed in Greek—the *Therapeutica* and *Therapeutica ad Glauconem*, Venice, 1500 (known in Latin as *De methodo medendi* and *De methodo medendi ad Glauconem*)—see below under 375:24 and 375:25. No other Galenic titles than these are known to have been issued in Greek during the fifteenth century, excepting the spurious work *De philosophica historia* attributed to Galen, in vol. II of the Greek *Opera* of Aristotle, Venice, 1497. [According to Durling's *Chronological Census*, no Greek texts except the *Opera* of 1525 appeared between 1500 and 1529, after which date—between 1529 and 1550—various titles are cited on p. 255–269 of his *Census*. Of 35 Greek texts listed, 33 were printed later than were their Latin translations. The texts of the *Therapeutica* and *Therapeutica ad Glauconem*, for instance, had been issued in the Latin *Opera* of 1490, as had 22 of the others cited. Two Greek texts, however—*De urinis*, issued by Simon de Colines at Paris about 1529–30, and *De remediis facile parabilibus I*, which he printed in 1530—antedate the printing of Latin versions in 1535 and 1533, respectively.]

Mon: SIGERIST, H. E. *Galen of Pergamum* (p. 68–77 in his *The great doctors, a biographical history of medicine*. New York, 1933). BEAUJEU, J. *Galen.* (p. 356–361 in Taton, René, ed. *Ancient and Medieval science*. New York: Basic Books Inc., 1963.) BERGSTRÄSSER, G. *Ḥunain ibn Isḥāq über die syrischen und arabischen Galen-Übersetzungen.* Leipzig, 1925 (reviewed and analyzed in p. 685–724 of *Isis* 8 1926). DURLING, R. J. *A chronological census of Renaissance editions and translations of Galen* (p. 230–305 in vol. XXIV of the *Journal of the Warburg and Courtauld Institutes* 24, nos. 3–4 1961), which lists editions of Galenic texts issued and re-issued from 1473 to 1600 as found in more than ninety European libraries and in the Cushing Collection at Yale University, the Osler Library at McGill University, the National Library of Medicine, and the Library of Congress. [See also p. 207–240 in NATIONAL LIBRARY OF MEDICINE. *A catalogue of sixteenth century printed books ... Compiled by Richard J. Durling.* Bethesda, Maryland, 1967.]

375   Opera [*Latin*] (Ed: Diomedes Bonardus).   Venice: Philippus Pincius, 27 Aug. 1490. f°.

Ref: H *7427; IGI 4129; Durling 250[10], 281–295; Choulant (H) 113; Klebs 432.1; Horblit 34; Schullian (ArMed) 199; Castiglioni (1947) 217–266; Stillwell G36; Goff G-37.

Con: 1) De affectorum locorum notitia (Tr: anon). 2) De alimentorum facultatibus (Tr: Guilielmus de Moerbeke, *d.* 1286). 3) De attenuante victus ratione (Tr: Nicolò da Reggio, *d.* 1350). 4) De bonitate aquae (Tr: ditto). 5) De bono corporis habitu (Tr: ditto). 6) De catharticis (Tr: anon). 7) De causis procatarcticis (Tr: N. da Reggio).   8) De complexionibus (Tr: anon).   9) De compositione medicamentorum secundum locos (Tr: N. da Reggio).   10) De constitutione artis medicae (Tr: ditto).   11) De crisibus (Tr: anon).   12) De cura icteri (Tr: N. da Reggio).   13) De cura lapidis [Bezoar] (Tr: anon).   14) De curandi ratione per venae sectionem (Tr: N. da Reggio).   15) De diebus decretoriis (Tr: anon).   16) De differentiis febrium (Tr: Burgundio of Pisa, *d.* 1193).   17) De dissolutione continua (Tr: Accursius of Pistoia, *fl.* 1200).   18) De elementis secundum Hippocratem (Tr: anon).   19) De hirundinibus (Tr: N. da Reggio).   20) De inaequali intemperie (Tr: anon).   21) De insomniis (Tr: anon).   22) Introductio sive medicus (Tr: anon).   23) Liber secretorum ad Monteum (Tr: Gherardo da Cremona, *d.* 1187).   24) De methodo medendi (Tr: ditto) [Issued in Greek at Venice in 1500, as the *Therapeutica*—Cen G35].   25) De methodo medendi ad Glauconem (Tr: N. da Reggio) [Issued in Greek at Venice in 1500 with the *Therapeutica*, as the *Therapeutica ad Glauconem*—Cen G35].   26) De morborum causis (Tr: anon).   27) De morborum differentiis (Tr: anon).   28) De morborum temporibus (Tr: N. da Reggio).   29) De optima corporis nostri constitutione (Tr: ditto).   30) De optima doctrina ad Favorinum (Tr: ditto).   31) De optima secta ad Thrasybulum (Tr: ditto).   32) De palpitatione, tremore, rigore, convulsione (Tr: Pietro d'Abano, *d.* 1316).   33) De partibus artis medicae (Tr: N. da Reggio).   34) De parvae pilae exercitio (Tr: anon).   35) De praecognitione ad Epigenem (Tr: N. da Reggio).   36) De probis et pravis alimentorum succis (Tr: ditto).   37) De purgantium medicamentorum facultate (Tr: anon).   38) De remediis facile parabilibus II, ad Solonem (Tr: N. da Reggio).   39) De sanitate tuenda (Tr: Burgundio of Pisa).   40) De sectis ad eos qui introducuntur (Tr: N. da Reggio?)   41) De spermate (Tr: anon).   42) De symptomatum causis (Tr: anon).   43) De symptomatum differentiis (Tr: anon).   44) De theriaca ad Pamphilianum (Tr: N. da Reggio).   45) De theriaca ad Pisonem, *frag.* (Tr: ditto).   46) De totius morbi temporibus (Tr: ditto).   47) De tumoribus praeter naturam (Tr: ditto).   48) De typis (Tr: ditto).   49) De vinis (Tr: ditto?).   50) De virtutibus nostrum corpus dispensantibus (Tr: ditto).   51) De voce et anhelitu (Tr: anon).   [For other titles contained in this volume, having occasional medical interest, see our entry for this edition under NATURAL SCIENCE. With regard to these and subsequent translations of the titles cited, see DURLING, p. 281–295, a basic work which offers data not here presented and is rich in data regarding subsequent editions and translators.

N.B: The first edition of Galen's *Opera*. The first printing of each of the texts listed above. The copy at the National Library of Medicine, described by Schullian, is inscribed "Nicolaus Pol Doctor 1494" and contains his list of contents. The first twenty volumes of C. G. KÜHN's *Medicorum graecorum opera quae extant*, Leipzig, 1821–1833 include the Greek text of Galen's works with Latin translations and in the final volume an index of Galen's works by Fr. W. Assmann. With regard to Nicolò da Reggio, *d.* 1350, the translator of many of the pieces found in this *Opera*, see THORNDIKE, Lynn. *Translations of works of Galen from the Greek by Niccolò da Regio* (p. 213–235 in *Byzantium Metabyzantina* I 1946).

Fac: Horblit 34 [b].

Galen (continued)

Fifteenth-Century Latin 'Firsts'

As the Galenic 'firsts' were frequently issued with other texts by Galen or by other writers, a name cited in capital letters in parentheses indicates the author of the leading item with which the first printing of the given text was issued. The numerals in parentheses, which accompany the majority of the listed titles, refer to the page and call-numbers appearing on p. 281–295 in Durling's Chronological census of Renaissance editions and translations of Galen, *where imprints, translators, and later editions are listed. [As is frequently done in the alphabetizing of early printed books, the preposition 'De' is discounted when it is the first word in a title. For an alphabetical list of Galen's works as cited here and elsewhere in the present volume, see the* INDEX, *under Galen.]*

Separate editions and texts issued together with other works [in addition to the 51 titles listed above in the Latin 'Opera' of 1490]:

376   1) Ars medica [*i.e.*, Ars parva *or* Tegni, (ARTICELLA—GW 2678), [Padua, *c.* 1476] (Durling 282:8).   2) De divisione librorum Galeni, (ARTICELLA—Cen A1011), Venice, 1483 (250[5]).   3) In Hippocratis Aphorismos, (ARTICELLA—GW 2678), [Padua, *c.* 1476] (294:149).   4) In Hippocratis Prognosticam, (ARTICELLA—GW 2678), [*ibid*] (295:158).   5) Introductorium ad medicinam, (F. FILELFO—Cen P554), [Milan, 1484[(250[6]).   6) De medicinis expertis, (RHASIS—Cen R169), Milan, 1481 (287:62).   7) De praesagitura, (VALLA—Cen N33), Venice, 1498 (289:88).   8) Praesagium experientia confirmatum, (VALLA—Cen N33), *ibid* (293:138).   9) De succedaneis, (VALLA—Cen N33), *ibid* (291:111).   10) De victus ratione in morbis acutis ex Hippocratis sententia sive In Hippocratis de regimine acutorum morborum, (ARTICELLA—GW 2678), [Padua, *c.* 1476] 295:160).   11) De virtute centaureae ad Papiam, (SERAPION *the Younger*—Cen S422), Milan, 1473 (293:128).   [TOTAL: 62 *fifteenth-century Latin 'firsts'*]

Sixteenth-Century Latin 'Firsts'

Separate editions and texts issued together with other works:

377   1) De affectus renum dignotione et medicatione, Mainz, 1530 (290:99).   2) De antidotis, (GALEN), Paris, 1533 (283:18).   3) Brevis denotatio dogmatum Hippocratis (HIPPOCRATES), Lyon, 1547 (282:9).   4) De

compositione medicamentorum per genera, Paris, 1530 (284:29).
5) Contra ea quae a Juliano in Hippocratis Aphorismos dicta sunt,
(GALEN), Venice, 1541/42 (283:12). 6) De curandi ratione per sanguinis
missionem, (GALEN), Paris, 1529 (284:37) [possibly no. 375.14 above].
7) Definitiones medicae, Paris, 1528 (285:48). 8) De Hippocratis et
Platonis decretis, Paris, 1534 (285:51). 9) In Hippocratis Epidemiarum
lib. I, (HIPPOCRATES), Paris, 1531 (295:152.1). 10) In Hippocratis
Epidemiarum lib. I & III, (HIPPOCRATES), Paris, 1534 (295:152.3).
11) In Hippocratis Epidemiarum lib. [I, III?] VI, (GALEN), Venice, 1541/
42 (295:152.4). 12) In Hippocratis de fracturis, (GALEN), *ibid.* (295:153).
13) In Hippocratis de medica officina, (GALEN), *ibid.* (295:155). 14) In
Hippocratis de natura humana, (HIPPOCRATES), Paris, 1531 (295:156).
15) In Hippocratis Praedictiones lib. I, Paris, 1535 (295:157). 16) In
Hippocratis de victus ratione privatorum, (HIPPOCRATES), Paris, 1529
(295:159). 17) De instrumento odoratus, (GALEN), Venice, 1541 (286:
58). 18) De libris propriis, (GALEN), Basel, 1531 (286:59). 19) De
melancholia ex Galeno Rufo, (GALEN), Venice, 1541/42 (287:63).
20) De oculis, (S. CHAMPIER), [Lyon], 1512 (288:74). 21) Oratio sua-
soria ad artes, (GALEN), Basel, Paris, 1526 (293:137). 22) De ordine
librorum suorum, (GALEN), Basel, 1531 (288:78). 23) De plenitudine,
[Paris], 1528 (289:84). 24) Pro puero epileptico consilium, (GALEN),
Basel, 1531 (293:139). 25) Prognostica de decubitu infirmorum,
(GALEN), Venice, 1535 (293:140). 26) De propriorum animi cuiusque
affectuum dignotione et curatione, (GALEN), Paris, 1528 (289:90). 27)
De ptisana, (GALEN), Basel, 1533 (289:91). 28) Quaestiones in Hippocratem, (VALLA), Strasbourg, 1528 (294:141). 29) Quod optimus medicus sit idem philosophus, (GALEN), Basel, Paris, 1526 (294:143). 30)
Quod qualitates incorporeae sint, (GALEN), Venice, 1541/42 (294:144).
31) Quos quibus et quando purgare oporteat, (GALEN), London, 1522
(294:146). 32) De remediis facile parabilibus I, (GALEN), Paris, Antwerp, 1533 (290:98. 1a, b) [*Issued in Greek*, Paris, 1530]. 33) De remediis
facile parabilibus III, (GALEN), Venice, 1541/42 (290:98.3). 34) De san-
guisugis et scarificatione, (GALEN), Paris, 1529 (?284:37). 35) De sub-
figuratione empirica, (GALEN), Pavia, 1515/16 (291:110). 36) De
urinae significatione, (GALEN), Pavia, 1515/16 (292:120). 37) De urinis,
(GALEN), Venice, *n.b.* 11 Jan. 1535 (292:121) [*issued in Greek*, Paris, *c.*
1529–30]. 38) Utrum medicinae sit vel gymnastices hygiene ad Thrasybulum, (GALEN), Venice, 1538 (282:3). 39) Vocum obsoletarum
Hippocratis explanatio, (HIPPOCRATES), Basel, 1538 (294:148).

GANIVET, Jean (Joannes Ganivetus), *fl.* 1430.

378 Amicus medicorum (Ed: Gondisalvus de Toledo). Lyon: Joannes Trechsel, 14 Oct. 1496. 4°. [LEK]

> *Add*: ABRĀHĀM ben-'Ezrā, *c.* 1092–1167. De diebus criticis.
> *Ref*: HC *7467; BMC VIII 299; BM-Fr 197; Oates 3219; IGI 4171; Klebs 436.1; Stillwell G63; Goff G-71.
> *N.B*: A manual of astrological medicine said to be the most influential treatise on the subject written during the fifteenth century. Analyzed at some length in *Thornd* (*HM*) IV 134–139. Issued at Lyon by Johann Cleyn [Hans Schwab] in 1508 and by Guillaume Roville in 1550 (NLMCat 1998, 1999).

GART der GESUNDHEIT.

379 Gart der Gesundheit [*German*] (Ed: Johann Wonnecke von Cube, *c.* 1484–1503). Mainz: Peter Schoeffer, 28 Mar. 1485. f°. [LEK]

> *Ref*: H *8948; BMC I 35; Klebs 507.1; Klebs (Gart) 1; Schullian (ArMed) 200; *Osiris* 5 118; Stillwell G87; Goff G-97.
> *N.B*: Although basically derived from the *Herbarius* printed by Schoeffer in 1484, the *Gart der Gesundheit* shows originality in its break from stylized to naturalistic figures and in its presentation of pharmaceutical matter in the language of the people. Sometimes called the *Herbarius zu deutsch*. A rival edition was issued by Johann Schönsperger at Augsburg on 22 August 1485 (Cen G88); and still another is assignable to the Strasbourg press of Johann Grüninger, *c.* 1485/86 (Cen G89). Known in at least a dozen editions. Issued also in Low German (Cen G99).
> *Mon*: SHAFFER, Ellen. *The garden of health*, 1957.
> *Fac*: *Hortus sanitatis deutsch* . . . (*issued with* SCHREIBER, W. L. *Die Kräuterbücher des XV. und XVI. Jahrhunderts*. München, 1924); *Osiris* 5 1938, *fig.* 48.

GENTILE da Foligno (Gentilis Fulginas; Gentilis de Fulgino), *c.* 1290–1348.

380 De balneis. [Padua:] Joannes de Reno, 24 March 1473. 4°.

> *Add*: CASINI, Francesco, da Siena. Dicta de balneo Petrioli. BONAVENTURA de' Castelli, *fl.* 1340. De utilitatibus aquae balnei de Porretta.
> *Ref*: H *4592; Klebs 444.1; Schullian (ArMed) 202; *Sart* III 849, 1684; Stillwell G121; Goff G-133.
> *N.B*: Relates to the value of mineral water baths at Pozzuoli and refers to various noted Italian spas. [For general accounts of Gentile and his works, see Crombie (A–G) 1961 I 161, 171, 226–7, 229, 233, and Sart III 848–852.]

381 Consilia medica. [Pavia: Antonius Carcanus, 1488?] f°.

> *Ref*: HC (Add) *7574; Pell 5028; Klebs 453.1; Stillwell G122; Goff G-134.

N.B: A record of the treatment of specific cases. The fifth of the systematically arranged records of this nature to be printed before 1490. Included in a compilation
printed at Venice for Octavianus Scotus about 1495-97 (Goff C-403).

382 Consilium contra pestilentiam. [Padua: Laurentius Canozius, 1475.]
4°. [LEK]

Ref: H *7575; Klebs 445.1; Klebs (P) 50; *Sart* III 848-852; *Crombie (A-G)* 1961 I 229;
Castiglioni (1947) 357.

N.B: Addressed to a conclave of physicians relative to the plague in Genoa in 1348.
Written at the request of the city of Perugia, apparently at the beginning of its
appearance there, since Gentile died at Perugia of the plague on June 18, 1348.
The work relates to causes of the plague, its preventive and curative measures,
and problems for special study and discussion. It discusses the seeds of disease
(*semina*) and is indicative of a somewhat new approach to the subjects of contagion
and infection. Known also in two editions assigned to Colle de Valdesa about
1479, and Venice or Lyon after 1500 (Goff G-135, G-136).

Mon: SUDHOFF, Karl. *Pestschriften aus den ersten 150 Jahren nach der Epidemie des "schwar-
zen Todes" 1348* (nos. 30, 31-34 in *Archiv für Geschichte der Medizin* V, 1911, p.
83-87, 332-340, 396). KLEBS, Arnold C. and Karl SUDHOFF. *Die ersten gedruckten
Pestschriften*, Munich, 1926, p. 31, 86, 118-125. SARTON, George. *Plagues* (p.
1650-1664 in vol. III of his *Introduction to the history of science*, Washington, 1947).
WIGHTMAN, W. P. D. *Miasm and contagion* (p. 264-283 in vol. I of his *Science and
the Renaissance*, Edinburgh, 1962).

383 De febre. [Padua: Petrus Maufer, about 1477.] f°. [LEK]

Ref: R190; Osler (IM) 134; Klebs 448.1; Stillwell G124; Goff G-137.

N.B: The entry in IGI 4208 assigns this to the press of Jacopo de Tyela possibly at
Piacenza about 1483. A dated edition was issued at Padua in 1486. An edition
produced for the heirs of Octavianus Scotus at Venice in 1514 reads on f. 144 *v*:
Explicit expositio Gentilis Fulginatis super prima fen quarti Canonis Avicenne...;
and includes the text of the latter, in the translation of Gherardo da Cremona
(NLMCat 2047).

De majoritate morbi. *See no. 385n.*

384 De proportionibus medicinarum. Pavia: Jacobus de Sancto Petro, 9
Feb. 1479. 4°. [LEK]

Ref: Klebs 450.1.

N.B: An edition is assigned to the press of Matthaeus Cerdonis at Padua about 1486
(Cen G130). Included in compilations issued in [1527], [1541], and 1549 (NLM-
Cat 3124-3126). Also known under the title, *De dosi medicinarum investigandis
libellus.*

385 Super prima fen quarti Canonis Avicennae. Padua: Nicolò Petri de Harlem, I) 19 Feb. 1476; II) 1476. f°. [LEK]

> *Add*: GENTILE da Foligno. De majoritate morbi.
> *Ref*: HR 7565; IGI 4201; Osler (IM) 113; Schullian (ArMed) 205; Klebs 446.1; Stillwell G127; Goff G-139.
> *N.B*: The first of his various commentaries on Avicenna to be printed. Followed by his *Super tertio libro*, Padua, 1477; *Super secundo libro*, [Pavia, 1488?]; and *Super quinto libro*, [Pavia, 1488?]—*see* Cen G131–G133. The commentary of the first book of Avicenna, *Expositiones in primum librum Avicennae*, was printed at Venice in 1501-3, and his *Expositio super tractatu De lepra Avicennae*, at Venice in 1499.

386 De utilitatibus aquae balnei de Porretta. Padua: Joannes de Reno, 1473. 4°.

> *Ref*: Sart III 850; Stillwell G121; Goff G-133.
> *N.B*: Relates to the value of the baths at Porretta, not far from Bologna. Possibly a separate of the tract of this title issued with his *Balneae*, [Padua], 24 March 1473 and attributed in the text to Bonaventura de' Castello, *fl.* 1340—*see* NLMCat 2233–2235.

GERSDORFF, Hans von, *fl.* 1475.

387 Feldtbüch der Wundarznei [*German*]. Strasbourg: Johann Schott, [after 22 Aug. 1517]. f°. [LEK]

> *Ref*: NLMCat 2059; Pr 10285; *Garrison* (1929) 202; *Castiglioni* (1947) 372.
> *N.B*: A field-book of wound surgery; written by an army surgeon of original ideas and methods. Contains the earliest known picture of an amputation and "some of the most instructive pictures of early surgical procedure in existence." Like Brunschwig he believed in applying boiling oil to gun wounds. Strasbourg editions of [1526], [1528], and 1540 are listed in NLMCat 2060, 2062.

GERSON (Jean Charlier de Gerson; *called* Johannes Gerson), 1363–1429.

388 De pollutione nocturna. [Cologne: Ulrich Zel, 1466/67.] 4°.

> *Add*: Forma absolutionis sacramentalis.
> *Ref*: HC *7694; BMC I 179; Oates 281; Voull (K) 476; Pell 5219; Klebs 459.1; *Garrison* (1929) 166n; Stillwell G234; Goff G-254.
> *N.B*: Zel group A, no. 3 (BMC). Another edition assigned to Zel, *c.* 1467, contains also Gerson's *De cognitione castitatis et pollutionibus diurnis* and is presumably slightly later than this imprint, since type analysis shows it to be Zel group B, no. 4 (BMC).

III. *Medicine*

GESNER, Konrad (Euonymus Philiatrus, *pseud.*), 1516–1565.

389 Enumeratio medicamentorum purgantium, vomitorium & aluum bonam facientium ordine alphabeti.   Basel: Johann Froben and Nicolaus Episcopius, 1543.   4°.   [LEK]

> *Ref*: Garrison (1929) 230.
> *N.B*: An index of purgatives. Listed in L. C. HARPER, *Catalogue* 15, no. 221. Issued at Lyon in 1544 (BM-Fr 81). Gesner's *Apparatus et delectus simplicium medicamentorum* had appeared at Lyon, with other works, in 1542 (BM-Fr 201; NLMCat 2064).

GILINO Corradino, *fl.* 1495.

390 De morbo quem gallicum nuncupant.   [Ferrara: Laurentius de Rubeis, not before 1497.]   4°.

> *Ref*: Klebs 463.1; *Sudhoff-Singer*, p. xl–xli; Stillwell G284; Goff G-306.
> *N.B*: A syphilis tract recommending the application of a red-hot iron to the head in the region of the coronal suture.
> *Fac*: Sudhoff-Singer 7.

GILLES of Corbeil (Aegidius Corboliensis), 1165–1223.

391 De urinis, sive De urinarum judiciis carmen (Comm: Gentile da Foligno, *c.* 1290–1348. Ed: Venantius Mutius).   Padua: Matthaeus Cerdonis, 12 July 1483.   4°.   [LEK]

> *Ref*: GW 269; HCR 100; BMC VII 921; IGI 56; Klebs 464.1; *Castiglioni* (1947) 316–317; *Garrison* (1929) *151*; Stillwell A84; Goff A-93.
> *N.B*: A popular textbook on uroscopy. Sart II 440 speaks of this as a metrical elaboration of Theophilos Protospatharios (seventh century); Castiglioni (1947) 317, as derived from the *Regulae urinarum* of the Salernitan writer, Magister Maurus (*d.* 1214). [For further comment, see entry under NATURAL SCIENCE. For early sixteenth-century editions, see NLMCat 2100–2103.]

GRASSUS, Benvenutus (Grassi *or* Graffeo ?), *11th–12th century?*.

392 De oculis eorumque aegritudinibus et curis.   [Ferrara:] Severinus Ferrariensis, [147]4.   4°.

> *Ref*: HR 7869; BMC VI 608; IGI 4381; Osler (IM) 57; Schullian (ArMed) 216; Klebs 472.1; *Garrison* (1929) 203; *Castiglioni* (1947) 316; Stillwell G315; Goff G-352.
> *N.B*: The first printed book on diseases of the eye and their cure; a classic for several hundred years. Written by a professor at Salerno and Montpellier, and according to Castiglioni known in 22 manuscripts and 18 printed editions, in Latin, English, French, and Provençal.
> *Mon*: WOOD, Casey A. *Benvenutus Grassus' De oculis.* San Francisco, 1929.

III. *Medicine*

GREGORIUS I, *Pont. Max., St., the Great, c.* 540–604.

393 Dialogi. Vita [*Italian*]. Venice: Johannes de Colonia and Johannes Manthen, 1475. f°. [LEK]

> *Ref*: HC 7975; BMC V 231; IGI 4424; Pell 5363; Stillwell G371; Goff G-410.
> *N.B*: According to F.N.L. Poynter's *Catalogue of Incunabula in the Wellcome Historical Medical Library*, London, 1954, this edition contains a section entitled *Come sana un fanciulo dal morbo ellefantino*, and two on gout.

THE GRETE HERBALL, London, 1526. (See under *Arbolaire*.)

GRÜNPECK, Joseph, 1473–*c.* 1503.

394 Libellus de mentulagra, morbo rabido et incognito. [Reutlingen: Michael Greif, after 5 May 1503]. 4°.

> *Ref*: NLMCat 2184; H *8089; Pr 11256; *Garrison* (1929) 190; *Castiglioni* (1947) 461; *Sudhoff-Singer* p. xxvii; Goff G-513.
> *N.B*: A rather sceptical review of treatments used for syphilis during the early years of the outbreak. Variously assigned also to the press of Albrecht Kunne at Memmingen, after 1500.

395 Tractatus de pestilentiali scorra. [Augsburg: Hans Schauer, after 18 Oct. 1496.] 4°. [LEK]

> *Ref*: H *8090; BMC III 393; BM-Ger 373; Polain 1759; Klebs 476.1; *Sudhoff-Singer* p. xxii–xxviii.
> *N.B*: A commentary on a poem by Sebastian Brandt which appears in the text. The text also discusses the influence of astrology and includes a diagram of the universe showing the position of the planets. The preface is dated 18 October 1496. Of four other Latin editions believed to have been issued before 1501, only that printed at Magdeburg in 1498 is dated (Klebs 476.4; Cen G471–G473). A German version was printed at Augsburg, 17 December 1496 (Klebs 477.1), and an unsigned edition is assigned to Nuremberg, Dec. 1496 or Jan. 1497 (Cen G474).

GUAINERI, Antonio (Guaynerius; Antonius Guainerius), *fl.* 1440.

396 Opera medica. [Padua:] Conradus de Paderborn, 1473–1474. f°. [LEK]

> *Ref*: Klebs 480.1.
> *N.B*: A compilation of works, subsequently re-issued at Pavia and Venice (Cen G475–G478), and apparently comprising remainders from the editions of the author's treatises on diseases of the head, pleurisy, stomach and intestinal disorders, diseases of women, joints and the stone, and fever and antidotes, which were separately issued during 1473–1474 (*see* IGI 4510, 4512, 4513, 4514, 4517; Cen C479–G481). His treatises on plagues and poisons, issued together, are assignable to Venice about 1487 (H *8101; Cen G482).

Mon: THORNDIKE, Lynn. *Antonio Guaineri.* (Chap. XLVII in vol. IV of his *History of magic and experimental science.* New York, 1934.)

GUIDI, Guido (*called* Vidius), *d.* 1569.

397 Chirurgia e graeco in latinum conversa.   Paris: Pierre Gautier, 1544. f°.

Ref: NLMCat 2204; *Garrison* (1929) 125; *Castiglioni* (1947) 472.

N.B: Derived from a manuscript possibly dating from the beginning of the Christian era or earlier. Illustrated with surgical scenes variously attributed to Primaticcio or the school of Salviati. A scene depicting three persons attempting the reduction of the dislocation of a patient's shoulder is cleverly drawn and dramatic to a degree—see Castiglioni (1947) 474. Garrison, following Sudhoff, traces the source of these drawings to early Byzantine manuscripts believed to have transmitted the Hippocratic tradition of surgical practice.

Mon: KELLETT, C. E. *The school of Salviati and the illustrations to the Chirurgia of Vidus Vidius,* 1544 (p. 264–268 in vol. 2 of *Medical History,* 1958).

GUY de Chauliac (Guido de Cauliaco), *c.* 1300–1368.

398 Chirurgia [*French*:] La practique en chirurgie (Ed: Nicolaus Panis). Lyon: For Barthélemy Buyer, 28 March 1478. f°. [LEK]

Ref: Klebs 491.1; Pell 3533; Osler (IM) 164; *Sart* III 1690–1694; *Castiglioni* (1947) 345–347, 357.

N.B: The work, which in the main is written from a surgical point of view, confirms Mondino's practice in dissection, as transmitted by his pupil Bertuccio. It consists of seven sections: I)Anatomy; II) Abscesses; tumors; cancer; the prevention of plagues, based on experience at Avignon in 1348 and 1360; III) Wounds and skull fractures; IV) Ulcers; V) Fractures and dislocations; VI) Diseases of the body, including ears, eyes, and teeth; VII) Medicines and antidotes. Guy de Chauliac, a reactionary in other matters although an advocate of teaching from the cadaver, ranks as the most eminent surgeon of the fourteenth century, and more than twenty editions of his *Chirurgia* are known within our period.

Presumably originally written in Latin; commonly known as the *Chirurgia,* even though the first printed edition is in French. Although Garrison (1929) 158 *note* cites a Latin edition of Venice, 1490, none has been found in the present survey earlier than that printed at Venice, 21 Nov. 1498 (Cen G510). An edition (Cen G513) formerly assigned to [Lyon, 1499] has been re-assigned to [Lyon:] Vincentius de Portonariis the Elder [not before 1506]—see Schullian (ArMed) 229, note; NLMCat 2233; Goff G-560. Italian and Catalan translations were issued at Venice in 1480 (Cen G515) and at Barcelona in 1492 (Klebs 493.1). An abridgment, the so-called *Chirurgia parva,* was issued in Dutch, French, and Latin before 1501 (Klebs 495–497; see also Cen G512).

Mon: NICAISE, Edouard. *La grande chirurgie de Chauliac.* Paris, 1890.

Fac: *Osiris* 5 *fig.* 35.

Guy de Chauliac (continued)

399 Chirurgia parva [*Dutch*]. [Delft: Anonymous printer, 1477–87.] [LEK]

> *Ref*: Camp 870; Klebs 495.1; *Sart* III 1692.
> *N.B*: A compendium of his *Chirurgia*, possibly made by a student. Issued in French at Paris about 1500 (Klebs 496.1). [For a note on the first Latin edition—printed at Venice by Bonetus Locatellus on 22 Feb. 1497—see NATURAL SCIENCE: Guy de Chauliac.]

HALY, Jesu, *11th century. See* 'ISA ibn 'ALI.

HALY ABBAS ('Ali ibn 'Abbās), *d.* 994.

400 Liber medicinae, sive Regalis dispositio (Tr: Stephanus of Antioch, *fl.* 1127. Ed: Anonius Vitalis). Venice: Bernardinus Rizus for Joannes de Nigro, 25 Sept. 1492. f°. [LEK]

> *Ref*: HC *8350; BMC V 403; BM-Ital 19; IGI 4644; Klebs 498.1; Choulant (H) 350; *Sart* I 677; *Browne (AM)* 53–57; Stillwell H2; Goff H-3.
> *N.B*: A leading Arabic treatise on theory and medical practice until superseded by the *Canon* of Avicenna a century later. Originally called the *Almaleki* or *Royal Book*, the *Liber regius*, because of the fact that Haly Abbas was Royal Physician to Prince Adhad ad Daula ben Buweih. [For further comment, see under NATURAL SCIENCE.]

HERBARIUM APULEI [*pseudo-*Apuleius].

401 Herbarium Apulei. [Rome:] Joannes Philippus de Lignamine [about 1481–83]. 4°. [LEK]

> *Ref*: GW 2300; H *1322; BMC IV 131; IGI 775; Klebs 505.2–3 (*var*); Choulant (H) 212–214; Stillwell H52; Goff H-58.
> *N.B*: One of the first printed herbals and instances of plant illustrations, although the latter are in rather stylized form. An early herbal to which additions had been made in the course of the centuries. Sometimes attributed to Apuleius Barbarus, *c. 5th century* [not to be confused with Apuleius Madaurensis, the author of the *Asinus aureus*].
> *Fac*: HUNGER, F. W. T., ed. and *comm. The Herbal of pseudo-Apuleius. Facsimiles of the 9th-century manuscript, Codex Cassinensis 97, together with a facsimile of the first printed edition of J. P. de Lignamine [c. 1481]. Leiden, 1935.*

HERBARIUS.

402 Herbarius [*Latin, with German synonyms.*] Mainz: Peter Schoeffer, [14]84. 4°. [LEK]

Ref: HC 8444; Klebs 506.1; Stillwell H56; Goff H-62.

N.B: The prototype from which both the *Gart der Gesundheit* and the *Hortus sanitatis* were in part derived [*q.v.*]. With decorative woodcut illustrations. Known in variant issues (Cen H56). Issued in Latin with Dutch synonyms, [Louvain, *c.* 1484–85] (Cen H53); and in Dutch with Latin synonyms, [Kuilenburg or Louvain] 1484 (Cen H61). Also issued in Latin with German synonyms, Passau, [14]85 (Cen H58), in Latin with French synonyms, [Paris, *c.* 1486] (Cen H55), and later without synonyms. For a Low-German version, see ORTOLFF von Bayrlandt. For editions of 1509 and 1520, see NLMCat 2268, 2269. [Sometimes called the *Herbarius in latino* to distinguish it from the *Herbarius zu deutsch* (the *Gart der Gesundheit*) published by Schoeffer in 1485—Cen G87.]

Mon: KLEBS, Arnold C. Herbals of the 15th century (BIBLIOGRAPHICAL SOCIETY OF AMERICA. *Papers*, vols. 11–12, 1917–1918).

403 ——: Herbolario volgare [*Italian*]. Venice: Alessandro Bindoni, 1522. 4°. [LEK]

Ref: NLMCat 2270; BM-Ital 325; Nissen 2315.

N.B: For editions of 1536 and 1539, see NLMCat 2271, 2272 (Nissen 2316, 2318).

HILDEGARD of Bingen, *Saint*, 1098–1178.

404 Physica S. Hildegardis [*and other works*]. Strasbourg: Johann Schott, 1533. f°. [LEK]

Ref: NLMCat 2307; BM-Ger 405; Choulant (H) 302–309; *Hunt (Quinby)* I 32; *Sart* II 386–388.

N.B: One of the earliest herbals. [For comment and a note on the works included in this edition, see under NATURAL SCIENCE.]

HIPPIATRICA. *See no. 346.*

HIPPOCRATES (Hippokrates; Ippokrate), 460–375 B.C.

Major Compilations of Hippocrates's Works

In the contents listed under nos. 405–407, a title in italics indicates that its text is known in an earlier printing than in the Opera cited. Each entry is divided into two sections. The first section gives the title followed by a numeral indicating its notation or sequence in the Opera cited, the latter in square brackets if the numeral is supplied. The second gives the date of the earlier printing with its call-number within the present volume.

For an alphabetical list of the Hippocratic titles as cited here and elsewhere in the present volume, see the INDEX: *Hippocrates.*

Hippocrates (continued)

405 Opera [*Greek*]. Venice: In aedibus Aldi et Andreae Asulani soceri, May 1526. f°. [LEK]

Ref: NLMCat 2316; BM-Ital 327; Choulant (H) 22, 12–21; Osler (BO) 142; Renouard (Alde) I 243; *Sart (Appr)* 9.

N.B: The first Greek edition. Contains various titles not known to have been published in Latin or Greek prior to the date of this edition. Edited by Franciscus Asulanus (Francesco Torresani); based in part on manuscripts not available to later editors. A critical Greek edition prepared by Janus Cornarius, 1500–1558, was published by Hieronymus Froben and Nicolaus Episcopius at Basel in 1538 (WellHMed (1962) 3174; NLMCat 2317).

Con: 1) *De aere, aqua, locis** [23]; (1481; no. 658). 2) De affectibus Polybi [32]. 3) De alimento quem esse Hippocrates negat Galenus [26]. 4) *De arte* [2]; (1525, no. 406:2). 5) De articulis [49]. 6) *De carnibus* [12]; (1525, no. 406:5). 7) *Coacae praecognitiones* [46]; (?1525, 406:6). 8) De corde [19]; (1525; no. 406:7). 9) De curandis luxatis [51]. 10) Decretum atheniensium [57]. 11) Definitae sententiae [43]. 12) De dentitione [17]. 13) De diebus indicialibus [42]. 14) De dissectione [18]. 15) *Epibomios* [*De simulachro Hippocratis super tumulum aram ve comparentis, quod Epibomos dicitur*] [58]; (1525, no. 406:61). 16) *Epistolae Hippocratis* [56]; (?1525, 406:11). 17) De extractione foetus [16]. 18) *De fistulis* [53]; (1525, no. 406:12). 19) *De flatibus* [29]; (1525, no. 406:13). 20) *De fracturis* [48]; (1525, no. 406:14). 21) De glandibus [20]; (?1525, no. 406:16). 22) *De haemorrhoidibus* [54]; (1525, no. 406:17). 23) *De humoribus* [28]; (1525, no. 406:21). 24) *De insomniis* [25]; (c. 1481, no. 413). 25) De internarum partium affectibus [33]. 26) De iuditiis [41]. 27) *Iusiurandum Hippocratis* [1]; (1483, no 414). 28) *Lex Hippocratis* [7]; (1483, no. 415). 29) De locis in homine [22]; (1525, no. 406:26). 30) *De medici munere* [50]; (?1525, no. 406:29). 31) *De medico* [4]; (1525, no. 406:30). 32) *De morbis* [31]; (?1525, no. 406:33). 33) *De morbis mulierum* [36]; (?1525, no. 34). 34) De morbis passim grassantibus [39]. 35) De morbis virginum [34]. 36) *De natura foetus* [11]; (29 Mar. 1483, no. 659). 37) *De natura hominis* [8]; (1481, no. 660). 38) *De natura muliebri* [35]; (?1525, no. 406:39). 39) *De natura ossium* [21]; (1525, no. 406:44). 40) *De octomestri partu* [14]; (1525, no. 406:45). 41) Oratio Thessali Hippocratis filii legati ad Atheniensis [59]; (?1525, no. 406:65). 42) Praecepta Hippocratis [6]; (1525, no. 406:50). 43) Praedictiones [45]. 44) Praenotiones [44]. 45) De prisca medicina [3]; (1525, no. 406:53). 46) De probitate [5]; (1525, no. 406:18). 47) De sacro morbo docti cuiusdam [30]; (1525, no. 406:56). 48) De semine Polybi [sive De genitura] [10]; (?1525, no. 406:43). 49) De septimestri partu [13]; (1525, no. 406:60). 50) De sterilibus [37]; (1525, no. 662). 51) *De superfoetatione* [15]; (1525, no. 406:63). 52) Supposititia quaedam calci primi de morbis mulierum adscripta [38]. 53) *De ulceribus* [52]; (1525, no. 406:19). 54) *De usu humidorum* [27]; (1525, no. 406:20). 55) *De victus ratione* [24]; (?1525, no. 406:68). 56) *De victus ratione acutorum* I–IV [40]; (1511, no. 422). 57) *De victus ratione salubris Polybi discipuli Hippocratis* [9]; (c. 1483, no. 407n). 58) *De visu* [55]; (1525, no. 406:70). 59) *De vulneribus capitis* [47]; (1525, no. 406:4).

Mon: LITTRÉ, E. *Œuvres complétes d'Hippocrate*, 10 vols., Paris, 1839–61.

406 Opera [*Latin*] (Tr: Marcus Fabius Calvus, *fl.* 1520). Rome: Ex aedibus Francisci Minitii Calvi Novocomensis, 1525. f°. [LEK]

Ref: NLMCat 2320; Choulant (H) 25; *Sart* I 96–102; *Castiglioni* (1947) 153.

N.B: An Opera, issued in Latin at Basel by Andreas Cratander, in 1526, contains 68 of the translations by Calvus; 2 by Gulielmus Copus, and 1 each by Nicolaus Leonicenus and Andreas Brentius (NLMCat 2321). The first edition in Greek was issued at Venice in May 1526—*q.v.*

Con: 1) *De aeribus, aquis, locis* (9); (1481, *no.* 658). 2) De arte (1). 3) *De aphorismis* (54); ([*b.* 1476], *no.* 408). 4) De capitis vulneribus (72). 5) De carnibus (63). 6) De Coacis praenotionibus (58). 7) De corde (66). 8) De corporum secatione, Anatome ve (65). 9) De decretoriis diebus (47). 10) De epidemiis, I–VII (38–44); (1483, *no.* 411). 11) De epistolis Hippocratis . . . (79). 12) De fistulis (74). 13) De flatibus (62). 14) De fracturis, fractis ve ossibus (69). 15) De furore, seu insania, mania ve (77). 16) De glandulis per omnia membra (51). 17) De haemorrhoidibus, mariscis ve (64). 18) De honestate, probitate ve, sive Euschemosyne (4). 19) De hulceribus (73). 20) De humidorum, liquidorum ve usu (10). 21) De humoribus, complexionibus ve, & Chymis (61). 22) De infoecundis (21). 23) *Iusiurandum* (7); (1483, *no.* 414). 24) De lauationibus (50). 25) *De lege* (8); (1483, *no.* 415). 26) De locis in homine (52). 27) De lotii notis, signis ve, quod Hippocratis esse nolunt (78). 28) De luxatorum, loco ve motorum repositione (70). 29) De medici vulnerarii munere (67). 30) De medico (3). 31) De mente, sensu ve (5). 32) De mochlico, qui luxata reponatur (76). 33) De morbis, I–IV (31–34). 34) De morbis feminarum, I–III (19–21). 35) De morbis, qui extra (35). 36) De morbis, qui intra (36). 37) De morborum decretorio (46). 38) De natura (11). 39) De natura feminae (23). 40) *De natura hominis* (24); (1481, *no.* 660). 41) De natura ossium (68). 42) *De natura pueri, foetus ve* (13); (1483, *no.* 659). 43) De natura seminis genitalis [sive De genitura] (12). 44) De natura virginum (17). 45) De octimestri partu (15). 46) De oraculis, definitionibus ve, & aphorismis (54). 47) De nutricatione (26). 48) De perniciosis, & periculosis vulneribus (71). 49) De potionibus medicis (48). 50) De praeceptis, mandatis ve (6). 51) De praedictorio, I–II (56–57). 52) De praescito, prognostico ve (55). 53) De prisca medicina (2). 54) De pueri dentitione (16). 55) De pueri, foetus ve in utero mortui extractione (22). 56) De sacro morbo [epilepsy], comitiali ve (37). 57) De salubribus, sanis ve rebus (25). 58) De Senatus consulto Atheniensium (81). 59) De septimanis (45). 60) De septimestri partu (14). 61) De simulachro Hippocratis super tumulum aram ve comparentis, quod Epibomos dicitur (80). 62) De somniis (59). 63) De superfoetatione (18). 64) De telorum extractione (75). 65) De Thessali Hippocratis filii oratione . . . (82). 66) De venerea re (53). 67) De veratro, helleboro ve (49). 68) De victus ratione, I–III (27–29). 69) *De victus ratione in gravibus, acutis ve, ptisanae ve laudibus contra Cnidias opiniones, & sententias* (30); (?1511, *no.* 442). 70) De visu, oculi ve acie (60). [71] Praeterea tractatum Aphricani de ponderibus & mensuris, quaedam Balbi de Asse, & eius minutis partibus, addidimus.

Hippocrates (continued)

407 Opera parva, *so-called* (Tr. and Ed: Andreas Brentius [Andreas Althamer of Brenz]). [Rome: Eucharius Silber, about 1483–1490.] 4°. [LEK]

> *Ref:* HC *8669; BMC IV 122; IGI 4787; Klebs 519.1; Schullian (ArMed) 242; Stillwell H254; Goff H-278.
>
> *N.B:* Sometimes listed as *De natura hominis et alia opuscula.* Re-issued and assigned to the press of Stephan Plannck at Rome about 1490.
>
> *Con:* 1) Demonstratio quod artes sunt. 2) Invectiva in obtrectatores medicinae. 3) *Iusurandum*; (29 Mar. 1483, *no.* 414). 4) *Medicinae lex*; (29 Mar. 1483, *no.* 415). 5) *De natura hominis*; (1481, *no.* 660). 6) De tuenda valetudine. 7) De victu.
>   (As noted in NLMCat 935, *nos.* 1 and 2 are part of *De arte* [1525, *no.* 406:2]; and *nos.* 6 and 7 are sections of the so-called *De victus salubri ratione, sive Liber de salubri diaeta.*)

Titles issued earlier or not found in the 'Opera'

408 Aphorismi, sive Sententiae cum commentationibus Galeni. (*Issued in* ARTICELLA. [Padua: Nicolaus Petri, before 1476].) [LEK]

> *Ref:* GW 2678; Osler (IM) 181; Klebs 116.1; O'Leary 34.
>
> *N.B:* Known also as *Determinationes.* Issued at Florence by Antonio di Bartolommeo Miscomini, 16 Oct. 1494 (Cen H249), together with the commentary of Galen; translated by Laurentius Laurentianus [*Fac.: Osiris* 5 125]. An undated edition of the *Aphorismi* is assigned to Nuremberg, after 5 April 1496—Cen H250. Included in the Latin *Opera* of 1525. A new translation by Theodorus Gaza, assigned to Paris about 1519, is cited in NLMCat 2559. The so-called Rabelais edition in Greek and Latin was brought out at Lyon by Sébastien Gryphe in 1532 and 1543 —Choulant (H) p. 33. At least ten editions with the text in Greek were printed before the end of our period—see NLMCat 2358–2367. Section VII with a commentary by Leonhart Fuchs was issued at Basel in 1544, and two editions were printed in Paris the following year—Hunt (Quinby) I 51.

409 De atrae bilis agitatione melancholia ve liber I (Tr: Marcus Fabius Calvus). (*Issued with* HIPPOCRATES. De morbis libri IV. Paris: Claude Chevallon [1526].) 4°.

> *Ref:* NLMCat 2343.

410 Capsula eburnea, sive Liber pronosticorum. (*Issued with* RHASIS. Liber de Almansorem. Milan: Leonardus Pachel and Uldericus Scinzenzeler, 14 Feb. 1481.) [LEK]

> *Ref:* BMC VI 749; Klebs 826.1; Schullian (ArMed) 399; Stillwell R169; Goff R-175.
>
> *N.B:* Reprinted at Venice in 1497; issued with Maimonides at Bologna in 1489—*see* Schullian (ArMed) 400, 297. Included in various sixteenth-century editions of *Articella, see* NLMCat nos. 328–332.

411 Epidemiarum libri VII; cum commento VIII particulas continens (Ed: Franciscus Argilagnes; Comm: Joannes Alexandrinus). (*Issued* in ARTI-CELLA. Venice: Hermannus Liechtenstein, 29 March 1483.) f°. [LEK]

> *Ref*: GW 2679; H *1869; Pell 1377; IGI 908; Klebs 116.2; *Sart* I 98; Stillwell A1011; Goff A-1143.
>
> *N.B*: Books I and III are generally accepted as authentic and as among the most remarkable products of Greek science. The remaining books are supposed to be the work of disciples. Included in various subsequent editions of *Articella* and in the Latin *Opera* of 1525 (38–44). According to Castiglioni (1947) 167, Books I and II provide "the foundation of the concept of the genius epidemicus," which prevailed in medicine for centuries. Book VI was issued in Greek at Hagenau in February 1532, with a Latin translation and commentary by Leonhart Fuchs, 1501–1566 (Hunt (Quinby) I 31). [For sixteenth-century editions of various sections of the *Epidemiarum libri*, see NLMCat p. 301–302. For *Greek-English* texts edited by W. H. S. Jones, see Loeb Library, 1923.]

412 De insania Democriti facetum epistolium. [Augsburg: Johann Frosch-auer, about 1495–1500.] 4°.

> *Add*: ULSEN, Dietrich. Carmina.
>
> *Ref*: HC *8676; BMC II 399; BM-Ger 407; Polain 1963; Klebs 522.1; Stillwell H252; Goff H-276.

413 De insomniis (Tr: Andreas Althamer of Brenz [Andreas Brentius], 1490–1540). [Rome: Oliverius Servius, *c.* 1481]. 4°.

> *Ref*: HC *3779; BMC IV 130; BM-Ital 330 [4]; IGI 4784; Klebs 517.1; Choulant (H) 30; Stillwell H253; Goff H-277.
>
> *N.B*: The fifth aphorism of *Liber* I of Hippocrates's *Aphorismi* (cf. NLMCat 2410). Subsequently issued with Rhasis's *Liber ad Almansorem*, [Venice], 7 Oct. 1497 (Cen R170); and with Maimonides's *Aphorismi*, Venice, 10 Jan. 1500 (Cen M64). Included in the Greek *Opera* of 1526. A Greek edition was brought out by Oporinus at Basel in 1540 and reprinted in 1543; and a Latin version with a commentary by Julius Caesar Scaliger was issued at Lyon by Sébastien Gryphe in 1539. Authenticity questioned. The *De languentium somniis insomniis 've liber* appeared in a Latin *Opera* printed at Basel in 1526 and is included in a students' manual issued at Paris by Simon Du Bois in 1527.

414 Iusiurandum (Tr: Petrus Paulus Vergerius). (*Issued in* ARTICELLA. Ven-ice: Hermannus Liechtenstein, 29 March 1483). f°. [LEK]

> *Ref*: GW 2679; H *1869; IGI 908; Pell 1377; Choulant (H) 14; Poynter 410; Klebs 116.2; *Castiglioni* (1947) 154; *Garrison* (1929) 96; Stillwell A1011.
>
> *N.B*: The so-called Hippocratic oath. A text of two leaves giving a brief exhortation to maintain high ethical standards and an indenture in which a candidate at the Medical School at Cos agrees to assume the financial support of his teacher and to instruct his own children and other student-interns in the tradition of the

III. *Medicine*

Hippocrates (continued)

Asklepiads. The first *dated* issuing of this text. It appeared also in the undated *Opera parva* [*no.* 407] assigned to the press of Eucharius Silber at Rome about 1483–90; and in the *De generibus metrorum* of Niccolò Perotti [Cen P263] assigned to the press of Boninus de Boninis at Verona about 1483. The text is included in various subsequent editions of *Articella*; in the Latin *Opera* of 1525; the Greek *Opera* of 1526; and in Benedetti compilations of 1514 and 1527 (see NLMCat 521, 522). A French version appeared in a compilation printed at Lyon by Jehan Monsnier in 1539 (NLMCat 2447).

Mon: JONES, W. H. S. *The doctor's oath.* Cambridge, 1924. (Contains the text of the oath; discussion; and Christian and Arabic versions.) EDELSTEIN, L. *The Hippocratic oath, text, translation, and interpretation.* Baltimore, 1943 (Supplement to the *Bulletin of the History of Medicine*, I).

415 De lege sive Medicinae lex (Tr: Arnaldo de Villa Nova, *c.* 1235–1311). (*Issued in* ARTICELLA. Venice: Hermannus Liechtenstein, 29 March 1483). f°. [LEK]

Ref: GW 2679; H *1869; IGI 908; Pell 1377; Klebs 116.2; Stillwell A1011; Goff A-1143.

N.B: The first *dated* issuing of this work, which appeared also in the so-called *Opera parva* assigned to the press of Eucharius Silber at Rome about 1483–90 (*no.* 407). Included in various subsequent editions of *Articella*; in the Latin *Opera* of 1525, and the Greek *Opera* of 1526.

416 De medicorum astrologia. Padua: [Matthaeus Cerdonis] 1483. 4°. [LEK]

Ref: R 557; Klebs 518.1; Stillwell H251; Goff H-275.

N.B: A work apparently known under various titles (Astronomia de infirmitatibus; Astronomia . . . de variis egritudinibus et morbis; De decubitu infirmorum; De esse aegrorum secundum lunam; De significatione mortis et vitae libellus; Prognostica de decubitu; Prognosticorum liber secundum lunam). Authenticity questioned. Attributed to Imbrasius of Ephesus. [For discussion of the attribution to him and to others, see NLMCat 2527; also, S. WEINSTOCK in the *Classical Quarterly*, 1948, 42, p. 41–43.] Included in the *Opusculum reportorii prognosticon* assigned to Firmin de Beauval and printed at Venice by Erhard Ratdolt in 1485 —Schullian (ArMed) 193.

417 De pharmaciis. (*Issued with* RHASIS. Liber ad Almansorem (*and other medical tracts*). Milan: Leonardus Pachel and Uldericus Scinzenzeler, 14 Feb. 1481.) [LEK]

Ref: HCR 13891; BMC VI 749; Klebs 826.1; Schullian (ArMed) 399; Stillwell R169; Goff R-175.

418 De praeparatione hominis ad Ptolemaeum regem (Tr: Johann Reuchlin). Tübingen: Thomas Anshelm, 1512. 4°. [LEK]

Ref: NLMCat 2434.
N.B: Re-issued in Latin in an otherwise Greek-Latin compilation published at Basel by Heinrich Petri and assigned to 1543 (NLMCat 2337).

419   De purgatoriis medicamentis libellus . . . (Tr: Junius Paulus Crassus). (*Issued with* THEOPHILUS PROTOSPATHARIUS, *7th century.* De corporis humani fabrica. Venice: Octavianus Scotus, 1537.)   4°.   [LEK]

Ref: NLMCat 4342.
N.B: The earliest printing of this text found in the present survey. Also issued in Latin at Paris in 1539 and 1540, at Lyon in 1541, and possibly in Greek at Basel in 1544—see NLMCat p. 297.

420   De regimine acutorum morborum. (*Issued in* ARTICELLA. [Padua: Nicolaus Petri, before 1476].)

Ref: GW 2678; Osler (IM) 181; Klebs 116.1; Sart I 98.
N.B: *See also* De victus ratione in morbis acutis libri IV, *no. 422.*

421   Secreta. (*Issued with other medical works in* RHASIS. Liber ad Almansorem. Milan: Leonardus Pachel and Uldericus Scinzenzeler, 14 Feb. 1481).   f°.   [LEK]

Ref: HCR 13891; BMC VI 749; Schullian (ArMed) 399; Stillwell R169; Goff R-175.
N.B: Title listed also in the Rhasis collections printed at Venice in 1497, 1500, and 1508 (Schullian (ArMed) 400; NLMCat 3311, 3311*n*). Also with the *Regimen sanitatis* of Magninus Mediolanensis in an undated volume assigned to the press of François Fradin at Paris about 1500–1505 (NLMCat 3041; Goff M-56); and in various sixteenth-century editions of *Articella* (see NLMCat p. 41–42).

422   De victus ratione in morbis acutis libri I-IV (Tr: Gulielmus Copus). (*Issued with* HIPPOCRATES. Praesagiorum libri I-III. [? Paris: ? Henri Estienne, 1511].)   4°.

Ref: NLMCat 2440.
N.B: Also known as *De victu acutorum, sive De ptisana liber* (NLMCat 2420); see also *De regimine acutorum morborum*, [b. 1476], no. 420. Included in the Latin *Opera* of 1525 and the Greek *Opera* of 1526. Greek-and-Latin editions were issued by two Parisian presses in 1543, and various Latin versions and commentaries during the years 1527–1549 (see NLMCat p. 300).

De victus ratione salubri, sive Liber de salubri diaeta, [1483–1490]. *See no. 407n.*

[*For titles of possible medical interest, see* NATURAL SCIENCE: Hippocrates.]

HOCK Von BRACKENAU, Wendelin, *fl.* 1502–1514.

423 Mentagra, sive Tractatus de causis praeservativis, regimine & cura morbi Gallici. [Strasbourg: Johann Schott] 1514. 4°. [LEK]

> *Ref*: NLMCat 2450.
>
> *N.B*: Reprinted at Lyon by Antoine Blanchard for Barthélemy Trot in 1529, both editions containing the author's *Tractatus de curandis ulceribus hunc morbum ut in plurimum consequentibus*. The tract on syphilis appeared also in Dutch, in a 1533 edition of the *Hortus sanitatis* assigned to the press of Claes de Grave at Antwerp (NLMCat 2472).

HORTUS SANITATIS.

424 Hortus sanitatis. Mainz: Jacob Meydenbach, 23 June 1491. f°. [LEK]

> *Ref*: LC(LJRCat) 138; HC *8944; BMC I 44; BM-Ger 418; Oates 55; IGI 4900; Klebs 509.1; Klebs (Hortus) 1; Schullian (ArMed) 244; *Hunt (Quinby)* I 8; *Arber* (1938) 28–37; Stillwell H416; Goff H-486.
>
> *N.B*: Derived from the *Herbarius*, but much expanded and profusely illustrated. In addition to its account of the medicinal properties of plants, including some from foreign lands, it contains a treatise *De urinis*. Variously assigned to Johann von Cube as compiler, identified with Dr. Johann Wonnecke von Caub, *c*. 1484–1503, town-physician of Frankfurt. [See also under NATURAL SCIENCE. For early sixteenth-century editions, see NLMCat 2468–2470.]

HUGO Senensis. *See* BENZI, Ugo, da Siena.

ḤUNAIN ibn Isḥāq (*called* Joannitius *or* Johannitius), 809/10–877.

425 Isagoge ad Tegni Galeni. (*Issued in* ARTICELLA. [Padua: Nicolaus Petri, about 1476.] f°. [LEK]

> *Ref*: GW 2678; Poynter 82; Osler (IM) 181; Choulant (H) 338, 398; *Sart (Appr)* 19, 187 [49]; *Sart* I 611–613; O'Leary 164–170.
>
> *N.B*: The most important writing by a Nestorian physician, famed as the translator of Greek texts into Arabic and as the leader of a group of learned translators at Baghdād. His translations of Hippocrates, Galen, Plato, Aristotle, and Dioskorides were the result of the study and collation of many texts. The present work, however, is his *Introduction* to the *Ars medica* of Galen, a summary of the latter's medical concepts. For early sixteenth-century eiditions, see NLMCat col. 2508. A list of 129 Galenic works prepared by Hunain, with a critical survey of the translations and revisions made by Syriac and Arabic scholars, was edited and issued in a German translation by Gotthelf Bergsträsser, Leipzig, 1925. An English analysis by Max Meyerhof appeared in *Isis* 8 1926 p. 683–724. [For the 1497 edition, printed at Leipzig by Wolfgang Stöckel, see Cen J424.]

'ISĀ ibn 'ALĪ ('Alī ibn 'Isā; *called* Jesu Haly), *10th–11th century.*

426 Liber memorialis ophthalmicorum seu De cognitione infirmitatum oculorum et curatione earum. (*Issued with* GUY de Chauliac. Chirurgia. Venice: Simon de Luere for Andreas Torresanus de Asula, 23 Dec. 1499.) f°. [LEK]

> *Ref:* HC *4812; BMC V 575; BM-Ital 321; IGI 4560; Polain 1770; Schullian (ArMed) 228; Klebs 494.2; Choulant (H) 339, 416:133; *Sart* I 731; Stillwell G511; Goff G-559.
>
> *N.B:* Relates to the anatomy, physiology, and diseases of the eye. An earlier collection known to Choulant (p. 416) as printed by Bonetus Locatellus at Venice in 1497 has not been found in the present survey. Issued in Guy's *Chirurgia parva* of 1500/01 (Cen G512; NLMCat 2251). The *De oculis*, credited to Canamusali (Abū-l-Qāsim 'Ammār) in both collections, is said to be spurious, the work of David Armenicus—*Sart* I 729.

ISḤĀQ al ISRĀ 'ĪLĪ (Isaac Israeli; Isaac *Judaeus*; Isaac *Medicus*), *fl.* 925.

427 De particularibus diaetis (Tr: Constantinus *Africanus, d.* 1087). Padua: Matthaeus Cerdonis, 23 Mar. 1487. 4°.

> *Ref:* H *9267; BMC VII 923; BM-Ital 341; IGI 5399; Klebs 535.1; *Choulant (H)* 348; *Sart* I 639; *Garrison* (1929) 131, 174; *Castiglioni* (1947) 273; Stillwell I149; Goff I-176.
>
> *N.B:* One of the earliest separately printed treatises on diet. Written in Arabic by one of the greatest physicians of Western Islam. The "hearing" of a text by Isaac *Judaeus* was one of the student requirements in the Cambridge Statutes of 1396. His works, together with various items in the translation of Constantinus *Africanus*, were printed at Lyon by Bartholomaeus Trott in 1515—*see* NLMCat 2557.

ISIDORUS Hispalensis. *See under* NATURAL SCIENCE, *no. 665n.*

JĀBIR ibn Ḥaiyān (*called* Geber), *fl.* 775.

428 Flos naturarum. [Rome: Johannes Schurener?] 2 Aug. 1473.

> *Ref:* Hain 7504; Klebs 440.1; *Thornd (HM)* V 536; *Sart* II 1044; *Taton (A&MS)* 413.
>
> *N.B:* A popular book on organo-therapeutic superstitions. Ascribed to Jābir, the alchemist, but authenticity questioned.
>
> *Mon:* DARMSTAEDTER, E. *Die Geber-Inkunabel Hain 7504* (p. 214–217 in *Archiv für Geschichte der Medizin,* XVI, 1925). KRAUS, P. *Jābir ibn Hayyān, Contribution à l'histoire des idées scientifiques en Islam.* Cairo, 1942–1943. 2 vols.
>
> *Fac:* *Osiris* 5, *fig.* 16.

JACOPO da Forlì (Giacomo della Torre; Jacobus de Forlivio; Jacobus For-liviensis), *c.* 1360–1413.

429 Expositio in Aphorismos Hippocratis. [Venice: Bartholomaeus Cre-monensis] 30 Oct. 1473. f°. [LEK]

> *Ref*: H *7247; BMC V 209; Osler (IM) 32; Klebs 546.1.
> *N.B*: At least six editions were issued before 1500. An edition printed at Venice in 1546/47 is cited in NLMCat 2565 as including the *Aphorismi* in three Latin versions by Theodoros Gaza, Nicolaus Leonicenus, and an anonymous translator.

430 Expositio in primum librum Canonis Avicennae. [Upper Italy?: Eponymous press, about 1475.]. f°. [LEK]

> *Ref*: R 1525; Osler (IM) 96; IGI 4982; Klebs 548.1; Stillwell J45; Goff J-48.
> *N.B*: A commentary on the medical section of the *Qānūn*, or *Canon*, of Abū 'Ali al-Ḥusain ibn 'Abdallah ibn Sīnā (*called* Avicenna), 980–1037, an encyclopaedia influential for nearly six centuries. The first dated edition was printed anony-mously at Venice, 21 Dec. 1479—Cen J46. Frequently found with the *Recol-lectae de urinis* of Antonius Cermisonus.

431 Scriptum super I, II, III Tegni Galeni. Padua: Joannes Herbort, 1475. [LEK]

> *Ref*: Osler (IM) 91; Klebs 547.1.
> *N.B*: Known in five editions printed at Pavia (2) and Venice (3) before 1497. The issuing of the text in the early sixteenth century, including in four instances three Latin translations of Galen's *Tegni* by Gerardus Cremonensis, Laurentianus, and Leonicenus, is noted in NLMCat 2563, 169–171.

JASME, Jean, *d.* 1384. *See no. 493 note.*

JEAN de Tournemire (Johannes de Tornamira), *fl.* 1330–1390.

432 Clarificatorium partis practice medicine super nono Almansoris cum textu Rhasis. Lyon: Johann Trechsel, 17 June 1490. 4°. [LEK]

> *Ref*: HC *15551; BMC VIII 293; BM-Fr 321; Klebs 984.1; *Sart* III 1696; Stillwell T351; Goff J-439.
> *N.B*: Believed to be a series of lectures given by the author at Montpellier on the 9th Book of the treatise dedicated by Rhasis to Almansor, the Prince of Chorosan. For editions of 1501, 1507, and 1521, see NLMCat 2587–2589.

JESU HALY. *See* 'ISA ibn 'ALĪ.

III. *Medicine*

JOANNES de Rupescissa (Juan de Peratallada; *called* Rupescissa), *fl.* 1350.

433   De consideratione quintae essentiae. (*Issued in* FERRARI, Gianmatteo, da Gradi. Consiliorum utile repertorium. Venice: Georgius Arrivabenus impensis heredum Octaviani Scoti, 1514.)   f °.   [LEK]

Ref: BM-Ital 247; *Thornd* (*HM*) V 536; *Sart* III 1572; *Wightman* (1962) I 171–174.

N.B: A "Lullified version" of Rupescissa's treatise relating largely to alchemy and the medicinal properties of alcohol. Rupescissa's claim to the founding of medical chemistry thus antedates and in some measure rivals that of Paracelsus, 1493–1541, as also does that of the alchemist, Giovanni Battista Abiosi, *c.* 1470–1523.

     Confusion evidently occurred in manuscripts and early editions between Rupescissa's original treatise and writings attributed to Raymòn Lul, *c.* 1235–1315, who is credited with having discovered the distilling process essential to producing absolute alcohol—*HTech* II 142. According to *Thorndike* (*HM*) III 355, 728, the present work is "a perversion of Rupescissa's text, combined with bits from the alchemical writings [*De secretis naturae*] ascribed to Raymond Lull," which in itself is presumably an apocryphal work. A continuation of Rupescissa's ideas on the "fifth essence" is cited in Wightman (1962) II 694, in the *Coelum philosophorum seu De secretis naturae liber* of Philip Ulstadt, printed at Strasbourg by Johann Grüninger in 1525.

Mon: THORNDIKE, Lynn. *John of Rupescissa: chemist and prophet* (p. 347–369; 725–730 in vol. III of his *History of magic*, New York, 1934). MULTHAUF, Robert P. *John of Rupescissa and the origin of medical chemistry* (p. 359–367 in *Isis* 45 1954).

JOANNITIUS (Johannitius). *See* ḤUNAIN ibn Isḥāq.

JOHANNES *Mercurius.*

434   Contra pestem ac contra omnem ipsius epidemiae perniciosissimam contagionem. [Rome: Johann Besicken, 1499–1505.]   4°.

Ref: Klebs 677.1; CPhCat (1931) 240; Stillwell J339; Goff J-378.

JUNG, Ambrosius, 1471–1548.

435   Regiment der Pestilenz [*German*].   Augsburg: Johann Schönsperger, 14 Nov. 1494.   4°.

Ref: H *9473; BM-Ger 465; Klebs 567.1; Klebs (P) 64; Schullian (ArMed) 268; Stillwell J448; Goff J-498.

N.B: On 20 Nov. 1494 the same press issued a Latin version (Cen J447). A note in NLMCat 2641 states that Jung's *Ain nutzliche trostliche und kurtze Underrichtung, wie man sich in disen schwären Leüffen der Pestilenz halten sol . . .*, printed early in the sixteenth century, has little in common with this earlier tract.

KETHAM (Johann von Kirchheim; Johannes de Ketham; *called* Ketham),
fl. 1460.

436   Fasciculus medicinae.   Venice: Joannes and Gregorius de Gregoriis,
de Forlivio, 26 July 1491.   f°.   [LEK]

> *Add*: PIETRO da Tossignano, *fl.* 1400. Consilium pro peste evitanda.
> *Ref*: H 9774; Klebs 573.1; Choulant (H) 402–405; *Choulant (Anat)* 115–122; *Garrison*
> (1929) 210–213; Stillwell K11; Goff K-13.
> *N.B*: The first medical text with realistic figures. Issued in at least eight editions within
> our period, including an Italian version in 1493 (Cen K15) and one in Spanish
> in 1494 (Klebs 575.1). As cited in Choulant, its various editions present an ac-
> cumulative compilation of medical and anatomical treatises. Among the illus-
> trations in the 1493 edition, which includes the *Anatomia* of Mondino, is one of
> the two earliest known woodcuts of a dissection, a handsome cut attributable to
> the school of Gentile Bellini, 1429–1507. [For various sixteenth-century editions
> of Ketham's works, see NLMCat p. 336–338.]
> *Fac*: SUDHOFF, Karl, and Charles SINGER, *ed. The Fasciculus medicinae of Johannes de
> Ketham, Alemannus. Facsimile of the first (Venetian) edition of 1491 with introduction
> and notes.* London, 1924 (reviewed, p. 547–549 in *Isis* 6 1924). [For other mono-
> graphs, see this entry under NATURAL SCIENCE.]

LANFRANCHI, Guido (Lanfranco; Lanfrancus Mediolanensis), *d.* 1315.

437   Chirurgia maior [*French*].   Lyon, 1479/80.]   [LEK]

> *Ref*: C 3483 [Vienne in Dauphiné, 1480]; Osler (IM) 185A; Klebs 585.1; *Sart* II 1079–
> 81; *Castiglioni* (1947) 337.
> *N.B*: A Latin text was issued with the *Chirurgia* of Guy de Chauliac, printed at Venice
> by Bonetus Locatellus, 21 Nov. 1498 (Cen G510). A French edition was issued
> at Lyon by Jean de la Fontaine in February 1490/91 (Cen L43). Issued also with
> his *Chirurgia parva* in a Spanish edition printed at Sevilla in 1495 (Schullian
> (ArMed) 276; Cen L44). The author, an Italian exile who taught at the Collège
> de St. Côme in Paris, was a thoughtful observer and a skillful surgeon of the new
> Italian school, whose techniques he introduced into France. According to
> Castiglioni, the *Chirurgia maior* was written during 1296, and the *Chirurgia parva*
> during Lanfranchi's earlier years at Lyon.

438   Chirurgia parva [*Dutch*].   Louvain: Conrad Braem, 24 Nov., 3 Dec.,
29 Nov. 1481.   4°.   [LEK]

> *Ref*: Pr 9294; BMC IX 159; Klebs 586.1; *Castiglioni* (1947) 337.
> *N.B*: Issued in Spanish with the *Chirurgia maior* and apparently also as a separate;
> printed at Sevilla by 'tres Alemanes compañeros' [Pegnitzer, Herbst, and Glock-
> ner], 15 May 1495—Schullian (ArMed) 276. Four German versions issued in
> 1528 and 1529 are listed in NLMCat 2722–2725.

III. *Medicine*

LE FOURNIER, André (Andreas Furnerius), *d.* 1533.

439 La decoration dhumaine nature et aornement des dames [*French*].
Paris: I. Sainct Denys et I. Longis, 1530. 8°. [LEK]

> *Ref*: BM-Fr 260; *Thornd (HM)* V 543.
> *N.B*: A popular book on cosmetics, printed at least three times within our period. Two
> editions assigned to 1533, printed at Paris and Lyon, are listed in NLMCat 2755
> and 2756.

LEONICENUS (Nicolò da Lonigo; *commonly called* Leonicenus, Nicolaus
Leonicenus, *or* Nicolò Leoniceno), 1428–1524.

440 De epidemia quam vulgo morbum Gallicum vocant.   Venice: Aldus
Manutius, Romanus, June 1497.   4°.   [LEK]

> *Ref*: HC *10019; BMC V 557; BM-Ital 466; Renouard (Alde) 34; Schullian (ArMed)
> 279; Klebs 599.1; *Castiglioni* (1947) 373–375; *Sudhoff-Singer* p. xxix–xxxi; Still-
> well L143; Goff L-165.
> *N.B*: An account of syphilis; by a prominent medical professor and scholar who be-
> lieved the disease was known in ancient times. He has been rated the greatest
> clinician of his time and the greatest critic, notable for his corrections of Pliny,
> his attacks on the practices of Avicenna, and other accepted texts.
> *Fac*: Sudhoff-Singer 4.

441 De Plinii et aliorum in medicina erroribus.   Ferrara: Laurentius de
Rubeis and Andreas de Grassis, 18 Dec. 1492.   4°.

> *Ref*: HC *10021; BMC VI 612; Oates 2244; Schullian (ArMed) 281; Klebs 598.1;
> *Garrison* (1929) 194–195; Stillwell L146; Goff L-168.
> *N.B*: Leonicenus here called Pliny's knowledge into question and brought upon him-
> self the condemnation of Collenuccio and other humanists, whose interests,
> however, were with letters rather than with the concerns of medical botany. For
> editions issued at Ferrara in 1509 and Basel in 1529, see NLMCat 2790, 2791.
> *Mon*: THORNDIKE, Lynn. *The attack on Pliny* (Chapter LXVI in vol. 4 of his *History of
> magic and experimental science*, New York, 1934).

MACER FLORIDUS, *pseudonym*(?).

442 Macer floridus de virtutibus herbarum carmen.   Naples: Arnaldus de
Bruxella, 9 May 1477.   f°.   [LEK]

> *Ref*: HC *10420; Osler (IM) 130; IGI 5916; Klebs 636.1; *Castiglioni* (1947) 345; *Arber*
> (1938) 44, 272; *Hunt* (*Quinby*) I 3; Stillwell M1; Goff M-1.
> *N.B*: The first printed herbal to relate solely to the medicinal properties of plants. In
> Latin hexameters describing, according to its *Incipit*, the properties of eighty-
> eight herbs. Attributed to Odo de Meung, a French physician of the eleventh

Macer Floridus (continued)

century, whose name is added to a Macer manuscript at Dresden. Issued in at least ten editions within our period. For various early sixteenth-century editions, see NLMCat 2884–2893.

MAGNINUS Mediolanensis (Mayno de' Mayneri), *d.* 1368.

443 Regimen sanitatis. Louvain: Johann de Paderborn, 1482. 4°. [LEK]

Ref: H 10483; BMC IX 141; Oates 3708; Polain 2559; Klebs 640.1; Schullian (ArMed) 292; *Sart* III 854; *Garrison* (1929) 163; Stillwell M41; Goff M-51.

N.B: A medical discourse relating among other things to hygiene with regard to age, sex, and climate, during illness, convalescence, and epidemics, and with regard to food for persons of given occupations. At least eleven editions were issued before 1550, among them an Italian version printed at Venice in 1549 (NLMCat 3046). Included in the 1504 *Opera* of Arnaldo de Villa Nova, to whom it is erroneously attributed (NLMCat 305 *note*).

MAIMONIDES, Moses (Abū 'Imrām Mūsā ibn Maimūn; Moses ben Maimon), *Rabbi*, 1135–1204.

444 Aphorismi secundum doctrinam Galeni [*with other works*]. Bologna: Franciscus (Plato) de Benedictus for Benedictus Hectoris, 29 May 1489. 4°. [LEK]

Ref: HC *10524; BMC VI 824; Klebs 644.1; Schullian (ArMed) 297; *Castiglioni* (1947) 277–278, 349; Stillwell M63; Goff M-77.

N.B: An analysis and critique of Galen's theories relative to anatomy, physiology, diagnosis, therapeutics, fevers, bloodletting, emetics, surgery, hygiene, dietetics, drugs, and so forth. (For contents, see Sart II 371–373.) Written in Arabic; translated into Hebrew and Latin. According to Sarton, the work contains 1500 aphorisms from Galen and 42 critical comments. Several works of Hippocrates and other writers are included with this first edition of Maimonides, which, however, had already been printed at an earlier date.

Mon: FRIEDENWALD, H., and D. I. MACHT. *Maimonides as physician and scientist: a tribute.* New York: Jewish Pharmaceutical Society of America, 1963 (reprinted from the *Bulletin of the History of Medicine* 3 July, 1935). BACON, S. W., ed. *Essays on Maimonides.* New York, 1941.

445 De regimine sanitatis ad Soldanum Babyloniae. Florence: Apud Sanctum Jacobum de Ripoli, [*c.* 1481]. 4°. [LEK]

Ref: HC *10525; BMC VI 623; BM-Ital 452; Osler (IM) 196; Klebs 643.1; Stillwell M66; Goff M-80.

N.B: A treatise on personal hygiene and diet, written by the court physician to Saladin, for the latter's use. Variously assigned to 1477–1481. An edition of 1518 is listed in NLMCat 3304.

Fac: FREIMANN, A. (Heidelberg, 1931.)

MANARDI, Giovanni (Joannes Manardus), 1462–1536.

446   Epistolae medicinales.   Ferrara: Bernardino de Odonino, 1521.   4°.
[LEK]

> *Ref*: NLMCat 2910; BM-Ital 407; *Sart* (*Appr*) 27, 191:96; *Castiglioni* (1947) 442.
>
> *N.B*: Frequently reprinted. NLMCat lists nine editions before 1550, at least four of
> which contain the author's *Annotationes & censura in medicamina simplicia & com-
> posita Mesue* [*i.e., De simplicibus medicamentis purgantibus* and the *Grabadin* of
> Mesuë the Younger]. Manardi, a pupil of Leonicenus, was among the first to
> oppose the authority of Galen.

MANFREDI, Girolamo di (Hieronymus de Manfredis), *d*. 1492.

447   Trattato della pestilenza [*Italian*].   [Bologna: Johannes Schriber, de
Annunciata, after 5 Dec. 1478.]   4°.

> *Ref*: HR 10694; BMC VI 818; BM-Ital 409; IGI 6119; Klebs 655.1; Klebs (P) 71;
> Osler (IM) 151; Stillwell M170; Goff M-197.
>
> *N.B*: An undated Latin version is assigned to the press of Johannes Walbeck at Bologna,
> after 31 Dec. 1479 (Cen M169). For early sixteenth-century editions of Manfredi's
> works, see NLMCat p. 374.

MARSIGLIO da Santa Sofia (Marsilius de Sancta Sophia), *c*. 1367–1405?

448   Expositio in particulam tertiam et septimam Aphorismorum Hippocratis. (*Issued with* JACOPO da Forlì, *c*. 1360–1413. In Aphorismos Hippocratis expositio.   [Padua: Anonymous printer, not after 1480]   f°.
[LEK]

> *Ref*: H *7246; BMC V 209; IGI 4979; Osler (IM) 97; Klebs 546.3; Stillwell J41;
> Goff J-44.
>
> *N.B*: Assigned by IGI to the press of Johann Herbort at Padua about 1477, who
> according to IGI 6201 also issued the *Expositio* as a separate, *c*. 1477. Re-issued
> in subsequent editions of Jacopo da Forlì (Cen J42–J44; NLMCat 1956, 2378–
> 80, 2565), but according to Klebs not included in the editions of 1473 and 1477.
> For various sixteenth-century editions of Marsiglio's *Tractatus de febribus*, see
> NLMCat p. 379.

MASSA, Nicolò, *d*. 1569.

449   Liber de morbo gallico.   Venice: Francesco Bindoni and Maffeo Pasini,
1536.   4°.   [LEK]

> *Ref*: BM-Ital 424.
>
> *N.B*: Included also in the collection called *Morbi gallici curandi ratio*, printed at Basel in
> 1536, and at Lyon in August of the same year—Fisch (Pol) Y15, C40. [For an
> appraisal of Massa as a man in the forefront of his time, see WIGHTMAN, W. P. D.

Massa (continued)

>> *Science and the Renaissance.* Edinburgh, 1962, vol. I, p. 231–234. For various six-teenth-century editions of Massa's works, see NLMCat p. 381–383.]

MATTIOLI, Pierandrea, 1500–1577.

450 Di Pedacio Dioscoride Anazarbeo libri cinque Della historia et materia medicinale tradotti in lingua volgare Italiana . . . Venice: Nicolò de Bascarini, 1544. f°. [LEK]

>> *Ref*: NLMCat 1160; *Arber* (1938) 276; *Garrison* (1929) 231; *Castiglioni* (1947) 485; *Sart (Appr)* 75–77.
>>
>> *N.B*: An Italian translation and commentary on the five books of the *De materia medica* of Dioskorides, a work first printed (in Latin) at Colle in 1478 [see no. 354]. Mattioli's Italian version and commentary were again printed at Venice in 1548, with a so-called "sixth book" comprising translations of the *De venenis* and *De venenatis animalibus* frequently found appended to Dioskorides's text (Hunt (Quinby) I 59; NLMCat 1162); and re-issued in 1550 (NLMCat 1163). A Mantua edition appeared in 1549, under the title *Il Dioskoride. Con l'aggionta del sesto libro* (BM-Ital 218). [A Latin version of the commentary, which Castiglioni describes as an encyclopaedia of Renaissance pharmacology, was printed with the Dioskorides text, by Vincenzo Valgrisi at Venice in 1554 (NLMCat 3008).] According to Garrison, Mattioli introduced between two and three hundred new plant species from southern Europe. The printing of editions revised and enlarged continued into the seventeenth century.

MESUË *the Elder. See* YŪḤANNĀ ibn MASAWAIH *the Elder, c.* 777–857.

MESUË *the Younger. See* YŪḤANNĀ ibn MASAWAIH al-Mārdīnī, *d.* 1015.

METHODIUS, *St., fl.* 300.

451 Revelationes divinae a sanctis angelis factae (Ed: Sebastian Brandt). Basel: Michael Furter, 5 Jan. 1498. 4°. [LEK]

>> *Ref*: HC *11121; BMC III 785; Oates 2833; Polain 2682; Stillwell M453; Goff M-524.
>>
>> *N.B*: Although not cited as in the edition published in 1496, according to Poynter 384 the Basel edition issued by Michael Furter on 5 Jan. 1498 contains 60 woodcut illustrations, one showing a plague scene and another the birth of Antichrist by Caesarean section.

METLINGER, Bartholomaeus, *d.* 1491/2.

452 Ein Regiment der jungen Kinder [*German*]. [Augsburg: Günther Zainer, after 7 Dec. 1473.] f°. [LEK]

Ref: HC 11127; BMC II 321; Schullian (ArMed) 322; Klebs 682.1; *Garrison* (1929) 198; Stillwell M456; Goff M-527.

N.B: The second book on pediatrics to be printed, the first being the *De aegritudinibus infantium* by Paolo Bagellardo [*q.v.*]. A household manual of which few copies are extant. The assigned date is derived from a statement at the end of the volume. The tract is listed as no. 15 in Zainer's first advertisement. Printed at Augsburg in at least five editions before the turn of the century (Klebs 682.1–5), and again in 1511 (NLMCat 3153).

Fac: Titlepage reproduced in Castiglioni (1947) 491.

MICHAEL *Scotus* (Michael *the Scot*; Michael Scott; Michel Lescot; *frequently called* Scotus), *c.* 1180–1235.

453 Liber phisiognomiae sive De secretis naturae. [Venice: Jacobus de Fivizano, Lunensis] 1477. 4°. [LEK]

Ref: HC *14550; BMC V 242; BM-Ital 619; IGI 6417; Klebs 899.1; Schullian (ArMed) 435; *Thornd (HM)* II 328–331; *Crombie (A–G)* 1961 I 225; Stillwell M480; Goff M-551.

N.B: Scotus is known mainly as an astrologer, an exponent of Averroism, and a translator from the Arabic. The present work includes a treatise *De urinis*; it also relates to generation and in later chapters to physiognomy, the determining of character from a study of various parts of the body. Dr. Klebs lists twenty Latin editions in the fifteenth century and NLMCat five in the early sixteenth century. A Spanish version was issued with Ketham's *Fasciculus medicinae*, Saragossa, 1494, and an Italian version is known to have been printed at Venice in 1533 and again in 1537 and 1540. A French version printed at [Paris] in 1540 is listed in NLMCat 4165.

Mon: HASKINS, Charles H. *Michael Scot* (p. 272–298 in his *Studies in the history of mediaeval science*. Cambridge [Mass.], 1927). THORNDIKE, Lynn. *Michael Scot*. London, 1965.

MONDINO (Raimondo de' Luzzi; Mundinus), *c.* 1275–1326.

454 Expositio super canones universales. (*Issued in vol. III of* YŪḤANNĀ ibn Masawaih al-Mārdīnī. Opera medicinalia. Venice: Peregrinus de Pasqualibus, I) 21 Nov. 1490; II) 2 Dec. 1489; III) 18 July 1491. f°. [LEK]

Ref: H *11110; BMC V 391; Klebs 680.13; Stillwell M444; Goff M-515.

N.B: A commentary on the *Canones universales*, one of the treatises included in the third volume of the *Opera*. Relates to some extent to the use and preparation of drugs and the value of herbs. [For further references to Mondino, see under NATURAL SCIENCE.]

Mon: WELBORN, Mary Catherine. *Mondino de' Luzzi's commentary on the Canones generales of Mesuë the Younger* (p. 8–11 in *Isis* 22 1934).

MONTAGNANA, Bartolomeo, *fl.* 1430–1470.

455 Consilia medica (Ed: Jacobus de Vitalibus). [Padua:] Petrus Maufer,
4 May 1476. f°. [LEK]

> *Ref:* HR 11551; Osler (IM) 111; IGI 6698; Klebs 689.1; Stillwell M700; Goff M-813.
> *N.B:* The first printed record giving the condition of a physician's patients and the
> treatment or diet prescribed. IGI 6697 assigns an anonymously printed edition
> to Lorenzo Conozio at Padua, 1472–1475. Cited in two compilations printed at
> Venice in 1514 and at Lyon in 1525 (NLMCat 3234, 3235). Goff M-813—M-816
> cites five fifteenth-century editions including that of 4 May 1476.

MONTE, Giovanni Battista da (Joannes Baptista Montanus), 1498–1552.

456 Typus trium librorum Artis parvae Galeni. Venice: Apud Iuntas
[1546]. f°.

> *Ref:* NLMCat 3281; BM-Ital 445; *Sart (Appr)* 31; *Castiglioni* (1947) 442, 451; *Wight-
> man* (1962) I 222.
> *N.B:* Written by an outstanding physician who reverted to and restored the bedside,
> clinical method of Hippocrates in the study of disease. Various works developing
> this theme and also his interest in melancholia and psychiatry were issued in the
> 1550s. During his travels Monte made a point of searching for manuscripts of
> Hippocrates and other early medical texts. [See also under CAIUS, *no.* 323.]

MONTESAURO, Natale, *fl.* 1495.

457 De dispositionibus quas vulgares mal franzoso appellant. [Bologna:
Giustiniano de Ruberia, 1497?] 4°.

> *Ref:* R 1284; BMC VI 850; BM-Ital 447; Klebs 691.1; *Sudhoff-Singer* p. xliv.
> *N.B:* Contains an identifiable description of the bone pains, *dolores osteocopi*, incident
> to syphilis. IGI 6728 assigns this to "prima del marzo 1498."
> *Fac:* SUDHOFF-SINGER 9.

MONTIS, Petrus de (Pietro Monti), *fl.* 1490.

458 De dignoscendis hominibus. Milan: Antonius Zarotus, 17 Dec. 1492.
f°.

> *Ref:* HC *11608; BMC VI 722; BM-Ital 447; Poynter 390; IGI 6731; Schullian
> (ArMed) 331; Stillwell M736; Goff M-857.
> *N.B:* Translated from the Spanish of Gundisalvus Ayora. Contains sections on exer-
> cise and games for keeping physically fit. His *Exercitiorum atque artis militaris col-
> lectanea* was issued at Milan by Scinzenzeler in 1509 (BM-Ital 447).

III. *Medicine*

MUSA, Antonius, *1st century* B.C., *spurious.*

459   De herba betonica. (*Issued in* THORER, Alban, 1489–1550. *ed.* Collectio. Basel: Andreas Cratander, August 1528.)   f°.

> *Ref:* NLMCat 4351; Choulant (H) 214–215; Sart I 231.
>
> *N.B:* Relates to the medicinal properties of veronica. Also printed in 1537 with the *Herbarium* of Apuleius Barbarus—*Hunt (Quinby)* I 40—and in the Aldine *Collectio* printed at Venice in 1547. Authenticity questioned.

NICANDROS (Nicander), *variously assigned to the 2nd or 3rd century B.C.*

460   Theriaca. Alexipharmaca [*Greek*]. (*Issued with* DIOSKORIDES. De materia medica [*Greek*]. Venice: apud Aldum Manutium, July 1499.)   f°. [LEK]

> *Ref:* GW 8435; HC *6257; BMC V 560; Klebs 343.1; Renouard (Alde) 49; Choulant (H) 62–65; Schullian (ArMed) 333; Sart I 158, 159; Stillwell D216; Goff D-260.
>
> *N.B:* Two poems, one dealing with poisonous animals and antidotes for the effects of their venom; the other, with twenty-one poisons and their remedies, involving the medicinal use of about 125 plants. Issued as a separate at Venice in 1523; in Greek-and-Latin at Cologne in 1530–1531 and Paris in 1549 (NLMCat p. 427–428). Choulant lists a Latin translation in prose printed at Cologne in 1531; another in hexameters by Euricius Cordus, printed at Frankfurt in 1532, and included in his poetical works published in Frankfurt in 1550. Included in editions of Dioskorides—see no. 354*n.*

NICOLAUS *Salernitanus (called* Praepositus).

461   Antidotarium Nicolai.   Venice: Nicolaus Jenson, 1471.   4°.   [LEK]

> *Ref:* HR 11764; BMC V 170; IGI 6855; Klebs 703.1; Schullian (ArMed) 334; Sart II 239; *Garrison* (1929) 150, 153; *Castiglioni* (1947) 304; Stillwell N139; Goff N-160.
>
> *N.B:* The earliest printed pharmacopoeia. Known in 13th- and 14th-century manuscripts; possibly of earlier origin. Comprises nearly 150 prescriptions alphabetically arranged and including an early formula for the *spongia somnifera* to induce anesthesia and mention of various Eastern drugs. Contains also a section on substitutes, *Quid pro quo,* and one of *Synonyma.* Written by a physician unknown except through this volume. Based on the Salernitan formulary. Klebs 703.2–.6 lists five editions printed at or assigned to Rome, Naples, Pavia, Milan, and Strasbourg before 1485. NLMCat col. 3345 notes the inclusion of the text in eleven compilations printed between 1502 and 1550.
>
> *Mon:* CHOULANT, L. *Nicolaus Praepositus* (p. 282–391 in his *Handbuch der Bücherkunde für die ältere Medizin.* Graz, 1956—Leipzig, 1841, reprint). SIGERIST, Henry E. *Studien und Texte zur frühmittelalterlichen Rezeptliteratur.* Leipzig, 1923 (Stud. z.

143

Nicolaus Salernitanus (continued)

> Gesch. d. Med. *Heft* 13).   HELD, F. H. *Nicolaus Salernitanus and Nikolaos Myre-*
> *psos.* Leipzig, 1916.   KRISTELLER, P. O. *The school of Salerno, its development and*
> *its contribution to the history of learning* (Institute of the History of Medicine. *Bulletin,*
> 17:2 1945).

ODO de Meung, *11th century. See under* MACER FLORIDUS.

OREIBASIOS (Oribasius), 325–403.

462   Commentaria in Aphorismos Hippocratis (Tr: Johann Günther, 1505–
1574).   Paris: Simon de Colines, 1533.   8°.   [LEK]

> *Ref:* NLMCat 3407; BM-Fr 226; Renouard (Colines) 217; *Sart (Appr)* 34–36; *Cas-*
> *tiglioni* (1947) 250; O'Leary 34.
> *N.B:* Printed also in 1533 at Venice; and in 1535 at Basel (NLMCat 3408, 3409).
> *Mon:* MØRLAND, H. *Die lateinischen Oribasius Übersetzungen* (Symbolae Osloenses.
> Fasc., Suppl., V. Oslo, 1932).

463   Euporista (Tr: Johannes Sichardt, *c.* 1499–1552).   Basel: Hieronymus
Petri, 1529.

> *Ref:* *Sart (Appr)* 35; *Castiglioni* (1947) 251; *Taton (A&MS)* 365.
> *N.B:* A manual for the traveller, with practical advice in case of illness or accident.
> NLMCat 2307 *note* identifies the second book of the *Euporista* as in the com-
> pilation of 1533, listed below under no. 464.

464   De simplicibus libri V. (*Issued with* HILDEGARD of Bingen, *Saint, 1098–*
1180.   *Physica.*   Strasbourg: Johann Schott, 1533).

> *Ref:* NLMCat 2307; Choulant (H) 121, 308; *Hunt (Quinby)* I 32.
> *N.B:* Said to be derived largely from the treatise *De simplicium medicamentorum facul-*
> *tatibus* of Galen, for the transmission of whose works Oreibasios was in large part
> responsible. NLMCat in a note accompanying no. 2307, however, identifies the
> work as follows: "Of the five books allegedly by Oribasius, only book 4 contains
> the second book of his *Euporista*; books 1–3 are excerpted from Apuleius' *De*
> *herbis* and the so-called *Dynamidia Hippocratis*, while book 5 is an alphabetical
> reworking of material from Dioscorides."

465   De victus ratione fragmentum. (*Issued in* THORER, Alban, 1489–1550,
ed. Collectio.   Basel: Andreas Cratander, August 1528.)   f°.

> *Ref:* NLMCat 4351*n*; Choulant (H) 122, 405.
> *N.B:* Included with the fragment are two items, the *De virtute vini* and the *De veneriis*
> *actibus*, identified as apparently chapters 10, 12, and 13 of Book I of the author's
> *Euporista.*

ORTOLFF von Bayrlandt (Ortolff of Bavaria).

466 Arzneibuch [*German*]. Nuremberg: Anton Koberger, 17 Mar. 1477.
f°. [LEK]

> *Ref*: H *12112; BMC II 414; BM-Ger 664; Klebs 715.2; Schullian (ArMed) 340;
> Stillwell O102; Goff O-110.
>
> *N.B*: A popular manual, an unsigned edition of which is assigned to Augsburg about
> 1477 (Klebs 715.1; Cen O101). Re-issued at Augsburg in 1479 and 1488. His
> manual for pregnant women—*Büchlein der schwangeren Frauen*—is assigned to
> Augsburg about 1495 (Cen O104), a facsimile of which edited by Gustav Klein,
> was issued at Munich in 1910. The *Arstedyge boek* of 1483, variously attributed to
> Ortolff, is treated in BMC II 595 as a Low-Saxon version of the *Herbarius* (Cen
> O100).

PARACELSUS (Philippus Aureolus Theophrastus Bombastus Paracelsus von
Hohenheim; *variously called* Paracelsus, Theophrastus, *or* Bombast), 1493–
1541.

467 Grosse Wund Artzney ... [*German*]. Ulm: Hans Varnier, 1536. f°.
[LEK]

> *Ref*: NLMCat 3447; Sudhoff (BiblP) 14; *Castiglioni* (1947) 444–450.
>
> *N.B*: Printed by Heinrich Steiner in two editions at Augsburg in 1536 and twice again
> in 1537. Written by an eccentric but brilliant physician and chemist, a contro-
> versial figure frequently rated as the founder of medical chemistry and pharma-
> cology. [See also, above under Abiosi and Joannes de Rupescissa.] The purpose
> of chemistry, so Paracelsus believed, was the purification of chemical substances
> for medicinal use. The majority of his texts were printed after 1550. He was
> a prolific writer, his interests including theology, religio-philosophy, astronomy,
> and magic as well as medicine, biology, chemistry, and natural philosophy. The
> works of medical and scientific interest and those relating to magic and philoso-
> phy comprise fourteen volumes—i.e., part I of the *Sämtliche Werke* edited by Dr.
> Karl Sudhoff and published at Munich, 1922–1933; re-issued in 1960 with an
> important index by Dr. Martin Müller. The printing of the theological and
> religio-philosophical works as started in 1955 and several recent monographs on
> Paracelsus are reviewed by Dr. Walter Pagel (p. 527–530 in *Isis* 53 1962).
>
> *Mon*: SUDHOFF, K. *Bibliographia Paracelsus*, Berlin, 1894 (Vol. I of *Versuch einer Kritik
> der Echtheit der Paracelsischen Schriften*); *Sämtliche Werke* ... [Paracelsus], Munich,
> 1922–1933; *Nachweise zur Paracelsus-Literatur*, Munich, 1932. WEIMANN, K.-H.
> Paracelsus-Bibliographie, 1932–1960, Wiesbaden, 1963. PACHTER, H. M. *Para-
> celsus, magic into science*, New York, 1951. MULTHAUF, R. *Medical chemistry and
> the "Paracelsians"* (Bulletin of the History of Medicine, 28 1954). PAGEL, W. *Para-
> celsus, selected writings*. J. Jacobi, ed., New York, 1951; *Paracelsus—an introduction
> to the philosophical medicine in the era of the Renaissance*, Basel, 1958; *Das medizinische
> Weltbild des Paracelsus ...*, Wiesbaden, 1962 (*Kosmosophie*, Bd. I), reviewed, p.
> 239–240 in *Isis* 55 1964. THEOPHRAST VON HOHENHEIM [Paracelsus]. *Sämtliche*

Paracelsus (continued)

> *Werke. Erste Abteilung: Medizinische, naturwissenschaftliche und philosophische Schriften . . . Registerband . . . von Martin Müller, . . . Supplementum.* Einsiedeln, [1960].
>
> *Fac:* CASTIGLIONI (1947) 447, 449.

468   . . . Vom Holz Guaiaco gründlicher heylung . . . [*German*].   Nuremberg: Friderich Peypus, 1529.   4°.   8 ff. (the last blank).

> *Ref:* BM-Ger 139 [19]; Sudhoff (BiblP) 1; *Wightman* (1962) I 255.
> *N.B:* A tract on treatments for syphilis, discussing the uses of guaiac and mercury, recognizing both the efficacy and the dangers of the latter. The title is introduced by the phrase: Durch den hochgelerten herren Theophrastum von Hochenheym beyder Artzeney Doctoren. A longer tract, *Von der Frantzösischen kranckheit Drey Bücher*, issued by the same press in 1530, contains sections beginning: Das Erst von der impostur der Artzney . . .; Das Ander vom corrigiren der selbigen . . .; Das Dritt von den verderbtē kranckheiten . . .—Sudhoff (BiblP) 7.
> *Mon:* ACHELIS, J. D. *Die Syphilisschriften Theophrasts von Hohenheim.* Heidelberg, 1939.

469   Vonn den Bad Pfeffers in Oberschwytz gelegen . . . [*German*].   Zurich: Anonymous printer, 1535.]   4°.

> *Ref:* Sudhoff (BiblP) 13.

470   Wundt vnnd Leibartznei . . . Wes iedem Wundartzt der Theoric vnd Practick zuwissen von noten, die gantze Chirurgie belangend . . . Dabei Von aussziehung der fünfften Wesenheit, Quinta Essentia, Auss bewerten stucken der Artznei, Zu wunderbarer Heylung leiblicher gebrechen, Durch verborgene Natürliche krafft derselbigenn, Raimundus Lullius . . . [*German*].   Frankfort-am-Main: Christian Egenolff, 1549.   4°.

> *Ref:* NLMCat 3449; Sudhoff (BiblP) 24.

PARÉ, Ambroise, 1510–1590.

471   La methode de traicter les playes faictes par hacquebutes et aultres bastons à feu [*French*].   Paris: Vivant Gaulterot, 1545.   8°.   [LEK]

> *Ref:* BM-Fr 337; *Garrison* (1929) 224–226; *Castiglioni* (1947) 474–479.
> *N.B:* A manual on the treatment of gunshot and other wounds, which from experience as an army surgeon Paré had learned were not necessarily poisonous and need not be treated with boiling oil—a discovery which he made when the supply of oil became exhausted and he tried other methods with greater success. His essay on obstetrics was printed at Paris in 1549 and his treatise on surgery, some years after our period. Paré has been ranked as the greatest surgeon of his century.
> *Mon:* SINGER, D. W. *Selections from the works of Ambroise Paré.* London, 1924. SIGERIST, H. E. *Ambroise Paré* (p. 130–137 in his *The great doctors, a biographical history*

of medicine. New York, 1933.   DOE, Janet. *A bibliography of the works of Ambroise Paré.* Chicago, 1937.   HAMBY, Wallace B., ed. *The case reports and autopsy records of Ambroise Paré. Translated from J. P. Malgaigne's "Oeuvres complètes d'Ambroise Paré . . ."* Springfield, Ill., 1960.

PAULOS of Aigina, *fl.* 640.

472   Opera [*Greek*].   Venice: In aedibus Aldi et Andreae Asulani, August 1528.   f°.   [LEK]

> *Ref*: NLMCat 3547; BM-Ital 494; Choulant (H) 142; Renouard (Alde) 251; *Sart (Appr)* 38; *Castiglioni* (1947) 253–255; *Garrison* (1929) 124; *O'Leary* 35.
>
> *N.B*: Also known as the *De re medica libri VII.* The only surviving work of a Byzantine physician, who lived in Alexandria during or directly after the Muslim invasion, and through this medical encyclopaedia came to have great influence upon Arabic medicine. According to Castiglioni's analysis, its seven Books treat of: I) dietetic hygiene; II) pathology; III) diseases of the head; IV) leprosy, skin diseases, *etc.*; V) poisons; VI) surgery; VII) pharmacology. Garrison emphasizes the fact that Paulos summarizes all that was known of pediatrics and obstetrics from classical antiquity, and indeed until the Renaissance. Re-issued in Greek at Basel in 1538, as collated and revised by Hieronymus Gemusaeus (NLMCat 3548). Textual notes supporting this edition were issued by Gemusaeus in 1543 (NLMCat 2044.) An English translation with commentary by Francis Adams was published by the Sydenham Society at London, 1844–1847.

473   Opera (Tr: Johann Günther, 1505–1574).   Paris: Simon de Colines, 1532.   4°.   [LEK]

> *Ref*: NLMCat 3551; Choulant (H) 142; Renouard (Colines) 251.
>
> *N.B*: Also known as the *Opus de re medica.* Another translation, issued at Basel by Cratander and Bebelius in 1532, was made by Albanus Torinus (Alban Thorer) from the Greek *Opera* of 1528—its sixth Book, an influential treatise on surgery, being omitted but issued as a separate at Basel in 1533 [*see no.* 474]. Issued in at least seven Latin editions and two in Greek, within our period. Separates are known for its various Books, as I) Paris, 1510; II) Cologne, 1546; VI) Basel, 1533; VII) Strasbourg, 1531—these, together with their subsequent printings, totaling eleven editions. At least three commentaries were issued before 1544. [See Choulant (H) p. 143–144 and NLMCat p. 454–455.]
>
> Paulos's writings were apparently looked upon with great respect. Not only did some of the leading publishing-houses in Venice, Paris, Basel, Strasbourg, Nuremberg, Cologne, Frankfurt, and Lyon print editions of this work or its separate sections, but leading scholars, many of them of our period, produced translations or edited the text in its numerous editions. Among these one finds Torinus, Günther, Linacre, Cornarius, Erasmus, Copus, Feliciano, Tolet, Dodoens, and Brunfels. The extreme practicality of the text and its consequent use doubtless accounts for its rarity today. Its section on surgery, Book VI, has been called the principal medical work of the Byzantine era. According to Gar-

Paulos of Aigina (continued)

rison (1929) 203, the visor-mask [later called stenopeic spectacles] recommended by Paulos for use in strabismus or squint, is mentioned in the Basel edition of 1546, lib. III, cap. 22, 182 (NLMCat 3556).

474 De chirurgia liber (Tr: Bernardo Feliciano). Castigationes praeterea Albani Torini in suam Aeginetae tralationem. Basel: [Andreas Cratander et Joannes Bebelius] 1533. f°.

Ref: NLMCat 3566; Choulant (H) 143; *Castiglioni* (1947) 254.

N.B: The sixth Book of the author's *De re medica*, which had been omitted in the translation of Albanus Torinus published by Cratander and Bebelius in 1532. Torinus's corrections to his translation of Books 1–5 and 7, as called for in the title, occupy five pages at the end of the volume. A French version is included in a compilation issued by Estienne Dolet at Lyon in 1540; also issued at Paris in 1540 by Arnould and Charles Les Angeliers (NLMCat 3567, 3568).

475 Praecepta salubria sive De tuenda valetudine (Tr: Guilelmus Copus). Paris: Henri Estienne, 4 April 1510. 4°. [LEK]

Ref: NLMCat 3569; Choulant (H) 143; Renouard (Estienne) 8.

N.B: The first Book of the author's *De re medica*. The earliest 16th-century printing of any of his works found in the present survey. Re-issued at Strasbourg in 1511, at Paris in 1512 and 1527, and at Nuremberg in 1525. Also published in part at Strasbourg in 1531, together with part of Book VII—the *Pharmaca simplicia*, in the translation of Otto Brunfels. [*See* NLMCat 3569–73, 3565.]

PETRARCA, Francesco, 1304–1374.

476 De remediis utriusque fortunae. [Esslingen: Conrad Fyner, 1475?] f°. [LEK]

Ref: HC *12790; BMC II 514; BM-Ger 685; Oates 1146; IGI 7576; Stillwell P361; Goff P-407.

N.B: Variously assigned to Strasbourg and the press of Heinrich Eggestein. Considers good and bad fortune; contains a plea for public libraries as against private collections, and "Dialogi" on such topics as bodily illness, memory, alchemy, sterility, old age, fevers, poisons, toothache, and deafness, *De auditu perdito*. Issued also at Heidelberg about 1490 and at Cremona in 1492 (Goff P-408, P-409); and included in the Opera printed at Venice in 1501 (NLMCat 3600).

PFERDEARZNEI-BÜCHLEIN.

477 Pferdearznei-Büchlein [*German*]. Erfurt: Hans Spörer, 1500.

Ref: GW 5679; C 4729; Klebs 756.1; LC (LJRCat) 186.

N.B: A manual on horse-physic. Also known as *Büchlein von bewährter Arznei der Pferde*.

PIETRO d'Abano (Abano, Petrus de; Petrus Aponensis; *called* Petrus Conciliator), 1250– *c.* 1315.

478 Conciliator differentiarum philosophorum et praecipue medicorum. Mantua: Johannes Vurster and Thomas Septemcastrensis, 1472. f°. [LEK]

> *Ref*: H *1; BMC VII 929; Osler (IM) 24; Klebs 773.1; *Sart* III 439; *Castiglioni* (1947) 330–332; Stillwell P387; Goff P-431.
>
> *N.B*: Consists of some two hundred questions on which the opinions of Greek, Latin, Arabic, and Jewish writers are discussed in an effort to organize and harmonize their thought. Although the questions are not confined to medicine, the main themes are medical or astrological. Thornd (HM) II 919 mentions an edition printed at Venice by Octavianus Scotus in 1471, not found in the present survey. Klebs 773 lists six fifteenth-century editions, and Sart III 440 notes thirteen of the sixteenth century. NLMCat 1–4 lists editions of 1520, 1521, 1523, and 1548.
>
> The present volume contains the first known printing of *De venenis*, the author's treatise on poisons.
>
> *Mon*: THORNDIKE, Lynn. *Peter of Abano* (p. 874–947 in vol. II of his *History of magic and experimental science*, New York, 1923). SIGERIST, H. E. *Pietro d'Abano* (p. 95–99 in his *The great doctors, a biographical history of medicine*. Translated by E. and C. Paul. New York, 1933).

479 De lapide bezoar ex Pandectis. (*Issued with* ARNALDO de Villa Nova. De arte cognoscendi venena. Mantua [Johannes Vurster and Johannes Baumeister] 1473.) 4°. [LEK]

> *Ref*: GW 2522; HC *7+*1805; BMC VII 929; Oates 2583; IGI 861; Osler (IM)41; Klebs 98.1+774.1; Stillwell A953; Goff A-1067.
>
> *N.B*: Discusses the use of bezoar stones as antidotes for poison. Also issued in the edition printed at Padua in 1473 (Cen A952).

480 De venenis eorumque remediis. (*Issued with his* Conciliator. Mantua: Johannes Vurster and Thomas Septemcastrensis, 1472.) f°. [LEK]

> *Ref*: H *1; BMC VII 929; Klebs 773.1; *Sart* III 442, 445; Stillwell P387; Goff P-431.
>
> *N.B*: The first printing of this treatise on poisons and their antidotes, the latter including folk methods, astrology, and medical practice. Issued at Padua and Mantua in 1473 (Schullian ArMed) 361, 362; Cen A952, A953), each edition usually including also the *De arte cognoscendi venena* of Arnaldo de Villa Nova and the *De epidemia et peste* of Valasco de Taranta. Klebs 774 lists ten fifteenth-century editions beginning with 1473.

PIETRO d'Argellata (Petrus de Azzelata), *d.* 1423.

481 Chirurgia, libri VI (Ed: Matthaeus Moretus). Venice: Benedictus Genuensis, 9 Aug. 1480. f°. [LEK]

Pietro d'Argellata (continued)

> *Ref*: GW 2321; BM-Ital 37; IGI 783; Pell 1161; Klebs 777.1; *Thornd (HM)* IV 132–134; *Sart* III 1195; *Garrison* (1929) 158; Stillwell A850; Goff A-951.
>
> *N.B*: A series of lectures at Bologna on Avicenna. Describes a post-mortem examination of Pope Alexander V made by the author in 1410. [The earliest known account of a post-mortem is in 1302—Crombie (A–G) 1961 I 169.] An edition of the *Chirurgia* printed at Venice in 1531 is listed in NLMCat 258.

PIETRO da Tossignano (Petrus Albergheti de Curialtis, de Tussignano), *fl.* 1375.

482   Consilium pro peste evitanda.   [Venice: Anonymous printer, 1470–1480.]   4°.   [LEK]

> *Ref*: H*15750; BMC VII 1143; Osler (IM) 208; Klebs 778.1; Klebs (P) 109; Schullian (ArMed) 366; *Castiglioni* (1947) 358; *Sart* III 1682; Stillwell P491; Goff P-536.
>
> *N.B*: A treatise on the prevention of plagues apropos of the plague of 1397, and relating also to paralysis, apoplexy, and epilepsy. Issued in the 1491 Venice edition of Ketham's *Fasciculus medicinae* and in its subsequent editions in Latin and Italian —*see* NLMCat 2659–60, 2667–68.
>
> *Mon*: MAZZINI, Giuseppe. *Vita e opera di Maestro Pietro da Tossignano*. Rome, 1926.

483   De regimine sanitatis.   Paris: Christien Wechel, 1535.   8°.   [LEK]

> *Ref*: NLMCat 3650; BM-Fr 430; *Sart* III 1681–84.
>
> *N.B*: A treatise on hygiene and dietetic rules including such "modern" ideas as the need of pure air; of not eating to satiety; of full mastication; the avoidance of anger, sadness, and fear; the changing of diet according to season; and the allowing of time for such enjoyments as music and the reading of history. Pietro da Tossignano also wrote a textbook of therapeutics, *Receptae super nonum ad Almansorem*, in which he added medical receipts to those of Rhasis (Cen R176), and which after its initial publication at Venice in 1483 ran through various fifteenth- and sixteenth-century editions. NLMCat 4293 lists an edition printed at Venice in 1518, containing the commentary *Super nono Almansoris* by Syllanus de Nigris.

PISTORIS, Simon, 1453–1523.

484   Declaratio defensiva cuiusdam positionis de malo franco.   [Leipzig: Conrad Kachelofen, after 3 Jan. 1500.]   4°.

> *Ref*: NLMCat 3669; HC(Add) *13021; BMC III 629; BM-Ger 699; Klebs 781.1; Schullian (ArMed) 367; *Sudhoff-Singer* p. ix; Stillwell P596; Goff P-653.
>
> *N.B*: A controversial work on the nature and origin of syphilis, which called forth from Martin Pollich, *c.* 1450–1513, a tract entitled *Responsio . . . in superadditos errores Simonis Pistoris*, assigned to Leipzig, 1501 (NLMCat 3702). According to a note accompanying this reference, the controversy is discussed in FUCHS, C. H.,

ed. Die ältesten Schriftsteller über die Lustseuche in Deutschland, von 1492 bis 1510 . . .
Göttingen, 1843, p. 127–288; and SUDHOFF, K. *Die medizinische Fakultät zu
Leipzig . . .* Leipzig, 1909, p. 136 ff.

PLATINA (Bartolomeo de' Sacchi, di Piadena; Bartholomaeus Sacchi, de Platina; *called* Platina), 1421–1481.

485 De honesta voluptate et valetudine. [Rome: Ulrich Han, *c.* 1475.]
4°. [LEK]

> *Ref*: HC(Add)R 13049; Pr 3380; IGI 7847; Schullian (ArMed) 368; Klebs 783.1;
> *Garrison* (1929) 208; Stillwell P692; Goff P-761.
> *N.B*: Garrison describes this as the first printed book on dietetics. It has also been
> described as a cookbook with a gourmet's touch. A dated edition was issued at
> Venice on 13 June 1475 (Cen P693). IGI 7848 lists an unsigned edition printed
> at Venice and bearing the same date. At least eight editions were printed in the
> fifteenth century, two of them in Italian. NLMCat p. 473 records four issues and
> a German translation printed during 1517–41, a Latin edition issued at [Paris] in
> 1530 having the descriptive title, *De honesta voluptate. De ratione victus & modo
> vivendi. De natura rerum & arte coquendi libri X.* The author was Papal Secretary
> and Librarian under Pope Sixtus IV.

PLATO, *c.* 423–347 B.C.

486 Opera (Tr: Marsilio Ficino, 1433–1499). Florence: Laurentius de
Alopa [May 1484; before April 1485]. f°. [LEK]

> *Ref*: HC *13062; BMC VI 666; Oates 2436; IGI 7860; Klebs 785.1; Stillwell P702;
> Goff P-771.
> *N.B*: A Greek edition was issued at Venice at the Aldine press in Sept. 1513—BM-Ital
> 524; Renouard (Alde) 148.
> *Mon*: OSLER, *Sir* William. *Physic and physicians as depicted in Plato* (p. 129–133, 153–156
> in *Boston Medical and Surgical Journal* vol. 128 1893).

PLINY *the Elder* (Plinius Secundus, Caius), 23–79 A.D.

487 Historia naturalis, libri XXXVII. Venice: Johann von Speier, [before
18 September] 1469. f°. [LEK]

> *Ref*: HC(+Add)R 13087; BMC V 153; BM-Ital 526; Choulant (H) 181–206; IGI
> 7878; Klebs 786.1; Horblit 84; LC(LJRCat) 192; *Wightman* (1962) I 188; Still-
> well P716; Goff P-786.
> *N.B*: An encyclopaedia on natural history. One of the great source books of antiquity.
> In 37 Books, of which Books 20–32 relate to drugs, medicinal herbs, and medical
> practices in Roman times. At least forty-six editions were printed within our
> period. Issued in Italian by Nicolaus Jenson at Venice in 1476. The medical
> sections, *De re medica libri V,* appeared in the 1528 *Collectio* of Alban Thorer
> (NLMCat 4351). Fourteen centuries after Pliny's time, his text was critically

Pliny (continued)

studied by Nicolaus Leonicenus, 1428–1524, and by the philologist and erudite scholar, Ermolao Barbaro, 1454–1493.

The terminal-date derives from the fact that this edition is mentioned as already published, in the five-year privilege granted Johann von Speier on 18 Sept. 1469, by the Signoria of Venice.

Mon: THORNDIKE, L. *The attack on Pliny* (p. 593–610 in vol. IV of his *History of magic and experimental science*. New York, 1934).

Fac: HORBLIT 84 [b].

POL, Nicolaus, *c.* 1470–1532.

488   De cura morbi gallici per lignum guaycanum.   [Venice: Joannes Patavinus and Venturinus de Ruffinellis] 1535.   8°.   [LEK]

Ref: BM-Ital 530; *Fisch (Pol)* C39.

N.B: A separate; but sometimes found appended to certain copies of the *Liber de morbo gallico* issued by this firm in 1535 (NLMCat 2812). The text was also included in the collection, *Morbi gallici curandi ratio*, printed by Joannes Bebelius at Basel in 1536, and for Scipio de Gabiano at Lyon in August of that year (NLMCat 3295, 3296). In addition to discussion of treatment for syphilis, it contains a recipe for guaiac powder and, in the 1535 edition, one for making German beer. The tract itself was completed by Dr. Pol in December 1517. It is dedicated to his patron, Cardinal Lang, and it is possible that Dr. Pol was a member of the medical mission apparently sent to Spain by Cardinal Lang earlier in the year to study the new cure for syphilis. But there is no evidence of the printing of the tract before 1535. Dr. Pol was a booklover, much of whose library is still extant in the Pol collections at the Cleveland Medical Library, at Yale University School of Medicine, and at San Candido in the Tyrol, with scattered volumes elsewhere. His books were almost invariably autographed: Nicolaus Pol Doctor 1494— possibly the year in which he obtained his medical degree.

A critical text of his guaiac tract edited and translated by Dr. Dorothy M. Schullian is included in the monograph noted below. According to the collation given by Dr. Fisch, the separate is in the same type and format as the Pol tract appearing in certain copies of the 1535 collection printed by Joannes Patavinus and his partner, from which the printer-assignment for the separate is derived.

Mon: FISCH, Max H. *Nicolaus Pol Doctor 1494 . . . Published for the Cleveland Medical Library Association by Herbert Reichner.* New York, 1947. BÜHLER, Curt F. *A Volume from the library of Dr. Nicolaus Pol* (p. 147–151 in *Gutenberg Jahrbuch*, 1954)

PONZETTI, Fernando, *Cardinal, c.* 1475–1528.

489   Libellus de venenis.   Rome: Jacobus Mazochius, 1521.   f°.

Ref: BM-Ital 534; *Thornd (HM)* V 472–474.

N.B: A work that continues the traditional interest in books on poisons.

PRISCIANUS. *See* THEODORUS PRISCIANUS.

PSELLUS, Michael, 1018 – *c.* 1079.

490   De victus ratione ad Constantinum imperatorem libri II (*and other works*)
(Tr: Giorgio Valla, 1447–1499).   Basel: Andreas Cratander, 1529.   4°.
[LEK]

> *Ref*: NLMCat 3769; *Sart* I 750.
> *N.B*: Edited by Andreas Leennius. Re-issued with Galen's *De euchymia et cacochymia*,
> Paris, 1530, with the title *Psellii commentarius de victus ratione* (NLMCat 1884).

RABANUS MAURUS (*called* Hrabanus; Raban), *Abbot of Fulda, Abp. of
Mainz, c.* 776–856.

491   Opus de universo sive De sermonum proprietate libri XXII.   [Stras-
bourg: The R-Printer (Adolf Rusch), before 20 July (or June), 1467.]
f°.

> *Ref*: HC *13699; BMC I 60; BM-Ger 420; Oates 98; IGI 8266; Osler (IM) 1; Schul-
> lian (ArMed) 383; Klebs 524.1; *Garrison* (1929) 147; Stillwell R3; Goff R-1.
> *N.B*: An early encyclopaedia of universal knowledge.   The terminal-date is derived
> from a contemporary note in the copy at the Bibliothèque Nationale in Paris.
> Written by Alcuin's favorite pupil, who was responsible for the introduction of
> learning into Germany.   Sections VI, VII, and XVIII have medical interest
> (Garrison), and are among the first texts treating of medical subjects to be issued
> in a printed book [but see the *Almanach für Wien*, 1462, the *Calendar for 1457*—
> both of which are broadsides—and works of Gerson assigned to 1466/67 (nos.
> 267, 324, and 388, respectively)].

RECEPT.

492   Ain Recept von ainem holtz zu brauchen für die kranckheit der Fran-
zosen . . . darzu das Regiment [*German*].   Augsburg [Sigismund Grim
and Marcus Wirsung], 1 Dec. 1518.

> *Ref*: *Fisch* (Pol) p. 43.
> *N.B*: This tract translated from Spanish into German (quoted from Zapf's *Augsburgs
> Buchdruckergeschichte*) is the earliest known printing of a recipe for the use of
> powdered *guaiacum* in the treatment of syphilis.   Various later tracts, however,
> refer to the use of the guaiac cure as early as 1504, 1508, 1516, and 1517.

RÉGIME.

493   Régime de l'épidémie [*French verse*].   [Lyon: Guillaume Le Roy
before 1476.]   4°.

> *Ref*: Pell 4449; Klebs 541.1; Klebs (P) 58; *Garrison* (1929) 188, 203; *Sart* III 1687.
> *N.B*: Attributed to Jean Jasme (Joannes Jacobi; Jacme), *d.* 1384.   According to Polain

2153, a Latin version of this work appeared under the title *Regimen pestilentiae*. [*See no. 494 and* note.]

Fac: Klebs-Droz 1.

REGIMEN CONTRA PESTILENTIAM.

494 Regimen contra pestilentiam. [Paris: Ulrich Gering, 1480.] 4°. [LEK]

Ref: H *9752; BMC VIII 27; BM-Fr 91; Osler (IM) 209; Klebs 245.1; Klebs (P) 10; *Sart* III 1687; *Garrison* (1929) 203; Stillwell J1; Goff J-1.

N.B: According to Polain 2153, a Latin prose version of the *Régime de l'épidémie* written in French verse and ascribed to Joannes Jacopi (Jean Jasme), *d.* 1384 [*see no. 493*]. Without the *Regimen sanitatis per circulum anni*, which was included in a second series, assignable to 1492–1500 (Klebs 245.12–.23). At least eleven editions of the present issue were printed before the second series was started. NLMCat 2560 and Goff J-13 cite an edition of the second series assigned to the early 16th century.

The frequent ascription of this Latin tract to Benedictus Canutus, Episcopus Arusiensis (Bengt Knutsson, Bishop of Vesterås in Sweden) has been seriously questioned. An English version crediting the *Regimen* to the Bishop of Arusiens was issued at London about 1485 (Klebs 246.1), presumably *A Passing Gode Lityll Boke Necessarye and Behovefull Agenst the Pestilence*, assigned to the London press of William de Machlinia, about 1485. A Portuguese version was printed at Lisbon about 1495, which named the author as Raminto (Klebs 247.1). NLM-Cat 3840 and 2194 list French versions issued—with other works—at Lyon, *c.* 1501 [reprinted at Lyon by Claude Nourry in 1503] and at Paris, *c.* 1512, entitled: *Remede tresutile contre fievre pestilencieuse, et autre maniere depydimie approuvee par plusieurs docteurs en medicine.*

REGIMEN SANITATIS.

495 Regimen sanitatis [*German:*] Die Ordnung der Gesundheit. Augsburg: Johann Bämler, 23 Apr. 1472. f°. [LEK]

Ref: H *13736; Schullian (ArMed) 384; Klebs 828.1; Stillwell R42; Goff R-45.

N.B: Health rules for German readers; a popular guide frequently reprinted in Germany. Issued in the same year by the same printer, in a compilation of tracts entitled *Lehre und Unterweissung* (Cen L105).

REGIMEN SANITATIS PARISIENSE.

496 Regimen sanitatis Parisiense [*German and Latin*]. [Leipzig: Conrad Kachelofen, about 1490.] 4°. [LEK]

Ref: R 1045; Klebs 832.1; Stillwell R48; Goff R-54.

N.B: Variant known. Although no English imprints are known, a Strasbourg edition of 1499 bears the interesting title: *Iste est tractatulus medicinalis quẽ doctores Parisieñ miserūt regi Anglie.* Dr. Klebs under the heading "Regimen sanitatis, Schul von Paris" lists eleven editions with German imprints.

REGIMEN SANITATIS PARVUM.

497 Regimen sanitatis parvum, sive Regimen per circulum anni. (*Issued with the* CALENDARIUM *perpetuum, 1479–1578.* Geneva: Henricus Wirczburg and Adam Steynschaber, 17 Oct. 1479.) [LEK]

Ref: Klebs, p. 272 (239.1).
N.B: Health rules issued with a calendar for easy consultation. Subsequently issued with various editions of ALBERTUS MAGNUS. *Liber aggregationis* (Cen A237–A239; Klebs 18.41–.52) and with other works.

REGIMEN SANITATIS SALERNITANUM.

498 Regimen sanitatis Salernitanum (Comm: Arnaldo de Villa Nova, *spurious*). [Cologne: Conrad Winters, about 1480.]   4°.   [LEK]

Add: ARNALDO de Villa Nova. Regimen sanitatis ad regem Aragonum.
Ref: NLMCat 3804 *note*; HC *13751; BMC I 250; Osler (IM) 189; Oates 672; Polain 3321; Voull (K) 1002; IGI 8294; Klebs 829.1; *Castiglioni* (1947) 309–315; *Garrison* (1929) 150; Stillwell R53; Goff R-59.
N.B: These rules of health, hygiene, and diet attributed to the Medical Faculty at Salerno apparently antedate the year 1311 and are presumably an accumulation from much earlier times. Both text and commentary are in verse. Two other editions are assigned to about 1480 and the press of Johann de Paderborn at Louvain (Cen R55, R56). A basic work; frequently reprinted in its present form, and with revisions made at Montpellier in 1480. For twenty printings during the early sixteenth century, including English versions of 1535 and 1541, see NLM-Cat p. 38, 490–494.
Mon: CHOULANT, Ludwig. *Regimen sanitatis Salernitanum* (p. 264–282 in his *Handbuch der Bücherkunde für die ältere Medicin.* Graz, reprinted 1956). LAWN, Brian. *The Salernitan questions. An introduction to the history of medieval and Renaissance problem literature.* Oxford, 1963 (reviewed, p. 386–388 in *Isis* 55 1964).

499 —— (——) Noviter correctum ac emendatum per doctores Montispesulani regentes, anno 1480. [Lyon?: Joannes Fabri *or* Mathias Huss? not before 1480.]   4°.   [LEK]

Ref: C 5059; Pell 1283; Klebs 830.7; Stillwell R62; Goff R-68.
N.B: The earliest *dated* edition containing the Montpellier revisions of 1480 was printed at Besançon in 1487 (Stillwell R66; Klebs 830.5). At least sixteen editions were printed during the fifteenth century at Lyon (7), Paris (1), Besançon (1), Strasbourg (2), Cologne (1), and Venice (4)—Stillwell R62–R77.

RHASIS (Abū Bakr Muḥammad ibn Zakarīyā al-Rāzī; Ar-Rāzī; *called* Razi, Rasis, Rhazes, Rhasis), *d.* 923/24.

500   Liber ad Almonsorem, libri X (*with other medical tracts*).   Milan: Leonardus Pachel and Uldericus Scinzenzeler, 14 Feb. 1481.   f°.   [LEK]

> *Add*: GALEN. De medicinis experimentatis. HIPPOCRATES. Secreta. Capsula eburnea. De humana natura. De aere et aqua et regionibus. De pharmaciis. JOANNES Damascenus [Mesue? or Serapion?] Aphorismi. [*See no.* 552.]
>
> *Ref*: HCR 13891; BMC VI 749; Schullian (ArMed) 399; Klebs 826.1; Choulant (H) 340–345; *Sart* I 609–610; *Castiglioni* (1947) 268; *Campbell* (AM) I 66–67; Stillwell R169; Goff R-175.
>
> *N.B*: In addition to the *Liber ad Almansorem* and the works noted above, the volume contains Rhasis's *Liber divisionum*; *De aegritudinibus iuncturarum*; *De aegritudinibus puerorum*; *De secretis in medicina sive aphorismi*; *De sectionibus et cauteriis et ventosis*; *Synonyma*; and a *Tabula de herbis medicinis*. Issued at Venice with variable contents in 1497 and 1500 (Cen R170, R171). The 1497 edition, for instance, printed at Venice by Bonetus Locatellus, contains also Rhasis's *Antidotarium*; *De preservatione ab aegritudine lapidis*; *Introductorium medicinae*; and *De proprietatibus membrorum et nocumentis sexaginta animalium*. BM-Ital 456 lists a Venetian edition of 1508. [For sectional analysis, see under NATURAL SCIENCE.] The third and ninth Books were issued as separates, the former in Italian verse, the *Cibaldone*; known in thirteen editions [1478–1500] (Klebs 825); the latter, the basis of various commentaries, issued in whole or in part in the *Practica* of Gianmatteo Ferrari, about 1472/73—*see no.* 502. The third Book, under the title *De simplicibus ad Almansorem*, is included in a compilation edited by Otto Brunfels and printed at Strasbourg in 1531 (NLMCat 2524).
>
> *Mon*: RANKING, G. S. A. *The life and works of Rhazes* (p. 246–268 in *Proceedings of the XVII International Congress of Medicine*. London, 1913).

501   Liber dictus Elhavi continens artem medicinae (Tr: Faraj ben Salīm, *13th century*. Ed: Joannes Bugatus).   Brescia: Jacobus Britannicus, 18 Oct. 1486.   f°.   [LEK]

> *Ref*: HC *13901; BMC VII 975; BM-Ital 456; IGI 8342; Klebs 827.1; Choulant (H) 342; *Sart* I 609, II 833; *Afnan* 204; *Browne* (AM) 47, 50; Stillwell R172; Goff R-178.
>
> *N.B*: A comprehensive and important medical encyclopaedia sometimes called *Continens*. The text discusses the theories of Galen and Hippocrates and combines the latter's common sense and simplicity with Eastern medical knowledge and the author's experience in therapeutics. According to Afnan, Rhasis cites for each disease the Greek, Syrian, Arabic, Persian, and Indian authors and then gives his own clinical experience and observations. Included also is a treatise, *De expositionibus vocabulorum seu synonimorum simplicis medicine*. [For a review of a modern edition of the *Elhavi*, 1955—issued under the auspices of the Ministry of Education in India—see p. 105–107 in *Isis* 51 1960. Parts I–III are listed as relating to diseases of the nerves, eye, ear, nose, throat, teeth, tumors, ulcers, and respiration. On

p. 585 in *Isis* 54, 1963 there is reference to Pts. XII and XIII issued at Hyderabad, India, 1962, as *New series*, no. IV, Osmania Oriental Publications Bureau. Part XII is described as relating to cancer, swellings, ulcers, abscesses, wounds, *etc.*; Part XIII, to contusion, sinus, ulcers on generative organs, *etc.*; Part XIV, on the diseases of fever, on excretion and vomiting, was issued in this series in 1963.]

Fac: *Osiris* 5 1938, p. 143.

502   Liber nonus Almansoris. (*Issued with* FERRARI, Gianmatteo. Practica cum textu noni ad Almansorem. [Milan: Philippus de Lavagina, 1472/73.]) f°. [LEK]

Ref: Osler (IM) 37; Klebs 392.1; Schullian (ArMed) 184; Stillwell F95; Goff F-119.

N.B: A noted textbook of pathology and therapeutics, the ninth book of Rhasis's *Liber ad Almansorem*. An unsigned edition. Variously assigned to Milan, as cited above, or to the press of Joannes de Sidriano at Pavia about 1474. A unique edition dated 8 June 1476 is assigned in IGI 8343 to Padua and the press of Bartolomeo Valdezochio.

    At least 9 editions—with commentaries by Giovanni Arcolani (3), Syllanus de Nigris (4), Cristoforo Barzizza (1), and Jean de Tournemire (1)—were issued during the years 1476–1497 at Padua (1), Venice (5), Milan (1), Pavia (1), and Lyon (1) (Cen R173–78, B224; Goff J-439). The text appeared in editions of the *Articella* produced at Venice in 1507 and at Lyon in 1515 and 1519 (NLMCat 326, 328, 329). An analysis of other entries in NLMCat shows 5 instances in which the text—with commentaries by Galeazzo de Santa Sofia (1), Gerardus de Solo (2) and Jean de Tournemire (2)—were issued during the years 1501–1533 at Hagenau (1), Lyon (2), and Venice (2). Revised in 1537 by Andreas Vesalius, and continued long in use (*see p. 3–9 in* CUSHING, H. *A bio-bibliography of Andreas Vesalius*, New York, 1943).

503   Libro tertio dell Almansor chiamato Cibaldone (*Italian verse*). [Venice:] Gabriel Petri [1478]. 4°. [LEK]

Ref: Osler (IM) 192; Klebs 825.1; Choulant (H) 344:4.

N.B: A version of Rhasis's rules for simples and diet, the third book in the treatise which he dedicated to Almansor, the Prince of Chorasan. A dozen or more editions were issued during our period with apparently variant titles.

Fac: SCHULLIAN (ArMed) 398 reproduces a page from the edition assigned to Venice and the press of Baptista de Tortis about 1493 (Cen R168).

504   De pestilentia. (*Issued with* NICEPHOROS, Gregoras, 1295–1359. De astrolabo. Giorgio Valla, 1447–1499, *ed*. Venice: Simon Bevilaqua, 30 Sept. 1498.) f°.

Ref: HC *11748; BMC V 523; Klebs 1012.1; Choulant (H) 342; *Sart* I 609; *Browne (AM)* 47; *Afnan* 203; *Castiglioni* (1947) 269–270; *Garrison* (1929) 129; Stillwell N33; Goff N-44.

Rhasis (continued)

N.B: The oldest treatise on smallpox and measles; the first accurate account of infectious diseases. Also called the *Liber de variolis et morbillis*. Choulant lists five editions within our period, among them a Basel edition of 1544 translated from the Arabic into Latin by Albanus Torinus (Thorer), and a Greek edition from the Syriac printed at Paris in 1548. An English translation by Greenhill was published by the Sydenham Society, London, 1847/48 [a portion of which is quoted by Castiglioni].

Mon: SIGERIST, H. E. *Rhazes and Avicenna* (p. 78–87 in his *The great doctors, a biographical history of medicine*. Translated by E. and C. Paul. New York, 1933).

ROCCA, Bartolomeo della (*known as* Cocles), 1467–1504.

505 Chryomantie et physionomie anastasis. Bologna: Joannes Antonius de Benedictis, 1504. sm. f °. [LEK]

Ref: NLMCat 972; *Thornd (HM)* V 50.

N.B: Although relating largely to divination and character analysis, the work contains a section on syphilis—the text of the latter, reproduced in Thornd (HM) V 671–672. As an astrologer Rocca correctly predicted the time of death of many prominent persons, including his own. Illustrated editions were issued at Strasbourg in 1533 and 1534 and a German version in 1533 (NLMCat 973–974).

Mon: THORNDIKE, Lynn. *Cocles and chiromancy* (chap. IV in vol. V of his *A History of magic and experimental science*. New York, 1941).

RODRIGUEZ de Castello Branco, João (*frequently called* Amatus Lusitanus), 1511–1568.

506 Index Dioscoridis. Antwerp: Vidua Martini Caesaris, 1536. [LEK]

Ref: Arber (1938) 275; *Sart (Appr)* 72–73, 201:59; *Castiglioni* (1947) 441.

N.B: The work of a famous Portuguese physician, whose *Centuriae*, or collections of case histories, were printed after our period.

Mon: FRIEDENWALD, H. *Jewish luminaries in medical history*, Baltimore, 1946, p. 35–37.

RÖSLIN, Eucharius (*called* Rhodion), d. 1526.

507 Der schwangeren Frauen und Hebammen Rosengarten [*German*]. Strasbourg: Martin Flach, 1513. 4°.

Ref: NLMCat 3893; Pr 10148; BM-Ger 743; *Garrison* (1929) 198; *Sart (Appr)* 208:134; *Castiglioni* (1947) 481.

N.B: A popular book on obstetrics reviving the podalic method, as derived and practiced since the treatise on midwifery written by Soranos of Ephesos in the second century A.D. With illustrations by Conrad Merkel, a friend of Albrecht Dürer. Translated and re-issued by William Raynalde at London in 1540 and

1545 under the title, *The Byrthe of Mankynde*. A Latin translation appeared under the title, *De partu homines*. For early editions of the sixteenth century, see NLM Cat p. 502–503. [An edition cited by Garrison as printed at Worms in 1513— possibly an error deriving from the signature, "Wurms, 1513," at the end of the dedication—has not been found in the present survey.]

Mon: HELLMAN, Alfred M. *A collection of early obstetrical books*, New Haven, 1952. HELLMAN, C. Doris. *Additions to the Alfred M. Hellman collection of early obstetrical books* (p. 2–11 in *The Academy Bookman* (N.Y. Acad. Med.), 11, no. 2, 1958).

Fac: Facsimile reprint edited by Gustav Klein, München, 1910.

RUFFO, Giordano, *13th century*.

508 Arte di conoscere la natura dei cavalli [*Italian*] (Tr: Gabriele Bruno). Venice: Petrus de Quarengiis, Bergomensis [1493]. 4°. [LEK]

Ref: HC 14034; BMC V 512; IGI 8468; Klebs 868.1; LC(LJRCat) 249; Goff R-350.

N.B: Issued at Venice in 1519 (NLMCat 3987). Apparently included in part in an edition of the *Opera de l'arte del malscalcio . . .* of Lorenzo Rusio printed at Venice in 1543 (NLMCat 4012). [A work by the latter, entitled *Liber marescalciae equorum* and issued before 1490, is assigned to the press of Johann and Conrad Hist at Speier (Cen R346; Schullian (ArMed) 413).] *See also no. 566n.*

RUSIO, Lorenzo. *See no. 508n.*

SALICETO (Guglielmo Saliceti, of Piacenza; *called* Guilielmus de Saliceto), 1210–1277.

509 La ciroxia vulgarmente fata [*Italian*]. [Venice:] Filippo di Pietro, 1 Mar. 1474. f°. [LEK]

Ref: HCR 14147; Pr 4254; Osler (IM) 55; Klebs 485.1; *Singer (SHA)* 1957 71–72; Castiglioni (1947) 336; Stillwell S25; Goff S-27.

N.B: A surgical work of special importance because it re-introduced the use of the surgical knife, counter to cauterization as employed and advocated by the great surgeons of the East. The text discusses fractures and the suturing of nerves, and gives an account of regional anatomy. Re-issued at [Brescia] in 1486 and at Venice in 1491 (Cen S26, S27). The first Latin version to be printed was issued with his *Summa conservationis*, Piacenza, 1476 (Cen S30). A French version was printed at Lyon in 1492 (Cen S24). See NLMCat 2194–96 for printing of the text in the early sixteenth century. [The author is commonly called Saliceto, although Castiglioni uses the form Saliceti.]

Mon: SCHAARSCHMIDT, Franz Otto. *Die Anatomie des Wilhelm von Saliceto.* Leipzig, 1919 (reviewed in *Isis* 1922 4, p. 585).

510 De salute corporis. [The Netherlands (Utrecht?): No printer known; not before 1458, not after 1472.]

Ref: Camp (+ 3rd Supp) 1493; BMC IX 1, 4; Polain 1837; Klebs 484.1.

Saliceto (continued)

N.B: A tract on hygiene, the earliest to be printed. The edition contains several non-medical works, among them two by Pope Pius II, who was elevated to the Papacy in 1458. The edition, therefore, cannot have been issued prior to that time. The Darmstadt copy contains a rubricator's date of 1472. The assignment of the date of printing is governed by these two factors. It is probable that the book was not issued until after the Pope's death in 1464. In technical terms this early volume, which is one of the so-called Costeriana, is printed in 123 Gothic type. Variant known. Copies are known at the British Museum and at Brussels, Darmstadt, and The Hague. Klebs lists five fifteenth-century editions.

511 Summa conservationis et curationis. Chirurgia. Piacenza: [Joannes Petrus de Ferratis], I) 1476; II) 25 May 1476. f°. [LEK]

Ref: HR 14146; BMC VII 1071; BM-Ital 322; Osler (IM) 118; Schullian (ArMed) 418; Klebs 487.1; *Sart* II 1078; Stillwell S30; Goff S-32.

N.B: Comprises five books—pathology and therapeutics; fevers; cosmetics and dermatology; toxicology; materia medica. According to Castiglioni (1947) 336, chapter 140 contains a notable description of dropsy due to the condition later called Bright's disease. Garrison (1929) 154 credits Saliceto with valuable contributions to gynecology and the subject of melancholia. Included in this edition is the first Latin version of Saliceto's treatise on surgery and anatomy, which had been published in Italian at Venice in 1474. Re-issued at Venice in 1489 and 1490 (Cen S31, S32), and also in 1502 (NLMCat 2196).

SAVONAROLA, Giovanni Michele (Michele Savonarola), *d.* 1462/64.

512 De balneis et thermis naturalibus omnibus Italiae. Ferrara: Andreas Belfortis, Gallus, 10 Nov. 1485. f°. [LEK]

Ref: HC *14493; BMC VI 603; BM-Ital 610; Oates 2241; Schullian (ArMed) 422; Klebs 884.1; *Castiglioni* (1947) 366, 895; Stillwell S265; Goff S-290.

N.B: An account of the baths and natural hot springs of Italy. Written by one of the leading physicians of the fifteenth century, of an earlier generation than Savonarola, the martyr. Re-issued at Bologna in 1493 and at Venice 20 Nov. [1496] (Cen S266, S267).

Mon: THORNDIKE, Lynn. Michael Savonarola (Chap. XLIV in vol. IV of his *History of magic and experimental science*, New York, 1934).

513 De febribus. Bologna: Dionysius Bertochus, 8 Mar. 1487. f°. [LEK]

Ref: H 14487; BMC VI 832; Klebs 885.1; *Castiglioni* (1947) 895; Stillwell S268; Goff S-293.

N.B: Re-issued at Venice in 1496 and 1498 (Cen S269, S270).

514 Practica medicinae, sive De aegritudinibus a capite ad pedes. Colle di Valdelsa: Bonus Gallus, 13 Aug. 1479. f°. [LEK]

Ref: HC 14480; BMC VII 1079; Osler (IM) 184; Klebs 882.1; Stillwell S271; Goff S-296.

N.B: Gives descriptions of cases, thus contributing to the revival of clinical interest after the long interval of medical scholasticism. Re-issued at Venice in 1486 and 1497 (Cen S272, S273). [For early sixteenth-century editions, see NLMCat 4079–4084.]

515 De pulsibus, urinis et egestionibus.   Bologna: Henricus de Harlem and Johannes Walbeck, 8 May 1487.   f °.   [LEK]

Ref: HC *14490; BMC VI 830; Klebs 886.1; Polain 3468; Schullian (ArMed) 429; Stillwell S274; Goff S-299.

N.B: Re-issued at Venice, 10 Feb. 1497 (Cen S275).

516 De vermibus. (*Issued with his* De febribus [*and other tracts*]. Venice: Bonetus Locatellus for Octavianus Scotus, 22 Nov. 1498.)

Ref: HC 14489; BMC V 451; Klebs 885.3; Schullian (ArMed) 426; Stillwell S270; Goff S-295.

SCANAROLI, Antonio (Scanarolus, Antonius), *fl.* 1495.

517 Disputatio utilis de morbo gallico.   Bologna: [Benedictus Hectoris] 26 Mar. 1498.   4°.   [LEK]

Ref: H *14505; BMC VI 844; Klebs 887.1; Stillwell S279; Goff S-304.

N.B: Issued in a compilation of medical tracts together with the commentary *Super nono Almansoris* by Marco Gatinaria (*d.* 1496) Venice, 1516 (NLMCat 2015).

Fac: SUDHOFF-SINGER 10.

SCHELLIG, Konrad, (Schelling), *fl.* 1495.

518 In malum de francia consilium. *Text begins:* In pustulas malas morbū quē malum de frācia vulgus appellat consilium.   [Heidelberg, Friedrich Misch, 1495.]   4°.   [LEK]

Ref: R 727; BMC III 668; BM-Ger 786; Polain 3472; Klebs 891.1; *Garrison* (1929) 190–191; *Sudhoff-Singer* p. xviii–xxi; Stillwell S287; Goff S-313.

N.B: The first regimen against syphilis. Written after the Diet of Worms in 1495, which Schellig as physician to Philip, Elector to the Palatinate, had attended. The first reference, in official use, to the disease occurs in the edict issued by the Diet, 7 August 1495. [Syphilis was known as *malum de francia, morbus gallicus, mala napoletana, mal serpentino,* or *bösen Blattern*, the evil pocks.] Garrison (1929) 190 gives the title of Schellig's tract as *Concilium breve contra malas pustulas*, from the caption which appears on leaf aii. Issued in German at Heidelberg on 24 Dec. 1501 (Klebs 892.1) and recently assigned to the press of Jacob Stadelberger; re-issued [Speier? Konrad Hist, 1502] (NLMCat 4106).

Fac: SUDHOFF-SINGER. *The earliest printed literature on syphilis, 1495–1498.* Florence, 1925, no. 1.

SCHMAUS, Leonard, *fl.* 1500.

519 Lucubratiuncula de morbo gallico et cura eius noviter reperta cum ligno indico. Augsburg: Sigismund Grim and Marcus Wirsung, 17 Dec. 1518. f°. [LEK]

> *Ref*: NLMCat 4124; *Fisch (Pol)* p. 43; *Garrison* (1929) 190.
> *N.B*: The author states that his essay is based on nineteen reports from the West Indies and Portugal, and refers specifically to the report of Hieronymus Carozolus to Cardinal Lang on the virtues of the wood called by the natives of Hispaniola *huaiacum*, and *guaiacum* by the Spaniards, as a cure for syphilis.

SCILLACIO, Nicolò, *15th century*.

520 Opuscula. Pavia: Joannes Andreas de Boscho, 9 Mar. 1496. 8°.

> *Ref*: BM-Ital 618; *Garrison* (1929) 190.
> *N.B*: A letter from Scillacio at Barcelona, included in the *Opuscula*, reveals that syphilis had broken out there in June 1495, simultaneously with the appearance of the scourge at Naples. The author was the editor of the *Rosa anglica practica medicine* by Joannes de Gaddesden, issued at Pavia in 1492 and at Venice in 1502 (Cen J289; NLMCat 2607, respectively).

SERAPION *the Elder. See* YŪḤANNĀ ibn SARĀBIYŪN *the Elder, 9th–10th century.*

SERAPION *the Younger. See* YŪḤANNĀ ibn SARĀBIYŪN *the Younger, 11th–12th century.*

SERMONETA, Giovanni, *fl.* 1430.

521 Quaestiones super Aphorismos Hippocratis et libros Tegni Galeni. Milan: Uldericus Scinzenzeler, 22 Nov. 1487. f°. [LEK]

> *Ref*: H 14700; Klebs 915.1.
> *N.B*: Issued at Venice for Octavianus Scotus, 31 Mar. 1498 (Cen S429).

SILVATICO, Matteo (Matthaeus Sylvaticus; *called* Pandectarius), *d.* 1342.

522 Liber pandectarum medicinae (Ed: Angelo Catone de Sepino, *fl.* 1470). Naples [Anonymous printer], 1 April 1474. f°. [LEK]

> *Ref*: HC 15194; BMC VI 859; BM-Ital 628; Osler (IM) 61; Klebs 919.1; *Crombie (A–G)* 1961 I 158; *Sart* III 816; Goff S-510.
> *N.B*: A dictionary of simples and their medicinal use, arranged in general alphabetical order and giving the plant names in Greek, Arabic, and Latin. The *Liber pandectarum medicinae*, edited by Matthaeus Moretus, was printed at Bologna by Johannes Vurster in July 1474, and the text was re-issued under various editors. The

Venice edition printed for Octavianus Scotus at Venice in 1498 contains the *Synonyma medicinae* of Simon of Genoa, which had been issued at Milan by Antonius Zarotus in 1473 (Cen S475), and from the text of which Silvatico is said to have derived much of his material. At least ten editions were issued during the fifteenth century (Goff S-510—S-518; Klebs 919.3). Five editions ranging from 1507-1541 are listed in NLMCat 4205-4209, printed at Venice (3), Turin (1), and Lyon (1).

SIMON of Genoa (Simone de Cordo; Simon Genuensis; Simon Januensis), *d.* 1330.

523   Synonyma medicinae sive Clavis sanationis.   Milan: Antonius Zarotus, 3 Aug. 1473.   f°.   [LEK]

Ref: HCR 14747; BMC VI 710; Osler (IM) 33; Schullian (ArMed) 455; Klebs 920.2; Garrison (1929) 166; Stillwell S475; Goff S-526.

N.B: The first dated edition of a polyglot dictionary; known also in an undated fragment assigned to Ferrara, 1471-72 (Klebs 920.1), and in at least four other fifteenth-century printings. Editions issued at Venice in 1507 and 1514 are listed in NLMCat 4214, 4215.

SOLDI, Jacopo (Jacobus Soldus), *d. about* 1440.

524   Opus de peste.   Bologna: Johannes Schriber, de Annunciata, for Thomas de Bononia, 1478.   4°.   [LEK]

Ref: HC *14870; BMC VI 818; BM-Ital 631; Osler (IM) 149; Oates 2478; Klebs 921.1; Klebs (P) 98; Schullian (ArMed) 457; Stillwell S548; Goff S-613.

N.B: An edition issued at Bologna in 1533 is listed in NLMCat 4232.

SOMMARIVA, Giorgio (Summaripa), *fl.* 1495.

525   Del mal franzoso [*Italian verse*].   Venice: Christophorus de Bottis, Dec. 1496.   4°.

Ref: R 1632; Klebs 923.1; Garrison (1929) 189(?).

SORANOS of Ephesos (Soranus of Ephesus), *fl.* 130.

526   Celerum passionum libri III (Ed: Johann Günther, 1505-1574).   Paris: Simon de Colines, 1533.

Ref: Choulant (H) 92, 206; Renouard (Colines) 204; Sart (Appr) 14-16; Castiglioni (1947) 202.

N.B: Relates to acute disease. Translated by Caelius Aurelianus, *fl.* 5th-6th century, to whom the text was erroneously ascribed in this edition—see note under *Tardarum passionum libri V.* Soranos, the most celebrated physician of the

III. *Medicine*

Soranos (continued)

Methodist school, ranks as the founder of obstetrics and gynecology. His great work on gynecology (issued, in translation, at Johns Hopkins University Press, 1956) is not known to have been printed before 1550.

Mon: SIGERIST, H. E. *Soranus of Ephesus* (p. 61–67 in his *The great doctors, a bibliographical history of medicine*. New York, 1933).

527 In artem medendi isagoge. (*Issued in* THORER, Alban, 1489–1550, *ed.* Collectio. Basel: Andreas Cratander, August 1528.) f°. [LEK]

Ref: Choulant (H) 94, 405, 408.

N.B: A manual on the art of the physician. Attribution to Soranos questioned; variously believed to be of later origin. Included in the compilation edited by Alban Thorer and printed at Basel in 1528 (NLMCat 4351); and, according to Choulant (H) 408, the text, again under the name of Soranos, appeared in the Aldine *Collectio* of 1547 (NLMCat 3050).

528 Tardarum passionum libri V (Ed: Johannes Sichardt, *c.* 1499–1552). Basel: H. Petrus, 1529. [LEK]

Ref: *Sart* I 282–283, 392; *Sart (Appr)* 16.

N.B: Although the original Greek had been lost, the Latin translation by Caelius Aurelianus, *fl.* 5th–6th century, preserved the text which centuries later was found by Johannes Sichardt in the abbey of Lorsch. The text relates to chronic suffering and is sometimes entitled *Aesculapius*, or *Esculapii liber unus, De morborum, infirmitatum, passionumque corporis humani caussis*—as listed in the *Physica* of Hildegard of Bingen, printed at Strasbourg by Johann Schott in 1533. Again issued in 1544 by the latter press, in a collection entitled *Experimentarius medicinae*.

Mon: DRABKIN, I. E. *Notes on the text of Caelius Aurelianus* (AMERICAN PHILOLOGICAL ASSOCIATION. *Transactions*. Vol. LXXVI, 1945 299–320); *Caelius Aurelianus, On acute and on chronic diseases*, Chicago, 1950. [In spite of his use of the name 'Caelius Aurelianus' in his titles, Drabkin in his texts gives full credit to Soranos and in his 1950 monograph, on p. xiv, footnote 5, he mentions that "Caelius constantly reminds the reader that he is rendering Soranus into Latin." Sarton refers to the continued assignment of the Soranos texts on acute and chronic diseases to Caelius Aurelianus as an instance of perverted tradition.]

STEBER, Bartholomaeus, *d.* 1506.

529 A malafranczos morbo Gallorum praeservatio ac cura. Vienna: Jo[hann] W[interburg] [1497–98]. 4°.

Ref: HC 15053; BMC III 811; BM-Ger 831; Klebs 931.1; Schullian (ArMed) 459 *var*; *Sudhoff-Singer* p. xlii–xliii; Stillwell S679; Goff S-762.

N.B: According to Sudhoff, the writer considered syphilis due to imbalance in the so-called *non-naturals* of Galen, "air, meat and drink, sleep and waking, motion and rest, excretion and retention, and lastly the affections of the mind."

Fac: SUDHOFF-SINGER 8.

III. *Medicine*

STEINHÖWEL, Heinrich, 1412–1482.

530   Büchlein der Ordnung der Pestilenz [*German*].   Ulm: Johann Zainer, 11 Jan. 1473.   4°.   [LEK]

     Ref: H *15058; BMC II 520; BM-Ger 831; Klebs 933.1; Klebs (P) 100.
     N.B: The earliest printed pest-tract. Six German editions are known before the end of the century. Utilized by Hieronymus Brunschwig in his *Pestbuch* of 1500 (NLMCat 765).
     Mon: KLEBS, Arnold Carl, and Karl SUDHOFF. *Die ersten gedruckten Pestschriften. Faksimile von Steinhöwel's Büchlein der Pestilenz*, Ulm, 1473. München, 1926 (reviewed in *Isis* 9 430–33).
     Fac: *Osiris* 5 1938, *fig*. 55.

STRABO, Walafrid, *c*. 809–849. *See under* NATURAL SCIENCE.

SYLVIUS, Jacobus. *See* DUBOIS, Jacques.

THEODORUS PRISCIANUS (Octavius Horatianus?), *4th century*.

531   Diaeta. (*Issued with* HILDEGARD, *Saint*. Physica. Strasbourg: Johann Schott, 1533.)   f°.

     Ref: NLMCat 2307; BM-Ger 405; Choulant (H) 217, 308; Hunt (Quinby) I 32.
     N.B: Attribution questioned. Also issued in the *Experimentarius medicinae*, printed by Johann Schott at Strasbourg in 1544 (NLMCat 1411).

532   Rerum medicarum libri IV (Ed: Heremannus Comes).   Strasbourg: Johann Schott, 26 Feb. 1532.   f°.

     Ref: BM-Ger 415 (Horatianus); Choulant (H) 217.
     N.B: According to its title and contents, its sections comprise I) *Logicus, De curationibus omnium ferme morborum*; II) *De acutis et chronicis passionibus*; III) *Gynecia, De mulierum accidentibus et curis eorundem*; IV) *De physica scientica, Experimentor*. Also issued in the *Experimentarius medicinae* printed by this press in 1544 (NLMCat 1411). Variously attributed to Octavius Horatianus.

THEOPHRASTOS, *c*. 374 – *c*. 286 B.C.

533   De historia et causis plantarum (Tr: Theodoros Gaza, *fl*. 1400–1475. Ed: Giorgio Merula, *d*. 1494).   Treviso: Bartholomaeus Confalonerius, 20 Feb. 1483.   f°.   [LEK]

     Ref: HC *15491; BMC VI 894; BM-Ital 668; Klebs 958.1; *Castiglioni* (1947) 181–182; *Garrison* (1929) 102; *Sart* I 143–144; Stillwell T132; Goff T-155.
     N.B: The ninth section of the *Historia*, on the medicinal property of plants, is believed to have been added somewhat after Theophrastos's time. Its text, however, ranks

Theophrastos (continued)

as the earliest extant herbal, except for manuscript fragments of a Greek herbal assigned to about 350 B.C. [For the Greek *Opera* printed at Venice by Aldus Manutius during 1497, see NATURAL SCIENCE.] Issued in an edition assigned to Lyon about 1505 and printed in part by Chrétien Wechel at Paris in 1529 (NLMCat 4345, 4346).

534 De vertigine oculorum [*Greek*]. (*Issued in vol III of* ARISTOTLE. Opera [*Greek*]. Venice: Aldus Manutius, 29 Jan. 1497.)

Ref: GW 2332; HC *1656; BMC V 559; Oates 2183; IGI 790; Stillwell A857; Goff A-958.

THORER, Alban (Albanus Torinus; Thoren), 1489–1550, *ed.*

535 Collectio. Basel: Andreas Cratander, August 1528. f°.

Ref: NLMCat 4351; BM-Ger 860; Choulant (H) 405.
N.B: A collection of ancient medical works, edited by a professor of medicine at Basel. The text begins: De re medica huic volumini insunt. . . .
Con: APULEIUS (?), *5th century.* De herbarum virtutibus historia. MUSA, Antonius, *1st century.* De herba betonica. OREIBASIOS, *fl. 325–400.* Fragmentum de victus ratione. PLINY, *23–79 A.D.* De re medica libri V. SORANOS, *1st–2nd century.* In artem medendi isagoge. [Two of the treatises, however, had already been printed, both the Pliny and the *Herbarium Apulei* having appeared in fifteenth-century editions—*q.v.*]

TORRE, Giacomo della. *See* JACOPO da Forlì.

TORRELLA, Gaspare (Caspar Torrella), *fl.* 1495.

536 Dialogus de dolore cum tractatu de ulceribus in pudendagra evenire solitis. Rome: Johann Besicken and Martinus de Amsterdam, 31 Oct. 1500. 4°.

Ref: NLMCat 4388; HC 15559; BMC IV 142; BM-Ital 676; Schullian (ArMed) 468; Klebs 980.1; *Sudhoff-Singer* p. xxxii; Stillwell T356; Goff T-391.
N.B: For other titles, see NLMCat 4385–4390.

537 Tractatus cum consiliis contra pudendagram sive morbum gallicum. Rome: Petrus de Turre, 22 Nov. 1497. 4°. [LEK]

Ref: Polain 3789; Klebs 979.1; *Sudhoff-Singer* p. xxxii–xxxiv.
N.B: Contains five *consilia* on syphilis written by the body physician of Alexander VI (Roderigo de Borgia). The work mentions the appearance of the disease in France in 1493.
Fac: SUDHOFF-SINGER 5.

TORRIGIANI, Torrigiano dei (Pietro Torrigiano de Torrigiani; Turisanus Carthusiensis), *c.* 1270–*c.* 1350.

538 Plusquam commentum in Microtegni Galeni. Bologna: Ugo de Rugeriis, 10 June 1489. f°. [LEK]

    Ref: HC *15683; Polain 3878; Klebs 983.1; *Castiglioni* (1947) 340.
    N.B: A commentary which, according to Castiglioni, was regarded as a classic for almost two centuries. The edition of 1504 includes the Latin text of Galen's *Ars parva*, known also as the *Ars medica*. For Venetian editions of 1504, 1512, 1517, and 1543, see NLMCat 4393–4396.

TROTULA.

539 Trotulae curandarum aegritudinum muliebrium ante, in, et post partum, Liber I, nusquam antea editus (Ed: Georg Kraut). (*Issued in* Experimentarius medicinae. Strasbourg: Johann Schott, 1544.) f°.

    Ref: NLMCat 1411; BM-Ger 292; Choulant (H) 406; *Garrison* (1929) 150.
    N.B: The first item in a collection of tracts on medicine and natural science. Also included in the Aldine *Collectio*, printed at Venice in 1547 (NLMCat 3050). [The term *Trotula* is open to question. By some authorities it is accepted as a woman's name, "Madame Trotte de Salerne"; by others, as a Salernitan nickname commonly applied to midwives.]

UGO da Siena. *See* BENZI, Ugo.

ULRICH von Hutten (Hutten), 1488–1523.

540 De guaiaci medicina et morbo gallico liber unus. Mainz: Johann Schoeffer, April 1519, 4°. [LEK]

    Ref: NLMCat 2509; Pr 9865; BM-Ger 426; *Fisch (Pol)* p. 41.
    N.B: The author, who had taken the guaiac treatment at Augsburg in 1518, here reports on its value. Latin editions of 1521, 1524, and 1531; a French translation issued about 1522; and an English version issued in 1539 are listed in NLMCat 2510–2514. A German version (NLMCat 2515) was printed at Strasbourg by Johann Grüninger in 1519 [Fac. of t.p.: Fisch (Pol) p. 163]. [For an account of early records of the use of the powdered wood from Hispaniola in treatments for syphilis, see *Pol's tract on the guaiac cure* (FISCH, Max H. *Nicolaus Pol Doctor 1494.* New York, 1947 chap. IV).]

ULSEN, Dietrich (Theodoricus Ulsenius), *fl.* 1486–1508.

541 Carmina. (*Issued with* HIPPOCRATES. De insania Democriti facetum epistolium. [Augsburg: Johann Froschauer, about 1495–1500].) 4°.

    Ref: HC *8676; BMC II 399; BM-Ger 407; IGI 4783; Polain 1963; Klebs 522.1; Stillwell H252; Goff H-276.

Ulsen (continued)

542 Pharmacandi substantia. Pharmacandi accidens. (*Issued with* HIPPO-
CRATES. Aphorismi seu Sententiae. [Nuremberg: Caspar Hochfeder,
after 5 April 1496]).

> *Ref*: H 8673, 16088; Schullian (ArMed) 241; Klebs 520.2; Stillwell H250; Goff H-
> 274.

543 Vaticinium in epidemicam scabiem.   Nuremberg: [Hans Mair], 1 Aug.
1496.   Bdsde.

> *Ref*: H *16089; Einbl 1467; Voull (B) 1886; *Garrison* (1929) 189–192; Klebs 1004.1.
> *N.B*: One of the earliest dated tracts on syphilis. With a figure of a syphilitic drawn
> by Albrecht Dürer. An undated edition is assigned to the press of Johann Frosch-
> auer at Augsburg about 1496.
> *Fac*: SUDHOFF-SINGER, no. 2.

ULSTADT, Philip, *16th century*.

544 Coelum philosophorum seu De secretis naturae liber.   Strasbourg:
Johann Grüninger, 1526.   f °.   [LEK]

> *Ref*: BM-Ger 879; *Wightman* (1962) I 175.
> *N.B*: A revival of interest in the ideas of Joannes de Rupescissa, *fl.* 1350. Possibly first
> printed in 1525. Editions printed at Strasbourg in 1528 and at Paris in 1543 are
> listed in NLMCat 4447 and 4448, the latter with a dedication signed and dated
> May 1543 by the author. French versions were printed at Paris in 1546 and 1550
> (NLMCat 4451).

VALASCO de Taranta (Valascus de Tarenta), 1382–1417.

545 De epidemia et peste. (*Issued in two 1473 editions of* ARNALDO de Villa
Nova. De arte cognoscendi venena.)   [LEK]

> *Ref*: GW 2521, 2522; BMC VII 909, 929; Oates 2549, 2583(–); IGI 862, 861; Osler
> (IM) 40, 41; *Castiglioni* (1947) 339; Stillwell A952, A953; Goff A-1066, A-1067.
> *N.B*: Both of these editions, issued at Padua and Mantua, respectively, are dated 1473.
> The printer in each case is anonymous. An undated separate of the *De epidemia
> et peste* is assigned to France about 1474 (Cen V5; BMC VIII 414). Also issued
> as a separate at Basel [1474] and at Hagenau, 1497 (Cen V4, V6). Included in
> *Archana medicine*, a compilation assigned to Geneva about 1498–1500 (Goff A-
> 947; Schullian (ArMed) 42. Translations were printed in Catalan, 1475 (Klebs
> 1009.1); in Low-German [1484] (Cen V7); and in Spanish, 1494, 1495 (2) (Klebs
> 575.1–.3), and 1517 (NLMCat 2669). A Hebrew translation is assigned to
> Constantinople about 1510 (Sart III 1200).

546 Practica seu Philonium pharmaceuticum et chirurgicum, libri VII.
Barcelona: Pedro Posa, 23 Dec. 1484.   [LEK]

Ref: Klebs 1010.1; Sart III 1199; Garrison (1929) 163; *Castiglioni* (1947) 339.

N.B: A well organized therapeutic treatise on medicine and surgery, considered under the headings: *nomina, causae, signa, prognosticatio sive judicia, curatio.* Two editions were issued at Lyon in 1490 and two presumably in 1501, each by a different printer (Cen V8–V9; NLMCat 4471, 4472). Also known to have been printed in 1502, 1521, 1523, 1526, and 1535 at Venice (3) and Lyon (2).

VESALIUS, Andreas (André Vésale), 1514–1564.

547 Epistola, rationem modumque propinandi radicis chynae dedocti . . . pertractans. Basel: Joannes Oporinus, Oct. 1546. f°. [LEK]

Ref: NLMCat 4587; BM-Ger 891; Cushing VII.1; *Garrison* (1929) 219.

N.B: The so-called letter on the China root. Relates to the anti-syphilitic properties of the *smilax china*, introduced into Western Europe about 1525. Editions printed at Lyon, 1547, and in part at Würzburg, 1548 (NLMCat 4589, 4590), are cited in Cushing VII.3 and .4. A note under Cushing VII.2 suggests that the BMC-Ital 722 assignment of a Venice edition to 1546 is probably based on internal evidence (NLMCat 4588 [dedication 1546]). [See also under NATURAL SCIENCE.] The publication of Vesalius's doctoral thesis, *Paraphrasis in nonum librum Rhazae . . . ad Regem Almansorem* at Louvain and at Basel (NLMCat 4591) in 1537, is cited in Cushing I.-1 and I.-2. An edition was issued by Heinrich Petri at Basel in March 1544 [Cushing I.-3].

Mon: CUSHING, Harvey. *Bio-bibliography of Andreas Vesalius.* New York, 1943 (reviewed in *Isis* 35 398ff.; reprinted Hamden, Conn., Archon Books, 1962).

VETERINARIAE MEDICINAE LIBRI II (Tr: Jean de la Ruelle). *See no. 693 note.*

VIGO, Giovanni da, 1460–1525.

548 Practica copiosa in arte chirurgica, libri IX (Ed: Giovanni Antracini). Rome: Étienne Guillery and Ercole Nani, 1514. f°. [LEK]

Ref: NLMCat 4606; *Garrison* (1929) 225–226; *Castiglioni* (1947) 470.

N.B: A surgical work treating of syphilis and gunshot wounds, recommending for the latter a dressing of boiling oil. Castiglioni, but without mentioning the period covered, speaks of more than forty editions, including French, Italian, Spanish, German, and English versions. Garrison speaks of some fifty-two editions and innumerable translations. For sixteenth-century editions at the National Library of Medicine, see NLMCat p. 594.

549 Practica in professione chirurgica. Rome: Jacobus Mazochius, 1517. 4°.

Ref: BM-Ital 726; *Castiglioni* (1947) 470.

N.B: A summary of his *Practica copiosa* relating to surgery and anatomical knowledge essential to its practice. Possibly the work known as *Practica in arte chirurgica*

Vigo (continued)

compendiosa or *Practica compendiosa*, for the 1520 Venice edition of which see NLMCat 4605. Vigo contributed to surgery a method of ligating the great vessels by inserting a needle beneath the vein and tightening the cord from above, a method not common since the days of Celsus, in the early years of the Christian era.

VINCENT de BEAUVAIS (Vincentius Bellovacensis), *c.* 1200 – *c.* 1264.

550 Speculum doctrinale, libri XVII. [Strasbourg: The R-Printer (Adolf Rusch), 1477, not after 1478.] f°. [LEK]

Ref: BMC I 65; BM-Ger 894; Klebs 1037.1; Polain 3938A; LC (Thach) 12; *Sart* II 929–932; *Taton (A&MS)* 490; Stillwell V249, V250; Goff V-278, V-279.

N.B: Known in two issues from the same press, distinguishable by the use of 'ābulet' (Cen V250) or 'ambulet' (Cen V249) in the last line. The 'ābulet' issue at the Library of Congress has a presentation date, 1478, thus affording a terminal date for the issue here cited.

The book itself is one of four mammoth works which together make up the author's encyclopaedic *Speculum maius*, comprising the *Speculum historiale*, *Speculum morale*, *Speculum doctrinale*, and *Speculum naturale*. Of these the last two have scientific interest, since they record the common, traditional knowledge and folklore of the time. As analyzed by Sarton, the *Speculum doctrinale*, augmented by the *Speculum naturale*, devotes over four hundred sections to medicine. The work as a whole ranks as the greatest encyclopaedia of the Middle Ages, important as a collection of extracts and quotations from earlier writers.

Mon: THORNDIKE, Lynn. *Vincent of Beauvais* (p. 457–476 in vol. II of his *History of magic and experimental science*. New York, 1923).

WIDMANN, Johann (*called* Mechinger), 1440–1524.

551 Tractatus de pustulis sive mal de franzos. [Strasbourg: Johann (Reinhard) Grüninger, after 1 Feb. 1497.] 4°.

Ref: HC 16160; BMC I 111; Voull (B) 2332; Klebs 1048.1; Sudhoff-Singer p. xxxv-xxxix; Schullian (ArMed) 486; *Garrison* (1929) 209; *Castiglioni* (1947) 461; Stillwell W14; Goff W-17.

N.B: A diagnosis of the symptoms of syphilis, with a discussion of means to prevent contagion and an attempt to differentiate between syphilis, leprosy, and other diseases. Written by a physician, who was also a writer of mathematical textbooks.

Fac: SUDHOFF-SINGER 9, 10a.

YŪḤANNĀ ibn MASAWAIH *the Elder* (Mesuë *the Elder*; Yūḥannā ibn Māssūya), *c.* 777–857.

552 Aphorismi. (*Issued with* RHASIS. Liber ad Almansorem, libri X. Milan: Leonardus Pachel and Uldericus Scinzenzeler, 14 Feb. 1481.) [LEK]

Ref: HCR 13891; BMC VI 749; Schullian (ArMed) 399; Klebs 826.1; Choulant (H) 340; *Sart* I 574, 608 *note*; *O'Leary* 163–166; Stillwell R169; Goff R-175.

N.B: In early texts the author is frequently given as Janus (Joannes) Damascenus, an attribution possibly intended for Joannes Serapion *the Elder*, who flourished in Damascus at about the end of the ninth century. Now generally attributed to Mesuë *the Elder*, who lived in Jundishāpūr and Baghdād and was the teacher of Ḥunain ibn Isḥāq (Johannitius, *c*. 810–877), the famous translator of Greek texts into Arabic. A note under NLMCat 4778 states that in a compilation printed at Basel by Heinrich Petri about 1543, the "Contents vary from the two preceding editions [*i.e.*, Lyon, 1525 and Venice, 1530]. Book I contains the Aphorisms (not present in earlier editions) . . ." The title, however, is cited in the *Articella* of 1502 and 1507 and as issued with Maimonides, 1508; Ivry, 1519; and Benedetti, 1528 (NLMCat 325, 326, 3302, 2559, and 524, respectively).

YŪḤANNĀ ibn MASAWAIH al-Mārdīnī (Mesuë, Johannes; Mesuë *the Younger*), *d*. 1015.

553   Opera medicinalia (Ed: Peregrinus Cavalcabovis).   [Venice:] Clemens Patavinus, [not before 18 May 1471.]   f°.   [LEK]

Ref: HC 11118; BMC V 185; BM-Ital 739; Choulant (H) 351–358; Schullian (ArMed) 314; Klebs 680.1; *Garrison* (1929) 133; *Thornd* (*HM*) II 734*n*, 880, 923; *Sart* I 728; Stillwell M437; Goff M-508.

N.B: A compilation comprising his *Canones universales*; *De simplicibus*; *Practica*; and the apothecary's manual known as the *Grabadin*. An edition dated 9 June 1471 (Cen M438) is assigned to Florence and includes additions by Pietro d'Abano, *c*. 1250–1316, on remedies for complaints of the heart and digestive organs, with incipit reading: Liber Joannis Mesue De complexionibus proprietatibus electionibus operationibusque simplicium medicinarum laxativarum. Klebs lists fifteen Latin editions, ten of which are included in Cen M437–M446. [The *Grabadin* was subsequently issued with the *Antidotarium* of Nicolaus Salernitanus [Strasbourg, 1483/84] (Cen 142); and in various sixteenth-century editions of Mesuë's works as listed in NLMCat p. 398–402.]

554   Il libro della consolatione delle medicine semplici solutive [*Italian*]. [Modena:] Johannes Vurster, 25 June 1475.   f° & 4°.   [LEK]

Ref: H *11114; BMC VII 1059; Oates 2690; Klebs 681.1; Osler (IM) 93; Stillwell M447; Goff M-518.

N.B: A popular Italian version of Mesuë the Younger's major work. Printed also at Florence in editions assigned to 1480 and 1492; and at Venice in 1487 and 1493.

YŪḤANNĀ ibn SARĀBIYŪN *the Elder* (Serapion *the Elder*; Johannes Serapion; Jahiah ben Serabi; Yaḥyā ibn Sarāfyūn), *9th–10th century*.

555   Breviarium medicinae (Tr: Gherardo da Cremona, *c*. 1114–1187). Venice: Reynaldus de Novimagio, 1 Aug. 1479.   f°.   [LEK]

Ref: H *14693; BMC V 255; BM-Ital 739; Choulant (H) 345–347; Poynter 546; Klebs 912.1; Schullian (ArMed) 443; Sart I 608; Stillwell S420; Goff S-465.

N.B: Also known as the *Practica* or *Therapeuticae methodus*. There has been some question about the identity of this Syrian writer and that of Yūḥannā ibn Sarābiyūn *the Younger*. BM-Ital 739, for instance, does not distinguish between them, but most bibliographies keep to the traditional distinction. Re-issued at Venice, 16 Dec. 1497 (Cen S421). Editions printed at Lyon, Venice, and Basel in 1525, 1530, [1543], and 1550 are listed in NLMCat 4776–4779.

YŪḤANNĀ ibn SARĀBIYŪN *the Younger* (Serapion *the Younger*; Johannes Serapion *the younger*; Ibn Serabi), *11th–12th century.*

556 Liber Serapionis aggregatus in medicinis simplicibus (Tr: Simon of Genoa, *d.* 1330, and Abraham *Judaeus* of Tortosa, *fl.* 1290). Milan: Antonius Zarotus, 4 Aug. 1473. f°. [LEK]

Add: GALEN, *spurious.* De virtute centaureae ad Papiam.

Ref: HC *14691; Choulant (H) 371–72; Schullian (ArMed) 445; Osler (IM) 34; Klebs 913.1; Stillwell S422; Goff S-467.

N.B: Known also as *De simplici medicinae, De medicamentis simplicibus,* and *De temperamentis simplicium.* A popular work on simples and drugs. Garrison (1929) 133 identifies this drug-list as translated by Simon of Genoa and Abraham ben Shemtob in 1290. Re-issued in Venice, 8 June 1479 (Cen S423). Compilations issued in 1525, 1530, and 1550 are recorded in NLMCat 4776–4779. An Italian translation was issued by the Instituto per la Collaborazione Culturale, Venice/Rome, 1962 (Civiltà veneziana. Fonti e testi 3. 3rd ser., no. 1).

ZERBIS, Gabriele de (Zerbi; Gabriel Zerbus), 1468–1505.

557 De cautelis medicorum. [Venice: Christophorus de Pensis, not before 1495.] 4°. [LEK]

Ref: HC *16286; BMC V 470; BM-Ital 743; Schullian (ArMed) 489; Klebs 1058.1; *Garrison* (1929) 176; Stillwell Z25; Goff Z-25.

N.B: Treats of medical etiquette and practice. Re-issued at Pavia in 1508, and Lyon in 1525 (NLMCat 3437, 3438).

Mon: MANCINI, Clodomiro, ed. *Un codice deontologico del secolo XV: Il "De cautelis medicorum" di Gabriele de Zerbi*, Pisa, 1963 (Collana Scientia Veterum, no. 44).

558 Gerontocomia scilicet de senum cura atque victu. Rome: Eucharius Silber, 27 Nov. 1489. 4°.

Ref: HR 16284; BMC IV 110; BM-Ital 743; Schullian (ArMed) 490; Klebs 1057.1; Sart (*Appr*) 210:153; Stillwell Z26; Goff Z-26.

N.B: The first treatise on gerontology to be printed; by the author of the first account of the anatomy of the infant.

SUBJECT ANALYSIS FOR
NATURAL SCIENCE

[1] ANATOMY: Achillini; Avicenna; Benivieni; Berengario da Carpi; Brunschwig; Celsus; Cicero; Dryander; Dürer; Estienne; Fuchs; Galen; Günther; Guy de Chauliac; Haly Abbas; Hundt; Ketham; Maimonides; Mondino; Peylick; Rhasis; Saliceto; Valasco de Taranta; Vesalius.—DISSECTION: *Anatomia porci*; Aristotle; Bartholomaeus Anglicus; Benedetti; Berengario da Carpi; Bertuccio; Canano; Dryander; Estienne; Massa; Mondino; Saliceto; Vesalius; Zerbis.—INFANT: Zerbis.—POST-MORTEM: Benivieni.—TERMINOLOGY: *Anatomia porci*; Pollux. [See also under Zoology and MEDICINE: Surgery.]

[2] BIOLOGY: Aristotle; Avicenna; Cardano; Columella; Galen; Jacopo da Forlì (Giacomo Della Torre). [See also Physiology.]

[3] BIRDS: Conrad von Megenberg; Hildegard; *Hortus sanitatis*; Pliny; Rabanus Maurus; Turner; Vincent de Beauvais.

[4] BOTANY: Amatus (see Rodriguez); Aristotle; Bock; Brunfels; Curtius Rufus; Dioskorides; Estienne; Fernández de Oviedo; Fuchs; Gesner; Ludolph von Suchen; Pliny; Polo; Rodriguez; Ruelle; Silvatico; Strabo; Theophrastos.—TERMINOLOGY: Estienne. [See also MEDICINE: Medicinal properties of plants.]

[5] CHIROMANCY and PHYSIOGNOMY: Achillini; Aristotle; Michael *Scotus*; Pietro d'Abano; Rocca; Tiberti.

[6] FISH: Conrad von Megenberg; Hildegard; *Hortus sanitatis*; Oppianos; Rabanus Maurus; Theophrastos; Vincent de Beauvais.

[7] GEOLOGY and MINERALOGY: Agricola; Albertus Magnus; Aristotle; Fernández de Oviedo; Leonardi; Polo.

HERBALS: [See under MEDICINE: Medicinal properties of plants, *etc.*]

[8] HUSBANDRY and AGRICULTURE: Cato; Columella; Crescenzi; Estienne; Fitzherbert; Palladius; Varro; Walter of Henley. [See also MEDICINE: Veterinary Practice.]

[9] METALS: Agricola; Conrad von Megenberg; Hildegard; Vergilius.

[10] NATURAL PHILOSOPHY: Aristotle; Averroës; Bacon; Bartholomaeus *Anglicus*; Isidorus Hispalensis; Lucretius Carus; Pliny; Vergilius; Vincent de Beauvais.

[11] PHENOMENA: Conrad von Megenberg; *Ein Erdbeben.*

PHYSIOGNOMY: [See above, under CHIROMANCY.]

[12] PHYSIOLOGY: Aristotle; Censorinus; Falcucci; Fernel; Galen; Gilles de Corbeil (Aegidius Corboliensis); Hippocrates; Marliani; Servetus; Theophilos.

[13] SPORTS (Falconry, Fishing, Hunting):   Barnes; Crescenzi; *Habichtbuch*; Henri de Ferrières; *Le Livre de la chasse*; *Le Livre du faulcon*; Tardif.

[14] STONES: Albertus Magnus; Conrad von Megenberg; *Hortus sanitatis*; Leonardi; Theophrastos.

[15] TERMINOLOGY: Agricola; Estienne; Fuchs; Silvatico; Simon of Genoa.

[16] ZOOLOGY: Agricola; Albertus Magnus; Aristotle; Breydenbach; Columella; Conrad von Megenberg; Fernández de Oviedo; Galen; Ludolf von Suchen; Pliny; Polo; Rabanus Maurus; Vergilius.

IV. NATURAL SCIENCE

and Allied Topics

ABŪ-l-WALĪD Muḥammad ibn Aḥmad. *See* AVERROËS.

ABŪ SINA. *See* AVICENNA.

ACHILLINI, Alessandro, 1463–1512.

559 In Mundini anatomiam annotationes (Ed: Philotheus Achillini). Bologna: Hieronymus de Benedictis, 23 Sept. 1520. 4°. [LEK]

> *Ref*: NLMCat 31 (?); BM-Ital 5; *Mayer* (1941) 7–9; *Castiglioni (Ren)* 39; *Castiglioni* (1947) 368.
>
> *N.B*: An early attempt to correct Galen's errors. Although basing his treatise on Mondino, Achillini included observations of his own regarding the bladder, bile ducts, cranial nerves, and various other elements. Possibly printed at Venice as early as 1516.
>
> *Mon*: THORNDIKE, Lynn. *Achillini: Aristotelian and anatomist* (Chap. III in vol. V of his *History of magic and experimental science*, New York, 1941).

560 De subjecto physionomiae et chyromantiae. Bologna: Joannes Antonius de Benedictis, 1503. f°. [LEK]

> *Ref*: NLMCat 32.
>
> *N.B*: The earliest edition of this tract found in the present survey. Also known under the title *De chyromantiae principiis et physionomiae*. Addressed to Bartolommeo della Rocca (known as Cocles), whose work *Chyromantie ac physionomie anastasis* was issued by the same press in 1504 and prefixed to that work as Achillini's "Approbatio." Included in a compilation of similar works assigned to the press of Bernardinus de Garaldis and dated 1515 (NLMCat 2542).

AGRICOLA (Georg Bauer; Georgius Agricola; *usually called* Agricola), 1491–1555.

561 De animantibus subterraneis liber. Basel: Hieronymus Froben and Nicolaus Episcopius, *the Elder*, 1549. 8°. [LEK]

> *Ref*: BM-Ger 8; *Hoover (Agricola)* 597, 600.
>
> *N.B*: A brief account of animals that live or hibernate under ground or have been forced to migrate by geological changes.

Agricola (continued)

> *Mon*: PRESCHER, Hans, *ed. Georgius Agricola—Ausgewählte Werke*. Berlin (East Germany), 1955–1956, a commemorative series of three volumes sponsored by the Staatliches Museum für Mineralogie und Geologie at Dresden—I) *Georg Agricola und seine Zeit*; II) *Bermannus*, with translation; III) *Schriften zur Geologie und Mineralogie* (reviewed, p. 368–369 in *Isis* 49 1958).

562　Bermannus sive De re metallica dialogus.　Basel: In aedibus Frobenianis, 1530.　8°.　[LEK]

> *Ref*: BM-Ger 8; *Hoover (Agricola)* 596, 599–600, 603; *HTech* II 39.
>
> *N.B*: An important book on mineralogy. Written as a conversation between Bermannus [presumably Lorenz Berman, Agricola's friend and a prominent miner] and two scholars, regarding the minerals seen as they walked through the Saxon mines.　It describes various minerals for the first time and records German designations which are still in common use. [See also Agricola's works under TECHNOLOGY.]

563　De natura eorum quae effluunt ex terra libri IV. (*Issued with his* De ortu et causis subterraneorum. Basel: Hieronymus Froben and Nicolaus Episcopius, *the Elder*, 1546.)

> *Ref*: BM-Ger 8; *HTech* III 28.
>
> *N.B*: Relates to subterranean waters and gases.

564　De natura fossilium libri X. (*Issued with his* De ortu et causis subterraneorum. Basel: Hieronymus Froben and Nicolaus Episcopius *the Elder*, 1546.)

> *Ref*: BM-Ger 8; Burndy (Dibner) 128; *Hoover (Agricola)* 594, 600, 603; *HTech* III 28–29; *Sart (SW)* 158.
>
> *N.B*: The first systematic treatise on mineralogy. Comprises also a glossary of mineralogical terms in Latin and German. Agricola believed rocks and metals to be formed through the precipitation of mineral solutions due to the action of gravity, heat, cold, and evaporation. In addition to his own classification of minerals, he reviews earlier accounts from the time of Aristotle.
>
> Ex-President Hoover in his monograph on Agricola, p. 594, analyzes the Books of the present work. Its text was translated into English by M. C. and J. A. Bandy, New York, 1955 (GEOLOGICAL SOCIETY OF AMERICA. Special paper, 63).

565　De ortu et causis subterraneorum libri V [*and other works*].　Basel: Hieronymus Froben and Nicolaus Episcopius, *the Elder*, 1546.　f°. [LEK]

> *Ref*: BM-Ger 8; Horblit 2a; *Hoover (Agricola)* 594–596, 600, 603; *Sart (SW)* 159.
>
> *N.B*: A treatise on geology discussing underground heat and vapors, the causes of volcanoes, earthquakes, and mountains, and the origin of ores. Particularly

IV. *Natural Science*

valuable in its description of ore-deposits. Contains also his *De natura eorum quae effluunt ex terra libri IIII. De natura fossilium libri X. De veteribus et novis metallis libri II. Bermannus sive De re metallica dialogus. Interpretatio Germanica vocum rei metallicae addito indice faecundissimo.* For an analysis of Agricola's theory of ore deposits as set forth in the *De ortu*, see Hoover (Agricola) 46–53.

An Italian translation of this edition was printed at Venice by Michele Tramezzino in 1550 (BM-Ital 10), and a Latin edition including Agricola's additions and revisions was issued by the original press in 1558.

Fac: HORBLIT 2a [2b, recto].

ALBERTUS MAGNUS (Albrecht von Bollstädt), *Saint, c.* 1200–1280.

566   De animalibus libri XXVI (Ed: Fernandus Cordubensis).   Rome: Simon Nicolai Chardella, de Lucca, 2 Apr. 1478.   f°.   [LEK]

> *Ref*: GW 587; HCR 545; BMC IV 75; Oates 1436; IGI 161; Klebs 14.1; *Sart* II 938; *Thornd* (*HM*) II 540–545; Stillwell A201; Goff A-223.
>
> *N.B*: One of the outstanding works of scientific interest written between the time of Pliny and the sixteenth century. Text based largely on Aristotle, but offset by occasional observations and an attitude of mind indicative of a scientific point of view. [For a brief analysis see Crombie (A–G) 1961 I 151–157.] Variant issue known. Issued at Mantua in 1479 and at Venice in 1495 (Cen A202, A203); and at Venice for the heirs of Octavianus Scotus in 1515 (NLMCat 94). An Italian version of Book XXII, *Trattato d'Alberto Magno sopra le malscaltie del cavallo*, is included in a manual printed at Venice in 1519 (NLMCat p. 12), the main work of which is attributed to Giordano Ruffo—*see no.* 508.

567   De mineralibus (Corr: Nicolaus de Pigaciis).   [Padua:] Petrus Maufer, for Antonius de Albricis, 20 Sept. 1476.   f°.   [LEK]

> *Ref*: GW 686; IGI 206; Klebs 21.1; *Crombie* (*A–G*) 1961 I 123–129; Stillwell A251; Goff A-279.
>
> *N.B*: See also under TECHNOLOGY.
>
> *Mon*: WYCKOFF, Dorothy. *Albertus Magnus on ore deposits* (p. 109–122 in *Isis* 49 1958).

568   Summa de creaturis.   Venice: Simon de Luere, for Andreas Torresanus, 19 Dec. 1498; 16 Feb. 1498/99.   f°.   [LEK]

> *Ref*: GW 779; H *569; BMC V 574; BM-Ital 13; IGI 238; Klebs 27.1; Schullian (ArMed) 26; Stillwell A304; Goff A-334.

'ALĪ ibn 'ABBĀS. *See* HALY ABBAS.

ANATOMIA PORCI (*the so-called* Anatomia Cophonis), *12th century.*

569   Anatomia porci. (*Issued with* Yūhannā ibn Massawaih al-Mardīnī. Mesuë vita [*and other works*]. Lyon: Impressa per Antonium du Ry, impensis

Anatomia Porci (continued)

vero Jacobi q. Francisci de Giunta & sociorum Florentini, 1523.)   8°.
[LEK]

Ref: NLMCat 3136; Baudrier V 112; Choulant (H) 260–263; *Sart* II 237.

N.B: An account of an anatomical demonstration, the public dissection of a pig. Important in its varied and transitional use of terminology. Although issued in a compilation devoted largely to MESUË *the Younger* (Yūḥannā ibn Masawaih al-Mardīnī), a section entered in the title as *Antidotarium domini Nicolai Cophonis . . . isagoge* relates to Copho, comprises his *Ars medendi*, and is followed by the *Anatomia porci*, sometimes erroneously ascribed to him. The compilation was reissued by the same publishing-house and press in 1531 (NLMCat 3137). The *Anatomia porci* and the *Ars medendi* are recorded as issued together by Valentinus Kobianus at Hagenau in 1532 (Choulant (H) 263); and the *Anatomia porci ex traditione Cophonis* with Dryander's *Anatomiae*, Marburg, 1537 (*no. 619n, below*).

Mon: CORNER, G. W. *Anatomical texts of the earlier Middle Ages, with a revised Latin text and English translation of Anatomia Cophonis*, Washington, 1927 (reviewed, p. 452–456 in *Isis* 9).

ARISTOTLE (Aristoteles), *c*. 384–322 B.C.

570   Opera [*Greek*].   Venice: Aldus Manutius, I) Nov. 1495; II) Feb. 1497; III) 29 Jan. 1497; IV) June 1497; V) June 1498.   f°.

Ref: GW 2334; HC *1657; BMC V 553, 556, 555, 556, 558; Oates 2162, 2172, 2170, 2173, 2182; IGI 791; Klebs 83.1; Renouard (Alde) 25; Stillwell A858; Goff A-959.

N.B: Since much of this five-volume set of Greek texts by classical writers consists of the life and works of Aristotle, it is generally entered under his name. In addition, however, the series contains Galen's history of philosophy (*spurious*) and works by Porphyrius; Theophrastos; Philo Judaeus; and Alexander of Aphrodisias.

Among Aristotle's works the following are included: vol. II) *De physico auditu s. Physica libri VIII*; *De coelo libri IV*; *De mundo ad Alexandrum liber I*—vol. III) *De historia animalium libri IX*, pt. of *liber X* (?); *De partibus animalium libri IV*; *De anima*; *De sensu et sensato*; *De motu animalium*; *De generatione animalium libri V*; *De respiratione*; *De animalium incessu*; *De coloribus*; *Physiognomia*—vol. IV *Problemata* (Comm: Alexander of Aphrodisias); *Mechanica* [authenticity questioned]; *Metaphysica*. For the *Mechanica* and *De animalium incessu*, inclusion in this Greek *Opera* is their first known printing. The others cited had appeared in Latin earlier in the fifteenth century, as listed herein. A Greek *Opera* edited by Erasmus was printed at Basel in 1531—Choulant (H) 54.

Mon: RANDALL, John Herman, Jr. *Aristotle*. New York, 1960 (reviewed, p. 248–249 in *Isis* 53 1962).

571   Opera [*Latin*].   Venice: Philippus Petri, 4 April 1482.   f°.

Add: AVERROËS. De substantia orbis.

Ref: GW 2336; IGI 792; Pell 1194; Voull (B) 3733.5; Klebs 82.6; Stillwell A860; Goff A-961.

Con: Physica.——De caelo et mundo.——De generatione et corruptione.——Meteorologica.——De anima.——De plantis.——De coloribus . . .——De inundatione Nili.——Physiognomia.——De motu animalium.——De sensu et sensato . . .——Metaphysica.——Etc., etc.

N.B: Text ends, fol. 349: *Expliciunt opera Aristotelis de naturali philosophia* . . . Three of the texts cited above—*De coloribus, De motu animalium*, and the spurious *De plantis*—saw their first printing in this volume.

> Three earlier compilations, however, are on record. A volume—possibly a compilation of remainders, issued at Padua, *c.* 1475 (Horblit 6)—contains other Aristotelian works of scientific interest printed by Laurentius Canozius, 22 Nov. 1472–24 June 1474. [For the works as separately issued, *see nos.* 25, 26, 572, 580, 733, 735, 736 *herein*]. The Opera cited in Copinger 615 as printed at [Lyon, 1468?] is not known today. The Opera printed at Augsburg in 1479 (Cen A859) includes the *Physica* but in general comprises works of philosophy rather than science.

572 De anima (Comm: Averroës, 1126–1198). Padua: Laurentius Canozius, de Lendenaria, for Joannes Philippus Aurelianus et fratres, 22 Nov. 1472. f°. [LEK]

Ref: GW 2349; HCR 1709; BMC VII 907; Oates 2542; IGI 800; Klebs 84.1; Choulant (H) 51; *Lewes* 221–245; *Garrison* (1929) 101; *Singer* (*SHA*) 25; Stillwell A867; Goff A-969.

N.B: One of seven tracts issued by this press and publisher and combined in a compilation issued at Padua about 1475 (Horblit 6). The text appeared in volume III of the Greek *Opera*, Venice, 29 Jan. 1497, and Greek editions of the text were printed at Basel in 1544 and 1548. Klebs lists seven Latin editions printed during 1472–1500 at Padua (1), Cologne (2), Leipzig (3), and Venice (1). Included in compilations issued at Venice in 1483, 1489, 1495, 1496 (GW 2337, 2339–41) and 1540 (NLMCat 272).

573 De animalibus. (Tr: Theodoros Gaza, *fl.* 1400–1475. Ed: Ludovicus Podocatharus.) Venice: Johannes de Colonia and Johannes Manthen, 1476. f°. [LEK]

Ref: GW 2350; HC *1699; BMC V 232; IGI 803; Choulant (H) 45–47; Poynter 69; Klebs 85.1; Schullian (ArMed) 47; *Lewes* 269–375; *Nordenskiöld* (*HB*) 37–43; *Taton* (*A&MS*) I 236–238; *Crombie* (*A-G*) 1961 I 140; Stillwell A870; Goff A-973.

Con: De natura animalium sive De historia animalium libri IX. De partibus animalium libri IV. De generatione animalium libri V.

N.B: The first compilation relating to biology to be printed, containing three of Aristotle's great works on biology and physiology as disclosed by the dissection and study of animals. Issued also at Venice in 1492, *c.* 1495, and 1498 (Cen A871–A873), by the Aldine press in 1504 and 1513, and by Hieronymus Scotus in 1545

Aristotle (continued)

(NLMCat 273). The texts appear in vol. III of the Greek *Opera* printed at Venice, 29 Jan. 1497 (*no. 570, above*), and in Gaza's translation in a compilation issued by Andreas Cratander at Basel in 1534 (NLMCat). A Greek edition of the *De generatione animalium* was printed at Venice in Feb. 1526 (Choulant (H) 51:9). Aristotle's theory rested upon a graduated hierarchy of living matter from invertebrate to vertebrate animals, a teleological concept and scale of living nature. [For discussion of Aristotle's powers of observation and inductive reasoning, see NEEDHAM, Joseph. *A history of embryology* issued in 1934; re-issued, New York, 1959.]

Mon: THOMPSON, W. D'Arcy. *On Aristotle as a biologist*. Oxford, 1913. LONES, Thomas East. *Aristotle's researches in natural science*. London, 1912. MICHEL, P.-H. *The Aristotelian school: Natural science* (p. 236–240 in TATON, René, ed. *Ancient and Medieval science* . . . New York; Basic Books, Inc., 1963).

Fac: SARTON, G. *A history of science*. Cambridge, 1952, vol. I, p. 528–529.

De animalium incessu [*Greek*]. *See volume III of the Greek* Opera, *no. 570*.

[For a Latin version by Nicolò Leonico Tomeo and his commentary printed at Venice in 1523 and 1525 respectively, *see* NLMCat 283 *and* 2794.]

574 Chiromantia: Cyromancia Aristotilis cum figuris. Ulm [Johann Reger] 21 July 1490. 4°.

Ref: GW 2358; HC *1778; BMC II 540; Oates 1170; Pell 1264; Voull (B) 2663.5; Klebs 86.1; Stillwell A877; Goff A-980.

N.B: The only edition found in the present survey.

575 De coloribus. (*Issued with his* Opera. Venice: Philippus Petri, 4 April 1482). f°. [LEK]

Ref: GW 2336; H 1682; IGI 792; Voull (B) 3735.5; Pell 1194; Klebs 82.6; Stillwell A860; Goff A-961.

N.B: Although not known to have been printed as a separate, the text is found in a compilation printed at Venice in 1496 (Cen A865) and in volume III of the Greek *Opera* printed at Venice, 29 Jan. 1497 (*no. 570, above*). A translation by Celio Calcagnini is included in a volume issued at Paris by Jacobus Gazellus in 1548 (NLMCat 2578).

De generatione animalium, libri V. *See no. 573*.

576 De generatione et corruptione (Comm: Averroës, 1126–1198). Padua: Laurentius Canozius, de Lendenaria, for Johannes Philippus Aurelianus et fratres, 18 June 1474. f°. [LEK]

Ref: *See below, under no. 733*.

N.B: Presents Aristotle's theory of the elements and the four qualities affecting matter. Issued in the second volume of the Greek *Opera*, Feb. 1497 (*no. 570*).

IV. *Natural Science*

De historia animalium. *See no.* 573.

De inundatione Nili. *See no.* 571, 581.

Lapidarius. *See no.* 581 *note.*

577 Meteorologica, libri IV (Liber 4, comm: Averroës, 1126–1198). Padua: Laurentius Canozius, de Lendenaria, for Johannes Philippus Aurelianus et fratres, 24 June 1474. f°. [LEK]

Ref: GW 2423; HCR 1696; Oates 2546; IGI 829; Klebs 91.1; *Sart* I 133; Stillwell A900; Goff A-1007.
N.B: One of the main sources of medieval geology. [For other editions, see no. 735.]
Mon: HELLMAN, G. *Bibliographie der gedruckten Ausgaben, Übersetzungen und Auslegungen der Meteorologie des Aristoteles.* Berlin, 1917. CROMBIE, A. C. *Geology* (p. 123–129 in vol. I of his *Augustine to Galileo,* London, Mercury Books, 1961).

578 De mineralibus (Tr: Alfredus Anglicus). (*Issued with* Secreta secretorum Aristotelis. Lyon: In edibus Antonii Blanchard, 1528.) 4°.

Ref: NLMCat 270; *Crombie (A–G)* 1961 I 133.
N.B: According to Aristotle's theory, minerals are produced by exhalations within the earth and metals by the combination of sulphur and mercury, as generated by dry and wet exhalations.

579 De motu animalium. (*Issued in his* Opera. Venice: Philippus Petri, 4 April 1482.) f°. [LEK]

Ref: GW 2336; H*1682; IGI 792; Pell 1194; Klebs 82.6; Stillwell A860; Goff A-961.
N.B: Included also in editions of the *Parva naturalia* printed at Padua in 1493 and Cologne in 1491 and 1498, also in the Latin *Opera,* Venice, 1496 (Cen A865). A Greek text appears in volume III of the Greek *Opera,* Venice: Aldus Manutius, 29 Jan. 1497 and in volume I of the Latin *Opera* printed at Basel in 1538. A commentary by Nicolò Leonico Tomeo (1456–1531?) was included in the latter's *Opuscula,* Venice, 1525, and re-issued by Simon de Colines at Paris in 1530 (NLMCat 2794, 2795).

De natura animalium. *See no.* 573.

De partibus animalium. *See no.* 573.

580 Parva naturalia (Comm: Averroës, 1126–1198). [Padua: Laurentius Canozius, de Lendenaria, about 1474.] f°. [LEK]

Add: AVERROËS. De substantia orbis.
Ref: GW 2427; Oates 2548; Pell 1213; Klebs 92.1; Horblit 6; *Lewes* 246–268; Stillwell A909; Goff A-1016.

181

Aristotle (continued)

N.B: A compilation of variable contents. This Padua edition consists of a commentary and tract by Averroës and four Aristotelian items—*De sensu et sensato*, *De memoria et reminiscentis*, *De somno et vigilia*, and *De longitudine et brevitate vitae*. The Leipzig editions of *c.* 1490/95 and *c.* 1498 are without the Averroës but include the tracts by Aristotle (GW 2425–26; Cen A908). To the latter the Padua edition of 1493 adds *De bona fortuna*, *De causis*, and a commentary by Thomas *Aquinas* (GW 2430; Cen 912), while the Cologne editions of 1491 and 1498 add to the original four the tracts, *De iuventute et senectute*, *De inspiratione et respiratione*, *De vita et morte*, *De motu animalium*, *De motu cordis*, and the commentary of Johannes de Mechlinia (GW 2428–29; Cen A910, A911). Editions containing 9 Aristotelian items and a commentary by Nicolò Leonico Tomeo, printed at Venice in 1523 and at Paris in 1530 are recorded in NLMCat 283 and 284.

One of seven items issued by this publisher about 1475, as an 'Opera' (Horblit 6). [See note under no. 571, above.]

581 Physiognomia. (*Issued with* De pomo. De inundatione Nili. [Cologne: Arnold Ther Hoernen, *c.* 1472]) 4°.

Ref: GW 2450; HC 1786; BMC I 204; Voull (K) 161; Pell 1266; Klebs 94.1.

N.B: A popular work, the first *dated* printing of which occurs in a volume introduced by the *Lapidarius* and issued at Merseburg, 20 Oct. 1473 (GW 2389). Issued in French together with the *Secreta secretorum* in at least eight editions issued between *c.* 1484 and the early years of the sixteenth century. Included in the third volume of the Greek *Opera*, published in Venice, 29 Jan. 1497, and in compilation of Latin texts issued at Venice in 1489, 1495/96, and 1496. NLMCat 276 lists an Italian version by Giovanni Manente issued with other texts at Venice in 1538.

582 De plantis, *spurious*. (*Issued in his* Opera. Venice: Filippo di Pietro, 4 April 1482.)

Ref: GW 2336; H *1682; IGI 792; Klebs 82.6; *Arber* (1938) 4; *Sart* I 226; *Crombie* (A–G) 1961 I 141, 147; Stillwell A860; Goff A-961.

N.B: A work whose authenticity was first questioned by Julius Caesar Scaliger, 1484–1558; now generally accepted as spurious—Hunt (Quinby) I 98*n*. A compilation from Aristotle and Theophrastos. Variously attributed to Nicolaus, *Damascenus*, 1st century B.C. Included with *De respiratione*, *De coloribus*, *De vegetabilibus* and other Aristotelian items in a compilation printed at Venice for Benedictus Fontana by Johannes et Gregorius de Gregoriis in 1496 (GW 2341; Cen A865).

De pomo. *See no. 581*.

583 Problemata (Tr: Theodorus Gaza, *fl.* 1400–1475). Mantua: Johann Vurster and Johann Baumeister [*c.* 1473]. 4°. [LEK]

Ref: GW 2452; HCR 1729; BMC VII 929; IGI 846; Pell 1217; Osler (IM) 42; Klebs 95.1; Stillwell A921; Goff A-1030.

N.B: In this and in the first dated edition—Rome, 1475 (Cen A922)—the text begins: Cur exuperantiae. In that assigned to Magdeburg, 1483/84 (GW 2454) and in subsequent editions, the text begins: Omnes homines. Of the latter group the *Gesamtkatalog der Wiegendrucke* records 24 editions before 1501, namely, 2 issued at Magdeburg, 3 at Leipzig, 2 at Antwerp, 1 at Augsburg, 7 at Cologne, and 3 at Paris; plus 3 German versions printed at Augsburg, 1 at Memmingen, and 2 at Ulm. Six undated editions are re-assigned to the early sixteenth century as printed at Paris (3), Antwerp (1), and Cologne (2). Latin editions printed at Venice in 1501 and Paris in 1550, and excerpts in German issued in 1515, 1531, and 1543 are listed in NLMCat 286, 287, 294–296. The Greek text appeared with the commentary of Alexander of Aphrodisias in volume IV of the Greek *Opera*, June 1498 (*see no. 570*).

De respiratione. *See no. 570 note, 580 note.*

584 Secreta secretorum (Tr: Philippus Tripolitanus). [Cologne: Arnold Ther Hoernen, *c.* 1472] 4°. [LEK]

Ref: GW 2481; HC 1782; BMC I 206; Oates 440; Voull (K) 162; Klebs 96.1; *Sart* I 544; *O'Leary* 159; Stillwell A934; Goff A-1047.

N.B: Authenticity questioned. A popular work including sections on physiognomy and dietetics. Translated from Syriac into Arabic by Yūḥannā ibn Batriq about 815. Known in at least fourteen Latin editions or versions and eight French versions issued during the fifteenth century, the latter frequently with the text of the *Physiognomania*.

De sensu et sensato. *See nos. 570 note, 571 note, 580 note.*

585 De signis aquarum, ventorum, & tempestatum (Tr: Bartholomaeus de Messana). (*Issued with* Secreta secretorum Aristotelis. Lyon: In edibus Antonius Blanchard, 1528). 4°.

Ref: NLMCat 270.

N.B: Authenticity questioned. A title listed in vol. II of the Greek *Opera*, Feb. 1497 reads: De signis aquarum & ventorum, incerti auctoris (GW 2334).

586 De vegetabilibus. (*Issued in his* Opera. Venice: Joannes et Gregorius de Gregoriis, de Forlivio, for Benedictus Fontana, 13 July 1496.) f°.

Ref: GW 2341; HC *1659; BMC V 349; IGI 797; Klebs 82.7; Cen A865.

N.B: The only 15th-century printing of the *De vegetabilibus* known.

IV. *Natural Science*

AVERROËS (Abū-l-Walīd Muḥammad ibn Aḥmad ibn Muḥammad ibn Rushd. *Variously called* Ibn Rushd; Muḥammad ibn Aḥmad; Averroës), 1126–1198.

587 Liber universalis de medicina qui dicitur Colliget [al-Kullīyāt]. Ferrara: Laurentius de Rubeis et socii, 5 Oct. 1482. f °. [LEK]

> *Ref*: GW 3107 and 3107 note (*var.*); HC *2189 (*var.*); BMC VI xi; IGI 1107; Klebs 128.1 and 128.1 (*var.*); *Campbell* (*AM*) I 95; *Sart* II 360; *Nordenskiöld* (*HB*) 71-72; Stillwell A1256; Goff A-1411.
>
> *N.B*: The chief work of a great natural philosopher who developed Aristotle's theory of potentiality into an independent thesis of his own, maintaining that, in nature, only that has potentiality which already exists, even though in undeveloped form —as the plant already exists in embryo in the seed. Two variants are known from this same press—one without place of printing; the other naming Venice (Schullian (ArMed) 72).

AVICENNA (Abū 'Alī al-Ḥusain ibn 'Abdallah ibn Sina. *Variously called* Avicenna; Alhossein; Ibn Sina; *or* Ḥusain), *c*. 985–1037.

588 De animalibus (Tr: Michael Scotus, *d*. 1235). [Venice: Joannes and Gregorius de Gregoriis, about 1500.] f °.

> *Ref*: GW 3112; HC *2220; BMC V 352; IGI 1112; Klebs 136.1; Schullian (ArMed) 74; Stillwell A1261; Goff A-1415.

589 Canon medicinae [al-Qanūn], libri V (Tr: Gherardo da Cremona, *c*. 1114–1187). Milan: Philippus de Lavagnia, 12 Feb. 1473. f °. [LEK]

> *Ref*: GW 3115; BMC VI 700; BM-Ital 336[7]; IGI 1115; Klebs 131.2; *Sart* I 709–711.
> *N.B*: The first *dated* edition of an influential work written in Arabic in the eleventh century and translated into Latin in the twelfth. Possibly first issued in separate parts, since GW 3125 cites a printing of Book III with the date 23 Dec. 1472. An undated edition is variously assigned to the press of Adolf Rusch at Strasbourg before 1473 (Horblit 7; Cen A1262). A new translation by Andrea Alpago, *d*. 1520, was issued at Venice in 1544 (BM-Ital 335). A Hebrew edition was printed at Naples, 9 Nov. 1491-[1492?] (Stillwell H493; Goff Heb-4). Klebs lists fourteen Latin editions printed during the fifteenth century.
> The anatomical sections of the *Canon*—Books I and III—were the most widely read anatomical texts until considerably after our period. According to Afnan, p. 204, they were still being studied in the late seventeenth century and at Louvain in the eighteenth. Thus the *Canon*'s transmission of the errors of Galen, on whose works it was largely based, held even after the illustrations published in Vesalius's works in the 1540s had shown that Galen's anatomical descriptions of animals were not applicable to the human form.
> De Koning's French translation from the Arabic, which cites corresponding sections from Galen and the text of Oreibasios, comprises part of the *Canon*'s

Book I, *De la nature des parties du corps et des parties qui les composent*, in 77 sections or fanns; and Book III, *De l'utilité de la tête*, in 22 fanns.

Mon: AFNAN, Soheil M. *Avicenna, his life and works*, London, 1958. DE KONING, P. *Trois traités d'anatomie arabes . . . Traduction*. Leide, 1903, p. 432–643; 644–781. [*See also* MEDICINE: Avicenna, *no.* 287.]

590 Cantica de medicina (Comm: Averroës, 1126–1198). Venice: Petrus Maufer and Nicolaus de Contugo, 24 Mar. 1483. f°. [LEK]

> *Ref:* GW 3128; IGI 1128; Schullian (ArMed) 81; *Choulant (Anat)* 21; Stillwell A1274; Goff A-1429.
>
> *N.B:* Said to have anatomical interest as well as medical. Re-issued the following year, at Venice, by the rival press of Andreas de Soziis.

BACON, Roger, *c.* 1214–1294.

591 De mirabili potestate artis et naturae, ubi de philosophorum lapide . . . libellus (Ed: Oronce Fine, 1494–1555). (*Issued with* COELESTINUS, Claudius. De his quę mundo mirabiliter eveniunt . . . opusculum. Paris: Simon de Colines, 1542.) 4°.

> *Ref:* NLMCat 979; *Sart* II 954, 963.
>
> *N.B:* Written by a philosopher and encyclopaedist who was a believer in experimental science. In spite of his many writings, no incunabula are known and early sixteenth-century imprints are rare. According to Sarton, the *Speculum alchemia* variously attributed to Bacon was printed at Nuremberg in 1541 and his *Epistola de secretis* at Paris in 1542. [For a note on the *Speculum alchemia*, see under TECHNOLOGY.]

BARBARO, Ermolao (Hermolaus Barbarus; Barbari), 1454–1493.

592 Castigationes Plinianae et Pomponii Melae. Rome: Eucharius Silber, 24 Nov. 1492; 13 Feb. 1493. f°. [LEK]

> *Ref:* GW 3340; HC *2421; BMC IV 113; Oates 1536; IGI 1210; Klebs 143.1; *Thornd (HM)* IV 601; Stillwell B88; Goff B-100.
>
> *N.B:* A factor in the controversy over Pliny instigated by Leonicenus, which developed into more of a humanistic contention over words and sources than over Pliny's statements regarding natural science, medicine, and other matters. According to Barbaro's analysis, Pliny derived much of his text from Aristotle, Theophrastos, and Dioskorides. In Wightman (1962) I 31, Barbaro's concern is described as mainly that of the balancing of rival authorities. An edition anonymously printed for Daniele Barbaro is assigned to Venice about 1493–1494. Barbaro's *Syllabus sive index omnium* to his *Castigationes Plinianae*, edited by Joannes Oporinus, was printed at Basel in 1534 (NLMCat 469).

Barbaro (continued)

593 In Dioscoridem corollariorum libri V.   Venice: Aloysius et Franciscus Barbari, 1516. f °. [LEK]

> *Ref*: BM-Ital 71, 218; Choulant (H) 82; *Sart (Appr)* 71–72.
>
> *N.B*: Edited by Giovanni Battista Cipelli (Joannes Baptista Egnatius, *pseud.*), 1473–1553. Also included in the author's translation of Dioscorides issued at Venice in 1516, at Strasbourg in 1529 and at Cologne in 1530 (NLMCat 1140, 1144, 470 respectively).

BARNES, Juliana (*called* Berners), *fl.* 1385?, *author, at least in part.*

594 The Book of hawking, hunting, and heraldry.   Saint-Albans: [The Schoolmaster printer] 1486. f °. [LEK]

> *Ref*: GW 4932; H 2465; Pr 9828; Oates 4212; Klebs 500.1; Stillwell B915; Goff B-1030.
>
> *N.B*: The earliest printed book in English on falconry and hunting. Frequently entered anonymously, under title, or under Berners. An inner page (Fol. 40a) ends with the words: Explicit Dam Julyans Barnes in her boke of huntyng. Issued by Wynkyn de Worde at Westminster in 1496, with the addition of *The treatyse of fysshinge wyth an angle* (Cen B916; LC(LJRCat) 412).
>
> *Fac*: London, 1881 (Blades).

BARTHOLOMAEUS *Anglicus, fl.* 1200–1240.

595 De proprietatibus rerum.   [Basel: Berthold Ruppel, 1471 or later.] f °. [LEK]

> *Ref*: GW 3402; HC *2499; BMC III 716; BM-Ger 67; Klebs 149.1; Schullian (Ar-Med) 89; *Sart* II 586–588; *Thornd (HM)* II 401–435; *Singer (SHA)* 1957, 170; Stillwell B115; Goff B-130.
>
> *N.B*: An encyclopaedia written for the common people, that went through many editions. Still important for its information on political geography and its accounts of natural history. It treats also of medicine, cosmology, form and matter, meteorology, minerals, metals, trees, plants, measures and weights, musical instruments, and many other matters. In the section relating to anatomy, the English translation printed at Westminster by Wynkyn de Worde about 1495 (Cen B128) shows a woodcut of a dissection, the first published in England—*Singer (SHA)* 1957, *fig.* 98. A variant but somewhat similar cut appears in the French version printed at Lyon in 1493—Castiglioni (1947) 334 *fac.* Apparently printed in the type of shorter body used by Ruppel after the printers' strike of 1471. An undated edition is variously assigned to William Caxton at Cologne about 1471 (Cen B116). A Dutch version was issued at Haarlem by Jacob Bellaert, 24 Dec. 1485 and in the same year a French version was printed at Lyon (Goff B-142, B-144). An English version by John Trevisa printed at London

in 1535 and a Spanish translation by Vincente de Burgos, Toledo, 1529 are recorded in NLMCat 476 and 477.

Mon: STEELE, Robert. *Mediaeval lore, an epitome of the science . . . of the middle age, being
classified gleanings from the encyclopaedia of Bartholomaeus Anglicus on the properties
of things.* London, 1893 (repr. in THE KING'S CLASSICS, London, 1907).

BENEDETTI, Alessandro (Alexander Benedictus), *c.* 1450–1512.

596   Historia corporis humani sive Anatomice, libri V.   Venice: Bernardinus Guerraldus, 1 Dec. 1502.   4°.   [LEK]

   Ref: NLMCat 520; BM-Ital 83; *Sart (Appr)* 123, 211:170; *Castiglioni* (1947) 369;
   Singer (SHA) 104; *Schullian (Benedetti)* 13, 32, 35, 240, 241.
   N.B: Written by a physician and philologist, notable for his skill in dissection and for
   his connection with the anatomical theater at Padua. Issued together with his
   Collectiones medicinales seu Aforismi at Paris in [1514] by Henricus Stephanus [Henri
   Estienne]; in an unsigned edition assigned to [Paris: Simon Du Bois] 1527; by
   Eucharius Cervicornus at [Cologne] in 1527; and at Strasbourg, Apud Johannem
   Hervagium, 1528 (NLMCat 521–524). Benedetti's edition of Pliny was printed
   at Venice in 1513, by Melchior Sessa.
   Mon: SCHULLIAN, D. M. *Alessandro Benedetti, Diaria de Bello Carolino . . . with introduction,
   translation, and notes.* New York; Renaissance Society of America, 1967. KICK-
   ARTZ, H. D. *Die Anatomie des Zahn-, Mund- und Kieferbereiches in dem Werk
   "Historia corporis humani sive anatomice" von Alessandro Benedetti* (Institut für
   Geschichte der Medizin der Medizinischen Akademie, Düsseldorf, 1964).

BENIVIENI, Antonio, 1443–1502.

597   De abditis nonnullis ac mirandis morborum et sanationum causis (Ed:
Giovanni Rosati, *fl.* 1480–1525, and Girolamo Benivieni, *d.* 1542).
Florence: Filippo Giunta, 24 Sept. 1507.   4°.   [LEK]

   Ref: NLMCat 528; BM-Ital 84; *Sart (Appr)* 119; *Castiglioni* (1947) 370.
   N.B: The first records of pathological anatomy to be printed, although post-mortems
   had been conducted at least two centuries before this date. Thorndike speaks of
   an edition of 1506 but used the known edition of 1507. Included in compilations
   published in Venice, 1516; Paris, 1528; and Basel, 1529 (LMCat 2015, 1917, and
   4168, respectively).
   Mon: THORNDIKE, Lynn. *A physician of Florence: Antonio Benivieni* (Chap. LXV in vol.
   IV of his *A History of magic and experimental science.* New York, 1934).
   Fac: A facsimile edition, with translation by Charles Singer and a biographical appreciation by Esmond R. Long, was issued at Springfield, Illinois, in 1954.

BERENGARIO da Carpi, Jacopo (Jacobus Berengarius; *called* Carpi), 1470–
1530.

598   Commentaria cum amplissimis additionibus super Anatomia Mundini.
Bologna: Hieronymus de Benedictis, 1521.   4°.   [LEK]

Berengario (continued)

Ref: NLMCat 530; BM-Ital 456; *Thornd (HM)* V 498–512; *Choulant (Anat)* 136–142; *Singer (SHA)* 97; *Castiglioni (Ren)* 42; *Castiglioni* (1947) 417.

N.B: A commentary on the *Anatomia* of MONDINO de' Luzzi and a critical survey of other texts, written from the angle of the author's long experience in surgical operations and in dissecting cadavers; with a corrected version of Mondino's text, which he admired. Berengario was an innovator, both in studying the anatomy of separate parts of the human body—the horsehoe kidney, the cranium, the ear, *etc.*—and in employing illustrations drawn from nature. In addition to drawings made direct from cadavers for purposes of anatomical study, the volume contains drawings designed for the use of artists. A tract entitled *Anathomia Mundini per [Jacobum] Carpum castigata* was printed at Venice: In officina D. Bernardini 1538 (NLMCat 3232).

Mon: PUTTI, V. *Berengario da Carpi* ... Bologna, 1937.

599 Isagogae breves in anatomiam humani corporis.   Bologna: Benedictus Hectoris, Dec. 1522.   4°.   [LEK]

Ref: BM-Ital 86; *Sart (Appr)* 119; *Castiglioni* (1947) 418.

N.B: An introduction to the study of anatomy for the use of students at the medical school at Bologna. One of the earliest printed books to display figures of internal organs based on drawings from life, for anatomical purposes and study. Castiglioni notes the anatomy of the heart as being well handled. Revised and re-issued in 1523, with improved text and illustrations; issued by Heinrich Sybold at Strasbourg in 1530—*cf.* SCHOLDERER, V. *Heinrich Sybold, physician and printer at Strasburg* (p. 168–170 in *Gutenberg Jahrbuch*, 1954)—and assigned to the press of Bernardinus de Vitalibus, in an edition printed at Venice in 1535 (NLMCat 534, 535, and 536 respectively).

Mon: LIND, L. R. and Paul G. ROOFE, ed. *Jacopo Berengario da Carpi. A short introduction to anatomy (Isagogae breves). Translated with an introduction and historical notes by L. R. Lind and with anatomical notes by Paul G. Roofe.* Chicago, 1959 (reviewed by C. D. O'Malley, p. 600–602 in *Isis* 51 1960).

Fac: SINGER, Charles. *A short history of anatomy.* New York: Dover, 1957, *fig.* 53.

600 Tractatus de fractura calve sive cranei.   Bologna: Hieronymus de Benedictis, 1518.   4°.   [LEK]

Ref: NLMCat 531; BM-Ital 86; *Thornd (HM)* V 513; *Garrison* (1929) 215; *Castiglioni* (1947) 417.

N.B: A treatise on fractures of the skull, produced during the time when Berengario, notable for his knowledge of anatomy and for his detailed study of the brain, was a professor at Bologna. An undated, second edition (NLMCat 532) identified as from the same press is assignable to 1525 or later; the volume contains Hippocrates's *De capitis vulneribus* in the translation of Marcus Fabius Calvus, which appeared in the Calvus translation of Hippocrates's works printed at Rome in 1525—*see no.* 406:4. Issued at [Venice] in 1535 (NLMCat 533).

Mon: PUTTI, V. *Berengario da Carpi. Saggio biografico e bibliografico seguito dalla traduzione del "De fractura calvae sive cranei."* Bologna, L. Cappelli, 1937.

BERGBÜCHLEIN.

601   Bergbüchlein (*also called* Bergwerkbüchlein).   Augsburg: Erhard Ratdolt, 1505.   8°.   [LEK]

    Ref: Sart (*SW*) 121–122; *Hoover* (*Agricola*) 610–614.
    N.B: The first book on mining and geology to be printed. A prospector's manual. Attributed to Ulrich Rühlein von Kalbe (Calbus of Freiburg), *d.* 1523. [For a note on the edition and on monographs discussing the work and its authorship, see TECHNOLOGY.] President Hoover in his translation and monograph on *Georgius Agricola: De re metallica*, New York, Dover, 1950, gives on p. 610 a reproduction of an Erfurt edition of 1527 of which the title begins, *Ein nützlich Bergbüchlin von allen Metallen*. Later editions, with variant texts and cuts, bear the titles—*Eyn Wolgeordent und Nützlich Bergbüchlein; Bergwerckbuch*, and so on. The 1505 edition cited above may no longer be extant, but an undated edition at the Bibliothèque Nationale in Paris may be of even earlier date. The earliest dated edition known to Mr. Hoover was printed at Worms in 1512.

BERTUCCIO, Nicolò (Nicolaus Bertucius; Vertuccio), *d.* 1347.

602   Collectorium (Ed: Michael de Capella).   Lyon: Claudius Davost for Bartholomeus Trot, 1509.   4°.   [LEK]

    Ref: NLMCat 563; BM-Fr 51; *Sart* III 847; *Castiglioni* (1947) 345.
    N.B: Written by a disciple of Mondino who continued the practice of cadaver dissections in the classroom and was the teacher of Guy de Chauliac. According to Sarton, the work contains a chapter on anatomy including a description of the brain. Printed at Lyon in 1518 and at Cologne in 1537 (NLMCat 564, 565). [See also under MEDICINE.]

BOCCACCIO, Giovanni, 1313–1375.

603   De montibus, silvis, fontibus, lacubus, fluminibus ...   Venice: [Wendelin von Speier] 13 Jan. [1]473.   f°.   [LEK]

    Ref: GW 4482; HC *3326; BMC V 162; BM-Ital 109; Oates 1618; IGI 1802; Klebs 189.1; *Sart* III 1806; Stillwell B675; Goff B-756.
    N.B: An alphabetical dictionary relating to physical geography, an interest in natural phenomena which is occasionally revealed in Boccaccio's other works. Issued also with the 1481 edition of his *Genealogiae deorum* printed at Reggio Emilia, in the Vicenza edition of 1487 and those issued at Venice in 1494/95 and 1497 (Cen B670–673).

BOCK, Hieronymus (*called* Tragus; Hieronymus Herbarius), 1498–1554.

604   New Kreutterbuch [*German*].   Strasbourg: Wendel Rihel, 1539.   f°.   [LEK]

Bock (continued)

Ref: NLMCat 595; *Nissen* 182; *Arber* (1938) 275.

N.B: Written by the second of the so-called German Fathers of Botany. Although issued without the lively illustrations which appeared in subsequent editions, Bock's text in its firsthand knowledge and descriptions shows a botanical understanding of flowers unknown to his predecessors. Issued by the same press in 1546 (NLMCat 596).

Mon: GREENE, E. L. *Hieronymus Tragus* (p. 220–262 in his *Landmarks of botanical history* —Smithsonian Miscellaneous Collections, vol. 54, 1909/10).

Fac: Fig. 27 and 28 in ARBER, Agnes. *Herbals. A new edition*, Cambridge, 1938, shows two cuts from the 1546 edition.

BREYDENBACH, Bernhard von, *d.* 1497.

605 Peregrinatio in terram sanctam. Mainz: Erhard Reuwich (with Peter Schoeffer's type], 11 Feb. 1486. f°. [LEK]

Ref: GW 5075; HC *3956; BMC I 43; BM-Ger 152; IGI 2055; Klebs 220.1; LC (LJRCat) 103; Stillwell B1058; Goff B-1189.

N.B: With maps and drawings by Erhard Reuwich, who accompanied Breydenbach to the Holy Land. On the verso of a picture of Rhodes is a cut showing seven animals—a giraffe and a great ape among them. Re-issued at [Speier] by Peter Drach, 29 July 1490 (LC(LJRCat) 134), with illustrations, views, and maps from the original blocks used in the 1486 Mainz edition. Known in eight fifteenth-century editions, including Latin, German, French, Low German, and Spanish versions (Goff B-1189—B-1196). An unsigned edition, formerly assigned to about 1495, has been re-assigned (GW col 656) to [after 24 Nov. 1502].

Mon: DAVIES, Hugh W. *Bernhard von Breydenbach and his journey to the Holy Land, 1483–4. A bibliography.* London, 1911.

Fac: For reproductions of the illustrations in various editions of Breydenbach, see vols. 4 and 15 of SCHRAMM, A. *Der Bilderschmuck der Führdrucke.* Leipzig, 1920–1943. 23 vols.

BRUNFELS, Otto, *c.* 1464–1534.

606 Herbarum vivae eicones: Appendix isagogica. Novi herbarii. Tomus herbarii. Strasbourg: Johann Schott, I) 1530–31, 1532 (App); II) 1531–32; III) 1536. f°. [LEK]

Ref: NLMCat 724–726; BM-Ger 155 (*var*); Horblit 33a; Nissen 257; Garrison (1929) 229; *Arber* (1938) 52–55; *Hunt (Quinby)* I 30.

N.B: Written by the earliest of the so-called German Fathers of Botany; illustrated by Hans Weydiz, whose work is eulogized in a poem at the beginning of the book. The text follows the traditional line, being based on Theophrastos, Dioskorides, and Pliny; but the work contains the important innovation of being illustrated with wood-engravings made for the first time from *actual* plants by a competent artist. Thus it stands as a milestone in the history of botany and as the forerunner of Leonhart Fuchs's *De historia stirpium* published a decade later. The first book of modern botanical illustration. The several parts of Brunfels's *Herbarum vivae eicones*, which were printed and reprinted individually by Johann Schott, are found in various combinations, each of which presents its special problems in technical bibliography.

Mon: ARBER, Agnes. *The Draughtsman of the Herbarum Vivae Eicones* (p. 131–132 in *Jour. Bot.* LIX, 1921). GREENE, Edward Lee. *Otho Brunfels* (p. 169–191 in his *Landmarks of botanical history* [Smithsonian Miscellaneous Collections, no. 54] Washington, 1909/10).

Fac: HORBLIT 33a [33b, recto].

BRUNSCHWIG, Hieronymus (Jeronimo Brunschweick; Hieronymus von Brawnschweig), *c.* 1450–1512.

607 Anathomia ossium corporis humani [*German*]. [Strasbourg: Johann (Reinhard) Grüninger, 1497.] f°.

Ref: GW 5593 *note*; Klebs 226.1; Stillwell B1087 *note*; Goff B-1225.

N.B: Generally found with the author's *Cirurgia* [see under MEDICINE]. Sometimes found as a separate, as in the Osler collection at McGill University. Known in 6-leaf and 4-leaf issues.

Mon: SUDHOFF, Karl. *Brunschwigs Anatomie* (p. 41–66, 141–156 in *Archiv für Gesch. d. Medizin* I 1908).

CANANO, Giovanni Battista (Joannes Baptista Cananus), 1515–1579.

608 Musculorum humani corporis picturata dissectio. [Ferrara: Francesco Rossi, 1543.] 4°.

Ref: BM-Ital 143; *Sart (Appr)* 119, 210:155; *Castiglioni* (1947) 418; *Castiglioni (Ren)* 42.

N.B: An illustrated account of the dissection of muscles in the human body, apparently issued in the same year as the *Fabrica* of Vesalius. By an anatomist who was the first to describe the valves in the veins. A portion of a text on anatomy the remainder of which was unpublished, possibly because of the issuing of the more spectacular work by Vesalius.

Fac: CUSHING, Harvey, and E. C. STREETER (*Monumenta medica*, no. 4. Florence, 1925).

CARDANO, Girolamo (*sometimes referred to as* Cardan), 1501–1576.

609 De subtilitate rerum libri XXI. Paris: Michel Fezandat and Robert Granjon, 1550. 8°. [LEK]

Ref: BM-Fr 91; *Garrison* (1929) 210; *Lindsay (JC)* 315–317.

N.B: A philosophical discussion of method, tending toward evolution in its biologic concepts. Wightman (1962) II 128 records an edition printed at Nuremberg by Joannes Petreius in 1550 and speaks of Cardano's views on heat as having a 'modern' character. The author was a scientist of advanced ideas and varied interests, his writings relating to medicine, physics, natural science, and in particular to mathematics.

Mon: ORE, Oystein. *Cardano, the gambling scholar*. Princeton, 1953.

IV. *Natural Science*

CATO, Marcus Porcius, 234–149 B.C.

De re rustica liber. *See under* SCRIPTORES REI RUSTICAE.

CELSUS, Aulus Cornelius, *early years of the first century*.

610   De medicina libri VIII (Ed: Bartolomeo Fonti, 1445–1513).   Florence: Nicolaus Laurentii, 1478. sm. f°. [LEK]

> *Ref*: GW 6456; HC *4835; BMC VI 627; Oates 2333; IGI 2674; Klebs 260.1; Schullian (ArMed) 140; *Sart (Appr)* 12–14, 185:28–31; *Sart* I 240; *Garrison* (1929) 108; Stillwell C325; Goff C-364.
>
> *N.B*: The first organized treatise on medicine to be printed. Books VII and VIII deal with surgery and anatomy. Variant known. Text recovered in 1426–1443. Four fifteenth-century editions were issued; Sarton notes fifteen in the following century. [For various early sixteenth-century editions, see NLMCat nos. 906–914.] Written in Latin; originally part of an encyclopaedic work, of which a few fragments of an agricultural section also remain. For a brief analysis of the text, see Castiglioni (1947) 205–213. [See also under MEDICINE.]
>
> *Mon*: TEMKIN, O. *Celsus' 'On medicine' and the ancient medical sects* (p. 249–264 in Institute of the History of Medicine, *Bulletin*, vol. 3, 1935). CASTIGLIONI, A. *Aulus Cornelius Celsus as a historian of medicine* (p. 857–873 in *ibid.*, vol. 8, 1940).

CENSORINUS, *3rd century*.

611   De die natali [*and other works*] (Ed: Philippus Beroaldus).   Bologna: Benedictus Hectoris, 12 May 1497. f°. [LEK]

> *Ref*: GW 6471; HC *4847; BMC VI 843; IGI 2682; Schullian (ArMed) 144; Stillwell C336; Goff C-376.
>
> *N.B*: Among several tracts included in this edition are Plutarch's essay on jealousy and hatred, and the essay *De invidia* of Basilius Magnus in the translation of Nicolaus Perottus. Printed in an unsigned edition assigned to the press of Bernardinus Venetus de Vitalibus at Venice about 1498–1500 (Cen C337).

CICERO, Marcus Tullius, 106–43 B.C.

612   De natura deorum (*with additions by* Raphael Zovenzonius).   [Venice:] Wendelin von Speier, 1471. 4°. [LEK]

> *Ref*: GW 6902; HC *5334; BMC V 158; BM-Ital 173–174; IGI 2878; Klebs 276.1; Stillwell C516; Goff C-569.
>
> *N.B*: Also issued in 1471 at Rome, in a compilation of Cicero's works (Cen C505) printed by Sweynheim and Pannartz. According to Singer (SHA) 38, in addition to its discussion of nature and the origin of the universe, this work not only includes an elementary exposition of anatomy and physiology but presents the first *formal* statement regarding the teleological design of the human body—a thesis later developed by Galen.

COLUMELLA, Lucius Junius Moderatus, *1st century A.D., fl. 50.*

613 De cultu hortorum carmen (Ed: Giorgio Merula, *c.* 1424–1494). [Rome: Printer of Silius Italicus, *c.* 1471.]   4°.   [LEK]

> *Ref*: GW 7180; Oates 1386; Klebs 287.1; *Nordenskiöld (HB)* 53; *Taton (A&MS)* 364.
> *N.B*: Book X of Columella's *De re rustica*, a work included in the so-called *Scriptores rei rusticae (no. 695)*. According to Klebs 902n, Columella's full text comprises 13 Books.

CONRAD von Megenberg, *c.* 1309–1374.

614 Buch der Natur [*German*].   Augsburg: Johann Bämler, 30 Oct. [14]75. f°.   [LEK]

> *Ref*: H *4041; BMC II 333; BM-Ger 476; Klebs 300.1; *Garrison* (1929) 165; *Sart* III 817–821; Stillwell C759; Goff C-842.
> *N.B*: The first printed book to contain figures of animals. The first notable scientific book in German. It discusses birds, fish, animals, anatomy, physiology, earthquakes, plagues, metals, and the medicinal value of plants and stones. According to Sarton, a somewhat expanded and free translation of the *De natura rerum* of Thomas of Cantipré, which is variously attributed also to Albertus Magnus. A popular book in Augsburg, where at least six editions were printed before 1500.

CORDUS, Valerius, 1515–1544. *See under* MEDICINE.

CRESCENZI, Pier de' (Petrus de Crescentiis), 1233–1321.

615 Ruralia commoda.   [Augsburg:] Johann Schüssler, 'circiter' 16 Feb. 1471.   f°.   [LEK]

> *Ref*: GW 7820; HC *5828; BMC II 328; BM-Ger 227; Oates 891; Klebs 310.1; *Sart* III 811–815; Stillwell C858; Goff C-965.
> *N.B*: Relates to the multitudinous problems of husbandry and agriculture incident to the management of a great estate. Based upon various traditional works on husbandry but written critically, from experience gained on Crescenzi's country place, the Villa d'Olmo, near Bologna. Includes sections on hunting and fishing, the making of wine, and the diseases of animals, as well as on the cultivation of cereals, trees, and plants. Issued in Latin, Italian, French, German, and apparently, Polish. Klebs lists thirteen editions issued in the fifteenth century.

CURTIUS RUFUS, Quintus, *fl. 50.*

616 Historiae Alexandri magni.   [Venice:] Wendelin von Speier [*c.* 1471]. 4°.   [LEK]

> *Ref*: GW 7871; HC *5878; BMC V 163; BM-Ital 207; IGI 3286; *Greene (LBH)* 133; Stillwell C883; Goff C-998.

Curtius Rufus (continued)

N.B: Issued in at least ten editions before the end of 1500, including translations in Italian (1478), Catalan (1481), Spanish (1496), and French [*c.* 1500]. Another undated edition, printed at Venice by Georgius Lauer, is assigned to about 1472 (BM-Ital 207). An English version by John Brende was issued at London in 1553. Alexander the Great, *d.* 323 B.C., had been a pupil of Aristotle, a fact no doubt accountable in some measure for his scientific curiosity. Among his troops he included scholars whose duty it was to record descriptions of plants and animals in the far countries to which he traveled, much of the botanical knowledge thus acquired eventually finding its way, it is said, into the text of Theophrastos.

Mon: BRETZL, Hugo. *Botanische Forschungen des Alexanderzuges.* Leipzig, 1903.

DELLA TORRE, Giacomo. *See* JACOPO da Forlì.

DIONYSIOS PERIEGETES, *first or second century.*

617 De situ orbis (Tr: Priscianus, *fl.* 500). (*Issued with* PRISCIANUS. Opera. [Venice: Wendelin von Speier] 1470.) f°. [LEK]

Ref: HCR 13355; BMC V 156; Klebs 806.1; Sart I 258, 440; Stillwell P877; Goff P-960.

N.B: A geographical poem describing the known world. Issued as a separate in the translation of Antonio Beccaria, at Venice in 1477 by the firm of Ratdolt, Maler, and Löslein (Cen D209) and included in subsequent editions of Priscianus.

DIOSKORIDES, Pedanios (Dioskurides; Dioscorides), *fl.* 50 A.D.

618 De materia medica (Comm: Pietro d'Abano, *c.* 1250–1316). Colle: Johannes de Medemblick, July 1478. f°. [LEK]

Ref: GW 8436; HC *6258; BMC VII 1078; BM-Ital 218; IGI 3492; Klebs 342.1; Sart I 258–260; O'Leary 170, 171; *Greene (LBH)* 151–154; *Arber (1938)* 6–12; Stillwell D217; Goff D-261.

N.B: The first edition of a standard work on medicines derived from animal, vegetable, and mineral sources. Describes over 600 plants. The first Greek edition—Venice: Aldus Manutius, July 1499 (Cen D216)—contains also two poems, the *Alexipharmaca* and *Theriaca* attributed to Nicandros, which describe about 125 plants as antidotes for poisons from various causes and for the venom of poisonous animals.

In five Books; in the translation attributed to Constantinus Africanus (*d.* 1087). Re-issued at Lyon about 1512 (NLMCat 1138). In a new translation—by the botanist Jean de la Ruelle (*d.* 1537), based upon the Greek edition of 1499 and issued at Paris about 1518—added titles *De venenis* and *De venenatis animalibus* are treated as Books 6–9. [For a note on this and other editions of Dioskorides, see under MEDICINE: Dioskorides, no. 354. See also NLMCat p. 143–146.]

The translation of Ermolao Barbaro (*d.* 1493), together with his *Corollariorum libri quinque* appeared at Venice in 1516 under the editorship of Otto Brunfels;

and again at Strasbourg in 1529 and at Cologne in 1530 (NLMCat 1140, 1144, 470 respectively). Added matter by Valerius and Euricius Cordus and by Konrad Gesner is included in the Frankfurt edition of [1549]. Four of six Italian versions of Dioskorides—those issued at Venice in 1544, 1548, 1549, and 1550—are in the translation of Pierandrea Mattioli (*d.* 1577) and contain his important commentary (Hunt (Quinby) I 59; NLMCat 1160–1163).

Mon: GUNTHER, Robert T. *The Greek herbal of Dioscorides.* (Illustrated by a Byzantine A.D. 512; Englished by John Goodyer A.D. 1655; edited and first printed A.D. 1933.) New York, 1959 (reviewed in *Isis* 51 1960, p. 588–590).

DRYANDER, Johannes (Johann Eichmann), 1500–1560.

619 Anatomia capitis humani in Marpurgensi Academia superiori anno publice exhibita. Marburg: Eucharius Cervicornus, Sept. 1536. 4°.

Ref: NLMCat 1214; BM-Ger 255; v. Dommer 68; *Sart (Appr)* 117; *Wightman* (1962) I 230.

N.B: An anatomical lecture and demonstration given at the University of Marburg. Re-issued, with additional illustrations and text, as *Anatomiae, hoc est, corporis humani dissectionis pars prior*..., Marburg, 1537; and the latter apparently included in whole or in part in Dryander's *Der gantzen Artzenei*, printed at Frankfurt-am-Main about 1542 (NLMCat 1215, 1216).

620 Anatomia Mundini . . . aliquot manu scriptorum codicum ad fidem collata . . . per Ioannem Dryandrum . . . Adiectae sunt, quarumcunq3 partium corporis, ad uiuum expressae figurae. Marburg: Christian Egenolff [1541]. 4°.

Ref: NLMCat 3233; v. Dommer 141, *Choulant (Anat)* 146, 149.

N.B: In passing reference to Dryander's revision of Mondino's text, Singer (SHA) 99 reproduces a figure of viscera from this edition, as the earliest figure showing the vermiform appendix. In fact, the printing of Mondino's *Anatomia* [*q.v.*] had already occasioned drawings of importance in the history of anatomic illustration. A decorative cut showing a classroom dissection of a cadaver introduces the edition of Mondino's *Anatomia* which is included in the 1493 Italian version of Ketham's *Fasciculus medicinae* [Choulant (Anat) 118, *fac.*] and which, in turn, includes a human-anatomy chart according to Mondino [Castiglioni (1947) 342, *fac.*]. And the 1521 commentary on Mondino by Berengario da Carpi includes the first printing of anatomic figures actually illustrative of the accompanying text—*see no. 598.*

621 Anatomiae hoc est corporis humani dissectionis pars prior in qua singula quae ad caput spectant recensentur membra atque singulae partes singulis suis ad vivum commodissime expressis figuris deliniantur. Marburg: Apud Eucharium Cervicornum, June 1537. 4°.

Dryander (continued)

Ref: NLMCat 1215; BM-Ger 255; v. Dommer 81; *Garrison* (1929) 211, 215; *Sart (Appr)* 117; *Thornd (HM)* V 520.

N.B: An oration delivered at the University of Marburg, October 25, 1536, praising Philip of Hesse for permitting public dissection of the corpses of criminals and advocating state or public support for the study of anatomy. Contains also the *Anatomia porci ex traditione Cophonis* and the *Anatomia infantis ex Gabriele de Zerbis*. The *Anatomia porci* [*no.* 569] had already been printed at Lyon in 1523.

DÜRER, Albrecht, 1471–1528.

622 Hierin sind begriffen vier Bücher von menschlicher Proportion [*German*] (Ed: Willibald Pirkheimer, 1470–1530). Nuremberg: Gedruckt durch Jeronymum [Hieronymus Andreae] Formschneyder, auff Verlegung Albrecht Dürers verlassen Witib, 31 Oct. 1528. [LEK]

Ref: NLMCat 1295; LC(LJRCat) 466; BM-Ger 256; *Smith (HM)* I 326; *Choulant (Anat)* 143–147.

N.B: The rare first edition of Dürer's treatise on the mathematical proportions of the human form developed from anatomical study. Illustrated with many woodcuts and diagrams which had formed the basis for anatomical proportion in his paintings and drawings. Published posthumously, although on the press at the time of Dürer's death in April 1528. Books I and II, translated into Latin by Joachim Camerarius (1500–1574), were issued about 1532, as *De sȳmetria partium in rectis formis hū anorum corporum libri in Latinum conuersi* (LC(LJRCat) 469; NLMCat 1297). Other editions appeared in French, Italian, Dutch, German, English, and possibly Portuguese, until well into the seventeenth century. A translation of Books III and IV, showing figures in action and entitled *De varietate figurarum*, was printed at Nuremberg for Dürer's widow in 1534 (NLMCat 1298).

Mon: PANOFSKY, Erwin. *Albrecht Dürer*. 2nd ed., revised. Princeton, 1945.

EIN ERDBEBEN.

623 Ein erschröckenliche newe Zeyttung so geschehen ist den 12 tag Junii in dem 1542 Jar in einem Stetlein Schgarbaria genent [*German*]. [Sine nota, 1542] 4°. [LEK]

N.B: An account of an earthquake at Scarperia, a village near Florence, and at a Turkish town near Salonika. A copy of this rare leaflet is at Harvard University, as also is the following version in English.

624 Heuy newes of an horryble erthquake in Scarbaria in this present yere of .xlii. the .xiii. day of June. And also how that a citie in Turky is sonke. London: Rychard Lant [1542]. sm. 8°.

N.B: The provenance of the German and English editions at Harvard is given in some detail in JACKSON, William A. *Heuy newes of an horryble earthquake in Scarbaria* (p. 248–250 in *Harvard Library Bulletin*. VI. 1952). A unique copy of an edition printed by Nicolas Bourman is registered as at the British Museum. No Italian editions have been found in the present survey, although such doubtless were issued at the time.

Fac: JACKSON, *ibid., fig.* 1.

ESTIENNE, Charles (Carolus Stephanus), 1504–1564.

625   Arbustum. Fonticulus. Spinetum.   Paris: Franciscus Stephanus (François Estienne), 1538.   8°.

Ref: BM-Fr 155; Renouard (Estienne) p. 97; *Hunt (Quinby)* I 42.

N.B: An Italian version was issued at Paris in 1545 (NLMCat 1400; Hunt (Quinby) I 54). [One of several tracts written by Charles Estienne; printed at Paris by his brothers François or Robert, during the years 1535–1543; re-issued by the author in his *Praedium rusticum*, Paris, 1554 (Hunt (Quinby) I 69); and here entered separately, *i.e.*—*De re hortensi libellus*, 1535 (*no.* 629); *Seminarium sive Plantarium*, 1536 (*no.* 630); *Vinetum*, 1537 (*no.* 632); *Arbustum*, 1538 (*no.* 625); *Sylva, frutetum, collis*, 1538 (*no.* 631); and *Pratum, lacus, arundinentum*, 1543 (*no.* 628). A French translation issued in 1564 bears the title *L'Agriculture et maison rustique*.]

Estienne was a member of an important family of scholar-printers whose publishing-house operated from 1502 until far into the seventeenth century. He himself was an anatomist and physician, a botanist, a classical scholar, and for a time the head of the family publishing-house. When his brother François fled from Paris for religious reasons in 1550, Charles Estienne took over the management of the firm. From 1551 to 1561 he served as *Imprimeur du Roi*.

626   De dissectione partium corporis humani libri III.   Paris: Simon de Colines, 1545.   f°.   [LEK]

Ref: NLMCat 1391; LC(LJRCat) 660; BM-Ital 155; *Sart (Appr)* 210:156; *Choulant (Anat)* 152–155; *Garrison* (1929) 224; *Castiglioni* (1947) 442; *Crombie (A–G)* 1961 II 272.

N.B: Illustrated with 56 figures based upon Estienne's dissections and observations. Contains the first published illustrations presenting the venous, arterial, and nervous systems in their entirety. Five of the cuts bear the Lorraine cross, the mark of Geofroy Tory. Several of the figures are dated 1530, 1531, or 1532, and the cuts reveal that blocks showing a detail of a given area were in various instances superimposed upon a more simply drawn figure, the detail being mortised into the main cut. According to Mr. Albert E. Lownes's description of the copy in his collection, for instance, "there are 62 full-page woodcuts, but six of them are repeated, so that there are only 56 different blocks. Thirty-eight of these have mortises with the anatomical details. Four of the blocks have two mortises." By 1539 the work itself was completed to the middle of the last section. Although not printed until after Vesalius's *Fabrica*, the writing of the present text antedated the latter's publication by some years. The cuts are transitional, in advance of the old school but without the anatomical surety introduced by Vesalius. [For discussion of the date and relation of this work to that of Vesalius, see Renouard (Colines) 409.] A French version was printed by Colines at Paris in 1546, entitled *La dissection des parties des corps* (NLMCat 1392).

Mon: KELLETT, C. E. *A note on Rosso and the illustrations of Charles Estienne's De dissectione* (p. 325–336 in *Journal of the History of Medicine and Allied Sciences* 12 1957); and p. 265–266 in *ibid.* 13 1958). RATH, G. *Charles Estienne: contemporary of Vesalius* (p. 354–359 in *Medical History* 8 1964).

627 De Latinis et Graecis nominibus arborum, fructicum, herbarum, piscium et avium liber. Paris: Robertus Stephanus (Robert Estienne), 1536. 8°. [LEK]

Ref: Renouard (Estienne) 42.

N.B: An important and popular work on terminology. Re-issued in 1544 (NLMCat 1393) and in two other editions before 1548. The text is based upon terms employed by Aristotle, Theophrastos, Dioskorides, Galen, Pliny, and other classical writers and upon those of the scholars Ermolao Barbaro, *d.* 1493, and Jean de la Ruelle, *d.* 1537. Its lists French terms as well as the Greek and Latin names of trees, fruit, herbs, fish, and birds.

628 Pratum. Lacus. Arundinetum. Paris: Simon de Colines and Franciscus Stephanus (François Estienne), 1543. 8°.

Ref: BM-Fr 156.

N.B: One of the six separately printed treatises later included in the author's *Praedium rusticum* of 1554. The present edition was printed by his brother at the printing-house of their step-father, Simon de Colines.

629 De re hortensi libellus vulgaria herbarum, florum, ac fructicum quae in hortis conseri solent nomina Latinis vocibus efferre docens ex probatis authoribus. Paris: Robertus Stephanus (Robert Estienne), 3 Nov. 1535. 8°. [LEK]

Ref: BM-Fr 155; Renouard (Estienne) p. 41.

N.B: Reprinted by Robert Estienne in 1536 (Hunt (Quinby) I 36). Issued at Paris or Lyon in more than half a dozen editions within a decade. An Italian version was issued at Venice in 1545 (NLMCat 1397; Hunt (Quinby) I 53), to which is appended *Un libretto di coltivare gli horti* that had first appeared in Latin in the Paris edition of 1539. Included by the author in his *Praedium rusticum*, printed at Paris "Apud Carolum Stephanum Typographū Regium, M.D.LIIII."

630 Seminarium sive Plantarium earum arborum, quae post hortos conseri solent quarum nomina, fructus...declarantur. Paris: Robertus Stephanus (Robert Estienne), 1536. 8°. [LEK]

Ref: NLMCat 1399; Hunt (Quinby) I 37; BM-Fr 156; Renouard (Estienne) p. 42.

N.B: One of several tracts that were combined and published by the author in 1554 as his *Praedium rusticum*. An Italian version, the *Seminario*, printed at Venice in 1545 together with *L'Arbusto*, is cited in BM-Ital 238; NLMCat 1400.

631   Sylva. Frutetum. Collis.   Paris: Franciscus Stephanus (François Estienne), 1538.   8°.   [LEK]

Ref: Renouard (Estienne) p. 97; Hunt (Quinby) I 43.

N.B: Reprinted by Charles Estienne in his *Praedium rusticum* of 1554.

632   Vinetum.   Paris: Franciscus Stephanus (Francois Estienne), 1537.   8°. [LEK]

Ref: BM-Fr 156.

N.B: Included in the author's *Praedium rusticum*, Paris, 1554. An Italian version printed at Venice in 1545 is recorded in BM-Ital 238; NLMCat 1401; Hunt (Quinby) I 55.

FALCUCCI, Nicolò (Nicolaus Falcutius), *d.* 1411/12.

633   Sermones medicinales, libri VII.   Pavia: Damianus de Confaloneriis, 1481–1484.   f°.   [LEK]

Ref: GW 9704; H *11767; BMC VII 1000 (II–VII); IGI 3800; Klebs 389.1; Sart III 1194; *Castiglioni* (1947) 332; Stillwell F32; Goff F-45.

N.B: An encyclopaedic work treating of medicine and physiology. Its seven Books comprise *De conservatione sanitatis*; *De febribus*; *De membris capitis*; *De membris spiritualibus*; *De membris naturalibus*; *De membris generationis*; *De chirurgia et de decoratione*. Issued at Venice in 1490–1491 (Cen F33; Schullian (ArMed) 178); and at Venice in 1507 (NLMCat 1423), although an eighth Book called for in the title of the latter appears not to have been published. Books II and V are known to have been issued as separates in 1491; and Books V and VI together, about 1495 [For fuller title see under MEDICINE.]

FERNÁNDEZ de OVIEDO y VALDÉS, GONZALO (*called* Oviedo), 1478–1557.

634   Natural hystoria delas Indias.   Toledo: Remon de Petras, 25 Feb. 1526. f°.

Ref: Harrissse (BAV) 139; Church 59.

N.B: The first natural history of the Indies, where, beginning in 1513, Oviedo lived for thirty-four years. Relates to plants, animals, and minerals. Oviedo was present at the Court of Spain when Columbus returned from his first voyage, and later held the post of official Chronicler of the Indies. His *Historia general delas Indias* was printed at Sevilla by Juan Cromberger in 1535, an edition in which (as noted in Sarah A. Dickson's *Panacea or precious bane*; *Tobacco in sixteenth century literature*, New York, 1954) the term "tabaco" first appeared in print, as the name of the tube through which the natives inhaled the smoke of a burning herb

IV. *Natural Science*

FERNEL, Jean, *d.* 1558.

635   De abditis rerum causis sive Dialogi.   Paris: Christien Wechel, 1548.

> *Ref*: Sart (*SW*) 195; Sart (*Appr*) 185:25.
> *N.B*: A series of dialogues on physiological questions by one of the most able thinkers
> of the time. An edition printed at Venice in 1550 is listed as NLMCat 1478.
> *Mon*: SHERRINGTON, *Sir* Charles. *The endeavor of Jean Fernel.* Cambridge, 1946 (reviewed in *Isis* 37 199; 41 212).

636   De naturali parte medicinae libri VII.   Paris: Simon de Colines, 1542. f°.

> *Ref*: Renouard (Colines) 357; Sart (*SW*) 194.
> *N.B*: A standard work that treats of physiology. Although eventually superseded by
> Harvey's *De motu cordis*, 1628, it remained in use until the latter had become fully
> accepted. Fernel is variously rated as the founder of physiology. At least, his
> conception of the structure and functioning of the organs of the human body was
> a start toward modern understanding. An edition printed at Venice in 1547 is
> assigned to the press of Giovanni Griffio (NLMCat 1480).

FITZHERBERT, John, *c.* 1460–1531.

637   Boke of husbandry.   London: Richard Pynson [1523].   8°.   [LEK]

> *Ref*: STC 10994; *Hunt (Quinby)* I 33*n*.
> *N.B*: Known only in a copy at the British Museum. Issued at London by Peter
> Treveris about 1525 and in two undated London editions by Thomas Berthelet,
> one of which has 1534 in the woodcut border of the titlepage. The text, according
> to Dr. E. Lamond's monograph on *Walter of Henley's Husbandry*, London,
> 1890, was largely derived from this earlier source, which was written in the
> twelfth or thirteenth century and printed about 1510.

FRIES, Lourenz (Laurentius Phryeren), *c.* 1490–1531.

638   Spiegel der Artzny [*German*].   Strasbourg: Johann Grüninger, 1518. 4°.   [LEK]

> *Ref*: Choulant (*Anat*) 130–135, 163–164; Garrison (1929) 214.
> *N.B*: An illustrated anatomy of the pre-Vesalian period. Two of its woodcuts are
> dated 1517, one bearing the name of Wendelin Hock of Brackenau in Württemberg. For editions printed at Strasbourg by the same or a rival press in [1519],
> [1529], 1532, and 1546, see NLMCat 1663–1666.

FUCHS, Leonhart, 1501–1566.

639   Errata recentiorum medicorum LX numero adiectis eorum confutationibus.   Hagenau: Johannes Secerius, 1530.   4°.   [LEK]

Ref: NLMCat 1699; BM-Ger 326; *Thornd* (*HM*) V 501.

Con: Errores, qui ad plantarum, medicaeque rei notitiam spectant. Errores, qui ad medendi methodium attinent. Errores, qui ad anatomiam spectant.

N.B: Containing criticism of Mondino and Benedetti because they disagreed with Galen, overlooking the fact that they were experienced in dissection. A controversial work which brought forth a rebuttal by Sébastien de Monteux in his *Annotatiunculae . . . in errata recentiorum medicorum per Leonardum Fuchsium . . . collecta*. Lyon: Benoit Bonin, 1533 (BM-Fr 318; NLMCat 3288). A revised and enlarged edition of Fuchs's *Errata* issued by Johann Bebel at Basel in 1535, entitled *Paradoxorum medicinae libri III*, brought a further reply from Monteux in 1537 and an answer from Fuchs in 1538 (NLMCat 1714, 3289, 3289n). [With regard to these and the works of other disputants, see STÜBLER.]

Mon: STÜBLER, E. *Leonhart Fuchs, Leben und Werk*. München, 1928 (Münchener Beiträge zur Geschichte und Literatur der Naturwissenschaften und Medizin, Heft 13/14).

640   De historia stirpium commentarii.   Basel: In officina Isingriniana [sic] (Michel Isengrin), 1542.   f°.   [LEK]

Ref: NLMCat 1675; BM-Ger 326; Horblit 33 b; *Nissen* 658; *Garrison* (1929) 229; *Greene* (*LBH*) 194; *Arber* (1938) 275; *Hunt* (*Quinby*) I 48.

N.B: A remarkably handsome volume having both botanical and medical interest. Written by a professor of medicine at Tübingen, sometimes ranked as one of the so-called Fathers of Botany. Illustrated by the artists, Füllmaurer, Meyer, and Speckle, whose portraits appear at the end of the volume. Contains 500 or more figures drawn from actual plants for purposes of identification and superior in their delineation and technique to those in Brunfels's *Eicones* [*q.v.*]. A Dutch version was issued by Isengrin the following year (NLMCat 1681). Sart (Appr) 96 lists seven editions in Latin, two in German, and two in French within our period. The NLMCat p. 200 lists eight, the Dutch or Low-German edition of 1543 and a French version, Lyon [1550?], included. A French version by Eloy de Maignan was printed at Paris by Jacques Gazeau in 1549—Hunt (Quinby) I 60.

   Garrison describes the purpose of the volume as being "entirely utilitarian, the work of a busy practitioner" seeking to improve knowledge of the *materia medica*. Fuchs's deep interest in medical botany is further shown in his *Annotationes aliquot herbarum et simplicium a medicis hactenus non recte intellectorum*, which according to Greene was included in the second volume of the first issue of Brunfels's *Eicones*, 1531.

Mon: ARBER, Agnes. *On a French version of the herbal of Leonard Fuchs* (p. 381–383 in *Notes and Queries* 154, 1928). CHOATE, H. A. *The earliest glossary of botanical terms; Fuchs 1542* (p. 186–201 in *Torreya* 17, 1917). GREENE, Edward Lee. *Leonhardus Fuchsius* (p. 192–219 in his *Landmarks of botanical history*, no. 54 in Smithsonian Miscellaneous Collections, pub. 1928, Washington, 1909/10).

Fac: HORBLIT 33 b [34, recto].

GALEN (Galenos, Galenus), 131 – *c.* 200.

Major Compilations of Galen's Works

641   Opera [*Greek*] (Ed: Andrea Torresani (Asulanus) and Giovanni Battista Opizo).   Venice: Ex aedibus Aldi et Andreae Asulani soceri, 1525. 5 vol. f °. [LEK]

> *Ref:* NLMCat 1748; BM-Ital 285; Renouard (Alde) 239; Choulant (H) 112–113; *Sart (Appr)* 20–22; *Castiglioni* (1947) 217–226.
>
> *N.B:* For monographs and for notes regarding Greek editions of Galen's works, see under MEDICINE, no. 374.

642   Opera [*Latin*] (Ed: Diomedes Bonardus).   Venice: Philippus Pincius, 27 Aug. 1490. f °.

> *Ref:* Hain *7427; Durling 250[10], 281–295; IGI 4129; Choulant (H) 113; Klebs 432.1; Horblit 34; Schullian (ArMed) 199; *Castiglioni* (1947) 217–226; *Crombie (A–G)* 1961 I 163–168; Stillwell G36; Goff G-37.
>
> *Con:* 1) An omnes partes animalis (Tr: Nicolò da Reggio, *d.* 1350). 2) De anatomia oculorum (Tr: ditto). 3) De atra bile (Tr: Pietro d'Abano, *d.* 1316). 4) De gynaeceis (Tr: N. da Reggio). 5) De motibus manifestis et obscuris (Tr: Marc of Toledo, *fl.* 1200). 6) De naturalibus facultatibus (Tr: anon.). 7) De naturalium facultatum substantia (Tr: N. da Reggio). 8) De pulsibus ad tyrones (Tr: Burgundio of Pisa, *d.* 1193). 9) De pulsuum causis (Tr: anon). 10) Pulsuum compendium I (Tr: anon). 11) De pulsuum differentiis (Tr: Burgundio of Pisa). 12) De respirationis causis (Tr: N. da Reggio). 13) De respirationis difficultate (Tr: ditto). 14) De respirationis usu (Tr: Pietro d'Abano, or N. da Reggio). 15) De respirationis utilitate (Tr: anon). 16) De semine (Tr: N. da Reggio). 17) De simplicibus medicaminibus ad Paternianum (Tr: anon). 18) De simplicium medicamentorum facultatibus (Tr: Constantinus, *Africanus, d.* 1087). 19) De temperamentis (Tr: Gherardo da Cremona, *d.* 1187). 20) De thoracis et pulmonis motu (Tr: anon). 21) De usu partium: Compendium, Bks. I–X (Tr: anon?) [see also 644.20 below]. 22) De uteri dissectione (Tr: N. da Reggio). [*See also the 1490 Opera, no. 375, for 51 titles, some of which upon further analysis may be found to relate to aspects of natural science.*]
>
> *N.B:* See under MEDICINE Galen, no. 375
>
> *Mon:* See under MEDICINE: Galen, no. 374.
>
> *Fac:* HORBLIT 34 [b].

Fifteenth-Century Latin 'Firsts'

Including the titles listed above in the Latin 'Opera' of 1490, and the following item:

643   De virtute centaureae ad Papiam (Tr: Nicolò da Reggio, *d.* 1350). (*Issued with* YŪḤANNĀ ibn Sarābiyūn *the Younger* [Serapion *the Younger*].

Liber aggregatus in medicinis simplicibus. Milan: Antonius Zarotus, 4 Aug. 1473.) f°. [LEK]

Ref: HC *14691; Durling 293:128; Osler (IM) 34; Klebs 913.1; Stillwell S422; Goff S-467.

N.B: Relates to the properties of the centaury plant. Authenticity questioned. Reissued in the Galen *Opera* of 1490. [TOTAL: 23 *fifteenth-century Latin 'firsts.'*]

Sixteenth-Century Latin 'Firsts'

Nota bene: As the Galenic 'firsts' were frequently issued in combination with other texts written by Galen or by other authors, a name in capital letters, in parentheses, indicates the author of the leading item with which the first printing of the given text was issued. Numerals in parentheses, which accompany the majority of the titles listed in no. 644, refer to the page and call-number appearing on p. 281–295 of Durling's Chronological census of Renaissance editions . . . of Galen, where imprints, translators, and subsequent editions are cited. [As is frequently done in the alphabetizing of early printed books, the preposition 'De' is discounted when it is the first word in a title. For an alphabetical list of Galen's works cited here and elsewhere in the present volume, see the INDEX: *Galen.*]

Separate editions and texts issued together with other works:

644   1) De anatomia parva, (GALEN), Pavia, 1515/16 (Durling, p. 283:15). 2) De anatomia vivorum, (GALEN), *ibid.* (283:16).   3) De anatomicis administrationibus, (BERENGARIO da Carpi), Bologna, 1529 (283:17). 4) De arteriarum venarumque dissectione, Paris, 1526 (285:43).   5) De foetuum formatione, (GALEN), Basel, 1535 (285:49).   6) In Hippocratis librum de articulis, (GALEN), Venice, 1541/42 (294:51).   7) In Hippocratis librum de natura humana, (HIPPOCRATES), Paris, 1531 (295:156).   8) De instrumento odoratus, (GALEN), Venice, 1541 (286:58).   9) De musculorum dissectione, (GALEN), Lyon, 1550 (287:70). 10) De musculorum motu, (GALEN), London, 1522 (287:68).   11) De natura et ordine cuiuslibet corporis, (GALEN), Pavia, 1515/16 (287:71). 12) De natura humana sive De compaigne membrorum, (GALEN), *ibid.* (284:28).   13) De nervorum dissectione, (GALEN), Paris, 1526 (285:42).   14) De ossibus ad tyrones, Lyon, Paris, Rome, 1535 (288:79 [35.2-4]).   15) De praesagatione ex pulsibus, (GALEN), Paris, 1532 (289:87).   16) De pulsibus dignoscendis, (GALEN), *ibid.* (290:93).   17) De pulsuum usu, (GALEN), Pavia, 1515/16 (290:96).   18) Quod qualitates incorporeae sint, (GALEN), Venice, 1541/42 (294:144).   19) De septimestri partu, (GALEN), Venice, 1541 (291:106b; also A7b in part in

Galen (continued)

Greek). 20) De usu partium corporis humani, Paris, 1528 (292:122) [see also 642.21 above]. 21) Utrum sanguis in arteriis secundum naturam contineatur, (GALEN), Paris, 1536 (282:7). 22) Utrum sit animal it quod utero contineatur, (A. LUDOVICUS), Lisbon, 1540 (282:5). 23) De venae sectione adversus Erasistrataeos, (GALEN), Basel [1536]; Paris, 1536 (292:126). 24) De venae sectione adversus Erasistratum, (GALEN), Basel [1536]; Paris, 1536 (292:125). 25) De vocalium instrumentorum dissectione, (GALEN), Lyon, 1550 (285:44).

GART der GESUNDHEIT. *See under* MEDICINE.

GEMINUS, Thomas (Thomas Gemini), *fl.* 1540.

645 Compendiosa totius anatomiae delineatio. London: John Herford, Oct. 1545. f°.

> *Ref:* NLMCat 2039; STC 11714; Cushing VI C-4; LC(LJRCat) 703; *Choulant (Anat)* 192–194.
>
> *N.B:* An imitation or compendium of the *De humani corporis fabrica libri VII* of Andreas Vesalius, which had been brought out at Basel in 1543. Illustrated with 40 anatomic copper-engravings derived from Vesalius's *Fabrica* of 1543 and his *Epitome*. One of the earliest instances of copper-plates produced in England. The first of a series of imitations which time and again reproduced the Vesalius illustrations and, in spite of the charge of plagiarism, did much in the years beyond our period to spread the 'new' anatomical knowledge.

GESNER, Konrad (Euonymus Philiatrus), 1516–1565.

646 Catalogus plantarum nomina latine, graece, germanice, et gallice proponens. Zürich: Christophorus Froschauer, 1542.

> *Ref:* Arber (1938) 276; *Sart (Appr)* 106–111.
>
> *N.B:* Gesner's *Bibliotheca universalis sive Catalogus omnium scriptorum*, upon which he spent ten years listing the books published in Latin, Greek, and Hebrew during the first century of printing, was printed by Froschauer at Zurich in 1545–1549. His accompanying classification of these titles under nineteen subjects, entitled *Pandectarum sive Partitionum universalium libri XXI*, was issued by Froschauer in 1548, and an *Appendix bibliothecae* in 1555.
>
> *Mon:* LEY, Willy. *Konrad Gesner, Leben und Werk*, München, 1929 (Münchener Beiträge zur Geschichte und Literatur der Naturwissenschaften, Heft 15–16).

647 Historia plantarum et vires ex Dioscoride [*and other works*]. Venice: Melchiorre Sessa, 1541. 16°. [LEK]

> *Ref:* BM-Ital 298; *Sart (Appr)* 108.
>
> *N.B:* A student's manual of botany. Also issued at Paris (BM-Fr 201) and at Basel during the same year. [Gesner's important biological and zoological work, the

Historia animalium—its illustrations including the famous rhinoceros drawn by Albrecht Dürer—was printed just after our period, in 1551–58, a fifth volume being issued in 1587. For a Gesner treatise on simples, see under MEDICINE: Medicinal properties of plants, *etc.*]

GILLES de Corbeil (Aegidius Corboliensis), 1165–1223.

648 De pulsibus carmen (Comm: Gentile da Foligno, *c.* 1290–1348. Ed: Venantius Mutius). Padua: Matthaeus Cerdonis, Jan. 1484. 4°. [LEK]

  Ref: GW 268; H *103; BMC VII 921; IGI 55; Klebs 465.1; Schullian (ArMed) 212; *Sart* II 440–441; *Garrison* (1929) 151; *Castiglioni* (1947) 316, 317, 328; Stillwell A83; Goff A-92.

  N.B: Frequently combined with his *De urinis carmen*, poems of great influence in transmitting the teachings of the school of Salerno; the latter a basic text for over four hundred years, first issued at Padua, 12 July 1483 (Cen A84).

GÜNTHER, Johann, 1505–1574.

649 Institutionum anatomicarum secundum Galeni sententiam ad candidatos medicinae, libri IV. Paris: Simon de Colines, 1536. 8°. [LEK]

  Ref: NLMCat 2227n; Renouard (Colines) 264; *Singer* (SHA) 113; *Cushing* (Vesalius) 44–50.

  N.B: A draft of Galen's anatomical theories drawn up by Günther for student use and known through copies at Boulogne-sur-Mer, Nancy, and the Bibliothèque Nationale at Paris. Günther, a teacher of anatomy, was a professional translator of ancient texts, twenty-two of which were brought out by Simon de Colines at Paris during the years 1528–1536. The fact that the printers at Basel were notorious for quickly reproducing popular books issued in Venice or Paris would make it seem possible that the Colines edition of 1536 may have been issued prior to that produced at Basel by Lasius and Platter in August of that year (NLMCat 2227). Two years later, an edition revised by Günther's pupil, Andreas Vesalius, was printed at Venice. Still other editions were subsequently issued at Basel, Venice, Lyon, and Padua.

GUY de Chauliac (Guido de Cauliaco), *c.* 1300–1368.

650 Chirurgia [*French*:] La practique en chirurgie (Ed: Nicolaus Panis). Lyon: For Barthélemy Buyer, 28 March 1478. f°. [LEK]

  Ref: Pell 3533; Osler (IM) 164; Klebs 491.1; *Sart* III 1690–1694; *Castiglioni* (1947) 345–347, 357.

  N.B: The work, which in the main is written from the surgical point of view, describes Mondino's methods of dissection as transmitted by Bertuccio. It consists of seven sections, the first of which treats of anatomy. Based largely on Galen and Avicenna. [For a note on contents, see under MEDICINE.] The section on anatomy was

Guy de Chauliac (continued)

printed, in Dutch, with a work by Lanfranchi of Milan, at Louvain in 1481 (Klebs 586.1).

Although Garrison (1929) 158 *note* cites a Latin edition of Venice, 1490, none has been found in the present survey earlier than that printed at Venice for Octavianus Scotus, 21 Nov. 1498 (Cen G510; Schullian (ArMed) 227). Italian and Catalan translations were issued at Venice in 1480 (Cen G515; Schullian (ArMed) 230) and at Barcelona in 1492 (Klebs 493.1). More than twenty editions are known within our period. For early 16th-century editions and adaptations, see NLMCat p. 271–273. An abridgment, the so-called *Chirurgia parva*, was issued in Dutch, French, and Latin before 1501 (Klebs 495–497).

Mon: NICAISE, Edouard. *La grande chirurgie de Chauliac*. Paris, 1890.
Fac: *Osiris* 5 *fig*. 35.

651   Chirurgia parva [*Dutch*]. [Delft: Anonymous printer, 1477–87.] [LEK]

Ref: Camp 870; Klebs 495.1; *Sart* III 1692.
N.B: A compendium of the *Chirurgia*, possibly made by a student. A popular manual, of which a French version was printed at Paris about 1500 (Klebs 496.1). The first Latin edition, printed at Venice by Bonetus Locatellus, 22 Feb. 1497 (Choulant (H) 416:133), contains the earliest printing of the eleventh-century treatise *De cognitione infirmitatum oculorum et curatione earum* of 'Isā ibn 'Alī, the famous Arabic oculist, giving an account of the anatomy and physiology of the eye, as well as its diseases and their cure. This apparently re-appeared in the edition issued by the same press, 27 Jan. 1500/01 (NLMCat 2251; Cen G512), together with the *Chirurgia* of Abū al-Kāsim (Albucasis), and the *Tractatus de oculis* of Canamusali de Baldach.

HABICHTBUCH.

652   Habichtbuch [*German*]. [Augsburg: Anton Sorg, 1480.] 4°. [LEK]

Ref: H 8341; BMC II 348; Klebs 501.1.
N.B: The earliest printed book on hawking.

HALY ABBAS ('Alī ibn 'Abbās), *d*. 994.

653   Liber medicinae, sive Regalis dispositio (Tr: Stephanus of Antioch, *fl*. 1127. Ed: Antonius Vitalis). Venice: Bernardinus Rizus for Joannes de Nigro, 25 Sept. 1492. f°. [LEK]

Ref: HC *8350; BMC V 403; BM-Ital 19; IGI 4644; Choulant (H) 350; Klebs 498.1; Schullian (ArMed) 233; *Sart* I 677; *Garrison* (1929) 129; *Browne* (AM) 53–57; Stillwell H2; Goff H-3.
N.B: By one of the three great Persian physicians whose writings translated from Arabic were largely responsible for medical knowledge in medieval Europe. Sometimes called the *Liber regius*. Divided into twenty discourses relating to

medical theory and practice. Sections II and III relate to anatomy [see De Koning] and section XIX to surgery. Also printed at Lyon by Jacobus Myt in 1523 (NLMCat 168; BM-Fr 11). An earlier translation—by Constantinus Africanus, *d.* 1087—is listed in NLMCat 2557 as printed at Lyon in 1515 in a volume ascribed to Isaac Israeli.

Mon: De KONING, P. *Trois traités d'anatomie arabes*, Leyde, 1903, p. 90–431 [Arabic text and French translation of Part I: Sections 2, chap. 1–16; and 3, chap. 1–37].

HENRI de Ferrières, *fl.* 1375.

654 De chasses [*French*]. (*Pt. I of* Les livres du roy Modus et de la royne Ratio. Chambéry: Antoine Neyret, 20 Oct. 1486.) f°. [LEK]

Ref: HC 11447; BMC VIII 386; BM-Fr 315; LC(LJR Cat) 331; Sart III 1183; Stillwell M629; Goff M-739.

N.B: A popular work on hunting. In prose and verse. Variant known. Printed in at least five editions during our period.

Mon: TILANDER, Gunnar, ed. *Les livres du roy Modus et de la royne Ratio.* Paris, 1931–32 (Société des anciens textes français). THIÉBAUD, J. *Bibliographie des ouvrages français sur la chasse.* Paris, 1934 (col. 388–395).

HERBARIUM APULEI; HERBARIUS; HERBOLARIO [*Italian*]. *See entries under* MEDICINE: Medicinal properties of plants, *etc.*

HILDEGARD of Bingen, *Saint*, 1098–1178.

655 Physica S. Hildegardis [*and other works*]. Strasbourg: Johann Schott, 1533. f°. [LEK]

Add: OREIBASIOS. De simplicibus. THEODORUS PRISCIANUS. Dieta. SORANOS. Asculapii de morborum . . . caussis [Tr: Caelius Aurelianus].

Ref: NLMCat 2307; BM-Ger 405; Choulant (H) 302–309; *Hunt (Quinby)* I 32; Sart II 386–388.

N.B: An early work on the natural sciences, including discussion of herbs and fruit, legumes, trees, and vineyards, as well as of fish, birds, and animal life, metals, and the rivers of Germany. One of the earliest herbals; written by a nun who founded the Convent of Rupertsberg.

HIPPOCRATES (Hippokrates; Ippokrate), 460–375 B.C.

656 Opera [*Greek*] (Ed: Franciscus Asulanus). Venice: In aedibus Aldi et Andreae Asulani soceri, May 1526. f°. [LEK]

Ref: NLMCat 2316; BM-Ital 327; Choulant (H) 22, 12–21; Osler (BO) 142; Renouard (Alde) I 243; Sart (Appr) 9.

N.B: The first Greek edition. Contains various titles not known to have been printed in Latin or Greek prior to the date of this *Opera*. A critical Greek edition prepared

Hippocrates (continued)

by Janus Cornarius, 1500–1558, was published by Hieronymus Froben and Nicolaus Episcopius at Basel in 1538 (NLMCat 2317).

Con: For list of contents, see above under no. 405.

657 Opera (Tr: Marcus Fabius Calvus, *fl.* 1520). Rome: Ex aedibus Fr. Minitii Calvi Novocomensis, 1525. f°. [LEK]

Ref: NLMCat 2321; Choulant (H) 25; Sart I 96–102; Sart (*Appr*) 8–10; *Castiglioni* (1947) 153.

N.B: Another edition, issued at Basel by Andreas Cratander in 1526, contains 68 of the Calvus translations, plus 2 by Gulielmus Copus and 1 each by Nicolaus Leonicenus and Andreas Brentius. An *Opera quae ad nos extant omnia*, compiled by Janus Cornarius, *d.* 1558, was issued at Basel, Paris, and Venice in 1546 (NLMCat 2322–2326), and revised and amended in later sixteenth-century editions.

Con: For list of contents, see above under no. 406.

658 De aere et aqua et regionibus. (*Issued with* RHASIS. Liber ad Almansorem. Milan: Leonardus Pachel and Uldericus Scinzenzeler, 14 Feb. 1481.) [LEK]

Ref: HCR 13891; BMC VI 749; Klebs 826.1; Schullian (ArMed) 399; *Castiglioni* (1947) 164–167; Stillwell R169; Goff R–175.

N.B: In addition to being the earliest known recognition of the action of climate on health, the text gives a comparison of the climatic conditions of Europe and Asia and their differences in flora and fauna. Included in the Latin *Opera* of 1525 and the Greek *Opera* of 1526. A Greek-Latin edition edited by Janus Cornarius, *d.* 1558, was published by Froben at Basel in 1529 and reprinted in 1542—NLMCat 2402, Choulant (H) 29. Also known as *De aeribus, acquis, et locis libellus*.

De anatome. *See* De corporum secatione.

De articulis [*Greek*], 1526 [49]. *See no.* 405:5.

De carnibus, 1525 (63). *See no.* 406:5.

De corde, 1525 (66). *See no.* 406:7.

De corporum secatione, Anatome ve, 1525 (65). *See no.* 406:8.

De dentitione [*Greek*], 1526 [17]. *See no.* 405:12.

De dissectione [*Greek*], 1526 [18]. *See no.* 405:14.

De flatibus, 1525 (62). *See no.* 406:13.

De genitura. *See* De natura seminis genitalis.

De glandulis per omnia membra, 1525 (51). *See no.* 406:16.

De humoribus, complexionibus ve, 1525 (61). *See no.* 406:21.

De infoecundus, 1525 (21). *See no.* 406:22.

De natura, 1525 (11). *See no.* 406:38.

De natura feminae, 1525 (23). *See no.* 406:39.

659   De natura foetus, pueri ve (Tr: Bartolomeo da Messina). (*Issued in* ARTICELLA. Venice: Hermannus Liechtenstein, 29 March 1483.) f°. [LEK]

> *Ref*: GW 2679; IGI 908; Klebs 116.2; Choulant (H) 398; Stillwell A1011; Goff A-1143.
>
> *N.B*: Included in various editions of *Articella*, for which see GW 2680 ff. and NLMCat 327–329. Also in the Latin *Opera* of Hippocrates, 1525, and the Greek *Opera* of 1526—*nos.* 406:4 *and* 405:36, *respectively*.

660   De natura hominis. (*Issued with* RHASIS. Liber ad Almansorem. Milan: Leonardus Pachel and Uldericus Scinzenzeler, 14 Feb. 1481.) f°. [LEK]

> *Ref*: HCR 13891; BMC VI 749; Schullian (ArMed) 399; Klebs 826.1; *Castiglioni* (1947) 160–162; *Sart* I 120; Stillwell R169; Goff R-175.
>
> *N.B*: The text is one of the main sources for the Hippocratic theory of the four humors (blood, yellow bile, black bile, phlegm) and the four qualities (wet, hot, dry, cold). Also known as *De natura humana*. Variously attributed to Polybus, the son-in-law of Hippocrates. Possibly preceded by an undated edition assigned to [Rome, 1480] in Reichling 556. Included as the first item in a compilaton assigned to [1483–1490], *see no.* 407:5. Another edition, in the translation of Andreas Brentius, is assigned to Rome, about 1490—Cen H255. Included in the Latin *Opera* of 1525 and the Greek *Opera* of 1526; also, in whole or in part, in various sixteenth-century compilations—*see* NLMCat p. 298. Issued at Paris by Simon de Colines in 1524 and 1534. A Greek edition was printed at Basel in 1536 under the editorship of Hollerius.

De natura humana. *See* De natura hominis.

661   De natura muliebri (*i.e.*, De natura feminae liber I). Paris: Claude Chevallon, 1526. f°.

> *Ref*: NLMCat 2416.
>
> *N.B*: Issued also in the Greek *Opera* of 1526 [35] and possibly as part of the *De natura feminae* in the Latin *Opera* of 1525 (23). *See nos.* 405:38 *and* 406:39.

De natura ossium, 1525 (68). *See no.* 406:41.

De natura pueri. *See* De natura foetus.

Hippocrates (continued)

De natura seminis genitalis, 1525 (12). *See no.* 406:43.

De natura virginum, 1525 (17). *See no.* 406:44.

De octimestri partu, 1525 (15). *See no.* 406:45.

De septimanis, 1525 (45). *See no.* 406:59.

De septimestri partu, 1525 (14). *See no.* 406:60.

662 De sterilibus (Tr: Marcus Fabius Calvus, *fl.* 1520). (*Issued with* HIPPO-
CRATES. De natura feminae liber I. Paris: Claude Chevallon, 1526.)   4°.
[LEK]

Ref: NLMCat 2416.
N.B: Issued also in the Greek *Opera* of 1526 [37]—see no. 405:50. In combination with
De mulierum morbis libri II, this tract comprises the so-called *De feminarum morbis
libri III*.

De superfoetatione, 1525 (18). *See no.* 406:63.

De visu, oculi ve acie, 1525 (60). *See no.* 406:70.

HORTUS SANITATIS.

663 Hortus sanitatis. Mainz: Jacob Meydenbach, 23 June 1491. f°.
[LEK]

Ref: HC *8944; BMC I 44; BM-Ger 418; Oates 55; IGI 4900; Klebs 509.1; Klebs
(Hortus) 1; LC(LJRCat) 138; Schullian (ArMed) 244; Hunt (Quinby) I 8; *Arber*
(1938) 28–37; Stillwell H416; Goff H-486.
N.B: Derived, like the *Gart der Gesundheit*, from the *Herbarius* but much expanded.
Profusely illustrated. In addition to its descriptive chapters *De herbis et plantis*
relating to plants, their geographical origin and medicinal properties, it contains
sections entitled *De avibus*, *De piscibus*, *De lapidibus*, and *De urinis*. Variously
assigned to Johann von Cube as compiler, identified with a town-physician of
Frankfurt, Dr. Johann Wonnecke von Caub, c. 1484–1503. Klebs lists four Latin
editions printed at Mainz (1) and [Strasbourg] (3) during 1491–c. 1499; also a
French version printed at Paris, c. 1500 (Cen H416–H420). NLMCat p. 308–309
lists six editions, 1511–1536, in Latin, German, and Dutch known or assignable to
presses at Venice (1), Strasbourg (3), Antwerp (1), and Utrecht (1).
Fac: HUDSON, Noel, *ed.* An Early English version of the *Hortus Sanitatis*. Facsimile of
The Noble Lyfe and Natures of Man, of Bestes, Serpentys, Fowles, and Fisshes . . .
Anvers, J. van Doesborgh, [c. 1521]. London, 1954.

IV. *Natural Science*

HUNDT, Magnus, *the Elder*, 1449–1519.

664 Antropologium de hominis dignitate, natura, et proprietatibus. Leipzig: Wolfgang Stöckel, 1501. 4°.

> *Ref:* NLMCat 2507; BM-Ger 423; Pr 11391; *Choulant (Anat)* 125.
>
> *N.B:* Illustrated with crude, stylized woodcuts which, however, give the most detailed representation of the internal organs known before the turn of the century. According to Garrison (1929) 210, the schematic drawing of the brain had already appeared, or is similar to one, in the *Philosophia naturalis* of Albertus Magnus, Brescia, 1490. Choulant (Anat) 123–4 cites the illustrations as having been re-engraved from cuts in the *Philosophie naturalis compendium* of Johannes Peyligk, Leipzig, 1499 (Cen P493).

ISIDORUS Hispalensis (Isidore, *Bishop of Sevilla*), Saint, *c.* 570–636.

665 Etymologiae libri XX. [Augsburg:] Günther Zainer, 19 Nov. 1472. f°. [LEK]

> *Ref:* H *9273; BMC II 317; BM-Ger 432; IGI 5404; Polain 2135; Klebs 536.2; Schullian (ArMed) 250; *Clagett (GSA)* 158–159; *Sart* I 471–472; Stillwell I153; Goff I-181.
>
> *N.B:* An encyclopaedia, which according to the captions of its twenty books treats of a wide variety of subjects—among them, *De quatuor disciplinis mathematicis* (Bk. III); *De medicina* (Bk. IV); *De temporibus*, listing solstices and equinoxes (Bk. V); *De animalibus* (Bk. XII); *De mundo et partibus* (Bk. XIII); *De terra et partibus* (Bk. XIV, with map); *De lapidibus et metallis* (Bk. XVI). Notable as containing the earliest printed map of the world, a schematic representation [see under TECHNOLOGY]. An unsigned and undated edition is variously assigned to Strasbourg about 1473 (Cen I154). Printed at least ten times during the fifteenth century. Book IV, on medicine, was issued with Symphorien Champier's *De triplici disciplina*. Lyon, 1508 (NLMCat 933).
>
> *Mon:* BREHAUT, E. *An encyclopedist of the Dark Ages, Isidore of Seville.* New York, 1912. ISIDORE of SEVILLE. *Medical writings. An English translation and commentary* [by] *William D. Sharpe.* Philadelphia, 1964 (*Transactions* of the American Philosophical Society, new ser., v. 54, pt. 2). ISIDORE of SEVILLE. *Traité de la nature.* Ed: L. Fontaine. Bordeaux, 1960 (French translation and Latin text; with introduction, p. 1–162. Reviewed, p. 632–634 in *L'Antiquité classique* 39 1961).

JACOPO da Forlì (Giacomo della Torre; Jacobus de Forlivio; Jacobus Forliviensis), *c.* 1360–1413.

666 Expositio in Avicennae aureum capitulum de generatione embryonis (Canon III, 21, 2). Pavia: Antonius Carcanus, 1479. 4°. [LEK]

> *Ref:* HCR 7234; BMC VII 996; IGI 4988; Osler (IM) 183; Schullian (ArMed) 255; Klebs 550.1; *Garrison* (1929) 167; Stillwell J39; Goff J-42.

Jacopo da Forlì (continued)

> N.B: Included in a compilation, edited by Bassianus Politus and printed at Venice in
> 1502, which contains commentaries by Dino del Garbo and Tommaso del Garbo
> (NLMCat 2562).

KETHAM (Johann von Kirschheim; Johannes de Ketham; *called* Ketham),
fl. 1460.

667 Fasciculus medicinae. Venice: Joannes and Gregorius de Gregoriis,
de Forlivio, 26 July 1491. f°. [LEK]

> *Add*: PIETRO da Tossignano, *fl.* 1400. Consilium pro peste evitanda.
> *Ref*: H 9774; Klebs 573.1; Choulant (H) 402–405; *Choulant (Anat)* 115–122; *Garrison*
> (1929) 210; Stillwell K11; Goff K-13.
> *N.B*: A book notable for its woodcut illustrations, attributable to the school of Gentile
> Bellini, 1429–1507. The first anatomical book to be illustrated. The *Fasciculus* in
> its various editions was an accumulative compilation of medical and anatomical
> tracts.
>
> An Italian version by Sebastianus Manilius was issued by this Venetian firm in
> 1493, in which is included the *Anatomia* of Mondino (Cen K15). A Spanish
> version was printed at Saragossa by Pablo Hurus, 15 Aug. 1494 (Klebs 575.1);
> and at Burgos by Juan de Burgos, 15 May 1495 (Cen K16; NLMCat 2669n).
> Known in four Latin editions in the last decade of the fifteenth century. For early
> sixteenth-century editions in Latin and the vernacular, see NLMCat p. 336–338.
> *Mon*: DONATI, Lamberto. Del "Fasciculus Medicinae," Venezia: 26 Luglio 1491–
> 5 Febraio 1493 (p. 71–76 in *Gutenberg Jahrbuch* 1961). SINGER, Charles. *The
> Fasciculo di Medicina, Venice, 1493, with introduction, discussion of art, language,
> sources and influence, a translation of the "Anathomia" of Mondino da Luzzi* [added
> to this edition], *an account of medieval anatomy and physiology and an atlas of illus-
> trative figures.* Milan, 1925.
> *Fac*: SUDHOFF, Karl and Charles SINGER, ed. *The Fasciculus Medicinae of Johannes de
> Ketham, Alemanus, Facsimile of the First (Venetian) Edition of 1491 with introduction
> and notes.* London, 1924. [The dissection cut, which accompanies the Mondino
> in the 1493 edition, is reproduced in Singer's *A short history of anatomy*, New York,
> 1957, *fig.* 35.]

Le LIVRE da la CHASSE.

668 Le livre de la chasse du grand seneschal de Normandie [*French*]. [Paris:]
Pierre Le Caron [*c.* 1500?].

> *Ref*: Klebs 609.1; *Sart* III 1185.

Le LIVRE du FAULCON.

669 Le livre du faulcon [*French*]. Paris [For Antoine Vérard, before 20
May 1496]. [LEK]

> *Ref*: Klebs 502.1; *Sart* III 1185.

IV. *Natural Science*

LEONARDI, Camillo, of Pesaro, *fl.* 1480.

670 Speculum lapidum. Venice: Giovanni Baptista Sessa, 1502. 4°.
[LEK]

> *Ref*: BM-Ital 375; *Sart (SW)* 157.
> *N.B*: Treats of over two hundred minerals, according to the traditional knowledge
> and concepts of earlier times.

LEONICENUS (Nicolò da Lonigo; *commonly called* **Leonicenus, Nicolaus
Leonicenus, Nicolò Leoniceno), 1428–1524.**

671 De Plinii et aliorum in medicina erroribus. Ferrara: Laurentius de
Rubeis and Andreas de Grassis, 18 Dec. 1492. 4°.

> *Ref*: HC *10021; BMC VI 612; Oates 2244; Klebs 598.1; Schullian (ArMed) 287;
> *Castiglioni* (1947) 373; *Garrison* (1929) 194, 195; Stillwell L146; Goff L-168.
> *N.B*: Castiglioni gives the title, possibly from a manuscript, as *Plinii et aliorum autorum,*
> *qui de simplicibus medicaminibus scripserunt, errores notati,* and adds with reference
> to Leonicenus that he refuted Pliny and the naturalists; and showed from original
> classical texts that translations by Serapion and Avicenna were distorted. Gar-
> rison speaks of Leonicenus's feat of courage in correcting botanical errors in
> Pliny's text. [For early sixteenth-century editions of this and other works and
> translations by Leonicenus, see NLMCat p. 354–355.]
> *Mon*: THORNDIKE, Lynn. *The attack on Pliny* (chapter LXVI in vol. 4 of his *History of*
> *magic and experimental science*, New York, 1934).

LUCRETIUS CARUS, Titus, *fl.* 95–55 B.C.

672 De rerum natura. [Brescia:] Thomas Ferrandus [1473]. 4°. [LEK]

> *Ref*: Osler (BO) 1; Klebs 623.1; *Nordenskiöld (HB)* 21, 22, 46–49; *Crombie (A–G)* 1961
> II 105.
> *N.B*: A scientific poem on the nature of things, and the best source regarding the
> ancient theory of atoms as developed by Demokritos, *fl.* 420 B.C., and discussed
> by Epikuros, *fl.* 300 B.C., in his philosophic school at Athens. Discovered by
> Poggio-Bracciolini about 1418. In theory, the universe consists of space in which
> atoms of varied shapes and sizes combine and disassociate themselves from others
> in eternal motion; and worlds arise and perish through the association and dis-
> association of atoms; the brain is the seat of thought; the soul, which is composed
> of the finest atoms, consists of four factors—spirit, understanding, the life-prin-
> ciple, and impulse; when its atoms disassociate, life ceases. According to Dr.
> Osler (*d.* 1919), the account of the origin of man as given in Lucretius, Book V,
> lines 925–1010, is so nearly correct it could be given in any textbook of anthro-
> pology. The first dated edition was printed at Verona by Paulus Fridenperger,
> 28 Sept. 1486 (Cen L298). At least five editions were printed in Italy during the
> fifteenth century. Editions edited by Pier Candido Decembrio (Florence, 1512)

Lucretius Carus (continued)

> and Andrea Navagero (Venice, 1515) are listed in NLMCat [2863] and 2864 respectively.
>
> *Mon*: See under PHYSICS: Lucretius Carus.

LUDOLF von Suchen (Ludolphus de Suchen), *fl.* 1335.

673 Iter ad Terram Sanctam. [Strasbourg: Heinrich Eggestein, 1475–1480.] f°. [LEK]

> *Ref*: HC *10307; BMC I 74; BM-Ger 532; Klebs 624.1; Stillwell L326; Goff L-362.
>
> *N.B*: Presumably the first printed account of the Holy Land and of a journey to Jerusalem; with descriptions of plants and animals. Another undated edition, set in two columns but in the same type, is attributed to the same press and period—Cen L327. The present edition, in long lines, is generally accepted as the earlier. An unsigned edition in German bears the imprint date, 1477 (Cen L329).

MACER FLORIDUS. *See under* MEDICINE: Medicinal properties of plants, *etc.*

MAIMONIDES (Moses ben Maimon; Abū 'Imrām Mūsā ibn Maimūn), 1135–1204.

674 Aphorismi secundum doctrinam Galeni [*and other works*]. Bologna: Franciscus (Plato) de Benedictis, for Benedictus Hectoris, 29 May 1489. 4°. [LEK]

> *Add*: DAMASCENUS, Janus [Mesuë? or Serapion?]. Aphorismi. RHASIS. De secretis in medicina, sive Aphorismi. HIPPOCRATES. Capsula eburnea.
>
> *Ref*: HC *10524; BMC VI 824; Klebs 644.1; Schullian (ArMed) 297; *Castiglioni* (1947) 277–278, 349; Stillwell M63; Goff M-77.
>
> *N.B*: An analysis and critique of Galen's doctrines, including his theories on anatomy and physiology. Two variants of an edition printed at [or assigned to] Venice in 1500 are known (Cen M65, M66), as also a page-for-page reprint at Venice in 1508 (NLMCat 3302). [For further comment, see under MEDICINE.] The other works included in this volume had seen their first printing in the edition of Rhasis's *Liber ad Almansorem* issued at Milan in 1481 (*no.* 500).
>
> *Mon*: BARON, S. W., *ed. Essays on Maimonides*. New York, 1941.

MARLIANI, Giovanni (Johannes Marlianus), *c.* 1425–1483.

675 Quaestio de caliditate corporum humanorum. [Milan:] Antonius Zarotus, 27 Aug. 1474. f°. [LEK]

> *Ref*: HC 10771; BMC VI 711; IGI 6189; Klebs 664.1; *Clagett (Mar)* 31, 34–36, 79; Stillwell M237; Goff M-274.
>
> *N.B*: A study of body heat and temperature, in which Marliani distinguishes between intensity [temperature] and heat quantity. An edition printed at Venice by

Bonetus Locatellus in 1501 for the heirs of Octavianus Scotus is listed as NLMCat 2966. Among the varied sources which Maliani cites are the works of Jacopo da Forlì (*d.* 1413), Giovanni Sermoneta (*fl.* 1430), and Ugo Benzi (*d.* 1439).

Mon: CLAGETT, Marshall. *Body heat and antiperistasis* (Chap. IV in his *Giovanni Marliani and late medieval physics*. New York, 1941).

MASSA, Nicolò, *d.* 1569.

676 Liber introductorius anatomiae.   Venice: Francesco Bindoni and Maffeo Pasini, Nov. 1536.   4°.

Ref: BM-Ital 424; *Thornd (HM)* V 514–519.

N.B: Relates in part to his clinical experience in Venice. Dedicated to Pope Paul III in 1536. [For an appraisal of Massa and his importance in introducing new concepts of anatomy, based upon dissection and factual observation, see WIGHTMAN, W. P. D. *Science and the Renaissance*. Edinburgh, 1962, vol. I, p. 231–234.]

MATTIOLI, Pierandrea, 1500–1577.

677 Di Pedacio Dioscoride Anazarbeo libri cinque Della historia et materia medicinale tradotti in lingua volgare Italiana . . . [*Latin-Italian*].   Venice: Nicolò de Bascarini, 1544.   [LEK]

Ref: NLMCat 1160; *Arber* (1938) 276; *Garrison* (1929) 231; *Sart (Appr)* 75–77.

N.B: Mattioli's translation of Dioskorides was also issued at Venice with his important commentary in 1548 and 1550 (NLMCat 1162, 1163; Hunt (Quinby) I 59); and at Mantua in 1549, under the title *Il Dioscoride. Con l'aggionta del sesto libro* (BM-Ital 218). According to Sart (SW) 137, the commentary was subsequently so revised, corrected, enlarged, and translated in various languages that it became a botanical treatise in itself. Wightman (1962) I 256 speaks of Mattioli's commentary as being "actually an 'up-to-date' and largely original work." Sarton speaks of Mattioli's travels, and notes that his correspondence increased with his fame, until he became a magnet of botanical information. [A Latin version of the commentary was printed with the Dioskorides text, by Vincenzo Valgrisi at Venice in 1554 (NLMCat 3008).]

MICHAEL *Scotus* (Michael *the Scot*; Michael Scott; *frequently called* Scotus), *c.* 1180–1235.

678 Liber phisiognomiae sive De secretis naturae.   [Venice: Jacobus de Fivizzano, Lunensis] 1477.   4°.   [LEK]

Ref: HC *14550; BMC V 242; BM-Ital 619; IGI 6417; Klebs 899.1; *Thornd (HM)* II 328–331; *Crombie (A–G)* 1961 I 225; *Taton (A&MS)* 482; Stillwell M480; Goff M-551.

N.B: Dr. Klebs lists twenty fifteenth-century, Latin editions. Spanish versions were issued with Ketham's *Fasciculus medicinae*, Saragossa, 1494, reprinted at Sevilla in

IV. *Natural Science*

Michael Scotus (continued)

1517 (NLMCat 2669*n*); and an Italian version is known to have been printed at Venice in 1533 and again in 1537 and 1540. Scotus is known mainly as an astrologer, an exponent of Averroism, and a translator from the Arabic.

Mon: HASKINS, Charles H. *Michael Scot* (p. 272–298 in his *Studies in the history of medieval science*. Cambridge [Mass.], 1927). THORNDIKE, Lynn. *Michael Scot*. London, 1965.

MONDINO (Raimondo de' Luzzi; Mundinus), *c.* 1275–1326.

679 Anatomia corporis humani. [Padua: Petrus Maufer, about 1476.] 4°. [LEK]

Ref: Klebs 688.1; *Sart* III 842–45; *Singer (SHA)* 1957, 74–88; *Taton (A&MS)* 529–530; *Choulant (Anat)* 88–96; *Thornd (HM)* V 499–502; *Castiglioni (1947)* 341–344.

N.B: A compendium of anatomy adhering to Galen's system in spite of the fact that Mondino re-introduced the public dissection of cadavers in his lectures. A popular dissecting manual frequently reprinted during our period.

The earliest edition with date was produced at Pavia, by Antonius Carcanus, 19 Dec. 1478 (Klebs 688.2). Eight editions in Latin, including a variant, were printed in the fifteenth century (Klebs 688.1–.8; Cen M747–M750). A decorative picture of a dissection in the classroom introduces Mondino's *Anatomia*, which is included in the 1493 Italian version of Ketham's *Fasciculus medicinae*. A new edition, based on a collation of Mondino's texts by Johannes Dryander [*see no.* 620], was published by Christian Egenolff at Marburg in 1541. [For early sixteenth-century editions, see NLMCat p. 412.] A translation of the *Anatomia* is given in Charles Singer's monograph on *The Fasciculo di Medicina*, Milan, 1925.

Fac: WICKERSHEIMER, Ernest. *Anatomies de Mondino dei Luzzi et de Guido de Vigevano* (p. 1–65 in vol. 3 of *Documents scientifiques du XVe siècle*. Paris, 1926). [For a reproduction of Ketham's 1493 chart of human anatomy according to Mondino, see Castiglioni (1947) 342.]

OPPIANOS (Oppianus), *2nd century.*

680 Halieutica, sive De piscatu (Tr: Laurentius Lippius). Colle di Valdelsa: Bonus Gallus, 12 Sept. 1478. 4°. [LEK]

Ref: HC *12015; BMC VII 1079; IGI 7006; Klebs 710.1; *McGill (VZ)* 2; Stillwell O59; Goff O-65.

N.B: A poem on the nature of fishes and fishing. Dr. Casey A. Wood, in *McGill (VZ)* 500, lists editions printed at Venice, Florence, and Strasbourg in 1508, 1515, and 1534, respectively. The 1534 edition of the *De piscibus libri V* is listed as NLMCat 3400.

OVIEDO y VALDÉS. *See* FERNÁNDEZ de Oviedo y Valdés, Gonzalo.

IV. *Natural Science*

PALLADIUS, Rutilius Taurus Aemilianus, *4th century, fl.* 340.

De re rustica libri XIV. *See under* SCRIPTORES REI RUSTICAE.

PAULUS *Venetus* (Paolo Nicoletti), *c.* 1368–1429.

681 Espositio in Aristotelem De generatione et corruptione (Ed: Jacobus Baptista Alouisius). Venice: Bonetus Locatellus, for Octavianus Scotus 21 May 1498. f°.

> *Add*: De mundi compositione.
> *Ref*: H *12518; BMC V 450; Oates 1999; Klebs 734.1; *Sart* III 1086; Stillwell P180; Goff P-209.
> *N.B*: Written by an Aristotelian who was the author of various commentaries.

PEYLICK, Johannes, 1474–1522.

682 De anathomia totius corporis humani suarumque partium principalium. (*In his* Philosophie naturalis compendium. Leipzig: Melchior Lotter, 12 September 1499.) f°. [LEK]

> *Ref*: HC *12861; BMC III 650; BM-Ger 689; Polain 3024; Klebs 754.1; *Choulant (Anat)* 123–124; Stillwell P493; Goff P-539.
> *N.B*: A brief anatomy of the human body. The final chapter of the larger work. With woodcuts, and caption reading *Compendiosa capitis physici declaratio*. Printed as a separate by Wolfgang Stöckel at Leipzig in 1516.

PIETRO d'Abano (Abano, Petrus de; Petrus Aponensis; *called* Petrus Conciliator), 1250–*c.*1315.

683 De physiognomia. Padua: Petrus Maufer, 1474. 4°.

> *Ref*: HC 18; BMC VII 912; Osler (IM) 68; Pell 13; Klebs 775.1; Stillwell P394; Goff P-438.
> *N.B*: According to Thornd (HM) V 53, the fifth Book of the *Chryomantie ac physionomie anastasis* of Bartolomeo della ROCCA [*see no.* 505] purports to be a treatise on chiromancy by Pietro d'Abano, with some additions. The *Decisiones physionomiae* of Pietro d'Abano, [Venice] 1548, is listed as NLMCat 6.
> *Mon*: See under MEDICINE: Pietro d'Abano.

PLINY *the Elder* (Plinius Secundus, Gaius), 23–79 A.D.

684 Historia naturalis, libri XXXVII. Venice: Johann von Speier, [before 18 September] 1469. f°. [LEK]

> *Ref*: HCR 13087; BMC V 153; BM-Ital 526; Choulant (H) 181–206; IGI 7878; Horblit 84; Klebs 786.1; LC(LJRCat) 192; Stillwell P716; Goff P-786.

Pliny (continued)

 N.B: An encyclopaedia of natural science, a strange combination of insight, erudition, and folktales, but of great value in revealing the knowledge of his and earlier times; made especially valuable by the fact that Pliny included his sources. The first important printed book in science. Variants known of this first edition. At least forty-six editions are known to have been printed within our period. This popularity was not due solely, however, to an awakening interest in natural science. Leoniceno, Barbaro, Merula, and Benedetti were among the humanists concerned with Pliny's text and its connotation. Book 1 is introductory; Book 2 relates to cosmological matters; Books 3–6, to geography; Book 7, to anthropology; Book 10, to birds; Books 8, 9, 11, to zoology; Books 12–19, to botany; Books 20–32, to medicine; Books 33–37, to mineralogy and sculpture, including the oldest known account of ancient art. [The Laocoön group now at the Vatican was identified through Pliny's text, when the statue was found among the ruins of the Baths of Titus in 1506.] The subjects as cited are not always contained within their specified sections; sixteen of its 37 books, for instance, describe plants, and the work as a whole is our best source on Roman plant-lore. A chapter is devoted to the origin and production of glass. For discussion of Pliny's translators and commentators, see Sart (Appr) 81–83. The terminal date in the imprint derives from the fact that this work is mentioned as already published, in the five-year privilege granted the printer on 18 September 1469 by the Signoria of Venice. [For early sixteenth-century editions in Latin and Italian, *see* NLMCat p. 474–475.]

 Mon: THORNDIKE, L. *The attack on Pliny* (p. 593–610 in vol. IV of his *History of magic and experimental science*. New York, 1934). STANNARD, Jerry. *Pliny and Roman botany* (p. 420–425 in *Isis* 56 1965).

 Fac: HORBLIT 84[b].

POLLUX, Julius, *c.* 134–192.

685 Onomasticon [*Greek and Latin*].   Venice: Apud Aldum [Aldus Manutius], April 1502. f°. [LEK]

 Ref: BM-Ital 531; Renouard (Alde) 78; *Choulant (Anat)* 21—N,P; *Singer (SHA)* 1957, 107.

 N.B: Arranged by subjects, one section containing a list of anatomical terms as employed at the time of Galen. Also known by its Latin title, *Vocabularium*. Used by the humanists in replacing Arabic terms, which were currently taboo in their society. Sarton I 313 cites editions printed at Florence in 1520 and Basel in 1536.

POLO, Marco, *c.* 1254–1324.

686 Buch des edlen Ritters und Landfahrers Marco Polo [*German*]. Nuremberg: Friedrich Creussner, 1477. f°. [LEK]

 Ref: HC *13245; BMC II 449; BM-Ger 709; Klebs 798.1; *Sart* II 1057–61; Stillwell P821; Goff P-901.

N.B: The first printed edition of Marco Polo's travels. A stirring account of his experiences in crossing and re-crossing Asia from the Mediterranean to the Pacific coast, Russia, and Japan. Contains observations on animals, plants, and minerals. Written or dictated while he was in prison at Genoa in 1298–1299. One of the surprising factors in the account of Polo's travels, which covered the years 1260 through 1295, was his mission in carrying letters from Kublai Khān to the Pope, during his return to Italy in 1269. Printed by Anton Sorg at Augsburg in 1481, in a volume containing the lives of Herzog Leopold and Wilhelm of Austria—LC (LJRCat) 70; Goff L-184. Columbus's copy of a 1485 Antwerp edition, with his annotations, is at the Colombina at Seville. Issued in many editions and in Latin, Italian, Portuguese, and Spanish versions during our period. A critical edition of Polo's narrative was undertaken by Giovanni Battista Ramusio, *d.* 1557, and included in his *Secondo Volume delle Navigationi et Viaggi.* Venice: nella stamperia de Giunti, 1559.

Mon: Meyer, E. H. F. *Geschichte der Botanik.* IV, 1857, p. 114–131. Yule, *Sir* Henry, *ed.* and *tr. The Book of Ser Marco Polo, the Venetian.* 3rd ed., revised. London, 1903. Benedetto, Luigi Foscolo. *Marco Polo, Il Milione.* Florence, 1928. Herriott, J. Homer. *The 'lost' Toledo manuscript of Marco Polo* (p. 456–463 in *Speculum* XII, 1937); discusses Ramusio's and Benedetto's critical studies.

RABANUS MAURUS (*called* Hrabanus; Raban), *Abbot of Fulda, Abp. of Mainz, c.* 776–856.

687 Opus de universo sive de sermonum proprietate, libri XXII. [Strasbourg: The R-Printer (Adolf Rusch), before 20 July (or June), 1467.] f°.

Ref: HC *13699; BMC I 60; BM-Ger 420; Oates 98; IGI 8266; Osler (IM) 1; Schullian (ArMed) 383; Klebs 524.1; *Sart* I 555; *Garrison* (1929) 147; *McGill* (*VZ*) 7, 527; Stillwell R3; Goff R-1.

N.B: The earliest printed book to treat of animals. Book VII includes the following sections: *De minutis animalibus*; *De serpentibus*; *De vermibus*; *De piscibus*; *De avibus*; and *De minutis avibus*. The terminal date is derived from a contemporary note in the copy at the Bibliothèque Nationale in Paris.

Mon: Fellner, Stefan. *Compendiun der Naturwissenschaften an der Schule zu Fulda im IX Jahrhundert.* Berlin, 1879 [which, according to Sarton, contains an analysis of the *Opus de universo*].

DE RE RUSTICA. *See under* Scriptores Rei Rusticae.

REISCH, Gregor, *d.* 1525.

688 Margarita philosophica. Freiburg [im Breisgau]: Johann Schott, *citra festum Margarethe* [before 13 July] 1503. 4°. [LEK]

Ref: Pr 11717; BM-Ger 731; LC(LJRCat) 429; *Choulant (Anat)* 126–129; *Sart (Appr)* 163–164; *Garrison* (1929) 210.

Reisch (continued)

> N.B: A popular encyclopaedia that treats the subjects of the *trivium* and *quadrivium*. Although not close to nature, the anatomical figures which appear in this popular digest of the sciences at least reveal the untutored conception of the internal organs and the structure of the eye—the latter said to be derived from a fifteenth-century drawing, the oldest schematic representation of the eye that is known. [The author's name is revealed in a poem dated 1496, and for a time this was erroneously taken for the date of printing. No fifteenth-century edition is known.] According to D. E. Smith's *Rara arithmetica*, 12 editions were issued before 1550.
>
> Mon: FERGUSON, John. *Bibliography of the Margarita Philosophica of Gregorius Reisch* (p. 194–216 in *The Library*, 4th Ser., X, no. 2, 1929).

RHASIS (Abū Bakr Muḥammad ibn Zakariyā al-Rāzī. *Called* Razi; Rasis; Rhazes; Rhasis), *d.* 923/24.

689 Liber ad Almansorem, libri X *(with other medical tracts)*.   Milan: Leonardus Pachel and Uldericus Scinzenzeler, 14 Feb. 1481. f°. [LEK]

> Ref: HCR 13891; BMC VI 749; Klebs 826.1; Schullian (ArMed) 399; *Sart* I 609; *Castiglioni (1947)* 268; *Campbell (AM)* I 66–67; Stillwell R169; Goff R-175.
>
> N.B: An important work by the most original physician of the East, one of the great physicians of all time. The Arabic text of part of the "Kitāb al-Manṣūrī"—known in Latin as cited above, or as the *Liber Almansoris*—together with a page-by-page translation in French, is given in De Koning's monograph. His text, which is derived from a manuscript at the Bibliothèque Nationale in Paris, presents twenty-six chapters treating of the anatomical structure of the bones, muscles, nerves, veins, arteries, the eyes, nose, thorax, heart, intestines, and so on. These chapters apparently derive from Book I, since according to the analysis given by Campbell, the full treatise comprises I) anatomy and physiology; II) temperaments; III) simple remedies; IV) health; V) skin diseases, cosmetics; VI) diet for travellers; VII) surgery; VIII) poisons; IX) diseases of the various organs; X) fevers. Issued at Venice in 1497 and in 1500 (Cen R170, R171); the latter, reprinted in 1508 (NLMCat 3311). [For further references and a note on various works included in the volume, see under MEDICINE.]
>
> Mon: DE KONING, P. *Trois traités d'anatomie arabes . . . Traduction*. Leide, 1903, p. 1–89 [Arabic text with French translation, chap. 1–26].

690 De proprietatibus membrorum et nocumentis sexaginta animalium. *(Issued with his* Liber ad Almansorem. [Venice:] Bonetus Locatellus for Octavianus Scotus, 7 Oct. 1497.) f°.

> Ref: HC *13893; BMC V 448; BM-Ital 456; Klebs 826.2; Schullian (ArMed) 400; Stillwell R170; Goff R-176.
>
> N.B: Eleven works by Rhasis are included in this compilation, an enlargement of the volume of medical tracts published at Milan in 1481.

IV. *Natural Science*

ROCCA, Bartolomeo della (*known* as Cocles), 1467–1504.

691 Chyromantie ac physionomie anastasis cum approbatione magistri Alexandri de Achillinis. Bologna: Joannes Antonius de Benedictis, 1504. sm. f°. [LEK]

    Ref: NLMCat 972; *Thornd (HM)* V 50.
    N.B: Written by a chiromancer and astrologer who correctly predicted the death of many prominent persons, including his own. The work, which relates to divination and character analysis, includes pungent comments on various contemporaries. An epitome of Books 1–2 is included in a *Physiognomiae & chiromantiae compendium* issued at Strasbourg in Latin and German in 1533 (NLMCat 973).
    Mon: THORNDIKE, Lynn. *Cocles and chiromancy* (Chap. IV in vol. V of his *History of magic and experimental science*, New York, 1941). [For other references to chiromancy and physiognomy, see the indexes in volume VI and earlier volumes of this work.]

RODRIGUEZ de Castello Branco, João (Amatus *Lusitanus*), 1511–1568.

692 Index Dioscoridis. Antwerp: Vidua Martini Caesaris, 1536.

    Ref: Arber (1938) 275; *Sart (Appr)* 72–73.
    N.B: The work of a famous Portuguese physician of Jewish origin, who fled under persecution to Antwerp and became a professor at Ferrara.

RUELLE, Jean de la (Jean Ruel; Joannes Ruellius), *c.* 1479–1537.

693 De natura stirpium libri tres. Paris: Simon de Colines, 1536. f°.

    Ref: BM-Fr 387; Renouard (Colines) 267; *Garrison* (1929) 230; *Hunt (Quinby)* I 39.
    N.B: The author—physician to Francis I and the translator of Dioskorides—was an able botanist in his own right; and the first botanist to give a full description of each plant. Valuable for terminology, as the book includes plant names in the French vernacular. A Venetian edition was produced by Bernardino Bindoni in 1538 (BM-Ital 591), and another *Apud Joan. Baptistam Pederzanum* (NLMCat 3985). Editions printed at Basel in 1537 and 1543 are listed in NLMCat 3984, 3986. An epitome by Leodegarius à Quercu [*i.e.*, Léger Duchesne], printed at Paris and Rouen in 1539, was subsequently brought out in several editions. Ruelle is known also as the translator of the *Veterinariae medicinae libri II* [*Hippiatrica*] published by Colines at Paris in 1530 (Choulant (H) p. 421; NLMCat 2310).

SALICETO (Guglielmo Saliceti, of Piacenza. *Called* Guilielmus de Saliceto), 1210–1277.

694 La ciroxia vulgarmente fata [*Italian*]. [Venice:] Filippo di Pietro, 1 Mar 1474. f°. [LEK]

    Ref: HCR 14147; Pr 4254; Osler (IM) 55; Klebs 485.1; *Singer (SHA)* 1957, 71–72; Castiglioni (1947) 336; Stillwell S25; Goff S-27.

Saliceto (continued)

N.B: The first printing of his *Chirurgia*. Possibly the earliest attempt to write on regional or surgical anatomy. The text relates to injuries, fractures, hernia, drugs, and
surgical anatomy. Although traditional in concept, it opposes cauterization. It
includes observation without, however, actually mentioning dissection. In
other words, it was written by a thirteenth-century surgeon, who had considerable independence of thought and had apparently seen some dissection.
Re-issued at [Brescia] in 1486 (Cen S26; Schullian (ArMed) 416) and at Venice
in 1491 (Goff S-29). The Latin version was first issued with his *Summa conserva-*
tionis et curationis printed at Piacenza in 1476 (Cen S30). Issued at least eight times
during the fifteenth century. A French version was printed at Lyon in 1492 (Cen
S24; Schullian (ArMed) 415). [Commonly called Saliceto, although Castiglioni
uses the form Saliceti.]

Mon: SCHAARSCHMIDT, Franz Otto. *Die Anatomie des Wilhelm von Saliceto*, Leipzig,
1919 (reviewed in *Isis* 4 585).

SCRIPTORES REI RUSTICAE.

695   Scriptores rei rusticae.   Venice: Nicolaus Jenson, 1472   f°.   [LEK]

Ref: H *14564; BMC V 173; Klebs 902.1; *HTech* II 86, 111, 114, *etc.*; Stillwell S318;
Goff S-346.

N.B: A compilation of four works relating to agriculture in ancient times. Written
respectively by Marcus Porcius CATO (234–149 B.C.); Marcus Terentius
VARRO (116–27 B.C.); Lucius Junius Moderatus COLUMELLA *fl.* 50); and Rutilius
Taurus Aemilianus PALLADIUS(*fl.* 340). The *De re rustica liber X* by Columella,
however, had already been issued as a separate and is assigned to the press of
the 'Printer of Silius Italicus' at Rome about 1471 (*no.* 613).

SERVETUS, Michael (Miguel Servet y Reves, of Villanueva de Sigena; Michel Villeneuve), *c.* 1511–1553.

696   Syruporum universa ratio ad Galeni censuram diligenter expolita. Vera
purgandi methodus.   Paris: Simon de Colines, 1537.   8°.   [LEK]

Ref: NLMCat 4193; BM-Fr 400; Renouard (Colines) 285; *Thornd (HM)* V 289;
Castiglioni (1947) 434; *Crombie (A–G)* 1961, II, 225.

N.B: A pharmaceutical work written by a physician, theologian, and mathematician
who was among the first to break the hold of Galen's theory of physiology. Galen
had maintained that the blood from the right side of the heart reached the left by
seeping through the pores of the muscular wall separating the two chief cham-
bers. Servetus discovered that the blood from the right side passed through the
lungs to the left side of the heart. This was mentioned in his manuscript-draft of
1546 although not printed until three years after our period.

His main interest, however, was in restoring Christianity to its original
teaching, and that proved his undoing. His discovery of the lesser circulation
was mentioned in his *Christianismi restitutio* printed at Vienne in 1553 and sub-

sequently burned. Consequently the latter is among the rare books of today, only three copies—at Paris, Vienna, and Edinburgh (imperfect)—being known to be extant. Servetus's simple Christian faith—too simple for Calvin—had occasioned Calvin's wrath when a Servetus tract, *De Trinitatis erroribus*, had been published in 1531. The printing of his *Christianismi restitutio* brought the controversy to a head, and it ended with Calvin's thunderous denunciations causing Servetus to be burned at the stake. [It was learned in 1924 that pulmonary circulation, the so-called "lesser circulation," had also been discovered by a Muslim physician, Ibn al-Nafīs al-Qurashī, *d.* 1288, several centuries before Servetus's time.]

Mon: OSLER, *Sir* William. *Michael Servetus* (p. 100–124 in his *A Way of life*. New York, Dover, 1958). SINGER, Charles. *The Discovery of the circulation of the blood.* London, 1922 (Classics of Scientific Method). NORDENSKIÖLD, Eric. *The Discovery of the circulation of the blood* (Chap. XIV in his *The History of biology*. [Tr. from the Swedish: L. B. Eyre.] New York, 1928. IZQUIERDO, José Joaquin. *A new and more correct version of the views of Servetus* [*on*] *the circulation of the blood* (p. 914–932 in vol. 5 of the Institute of the History of Medicine. *Bulletin*. Baltimore, 1937). O'MALLEY, Charles Donald. *Michael Servetus: A translation of his geographical, medical, and astrological writings, with introduction and notes* (American Philosophical Society. *Memoirs*. v. 34. Philadelphia, 1953). FULTON, John F. *Michael Servetus, humanist and martyr. With a bibliography of his works and a census of known copies by Madeline E. Stanton*. New York, 1953.

SILVATICO, Matteo (Matthaeus Sylvaticus; *called* Pandectarius), *d.* 1342.

697 Liber pandectarum medicinae (Ed: Angelo Catone de Sepino, *fl.* 1470). Naples: [Anonymous printer], 1 April 1474. f°. [LEK]

Ref: HC 15194; BMC VI 859; BM-Ital 628; Osler (IM) 61; Klebs 919.1; *Sart* III 816; Goff S-510.

N.B: A dictionary of simples and their medicinal use, arranged in general alphabetical order and giving the plant names in Greek, Arabic, and Latin. In matters of medicine, Silvatico's text keeps to the traditional line, but it contains various botanical observations of his own. His botanical garden, containing foreign as well as domestic plants, is one of the earliest known—aside from the customary gardens of herbs. An edition edited by Matthaeus Moretus was printed in 1474, by Johannes Vurster at Bologna (Cen S461). At least fifteen editions are known within our period (Klebs 919.1–.10; NLMCat 4205–4209). The Venice edition printed for Octavianus Scotus in 1498 contains the *Synonyma medicinae* of Simon of Genoa, *d.* 1330, which—already issued at Milan by Antonius Zarotus in 1473 (Cen S475; Schullian (ArMed) 455) and in an unsigned edition assigned to Ferrara about 1471–1472 (Klebs 920.1)—was one of the first polyglot dictionaries of drugs and simples to be printed.

SIMON of Genoa. *See no. 697 note.*

IV. *Natural Science*

STRABO, Walafrid (Walahfridus Strabus), *c.* 809–849.

698 Hortulus.   Vienna: Hieronymus [Vietor] Philovallus, 31 Oct. 1510. sm. 4°. [LEK]

> *Ref*: Choulant (H) 230; *Hunt (Quinby)* I xxiii, 11.
>
> *N.B*: In 444 hexameters, describing 23 plants grown in the garden at the Abbey of Reichenau on the Bodensee, among them *salvia, ruta, gladiola, lilium, rosa,* and various medicinal herbs. The poem written by this gentle garden-lover about 842 A.D. was addressed to the Abbot of St. Gall in Switzerland, where the manuscript was found in 1509. Variant known. An edition edited by Joachim von Watt was printed at Nuremberg in 1512 (NLMCat 4698).
>
> *Mon*: NÄF, Werner, and Mathäus GABATHULER. *Walahfrid Strabo Hortulus vom Gartenbau,* St. Gallen, 1942. An English translation, *Hortulus or The little garden,* by Richard S. Lambert, was issued at Wembly Hill, Middlesex, by the Stanton Press, 1924. [A facsimile of a ninth century manuscript of the *Hortulus,* with English translation, bibliography, and an account of the plants mentioned, was published by The Hunt Botanical Library, Pittsburgh, 1966 (commentary by Wilfrid Blunt).]
>
> *Fac*: SUDHOFF, K., H. MARZELL, and E. WEIL, ed. *Des Walahfrid von der Reichenau Hortulus, Wiedergabe des ersten Wiener Druckes.* Munich, 1926 (Münchener Beiträge zur Geschichte und Litteratur der Naturwissenschaften und Medizin. I Sonderheft). Hunt (Quinby) plate III.

TARDIF, Guillaume, *fl.* 1480.

699 Lart de faulconnerie et des chiens de chasse [*French*].   Paris: For Antoine Vérard, 5 Jan. 1492.   4°. [LEK]

> *Ref*: Klebs 950.1; *Sart* III 1185.
>
> *N.B*: A sixteenth-century edition of unassigned date was apparently issued at Paris by the press of Jean Tréperel (Cop 5703).

THEOPHILOS (Theophilos *Protospatharios*; *called* Philotheus; or Philaretus), *fl.* 610.

700 De pulsibus. De urinis. (*Issued with* ARTICELLA. [Padua: Nicolò Petri, about 1476.])   f°. [LEK]

> *Ref*: GW 2678; Poynter 82; Choulant (H) 398; Klebs 116.1.
>
> *N.B*: In addition to being included in various editions of the *Articella,* each of these titles was separately produced at Basel in 1533 by Hieronymus Petrus—Choulant (H) 140, 141. [*See also* Schullian (ArMed) 61, 62; NLMCat p. 560.]

THEOPHRASTOS, *c.* 374 – *c.* 286 B.C.

701 Opera [*Greek*]. (*Issued with* ARISTOTLE. Opera [*Greek*]. Venice: Aldus Manutius, II) Feb. 1497; III) 29 Jan. 1497; IV) 1 June 1497.)   f°.

Ref: GW 2334; HC *1657; BM-Ital 42; IGI 791; Klebs 83.1; Stillwell A 858; Goff
A-959.

N.B: In the 5-volume set of Aristotle and other Greek classics issued by Aldus Manutius, 1 Nov. 1495–June 1498, the *Vita Theophrasti* ascribed to Laertius appears in
volume II, and the works of Theophrastos appear as follows: II) *De igne*; *De
ventis*; *De lapidibus* [containing the earliest reference to the use of flints in making
glass clear]. III) *De piscibus*; *De vertigine oculorum*; *De laboribus*; *De odoribus*; *De
sudoribus*. IV) *De historia plantarum libri X*; *De causis plantarum libri VI*; *Metaphysica, liber I*. The *De historia et causis plantarum*, however, had been printed in
the Latin version of Theodoros Gaza, at Treviso in 1483 (*q.v.*).

702 De historia et causis plantarum libri IX (Tr: Theodoros Gaza, *fl.* 1400–
1475; Ed: Giorgio Merula, *d.* 1494).   Treviso: Bartholomaeus Confalonerius, 20 Feb. 1483.   f°.   [LEK]

Ref: HC *15491; BMC VI 894; BM-Ital 668; Klebs 958.1; *Garrison* (1929) 102;
Castiglioni (1947) 181–182; Stillwell T132; Goff T-155.

N.B: The earliest book of scientific botany. A study of about 500 plants described according to a rather primitive classification which held, however, until the mid-
sixteenth century. Included also in the Greek *Opera* cited above; and with
Aristotle in the Aldine editions of 1504 and 1513 (Renouard (Alde) 107, 142), and
the Basel edition of 1534 (NLMCat 271). Issued at Lyon in [1505] and 1529
(NLMCat 4346, 4345). Its ninth section, on the medicinal properties of plants—
the earliest extant herbal, except for fragments of a Greek herbal, c. 350 B.C.—
is believed to have been added somewhat after Theophrastos's time.

Mon: GREENE, Edward Lee. *Theophrastus of Eresus* (p. 52–142 in vol. 54 of *Smithsonian
Miscellaneous Collections*. Washington, 1909/10).

TIBERTI, Antiocho (Antiochus Tibertus), *c.* 1445 – *c.* 1498.

703 Chyromantia.   Bologna: Benedictus Hectoris, 1494.   4°.   [LEK]

Ref: H *15519; BM-Ital 673; *Thornd (HM)* V 54.

N.B: One of various popular books on chiromancy, which was closely allied to the
study of anatomy. Apparently a part of a work relating to physiognomy and
pyromancy of which only that on chiromancy is extant—unless, indeed, the
missing parts appear in the text published under Dryander's name as *De chyromantia libri tres authoris cuiusdam vetustissimi per Joannem Dryandrum restituti*, Mainz,
J. Schoeffer, 1538—*see* Thornd (HM) V 521. For an edition printed at Mainz in
1541, *see* NLMCat 4360.

TURNER, William, 1515–1568.

704 Avium praecipuarum, quarum apud Plinium et Aristotelem mentio
est, brevis et succincta historia ...   Cologne: Joannes Gymnicus, 1544.
8°.

Turner (continued)

Ref: BM-Ger 876; *McGill (VZ)* 605.

N.B: Although ostensibly based on Pliny and Aristotle, the prefatory letter which it contains shows that the text is based to considerable extent upon Turner's own observations and knowledge of birds. It thus ranks as the earliest modern book on ornithology.

Mon: EVANS, Arthur H. *Turner on birds: a short and succinct history of the principal birds noticed by Pliny and Aristotle . . . With introduction, translation, notes, and appendix.* Cambridge, 1903.

Fac: Reproduction of titlepage in Evans, as noted above.

705 Libellus de re herbaria novus. London: Joannes Byddellus, 1538. 4°. [LEK]

Ref: *Hunt (Quinby)* I 65 *note*; *Arber* (1938), 275, 276.

N.B: A brief list of British plants, noting their locality. Enlarged and printed at London by Day and Seres in English, in 1548, as *The Names of Herbes in Greke, Latin, Englische, Duche and Frenche wyth the Commune Names that Herbaries and Apotecaries Use* [reprinted, London, 1881. James Britten, *ed.*].

VALASCO de Taranta (Valescus de Tarenta), *c.* 1382–1417.

706 Practica seu Philonium pharmaceuticum et chirurgicum, libri VII. Barcelona: Pedro Posa, 23 Dec. 1484. [LEK]

Ref: Klebs 1010.1; *Sart* III 1199; *Garrison* (1929) 163; *Castiglioni* (1947) 339.

N.B: A well organized treatise on medicine and surgery with brief anatomical descriptions. Written by a physician of the Montpellier group who was Court Physician to Charles VI of France. Two editions were issued at Lyon in 1490 and two presumably in 1501, each by a different printer (Cen V8, V9, V10; Goff V-6, V-7, V-8, V-9; *see also* NLMCat p. 579–580).

VARRO, Marcus Terentius, 116–27 B.C.

De re rustica libri III. *See under* SCRIPTORES REI RUSTICAE.

VERGILIUS, Polydorus (Polidoro Vergilio), *c.* 1470–1555.

707 De inventoribus rerum. Venice: Christophorus de Pensis, de Mandello, 31 Aug. 1499. 4°. [LEK]

Ref: H *16008; BMC V 473; Klebs 1025.1; *Hay* 60, 180; Stillwell V130; Goff V-146.

N.B: A popular reference work which, atune to the interests of its time, presents a wide range of topics, among them precious metals, agriculture, and the nomenclature of animals. [For a further note on contents and for other monographs, see TECHNOLOGY: Vergilius.]

IV. *Natural Science*

Mon: FERGUSON, John. *Notes on the work of Polydore Vergil* (p. 71–93 in *Isis* 17 1932).
   HAY, D. *Polydore Vergil, Renaissance historian and man of letters*. Oxford, 1952.
Fac: *Osiris* 5 1938, p. 122, 178.

VESALIUS, Andreas (André Vésale), 1514–1564.

708   Anatomiae tabulae sex.   Venice: Bernardinus Vitalis for Johannes
Stephanus Calcarensis, 1538.   6 bdsdes.

> *Ref*:   *Choulant (Anat)* 173–177; *Wightman* (1962) I 227–230.
> *N.B*: Six single-leaf prints displaying various anatomical sections and three views of
> the human skeleton; with occasional text by Vesalius. Designed for student use.
> Published at the expense of the artist known as John or Stephen Calcar (J. S. van
> Calcar), whose name as publisher appears on the print showing the back of a
> skeleton. Both the 1538 prints and the subsequent plagiarisms are described in
> minute detail in Dr. Mortimer Frank's 1945 edition of Choulant, p. 175–177 and
> 185–192; with reproductions of the three positions of the skeleton. See also the
> textual translations and reproductions in Chapter II of Dr. Cushing's monograph.
> *Mon*: CUSHING, Harvey. *Bio-bibliography of Andreas Vesalius*, New York, 1943 (re-
> viewed, p. 398–441 in *Isis* 35; reprinted: Hamden, Conn., Archon Books, 1962).
> ERIKSSON, Ruben, *ed.* and *tr. Baldasar Heseler: Andreas Vesalius' first public anatomy
> at Bologna, 1540. An eyewitness report . . .* Uppsala, 1959 (reviewed, p. 602–603 in
> *Isis* 51 1960; p. 42–52 in *Gesnerus* 17 1960).

709   Epistola rationem modumque propinandi radicis chynae decocti . . .
pertractans.   Basel: Joannes Oporinus, Oct. 1546.   f°.   [LEK]

> *Ref*:   NLMCat 4587; BM-Ger 891; *Sart (Appr)* 129, 212:183; *Cushing* 156, VII.1.
> *N.B*: A letter of biographical interest since toward its end Vesalius refers to the hostility
> of the faculty at Padua occasioned by the printing of his *Fabrica* in June 1543 and
> his own impetuous act in burning his books and manuscripts as he left Padua at
> the turn of the year. It discusses also his correspondence with his teacher and
> present opponent, Jacques Dubois, and incidentally includes a regimen for the
> use of the China root, *smilax China*, which gives the work its title. Garrison (1929)
> 219 cites this work as containing criticism of Galen; also refers to an edition of
> 1542. [For other editions, see NLMCat p. 591.]
> *Mon*: CUSHING, H. *The China-root epistle and the aftermath of the 'Fabrica'* (p. 154–170
> in his *Bio-bibliography of Andreas Vesalius*, New York, 1943).

710   De humani corporis fabrica libri VII.   Basel: Joannes Oporinus, June
1543.   f°.   [LEK]

> *Ref*:   NLMCat 4577; LC(LJRCat) 776; BM-Ger 890; Horblit 98; *Sart (Appr)* 210:162;
> *Garrison* (1929) 219; *Singer (SHA)* 111–119; *Castiglioni* (1947) 418–426; *Crombie
> (A–G)* 1961, II 274; *Cushing* VI.A.-1, p. 73–125.
> *N.B*: One of the landmarks in the advance of anatomical knowledge. Replete with
> anatomic drawings of great elegance and accuracy. The drawings, however,

Vesalius (continued)

were more revolutionary than the text, which in some instances repeats the errors of the past. A revised edition was issued by Oporinus at Basel in August 1555. For discussion of the various cuts and editions, see p. 169–199 in CHOULANT, Ludwig. *History and bibliography of anatomic illustration. Translated and annotated by Mortimer Frank.* New York, 1945.

Mon: SAUNDERS, J. B. de C. M., and C. D. O'MALLEY. *The illustrations from the works of Andreas Vesalius of Brussels.* Cleveland and New York, 1950. (See also CUSHING, as cited above.) BAKELANTS, Louis, *ed.* and *tr. Préface d'André Vésale à ses livres sur l'anatomie, suivie d'une lettre à Jean Oporinus, son imprimeur.* Brussels, 1961. O'MALLEY, C. D. *Andreas Vesalius of Brussels, 1514–1564.* Berkeley/Los Angeles, 1964 (reviewed by J. O. Leibowitz, p. 362–365 in *Isis* 56 1965).

Fac: VESALIUS, Andreas. *De humani corporis fabrica libri septem. Basiliae . . . 1543.* Impression anastatique. Bruxelles, Culture et Civilisation, 1964 [complete reproduction]. *Andreae Vesalii Bruxellensis Icones anatomicae.* Munich and New York, 1934 [–1935]—containing a re-issue of the illustrations from the original blocks (then in existence); published jointly by the New York Academy of Medicine and the University of Munich. LAMBERT, S. W., W. WIEGAND, and W. M. IVINS, Jr. *Three Vesalian essays to accompany the Icones anatomicae of 1934,* New York, 1952. HORBLIT 98 [b–d].

711 De humani corporis fabrica librorum epitome. Basel: Joannes Oporinus, June 1543. f°.

Ref: NLMCat 4581; LC(LJRCat) 775; *Choulant (Anat)* 180–181, 184; *Cushing* VI.B.-I, p. 109–115.

N.B: A large folio of 14 leaves published more or less simultaneously with his *De humani corporis fabrica libri VII* and intended, as stated in the dedication of the latter, "as a short cut to these books and an index of the matters shown therein." Several of the latter's illustrations are repeated and seven new figures are added. It was intended for use in separate sheets, and instructions are cited for pasting certain figures together. A German version prepared by Alban Thorer, 1489–1550, was printed at Basel "bey Johann Herpst, genannt Oporino," 9 Aug. 1543.

Mon: SPENCER, W. G. *The 'Epitome' of Vesalius on vellum in the British Museum Library* (p. 237–244 in *Essays on the history of medicine presented to Karl Sudhoff on the occasion of his seventieth birthday November 26th, 1923.* Charles Singer and H. E. Sigerist, *ed.* Zürich, 1924).

VINCENT de Beauvais (Vincentius Bellovacensis), *c.* 1200 – *c.* 1264.

712 Speculum naturale, libri XXXII. [Strasbourg: The R-Printer (Adolf Rusch), not after 1478.] f°. [LEK]

Ref: Pr 255; BMC I 64; BM-Ger 894; Oates 106; Osler (IM) 138; LC (Thach) 11; Klebs 1036.1; *Sart* II 929–932; Stillwell V263; Goff V-292.

N.B: A work which according to Sarton has some concern with meteorology, geography, geology, astronomy, botany, zoology, anatomy, physiology, and chemistry as commonly conceived in the early thirteenth century. According to Dr. Casey Wood—McGill (VZ) p. 9—Book XVII describes birds, in alphabetical order; Book XVIII, fishes; Book XIX, domestic animals; Book XX, wild animals; Book XXI, other animals, serpents, reptiles, and worms. It forms part of an enormous but uncritical encyclopaedic work, the *Speculum maius*, which also includes the *Speculum doctrinale*, the *Speculum historiale*, and the *Speculum morale* [of questioned authenticity]. It is probable that the production of the enormous volumes of the encyclopaedia began early in the decade, possibly before 1473 since the last volume of the otherwise undated Mentelin edition of the *Speculum historiale* bears the date, 4 Dec. 1473 (Cen V254). The Thacher copy of the Rusch edition of the *Speculum naturale*, which is at the Library of Congress, has a presentation inscription dated 1478.

Mon: MEYER, E. H. F. *Geschichte der Botanik*. III, 1857, p. 96–106. THORNDIKE, Lynn. *Vincent of Beauvais* (p. 457–476 in vol. II of his *History of magic and experimental science*. New York, 1923).

WALTER of Henley, *12th or 13th century*.

713 Boke of Husbandry whiche mayster Groshede sōtyme bysshop of Lyncoln made & translated it out of Frensche into Englysche. [London: Wynkyn de Worde, *c.* 1510.]

Ref: STC 25007; *Hunt (Quinby)* I p. 429, 449; Sart II 647.

N.B: The earliest agricultural work by an Englishman; possibly the first to be written after Cato, Varro, and Columella. The citing of Grosseteste as translator is open to question. Only one copy known, at the University of Cambridge. Fitzherber's *Boke of husbandry* [*q.v.*] is said to be derived from this work. A manuscript version in an anglicised Norman-French dialect circulated in the early part of the 13th century.

Mon: LAMOND, E., *tr.* and *ed. Walter of Henley's husbandry* [and other works] ... London, 1890.

Fac: CRIPPS-DAY, F. H. *The manor farm, to which is appended . . . a facsimile of Walter of Henley's Boke of husbandry . . .* [*c.* 1510]. London, 1931.

YŪḤANNĀ ibn SARĀBIYŪN *the Younger* (Serapion *the Younger*; Johannes Serapion *the Younger*; Ibn Serabi), *11th–12th century*.

714 Liber Serapionis aggregatus in medicinis simplicibus (Tr: Simon of Genoa, *d.* 1330, and Abraham *Judaeus* of Tortosa, *fl.* 1290). Milan: Antonius Zarotus, 4 Aug. 1473. f°. [LEK]

Add: GALEN. De virtute centaureae ad Papiam.

Ref: HC *14691; Choulant (H) 371–372; Osler (IM) 34; Schullian (ArMed) 445; Klebs 913.1; Stillwell S422; Goff S-467.

N.B: Relates to simples and drugs. Sixteenth-century publications of the text are listed in NLMCat p. 316, 614, 615.

ZERBIS, Gabriele de (Gabriel Zerbus), 1468–1505.

715 Anatomia infantis ex Gabriele de Zerbis. (*Included in* DRYANDER, Johannes. Anatomiae hoc est corporis humani dissectionis pars prior. Marburg: Apud Eucharium Cervicorum, June 1537.)   4°.

> *Ref*: NLMCat 1215; BM-Ger 255; v. Dommer 81; Garrison (1929) 211, 215; *Sart (Appr)* 117; *Thornd (HM)* V 520.

716 Liber anathomie corporis humani et singulorum membrorum illius . . . Venice: Bonetus Locatellus, for the heirs of Octavianus Scotus, 1502. f°.

> *Ref*: NLMCat 4798; BM-Ital 743; *Castiglioni (1947)* 369; Garrison (1929) 215; *Sart (Appr)* 210:153.
>
> *N.B*: A work describing the muscles of the stomach and the outlet of the lachrymal ducts. The volume includes his *Liber tertius in quo ostenditur anathomia membrorum simplicium & eis similium*, and *Anathomia matricis pregnantis: et est sermo de anathomia & generatione embrionis*.

SUBJECT ANALYSIS FOR
PHYSICS

[1] HEAT: Al-Kindi; Duns *Scotus*; Grosseteste; Marliani.

[2] MAGNETISM and ELECTRICITY: Affaitatus; Cardano; Faleiro; Hartmann; Mercator; Pierre de Maricourt (Peter Peregrinus); Pliny.

[3] MECHANICS: Achillini; Aegidius (Giles of Rome); Albertus Magnus; Albertus de Saxonia; Alexander of Aphrodisias; *Aliud commentum* [see under Jordanus de Nemore]; Angelo da Fossombrone; Archimedes; Aristotle; Averroës; Bouelles; Bradwardine; Bricot; Buridan; Burley; Celaya; Coronel; Dullaert; Duns *Scotus*; Eutocios; Gaetano di Thiene; Georges de Bruxelles; Giovanni di Casali; Grosseteste; Heytesbury; Jacopo da Forlì; Jacopo da San Martino; Joannes *Canonicus*; Jordanus de Nemore; Le Fèvre d'Étaples; Lockert; Lucretius; Marliani; Marsilius ab Inghen; Nicolaus de Cusa; Nifo; Ockham; Oresme; Paulus *Venetus*; Pelacani (Blasius of Parma); Piccolomini; Politus; Pomponazzi; Simon de Lendenaria; Swineshead; Tartaglia; Tartaret; Thomas *Aquinas*; Thome; Torni; Urbano of Bologna.

[4] METEOROLOGY: Abū Alī al-Hasan (Alhazen); Al-Kindi (Ya Kūb ibn Ishāk . . . al-Kindi); Aratos; Aristotle; Averroës; Estwood; Firmin de Beauval; Grosseteste; Leopoldus; Nunes; Themo; Theophrastos; Thomas *Aquinas*.

   OPTICS [See MATHEMATICS: Applied Mathematics. In the period of our survey, however, optics was considered as related to meteorology.]

[5] VACUUM and VOID: Aegidius *Romanus*; Albertus Magnus; Aristotle; Burley; Thomas *Aquinas, St.*

[6] WEIGHTS and MEASURES: Agricola; Archimedes; Euclid(?), *Liber de ponderoso et levi*; Priscianus.

[For analysis of the scientific philosophy and theories which various physicists in our list contributed to the times, see CROMBIE, A. C. *Augustine to Galileo*, London (Mercury Books, nos. 3-4), 1961, vol. II, p. 1-132; WIGHTMAN, W.P.D. *The nature of the physical world* (p. 148-206 in his *Science and the Renaissance*, I, Edinburgh, 1962).

See also MAIER, Anneliese. *Der naturphilosophische Bedeutung der scholastische Impetus-theorie* (*Scholastik*, 30 Jahrg., Heft 3, 1951); *Zwei Grundprobleme der scholastische Naturphilosophie*. 2nd ed., Rome, 1951; *Zwischen Philosophie und Mechanik*, Rome, 1958. For the text, translation, or discussion of various theorems, see the reference works cited below under our entries, especially those of Professor Clagett and Professor Moody—to which I am much indebted. For definitions see CLAGETT, M. *Some general aspects of physics in the Middle Ages* (p. 29–44 in *Isis* 39 1948.]

V. PHYSICS
and Allied Subjects

ABŪ ALĪ al-ḤASAN ibn al-Haitham (Alhazen; Allacen; Ibn al-Haitham), *c.* 965–1038.

717 De crepusculis et nubium ascensionibus (Tr: Gherardo da Cremona, *c.* 1114–1187). (*Issued with* NUNES, Pedro, 1502–1578. De crepusculis. Lisbon: Luis Rodriguez, 1542.) 4°. [LEK]

Ref: BM-Port 280; Car p. 140; *Sart* I 721.

N.B: Relates to atmospheric refraction and twilight. Translated from the Arabic into Latin. For note regarding date, see under NUNES. [For the author's *De speculis comburentibus* mentioned in the text, see MATHEMATICS.]

Mon: SCHRAMM, Matthias. *Ibn al-Haythams Weg zur Physik.* (Boethius. Texte und Abhandlungen zur Geschichte der exakten Wissenschaften, Band I.) Wiesbaden, 1963 [reviewed by G. J. Toomer, p. 463–465 in *Isis* 55 1964].

ACHILLINI, Alessandro, 1463–1512.

718 De distributionibus ac De proportione motuum. Bologna: Benedictus Hectoris, 1494. [LEK]

Ref: *Duhem (Études)* III 500; *Thornd (HM)* V 39, 41; *Clagett (SM)* 443.

N.B: Written by one of the critics of Bradwardine's dynamic law of motion. The *Gesamtkatalog der Wiegendrucke* (GW 191n) cites this edition as recorded by Hain 71, Maittaire, and Panzer but finds no copy extant. Duhem, although he cites this 1494 edition, based his analysis upon the text in the Venice edition of the *Opera* printed by Girolamo Scoto in 1545 (BM-Ital 941; NLMCat 29). Since the 1494 edition has apparently been lost, the Venetian printing of 1545 stands as the earliest available. [A chapter on *Achillini: Aristotelian and anatomist* in Thornd (HM) V 37–49 gives an account of Achillini, although only slight references to the work in hand.] Achillini's *Expositio primi Physicorum* was printed at [Bologna] by Hieronymus de Benedictis in 1512 (NLMCat 35).

AEGIDIUS Romanus (Giles of Rome; Egidio Colonna *or* Columna), *c.* 1245–1316.

719 In Aristotelis Physica commentum (Ed: Bernardus Granellus and Aegidius Viterbiensis). Padua: Hieronymus de Durantibus, 15 Oct. 1493. f°. [LEK]

Aegidius Romanus (continued)

      Ref: GW 7197; H *128; BMC VII 1152; BM-Ital 51; IGI 3086; Klebs 364.1; *Crombie*
          (A–G) 1961, II 39; *Maier (AG)* 195–196; *Clagett (SM)* 207, 550; Stillwell A66;
          Goff A-75.

      N.B: With text. Written by an advocate of the dynamic aspect of motion, who sub-
          mitted that the speed of fall increases as the distance from the beginning of the
          fall. An edition was published by the heirs of Octavianus Scotus at Venice in
          1502 (NLMCat 998).

      Mon: MOODY, Ernest A. *Ockham and Aegidius of Rome* (in *Franciscan Studies* 9 1949).

AFFAITATUS, Fortunius.

720 Physicae ac astronomiae considerationes. Venice: Apud Nicolaum de
      Bascarinis, 1549. 8°.

      Ref: Riccardi I 6; *Mottelay* 71.
      N.B: Relates to the declination of the magnetic needle.

AGRICOLA (Georg Bauer; Georgius Agricola; *usually called* Agricola), 1491–1555.

721 Libri quinque de mensuris et ponderibus. Paris: Christien Wechel,
      1533. 8°. [LEK]

      Ref: *Hoover (Agricola)* 593, 597, 599–600; Burndy (Dibner) 23, 128.
      N.B: Relates to weights and measures as in use in Greek and Roman times, and to
          some extent in Saxony. Also published under the same date at Basel, *ex officina
          Frobeniana.* Ex-President Hoover rated this among Agricola's works as seventh
          in importance in present-day usage, and in his bibliography cited four editions
          of the present work printed before the end of our period, plus Agricola's *Epistolae
          ad Plateanum, cui sunt adiecta aliquot loca castigata in libris de mensuris et ponderibus
          nuper editis*, printed at Basel by Froben in 1534.

          In addition to the *De mensuris et ponderibus*, the 1550 edition contains *De
          externis mensuris et ponderibus, libri II. Ad ea quae Andreas Alciatus denuo disputavit
          De mensuris et ponderibus brevis defensio liber I. De mensuris quibus intervalla metimur,
          liber I. De restituendis ponderibus atque mensuris, liber I. De precio metallorum et
          monetis, libri III.*

ALBERTUS MAGNUS (Albrecht von Bollstädt), *Saint, c.* 1200–1280.

722 Physica. Venice: Joannes and Gregorius de Gregoriis, 8 Jan. 1488/89.
      f°. [LEK]

      Ref: GW 716; Pell 334; IGI 223; Klebs 24.1; *Crombie (A–G)* 1952 240–242, 1961 II 40;
          Stillwell A270; Goff A-299.
      N.B: In physics Albertus accepted the Aristotelian theories, including the concept of

the impossibility of vacuum. With additions by Matteo Battiferri. Re-issued by this press, 31 January 1494/95—Cen A271.

ALBERTUS de Saxonia (Albertus de Ricmestorp), c. 1330–1390.

723 Quaestiones in Aristotelis libros De caelo et mundo. Pavia: Antonius Carcanus, 11 May 1481. f°. [LEK]

> Ref: GW 795; H 575; IGI 250; Klebs 30.1; Sart III 1428–1432; Clagett (SM) 554–555; Stillwell A316; Goff A-346.
>
> N.B: The Latin text and translation of the section of Book II relative to acceleration of natural movement are given in Clagett's Science of mechanics, 1959, p. 565–569, with commentary. In his reasoning, Albertus showed the influence of Buridan in the matter of impetus and of Oresme in the measure of the acceleration of falling bodies, but he believed that the speed increases in direct proportion to the distance of the fall.

724 Quaestiones in Physica Aristotelis [with other works]. [Venice: Jacobus Pentius, 13 Jan. 1504.] f°.

> Ref: R 373; Klebs 31.1; Crombie (A–G) 1961 II 73–74.
>
> N.B: A treatise that among other matters distinguishes between angular and curvilinear velocities as applicable to measurement. For the Latin text and translation of the portion of Book VI relative to measuring the velocity of circular movement, see Clagett (SM) 223–229. [GW col. 392 finds this to be an undated section from a volume of the above date, and notes that a 1493 Padua edition cited as Hain 578 is not known today.] For an edition published at Venice in 1516, see NLMCat 82.
>
> According to the theory of Albertus, the trajectory of a projectile comprised three periods—the initial, forceful impact of the projector producing the initial motion and impetus; the continuance of the movement resulting from the impetus; and the lessening of that movement due to air resistance and the pull of gravity.

725 Tractatus proportionum. [Padua: Johann Herbort, 1476/77.] f°. [LEK]

> Ref: GW 786a; BMC VII 916; IGI 244; Klebs 29.1; HEHCat 3721; RA 9; Crombie (A–G) 1952 216; Clagett (SM) 442n, 443n; Stillwell A311; Goff A-341.
>
> N.B: Variously attributed also to the press of Michele Manzulo at Treviso, 1476/77. The first dated edition was printed at Padua by Matthaeus Cerdonis, 15 Aug. 1482 (GW 787; Klebs 29.2). Relates to Bradwardine's dynamic law of movement, Albertus agreeing that in circular movement the measure is the space described by the most rapidly moving point. A work entitled Commentaria in tractatum proportionum Alberti de Saxonia by Benedetto Vittorio is cited in Clagett (SM) 443n as printed at Bologna in 1506 (Riccardi I col 624).

AL-BIṬRŪJĪ (Alpetragius), fl. 1200. See under ASTRONOMY.

V. *Physics*

ALEXANDER of Aphrodisias, *3rd century.*

726 Super nonnullis Physicis quaestionibus solutionum liber (Tr: Angelo Poliziano, 1454–1494). Basel: Ex aedibus Andreae Cratandri, Aug. 1520. 4°.

> *Ref*: NLMCat 138; BM-Ger 19; *Clagett (SM)* 543–545, 555.
> *N.B*: Written by a third-century commentator interested in the velocity of falling bodies and other Aristotelian theories.

ALIUD COMMENTUM. *See under* Jordanus de Nemore.

AL-KINDĪ (Ya 'qūb ibn Isḥāq ibn aṣ-Ṣabbāḥ al-Kindī), *fl.* 870.

727 De medicinarum compositarum gradibus investigandis libellus. (*Issued with* IBN BUṬLĀN, *d. about* 1068. Tacuini sanitatis . . . de sex rebus non naturalibus, earum naturis, operationibus & rectificationibus . . . recens exarati. Strasbourg: Joannes Schott, 1531.) f°. [LEK]

> *Ref*: NLMCat 2520, 2521 var; Sart I 559; *Clagett (Marliani)* 35; *Campbell (AM)* I 64.
> *N.B*: Relates to calculating the temperature of medicinal compounds through the temperature of their several parts. Variant known. Included in a compilation printed at Venice in 1549 and in an unsigned collection of tracts issued about 1541 (NLMCat 3126, 3125).

728 De pluviis imbribus et ventis ac aeris mutatione. Venice: Petrus Liechtenstein, 1507. 4°.

> *Ref*: BM-Ital 739; Car p. 80.

ANGELO da Fossombrone (Angelus de Fossambruno), *c.* 1375–1402.

729 De velocitate motus. [Pavia: Antonius Carcanus, *c.* 1482.] f°.

> *Ref*: GW 1947; Klebs 70.1; *Clagett (SM)* 648–649.
> *N.B*: Written by a professor at Padua, well-versed in the theories of the English physicists and for the most part in accord with them. Heytesbury's method of measuring velocity he questions, however.
>   Possibly the text, or part of the text, of Angelo's *Recollecte super Hentisberi de tribus predicamentis* (issued with the second edition of Heytesbury's *De sensu composito*, Venice: Locatellus for Scotus, 27 May 1494—Cen H51), since a section of the *Recollecte* is devoted to the velocity of movement, *i.e., De velocitate motus penes effectum.*

V. Physics

ARATOS of Soli, *fl.* 275 B.C.

730   Phaenomena (Tr: Germanicus Caesar). (*Issued with* MANILIUS, M. Astronomicon. Bologna: Ugo Rugerius and Doninus Bertochus, '20 Mar.' 1474.)   f°.   [LEK]

Ref: HCR 10707; BMC VI 805; Klebs 661.2; Sart I 157; Stillwell M175; Goff M-203.

N.B: An astronomical poem consisting of three parts—the *Phaenomena*; the common risings and settings of the stars; and weather signs as derived from Theophrastos, *c.* 372–288 B.C.

With regard to the date of this edition, see Polain 2589. Klebs 77.1 refers to an undated edition of Aratos at the Laurentian Library in Florence, which may antedate the edition cited above, as it is assigned to about 1474. Issued at Venice in 1488 with the commentary of Rufus Festus Avienus (Cen A1277; Schullian (ArMed) 82); and in 1499 [Latin-Greek edition] with Greek commentary of Theōn (Cen F169), in a collection—the so-called *Scriptores astronomici veteres*—published at Venice by Aldus Manutius.

ARCHIMEDES of Syracuse (Archimenides), *c.* 287–212 B.C.

731   Opera [*Greek and Latin*] (Comm: Eutocios, *fl.* 500 Tr: Jacopo da Cremona, *fl.* 1450. Corr: Regiomontanus [Johann Müller of Königsberg], 1436–1476. Ed: Thomas Geschauff, *called* Ventorius, *fl.* 1540).   Basel: Johann Herwagen, 1544.   f°.   [LEK]

Ref: BM-Ger 39; Horblit 5; Sart (HS) II 72–84; Clagett (Arch) I 12, 13n.

N.B: The first edition of Archimedean texts in Greek and a more important work than the Latin version issued the preceding year. In four parts: I–II, Archimedes in Greek and Latin; III–IV, the commentaries of Eutocios of Ascalon, *fl.* 500, in Greek and Latin, including *In primum et secundum aequeponderantium*. The section devoted to Eutocios, although having a separate titlepage and signaturing, is listed in the general table of contents. It is thus an integral part of the volume, although apparently planned to be issued as a separate. The Latin *Opera* of 1543 and particularly this Greek-Latin edition mark the beginning of the so-called Archimedean renaissance, which gained further impetus after a new Latin version by Federigo Commandino was issued by Paolus Manutius at Venice in 1558. [The Commandino text of Archimedes's treatise *On floating bodies* (*De corporibus fluitantibus*) was issued at Bologna in 1565.]

Mon: VAILATI, G. *Del concetto di centro di gravità nella statica di Archimede* (p. 79–90 in his *Scritti*, Florence, 1911).   CHILD, J. M. *Archimedes' principle of the balance and some criticisms upon it* (p. 490–520 in Vol. II of SINGER, Ch., ed. *Studies in the history and method of science*. Oxford, 1921).   CLAGETT, Marshall. *The use of the Moerbeke translation of Archimedes in the works of Johannes de Muris* (p. 236–242 in *Isis* 43 1952); *Archimedes and the application of mechanics to geometry* [and] *Archimedes' proof of the law of the lever* (Append. II and IV in his *Greek science in antiquity*, New

Archimedes (continued)

> York, 1955); *Archimedes, On the equilibrium of planes or On centers of gravity, Book I, Postulates* (p. 31–37 in his *The science of mechanics in the Middle Ages*, Madison, 1959); *The impact of Archimedes on Medieval science* (p. 419–429 in *Isis* 50 1959) or (p. 1–14 in his *Archimedes in the Middle Ages*, vol. I, Madison, 1964).
>
> *Fac*: HORBLIT 5 [b].

732 Opera (Tr: William of Moerbeke, *c.* 1215–1286. Ed: Nicolò Fontana, *called* Tartaglia, *c.* 1506–1577). Venice: Venturino Ruffinelli, 1543. 4°. [LEK]

> *Ref*: BM-Ital 36; Sart (*HS*) II 76–77, 82–83; *Clagett (SM)* 9–13, 71, 170–175, *etc.*; Clagett (*GSA*) 74–75.
>
> *N.B*: Contains the first printing of two basic works on statics and hydrostatics— Archimedes's propositions relative to the *Equilibrium of planes* (*Planorum aeque-ponderantium*) and Book I of the treatise *On floating bodies* (*De corporibus fluitanti-bus*), demonstrated through an abstract mathematical approach. A reconstruction of the latter text made by Federigo Commandino was issued at Bologna in 1565. Although possibly antedated by the treatise on the balance attributed to Euclid, Archimedes's works—in addition to introducing the concept of gravity and utilizing the element of geometrical symmetry—stand as the exponent of the application of geometrical analysis to statical theorems of mechanics. [For other works, see under MATHEMATICS.]
>
> *Mon*: See above, under the Greek and Latin *Opera* of 1544.

ARISTOTLE (Aristoteles), *c.* 384–322 B.C.

733 De generatione et corruptione libri II . . . (Comm: Averroës, 1126–1198). Padua: Laurentius Canozius, de Lendenaria, for Johannes Philippus Aurelianus et fratres, 18 June 1474. f°. [LEK]

> *Ref*: GW 2388; HCR 1691; IGI 827; Oates 2545; Pell 1196; Osler (IM) 62; Klebs 88.1; *Taton (A&MS)* 228, 231–232; Stillwell A891; Goff A-996.
>
> *N.B*: Presents Aristotle's theories of the four elemental qualities—cold-dry, cold-humid, hot-dry, and hot-humid—which in affecting original matter produce, respectively, earth, water, fire, and air. Further discussion of the theory of the elements occurs in Books III and IV of Aristotle's *De caelo* (*no.* 25). [For analysis, see P.-H. Michel in Taton as cited above.]
>
> Also issued by this firm in a compilation of Aristotelian titles individually dated or assigned to the years 1472–1474 (Horblit 6). Included in volume II of the Greek *Opera* published at Venice by Aldus Manutius, February 1497 (*no.* 570 *above*). Issued about 1498 by Martin Landsberg at Leipzig (GW 2387), without commentary. Included in compilations of Aristotle's works issued by various presses at Venice in 1482, 1483, 1489, 1495/96, and at Cologne by Heinrich Quen-tell in 1497 (Cen A860, A861, A863, A864, A866). Discussed in the commentaries of Aegidius (Egidio Colonna), Naples, *c.* 1476 (Cen A62); Marsilius ab Inghen,

Padua, 1480 (Cen A63; Paulus *Venetus*, Venice, 1498 (Cen P180); Joannes de Celaya, Paris, 1518 (BM-Fr 26); and Joannes Grammaticus Philoponus, Venice, 1540 (BM-Ital 45). The text appears with the commentary of Thomas Aquinas, Lyon, 1520; with that of Agostino Nifo, Venice, 1526; and with that of Joannes Grammaticus Philoponus, Venice, 1543 (NLMCat 4348, 3351, 2591, respectively).

Mon: SOLMSEN, Friedrich. *Aristotle's system of the physical world.* Ithaca, 1960 (reviewed, p. 151–152 in *Isis* 54 1963).

734 Mechanica, liber I, *spurious?* (In vol. IV, ARISTOTLE, Opera [*Greek*]. Venice: Aldus Manutius, 1 June 1497.) [LEK]

Ref: GW 2334; HC *1657; IGI 791; Pell 1175; Klebs 83.1; *Clagett (SM)* 4–9, 71–72; *Sart* I 132; Stillwell A858; Goff A-959.

N.B: The start of the dynamic tradition as an approach to problems of statics. Possibly the earliest extant treatise on theoretical mechanics. Of unknown origin and history. Variously attributed to Aristotle or to an Aristotelian soon after his time, possibly Straton of Lampsacos, *fl.* 287 B.C. The only recorded printing of the *Mechanica* in the fifteenth century. The text was issued in Latin with a commentary by Nicolò Leonico Tomeo (1456–1531?) in a compilation printed by Bernardino dei Vitali at Venice in 1525 (NLMCat 2794).

Mon: FORSTER, E. S., *tr. Mechanica.* Oxford, 1913. DIJKSTERHUIS, E. J. *The origins of classical mechanics from Aristotle to Newton* (p. 163–184 in *Critical problems in the history of science.* Ed: Marshall Clagett. Madison, 1959).

735 Meteorologica, libri IV (Liber IV, comm: Averroës, 1126–1198). Padua: Laurentius Canozius, de Lendenaria, for Johannes Philippus Aurelianus et fratres, 24 June 1474. f°. [LEK]

Ref: GW 2423; HCR 1696; Oates 2546; IGI 829; Pell 1202; Klebs 91.1; *Clagett (SM)* 140; *Taton (A&MS)* 228, 234; *Lewes* 143–147; Stillwell A900; Goff A-1007.

N.B: The section on rainbows is discussed by C. B. BOYER in his *Refraction and the rainbow in antiquity*; in *The tertiary rainbow: an historical account*; and in *The theory of the rainbow: medieval triumph and failure* (p. 383–386 in *Isis* 47, 1956; and p. 114–154 and 376–390 in *Isis* 49, 1958, respectively). Specific gravity is touched upon in Aristotle's discussion of the effect of the "thickness" of a liquid upon its weight, as the difference in the weight of fresh and salt water.

Also issued by this firm in a compilation of Aristotelian titles individually dated or assigned to the years 1472–1474 (Horblit 6). Printed at Leipzig by Martin Landsberg *c.* 1492 (GW 2420) and included in compilations published at Venice in 1482, 1483, 1489, 1495/96 and at Cologne, 22 Sept. 1497 (GW 2336, 2337, 2339, 2340, 2342). Included also in volume II of the Greek *Opera* published at Venice in February 1497 (*no. 570, above*).

Books I–IV appeared with the commentary of Gaietanus de Thienis at Venice in 1491 and *c.* 1496 (Cen A901; GW 2421–22). Books I–III together with the commentary of Johannes de Amersfordia were issued at Cologne, 20 Nov. 1497 (GW 2424).

V. *Physics*

Aristotle (continued)

> *Mon*: THORNDIKE, Lynn. *Oresme and fourteenth century commentaries on the Meteorologica* (p. 145–152 in *Isis* 45, 1954). [Although treating of manuscripts, this also discusses the authenticity of texts and the authorship of various commentaries.]

736 Physica, libri VIII (Comm: Averroës, 1126–1198). [Padua: Laurentius Canozius, *c.* 1472/75.] f°. [LEK]

> *Ref*: GW 2443; HC 1683; Oates 2547; Pell 1192; Klebs 93.1; *Lewes* 128–136; *Sart (HS)* 515; *Crombie (A–G)* 1952 82, 212–273, and 1969 I 68–75, II 35–37; Stillwell A913; Goff A-1021.

> *N.B*: Known also as *De naturali ausculatione* or *De physico auditu*. One of seven Aristotelian works of scientific interest published by this press during 1472–1474 and cited in Klebs 82.1 as issued as an *Opera* in 1474 or later (Horblit 6). Included in a Latin *Opera* printed at Augsburg in 1479 (Cen A859) and in volume II of the Greek *Opera* published at Venice by Aldus Manutius, February, 1497 (*no. 570, above*).
>
> Issued as a separate at Louvain, at Rome in the translation of Johannes Argyropylus, and at Leipzig about 1475, 1481, and 1492 respectively (Goff A-1020; GW 2442, 2441); also at Pavia in 1520 (NLMCat 285). Included in various compilations published in Venice in 1482, 1483, 1489, 1495/96, and 1496 (Cen A860, A861, A863–A865). NLMCat 998 notes that the commentary of Aegidius printed at Venice in 1502 includes the text of the *Physica* in a revised Latin version by Guilelmus of Moerbeke.
>
> Aristotle's theories of physics and mechanics—as expressed here and in his *Metaphysica*, Padua, 1473 (Cen A898); *De caelo*, Padua, 1473 (Cen A874); and *Meteorologica*, Padua, 1474 (Cen A900)—were subject to study and re-valuation by fourteenth-century scholars at Oxford and the University of Paris, and subsequently served as the basis for innumerable commentaries.

> *Mon*: DRABKIN, I.E. *Notes on the laws of motion in Aristotle* (p. 60–84 in *American Journal of Philology*, 59, 1938). MOODY, Ernest A. *Laws of motion in medieval physics* (p. 18–23 in *The Scientific Monthly*, vol. 72, 1951. CLAGETT, Marshall. *Aristotelian mechanics and Bradwardine's dynamic law of movement* (chapter 7 and elsewhere in his *The science of mechanics in the Middle Ages*, Madison, 1959).

AVERROËS (Abū-l-Walīd Muḥammad ibn Aḥmad ibn Muḥammad Rushd; *called* Averroës; Muḥammad ibn Aḥmad; Ibn Rushd), 1126–1198.

737 Commentarium in Physicam. (*Issued with* ARISTOTLE. Physica. [Padua: Laurentius Canozius, *c.* 1472–1475.]) f°.

> *Ref*: GW 2443; HC 1683; Klebs 93.1; *Sart* II 355–361; *Clagett (SM)* 207; Stillwell A913; Goff A-1021.

> *N.B*: A commentary which stimulated discussion of the dynamic approach and the determining factors in movement, and which opposed the kinematic approach that later was to be upheld by Thomas Aquinas.

738 In Meteorologica Aristotelis liber IV (*Issued with* ARTISTOTLE, *c.* 384–322 B.C. Meteorologica. Padua: Laurentius Canozius, 24 June 1474). f°.

> *Ref*: GW 2423; HCR 1696; Oates 2546; IGI 829; Pell 1202; Klebs 91.1; Stillwell A900; Goff A-1007.

BLASIUS of Parma. *See* PELACANI, Biagio.

BOUELLES, Charles de (Carolus Bovillus), *c.* 1470–1553.

739 Physicorum elementorum libri X. Paris: In aedibus Ascensianis, 13 Dec. 1512. 4°.

> *Ref*: BM-Fr 78.
> *N.B*: Issued to be sold by Jodocus Badius Ascensius and also by Jean Petit, each of whom had his own device upon the titlepage of the copies in his consignment.

BRADWARDINE, Thomas, 1290?–1349.

740 Tractatus de proportionibus velocitatum in motibus. (*Issued with* ALBERTUS de Saxonia, *c.* 1330–1390. De proportionibus. Paris: For Geoffrey de Marnef [not before 1481].) f°.

> *Ref*: GW 792; Klebs 29.9; Sart III 668; *Clagett (SM)* 207–208, 454–462, 481–494, 676.
> *N.B*: A treatise making an early and careful distinction between dynamics and kinematics. A work which—influenced by the *Tractatus de motu* of Gerard of Brussels, written in the thirteenth century—was largely responsible for arousing the interest in mechanics and kinematic studies at Merton College, Oxford, during the fourteenth century. [The treatise by Gerard is not known to have been printed during our period. For discussion of his place in the evolution of mechanics, see Clagett (SM) 163–197, or his paper on Gerard in *Osiris* 12 1956, p. 73–175.] An edition of the Bradwardine, printed at Vienna in 1515, contains an anonymous *Abbreviatus ex libro de proportionibus D. Thome Braguardini*, assigned to the mid-fourteenth century. An anonymous *Sumulus de motu* appears as an introduction to the Bradwardine issued at Venice in 1505.
> No reason has been found for the date assignment of the present edition, which may be derived from the period or state of the printer's device (Silvestre 151).
> *Mon*: CLAGETT, Marshall. *Aristotelian mechanics and Bradwardine's dynamic law of movement; Gerard of Brussels and the origins of kinematics in the West; The emergence of kinematics at Merton College* (p. 421–444, 163–197, and 199–222, respectively, in his *Science of mechanics in the Middle Ages*, Madison, 1959). CROMBIE, A. C. *Oxford's contribution to the origins of modern science*, Oxford, 1954. CROSBY, H. Lamar, Jr., *tr.* and *ed. Thomas of Bradwardine his Tractatus de proportionibus*. Madison, 1955.

BRICOT, Thomas, *fl.* 1475.

741 Textus abbreviatus in cursum totius Physices et Metaphysicorum Aristotelis. Lyon: Anonymous press] 13 Apr. 1486. f°. [LEK]

> *Add*: GEORGES de Bruxelles, *late 15th century*. Quaestiones super Physica.
>
> *Ref*: GW 5542; HC 3974; IGI 2161; Klebs 222.1; *Clagett (SM)* 638–640; Stillwell B1069; Goff B-1202.
>
> *N.B*: Issued by at least four other presses at Paris and Lyon. Both Bricot and Georges de Bruxelles belonged to the small group of scholars who in fifteenth-century France retained an interest in Buridan's theory of impetus, although ignoring the early kinematics of the Merton school.

BURIDAN, Jean, *fl.* 1340–1350.

742 Questiones super octo Physicorum libros Aristotelis (Ed: Jean Dullaert, *c.* 1470–1513). Paris: Pierre Le Dru for Denis Roce, 25 Oct. 1509. f°.

> *Ref*: BM-Fr 87; *Sart* III 542–543; *Duhem (Études)* III 21; *Crombie (A–G)* 1961 II 66–73; *Clagett (SM)* 519, 653, 678, 686.
>
> *N.B*: Written by the founder of the Parisian school of theoretical mechanics, who introduced the fourteenth-century theory of impetus dynamics, a forerunner of the modern concept. Edited a century and a half later by a sixteenth-century master of the Collège de Montaigu, where interest in mechanics occasioned the printing in Paris of various early works.
>
> *Mon*: CLAGETT, Marshall. *John Buridan and the impetus theory of projectile motion* (p. 505–525, 532–540 in his *The science of mechanics in the Middle Ages*, Madison, 1959).

BURLEY, Walter (Gualtherus Burlaeus), 1275 – *c.* 1337.

743 Expositio in Aristotelis Physica [*without text*]. Padua: Bonus de Francia [Gallus] and Thomas de Asula, 18 July 1476. f°. [LEK]

> *Ref*: GW 5774; HC 4136; BMC VII 918; BM-Ital 131; IGI 2267; Klebs 232.1; *Clagett (SM)* 550; *Crombie (A–G)* 1961 II 40; Stillwell B1150; Goff B-1302.
>
> *N.B*: Published, with Aristotle's text, by Johannes Herbort at Venice, 15 Apr. 1482, under the editorship of Nicoletto Vernias da Chieti, *fl.* 1480 (Cen B1151). Aristotle's premise maintaining the impossibility of void was refuted by Burley as a denial of the power and infinity of God.

744 De intensione et remissione formarum. Venice: Bonetus Locatellus, for Octavianus Scotus, 28 Nov. 1496. f°.

> *Add*: JACOPO da Forlì (Jacobus de Forlivio), *c.* 1360–1414. De intensione et remissione formarum. ALBERTUS de Saxonia, *fl.* 1330–1390. De proportionibus. [The first edition of the Albertus is assigned to Treviso about 1476, and that of Jacopo da Forlì to Padua about 1477.]

Ref: GW 5780; IGI 2271; Pell 3081; Klebs 233.1; Stillwell B1162; Goff B-1314.

Mon: SHAPIRO, Herman. *Walter Burley and the intension and remission of forms* (p. 413–427 in *Speculum* 34 1959).

CARDANO, Girolamo (*often* Cardan *in English usage*), 1501–1576.

745 De subtilitate rerum libri XXI. Paris: Michel Fezandat and Robert Granjon, 1550. 8°. [LEK]

Ref: BM-Fr 91; *Mottelay* 14, 17; *Lindsay (JC)* 315–317.

N.B: Wightman (1962) II 128 lists an edition printed by Joannes Petreius at Nuremberg in the same year as this Paris edition. Cardano refers to the electro-magnetic powers of the lodestone, magnetic declination, and electrification by friction. He describes pumps, syphons, the water-screw of Archimedes, and machinery for raising sunken vessels. His concepts regarding heat and various other matters veered toward the modern. His autobiography, *De vita propria sua*, translated by Jean Stoner (Dutton, 1930), refers to all of his books, but with only brief comment on p. 225 regarding the present work. Other references occur in *Cardano, the gambling scholar* by Oystein Ore (Princeton University Press, 1953), p. 22, 30, 43, 44, 55, 121, 134, 212. [One of the few books known to have been printed by Robert Granjon, the famous type-cutter and designer.]

CELAYA, Juan, *fl.* 1500.

746 Expositio in octo libros Phisicorum Aristotelis, cum questionibus eiusdem. Paris: Jean Du Pré and Jacques Le Messier, for Hémond Le Fèvre, 7 Dec. 1517.

Ref: BM-Fr 29; *Duhem (Études)* III 135; *Clagett (SM)* 655–657.

N.B: An exposition of Buridan's theory of inertial impetus as offset and destroyed by the resistance and weight of the projectile, and a revival of other factors characteristic of thirteenth- and fourteenth-century theories.

CORONEL, Luiz, *fl.* 1500.

747 Physicae perscrutationes. [Paris, not before 1511.] [LEK]

Ref: *Duhem (Études)* III 135; *Clagett (SM)* 655–657.

N.B: An exposition of impetus mechanics and Merton kinematics, accepting a theory of Marsilius ab Inghen regarding an interval of rest in the fall of projectiles when the force of impetus and gravity are in balance. Written by a Spanish scholar at Paris, who saw in impetus an effect as well as a cause of motion. Although without colophon or imprint, the work includes a testimonial letter dated at Paris in 1511, thus indicating that this edition can not have been printed prior to that year. A dated edition was printed at Lyon in 1530.

DELLA TORRE, Giacomo. *See under* JACOPO da Forlì.

DULLAERT, Jean, *c.* 1470–1513.

748 Quaestiones super octo libros Phisicorum Aristotelis. Paris: Nicolas De Pratis, 23 Mar. 1506.

> *Ref:* *Duhem (Études)* III 134, 527; *Clagett (SM)* 653–654, 689.
>
> *N.B:* Written by a member of the Collège de Montaigu who maintained that the quantity of impetus depended upon the weight or resistance of the object to be projected. Like other members of the sixteenth-century physicists at Montaigu, Dullaert was both an original thinker and an earnest student of the theories of Buridan, whose *Quaestiones* he edited, and of the kinematic theories of the Merton school.

DUNS SCOTUS. *See no. 778 note.*

ESTWOOD, John (Eschuid; John of Ashendon), *fl.* 1340–1370.

749 Summa astrologiae judicialis de accidentibus mundi. Venice: Johannes Lucilius Santritter, for Franciscus Bolanus, 7 July 1489. f°.

> *Ref:* GW 9392; HC *6685; BMC V 462; IGI 3711; Klebs 381.1; Car p. 171; *Sart* III 672; Stillwell E84; Goff E-109.
>
> *N.B:* Book II treats of meteorology and predictions regarding catastrophes.

EUCLID (Eucleides), *fl.* 300 B.C.

750 Liber de ponderoso et levi. (*Issued with his* Elementa, libri XV, *Greek and Latin* [Ed(?): Philipp Melanchthon, 1497–1560]. Basel: Johann Herwagen, Aug. 1537.) [LEK]

> *Ref:* BM-Ger 288; Th-Stan 9; *Heath (HGM)* I 445–446; *Crombie (A–G)* 1961, I 36; *Moody-Clagett (MSW)* 21–31.
>
> *N.B:* Applies geometric methods of proof to theorems relative to freely falling bodies. Possibly a fragment of the original text. Authenticity questioned, but inconclusively. A translation presumably based upon an Arabic version.
>
> *Mon:* CURTZE, M. *Das Buch Euclids de Gravi et Levi* (p. 51–54 in *Bibliotheca Mathematica*, 1900). MOODY, Ernest A. *Liber Euclidis de ponderoso et levi et comparatione corporum ad invicem, propositiones I–IV* (p. 11, 23–31 in MOODY and CLAGETT. *The medieval science of weights*, Madison, 1952, with introduction, Latin text, and translation).

EUTOCIOS of Ascalon, *fl.* 500.

751 In eosdem Archimedis libros commentaria [*Greek and Latin*]. (In ARCHIMEDES, *c.* 287–212 B.C. Opera [*Greek and Latin*]. Basel: Johann Herwagen, 1544.) f°.

Ref: BM-Ger 39; Horblit 5; *Sart (HS)* II 81, 84 *fac.*

N.B: Contains his commentary on the *Equilibrium of planes* and also those on the *Measurement of the circle* and the *Sphere and cylinder.*

Fac: HORBLIT 5 [b].

FALEIRO, Francisco (Falero).

752 Tratado del esphera y del arte del marear.   Sevilla, 1535.

Ref: *Sart (SW)* 92; *Mottelay* 65, 67.

N.B: The first discussion of magnetic declination to be printed. Magnetic variation, however, had been observed by Columbus in reading his compass in 1492, during his first voyage of discovery.

Mon: HARRADON, H. D. *Treatise on the sphere and the art of navigation, Francisco Falero* (p. 79–91 in *Terrestrial Magnetism*, June 1943).

Fac: HELLMAN, G. *Neudrucke*, 1890 (no. 10).

FIRMIN de Beauval, *fl.* 1335–1345.

753 De mutatione aëris.   Venice: Erhard Ratdolt, 1485.   4°.   [LEK]

Ref: HCR 13393; BMC V 291; Klebs 406.1; Schullian (ArMed) 193; *Sart* III 657; Stillwell P920; Goff P-1006.

N.B: An anonymous work attributed to Firmin de Beauval. Relates to meteorology, phenomena, and astrology. Derived largely from the writings of Ptolemy, Pliny, Al-Kindī, Abū Ma'shar, 'Alī ibn Abū-l-Rijāl, Alī ibn Riḍwan, Joannes Hispalensis, Abrāhām ben 'Ezrā, Albertus Magnus, and Leopoldus, *dux Austriae* (Sart III 658). [For the reference to Pliny as identified by Dr. Pearl Kibre, see THORNDIKE, Lynn. *Pliny and Liber de presagiis tempestatum* (p. 28 in *Isis* 34 1942).]

GAETANO di Thiene (Gaietanus de Thienis), 1387–1465.

754 Commentarium. (*Issued with* STRODE, Ralph, *fl.* 1350–1400. Consequentiae. Venice: [Johannes Leoviler] 1488.)   4°.

Ref: HCR 15096; BMC V 406; Clagett (SM) 634n, 651–652; Stillwell S711; Goff S-801.

N.B: An unidentified work. Possibly Gaetano's *Recollecte super consequentias Strodi*, which is known in a manuscript at Venice, Bibl. Naz. San Marco, Lat. VI, 160, ff. 109r–118r.

755 Expositio Regularum et Sophismata Hentisberi (*Rev*: Franciscus Agubiensis).   Venice: Andreas de Bonetis, 9 Dec. 1483.   f°.

Ref: HCR 8441; BMC V 360; IGI 2346; Klebs 429.2; *Clagett (SM)* 647, 651; Stillwell G30; Goff G-31.

N.B: Written by a member of the new school of physicists at Padua. Also printed at Pavia by Durantis in 1483 (Klebs 429.1; R II p. 186). Comprises in part Gaetano's

Gaetano di Thiene (continued)

commentary on the important *De motu tractatus* in the *Regulae* of William Heytesbury.

Collation is needed to determine whether or not this text is the same as that accompanying the Aristotle of 1491, and the Heytesbury of 1494 where, in text quoted from the latter in Clagett (SM) 647*n*, it is stated that the treatise was begun by a Doctor Messinus—a hitherto unknown writer whom Clagett (in the second edition of his *Science of mechanics*, p. 671*n*) shows to have been Masino Codronchi, a lecturer at Pavia on astrology and natural philosophy.

Mon: VALSANZIBIO, P. S. da. *Vita e dottrina di Gaetano di Thiene*. 2nd ed. Padua, 1949.

756   De intensione et remissione formarum. (*Issued with* ARISTOTLE. Meteorologica.   Venice: Joannes and Gregorius de Gregoriis, 22 Oct. 1491.) f°.

Ref: GW 2421; H *1697; BMC V 342; Oates 1807; IGI 830; Klebs 91.2; Stillwell A901; Goff A-1008.

757   De reactione. (*Issued with* ARISTOTLE. Meteorologica. Venice: Joannes and Gregorius de Gregoriis, 22 Oct. 1491.) f°.

Ref: GW 2421; H *1697; BMC V 342; Oates 1807; IGI 830; Klebs 91.2; Stillwell A901; Goff A-1008.

758   Recollectae super Physica Aristotelis.   [Treviso: Joannes de Hassia, *c.* 1476.] f°. [LEK]

Ref: H 15496; BMC VI 891; Oates 2460; IGI 2348; Klebs 427.1; Stillwell G32; Goff G-33.

N.B: An unsigned edition dated 1477 is cited in Klebs 427.2. Also known in editions printed at Vicenza in 1487 (Cen G33) and at Venice in 1496 and 1500 (Cen G34; Goff G-35, G-36).

GEORGES de Bruxelles (Georgius Bruxellensis), *late 15th century*.

759   Quaestiones super Physica. (*Issued with* BRICOT, Thomas, *fl.* 1475. Textus abbreviatus. Lyon: [Anonymous press] 13 Apr. 1486.) f°. [LEK]

Ref: Clagett (SM) 638; Stillwell B1069; Goff B-1202.

N.B: Beginning with an edition printed at Paris, by Johann Higman and Wolfgang Hopyl, 23 June 1491 (Klebs 455.1), this text was issued several times as a separate. Possibly the same text as his *Expositio super octo libros Physicorum Aristotelis* printed as a separate at Lyon by Janon Carcain about 1490 (Goff G-149). Written by one of the four Parisian physicists of the period who were interested in Buridan's theory of impetus dynamics, the others being Thomas Bricot and Peter Tartaret, together with John Hennon, whose works, however, have not been found in the present survey of printed texts.

V. *Physics*

GERARD of Bruxelles, *13th century. See note under* BRADWARDINE.

GIOVANNI de Casali (Giovanni da Casale; *called* Casali), *c.* 1325–1375.

760 Quaestio subtilis de velocitate motus alterationis.   Venice: Bonetus Locatellus, for the heirs of Octavianus Scotus, 1505.   f°.

> *Ref*: *Sart* III 739; *Clagett (SM)* 331–333.
> *N.B*: An early instance of Italian interest in the theorems of the Merton school. Casali's system of graphs in measuring velocity possibly antedates that of Oresme. A manuscript of the former's text bears the date 1346.
> For Latin text, translation, and commentary, see p. 382–391 in CLAGETT, Marshall. *The science of mechanics in the Middle Ages*, Madison, 1959—which notes (p. 385) that Galileo employs figures oriented in the manner of Casali for his proof of the mean law rather than in that of Oresme. Issued also by this same press on Sept. 1, 1505 in a compilation of treatises by Politus, Swineshead, Bradwardine, Oresme, and Pelacani.

GROSSETESTE, Robert (Robertus Lincolniensis; *sometimes called* Lincoln), *c.* 1175–1253.

761 Super octo libris Physicorum Aristotelis.   Venice: Petrus de Quarengiis, 22 Apr. 1500.   f°.

> *Add*: THOMAS *Aquinas, c.* 1225–1274. Super Physica Aristotelis. [*For the first edition, see* THOMAS *Aquinas.*]
> *Ref*: HCR 10110; BMC V 514; BM-Ital 51; Klebs 851.1; *Sart* II 585; *Crombie (A–G)* 1952, 218–223 *and* 1961, II, 11–23, 39, *etc.*; *Taton (A&MS)* 490–491; Stillwell R200; Goff R-206.
> *N.B*: A commentary by the first Chancellor of the University of Oxford, who was one of the first to practice and advance the in-coming concept of experimental science. As shown by quotations cited by Crombie, in his investigation of nature Grosseteste employed a deductive method, eliminating such theories as proved contrary to experience and experiment. Thus he endeavored to evolve concepts of heat and the causation of comets and the rainbow. Taton (A&MS) 491 emphasizes Grosseteste's belief in light as the activating source of the universe; his recognition of the problem of error; and his concept that all natural phenomena could be explained by lines, angles, and geometric figures.
> *Mon*: CROMBIE, A. C. *Robert Grosseteste and the origins of experimental science, 1100–1700*, Oxford, 1953.   TURBAYNE, Colin M. *Grosseteste and an ancient optical principle* (p. 467–472 in *Isis* 50 1959).   DALES, Richard C. *Robert Grosseteste's scientific works* (p. 381–402 in *Isis* 52 1961); *Robert Grosseteste's 'Commentarius in octo libros Physicorum Aristotelis'* (p. 10–33 in *Medievalia et Humanistica* 11 1957); *The authorship of the 'Summa in Physica' attributed to Robert Grosseteste* (p. 70–74, 324 in *Isis* 55 1964).

HARTMANN, Georg, 1489–1564. Although a reference to Hartmann in Mottelay p. 611 with regard to the earliest determination of magnetic declination on land, on March 4, 1544, may refer to a printed item, no contemporary printed text has been found during the present survey. [*See also* DOVE, Wilhelm and Ludwig MOSER, *ed. Repertorium der Physik.* Berlin, 1837–49, vol. II, p. 129.]

HEYTESBURY, William (Guilielmus Hentisberus; Hentisbury; *also called* Tisberus), *c.* 1310–1371.

762 De moto locali (*in Part VI of his* Regule solvendi sophismata. [Pavia:] Antonius Carcanus, 1481.)

> *Ref*: For references and notes see below, under *Regule*.
> *N.B*: Issued also in a compilation beginning *De sensu composito et diviso*, printed at Venice by Joannes and Gregorius de Gregoriis in 1491 (Cen H50), and by Bonetus Locatellus, for Octavianus Scotus in 1494 (Cen H51). [It is the 1494 edition that is most frequently cited, doubtless because it contains the *Probationes conclusionum* and commentaries on Heytesbury by Gaetano di Thiene and Messinus; Angelo da Fossombrone; Bernardo Torni; and Simon de Lendenaria. All of these, however, are listed in earlier editions, excepting the Simon de Lendenaria (*q.v.*), the first printing of which seems to be in this 1494 compilation.]

763 Probationes conclusionum in regulis positarum. [Pavia:] Nicolaus Girardengus, 24 Jan. 1483. f°.

> *Ref*: HR 8442; Polain 1803; IGI 4615; Klebs 513.1; Wilson (WH) 116, *etc.*; Stillwell H48; Goff H-54.
> *N.B*: Contains direct arithmetical proof of certain theorems set forth in Heytesbury's *Regule*. Of unknown authorship. Variously assigned to Heytesbury or to an author of later date. Included in the 1494 compilation noted above, *no. 762n.*
> *Mon*: CLAGETT, Marshall. *Proofs of propositions posited in the rules for solving sophisms, attributed to William Heytesbury* (p. 200, 265–266, 284–289 in his *The science of mechanics in the Middle Ages.* Madison, 1959).

764 Regule solvendi sophismata. Sophismata (Ed: Joannes Petrus de la Porta.) [Pavia:] Antonius Carcanus, 1481. f°. [LEK]

> *Add*: STRODE, Ralph, *fl.* 1350–1400. Consequentiae.
> *Ref*: BMC VII 997; BM-Ital 323; Klebs 512.1; *Clagett (SM)* 200, 218, 273 (1494, *fac.*), *etc.*; *Maier (AG)* 266.
> *N.B*: According to Duhem (Études) III 407, the *Regule* comprises six brief treatises entitled *De insolubilibus*; *De scire et dubitare*; *De relativis*; *De incipit et desinit*; *De maximo et minimo*; and *De tribus praedicamentis* (comprising *De motu locali*; *De motu augmentationis*; *De motu alterationis*). Proofs of theorems are given in the *Probationes conclusionum*, which is variously assigned to Heytesbury or to an anonymous writer of later date. The *Sophismata* treats of thirty-two fallacies.

Both the *Regule* and the *Sophismata* appeared in Heytesbury's *De sensu composito et divisio* printed at Venice in 1491, together with the *Consequentiae* and the *Obligationes* of Ralph Strode (Cen H50; Schullian (ArMed) 240).

The *Regule*, written in 1335, contains the first known statement of the Merton uniform acceleration theorem. The text as known in early manuscripts is given in Clagett (SM). [For definitions of Heytesbury's concepts of uniform velocity, uniform acceleration, and instantaneous velocity, see Clagett (SM) 235–237.]

The *De motu locali* was evidently one of the most influential treatises produced by a member of the Merton College group. A portion of its text, treating of the concept of instantaneous velocity, is given in translation in E. A. Moody's *Laws of motion in medieval physics* (p. 18–23 in *Scientific Monthly*, LXXII, I, 1951). In the course of his discussion, Dr. Moody cites Heytesbury's text as proof that the kinematic law of uniformly accelerated motion, a factor in Galileo's mechanics, had been understood and clearly stated as early as 1340. A somewhat longer selection of the text, quoting three categories of motion as defined by Heytesbury, is given in Latin with translation in Clagett (SM) 235–242, 270–283. Proof of two theorems is given on p. 284–289.

Mon: WILSON, C. *William Heytesbury: Medieval logic and the rise of mathematical physics*, Madison, 1956.

765 Sophismata. (*Issued with his* Regule. [Pavia:] Antonius Carcanus, 1481.)

N.B: With regard to Heytesbury's introduction of mathematical and physical considerations into the analysis of sophisms, see the monograph on *William Heytesbury* by Curtis Wilson, noted above. Based on the 1494 edition of Heytesbury's works, pages 153–163 of the Wilson monograph list Heytesbury's 32 sophisms together with references to the works of other authors which discuss them.

JACOPO da Forlì (Giacomo della Torre; Jacobus de Forlivio; Jacobus Forliviensis), *c.* 1360–1413.

766 De intensione et remissione formarum. [Padua: Johannes Herbort, 1476/77.] f°. [LEK]

Ref: R 1211; BMC VII 916; BM-Ital 345; Klebs 549.1; Clagett (SM) 648–652.

N.B: A text indicative of the in-coming interest in the new physics at Padua. Also issued by the same press in combination with the *De proportionibus tractatus* of ALBERTUS de Saxonia (Cen A311). Subsequently issued at Venice in a compilation printed for Octavianus Scotus by Bonetus Locatellus in 1496 (Cen B1162).

Mon: RANDALL, J. H. *The development of the scientific method in the school of Padua* (p. 13–68 in his *The school of Padua and the emergence of modern science*. Padova, 1961. [Saggi e testi I]).

JACOPO da San Martino (Jacobus de Sancto Martino), *late 14th century.*

767 De latitudinibus formarum. Padua: Matthaeus Cerdonis, 25 Sept. 1482. [LEK]

Jacopo da San Martino (continued)

Ref: Klebs 713.1; *Clagett (SM)* 345–346.

N.B: Variously attributed either to Oresme or Jacopo da San Martino in manuscripts, and frequently to Oresme in printed texts. The present count, however, favors Jacopo on the basis of textual analysis; and Professor Thomas Smith has ventured the suggestion that the original text may have stated that it was written by Jacopo "according to the doctrine of Oresme," thus causing the confusion.

For a selection of its propositions relative to the latitude of forms as identifiable through geometric figures, see the Latin text and translation in Clagett (SM) 392–401.

JOANNES *Canonicus, fl.* 1329.

768 Quaestiones super libros Physicorum Aristotelis.   Padua: [Albertus de Stendal, or Bonus Gallus] 25 Apr. 1475.   f°.   [LEK]

Ref: H *4344; Pr 6785; IGI 2411; *Sart* III 739; Stillwell J230; Goff J-262.

N.B: A treatise upholding various Aristotelian theories, among them the impossibility of a vacuum. Authenticity questioned. Assigned to Jean de Jandun, *d.* 1328, in Klebs 553.1. [For a note on authorship, see Schullian (ArMed) 261.] An edition issued at Venice in 1488—the fifth of the six editions listed in Klebs 553—contains three works by Elias Cretensis, his *De primo motore quaestio*; *De efficentia mundi*; and *Annotationes in Physica Aristotelis* (Cen J316; Schullian (ArMed) 260).

JORDANUS de Nemore (Jordanus *Nemorarius*), *fl.* 1246(?).

769 Liber de ponderibus propositiones XIII (Ed: Petrus Apianus, *i.e.*, Peter Bienewitz, 1495–1552).   Nuremberg: Joannes Petreius, 1533.   4°.

Add: Aliud commentum [*An anonymous but important 14th-century commentary on the Elementa de ponderibus of Jordanus*—cf. Clagett (SM) 78–80, 100–101; Moody-Clagett (MSW) 231, 293–305.]

Ref: BM–Ger 462; Van Ortroy (Apian) 103; Crombie (A–G) 1952 83–87, 279, 1961 I 118–119; *Taton (A&MS)* 494.

N.B: One of three works attributed to Jordanus, comprising original attempts to derive the laws of statics through a dynamical approach. Relates to the theory of balance. Attribution sometimes questioned.

Mon: CLAGETT, Marshall. *Jordanus de Nemore and Medieval Latin statics* (p. 69–103 in his *Science of mechanics in the Middle Ages*, Madison, 1959).   MOODY, Ernest A. *Liber Jordani De ponderibus* (p. 121–123, 145–165 in MOODY and CLAGETT. *The Medieval science of weights*, Madison, 1952, with Latin text and translation). [In his introduction to this section, Dr. Moody ventures the suggestion that the author of the *Aliud commentum*, included in this 1533 edition, may have been a member of the fourteenth-century Merton school, even Bradwardine himself.]

V. *Physics*

LE FÈVRE d'Étaples, Jacques (Jacobus Faber Stapulensis), *c.* 1455–1536.

770 In Aristotelis octo Physicos libros paraphrasis (Ed: Josse Clichtove, 1472–1543). Paris: Johannes Higman, 1492. 4°. [LEK]

> *Add*: Dialogus in Physicam introductorius.
> *Ref*: GW 9638; HC 6839; BMC VIII 133; BM-Fr 25; Klebs 591.1; Stillwell F6; Goff F-12.
> *N.B*: Variant known. For a 1514 edition of Le Fèvre's *Introductio in Physicam paraphrasim* printed at Strasbourg, see NLMCat 2752.

LEOPOLDUS, *ducatus Austriae, 13th century*.

771 De mutatione aeris (Bk. VI of his *Compilatio de astrorum scientia*. Augsburg: Erhard Ratdolt, 9 Jan. 1489). 4°. [LEK]

> *Ref*: HC *10042; BMC II 382; BM-Ger 494; Oates 958; IGI 5747; Klebs 601.1; Car p. 171; *Sart* II 996; Stillwell L161; Goff L-185.
> *N.B*: A treatise on meteorology frequently quoted by the fourteenth-century writer, Firmin de Beauval. Sarton cites an edition of the *Compilatio* printed at Venice by Melchior Sessa in 1520.

LOCKERT, George (Georges Lokert), *fl.* 1510, *ed*.

772 Quaestiones et decisiones physicales insignium virorum Alberti de Saxonia ... Thimonis ... Buridani ...   Paris: Jodocus Badius Ascensius et Conradus Resch, 1516. [LEK]

> *Ref*: *Thornd (HM)* III 587; *Duhem (Études)* III 133, 583; *Clagett (HM)* 653.
> *N.B*: A collection of treatises edited by a Scotch master of the Collège de Montaigu and indicative of the interest in early mechanics which centered at Paris in the first half of the sixteenth century. Re-issued at Paris by this same firm in 1518— Wightman (1962) II 405.

LUCRETIUS CARUS, Titus, *fl.* 95–55 B.C.

773 De rerum natura. [Brescia:] Thomas Ferrandus [1473]. 4°. [LEK]

> *Ref*: Klebs 623.1; *Sart (HS)* II 263–279; *Crombie (A–G)* 1952 236–239.
> *N.B*: A great philosophical poem, which reveals the scientific knowledge of Lucretius's time, including the atomic theory derived from Demokritos, *fl.* 420 B.C. and Epikuros, *fl.* 300 B.C. From a manuscript discovered by Poggio Bracciolini about 1418. The first dated edition was issued at Verona in 1486 (Cen L298). Subsequent editions are known in 1495, 1496 and 1500 (Klebs 623.3–.5), and in 1515 (NLMCat 286[3], 2864). [See also under NATURAL SCIENCE: Lucretius Carus.]

Lucretius Carus (continued)

>   Translated by W. H. D. Rouse in the Loeb Classical Library, Cambridge, Mass., 1947. For brief analyses of Lucretius, see Sartos as noted above, and p. 101–104 in CLAGETT, Marshall. *Greek science in antiquity*, New York, 1955.
>
>   *Mon*: HADZSITS, G. D. *Lucretius and his influence*. London, 1935. LEONARD, Wm. E. and Stanley Barney SMITH. *T. Lucretii Cari De rerum natura*. Madison, 1942 (reviewed in *Isis* 34 1942, p. 514).
>
>   *Fac*: *Sart (HS)* II 277.

MARLIANI, Giovanni (Johannes Marlianus), *c*. 1425–1483.

774   Disputatio cum Joanne Arculano de diversis materiis ad . . . medicinam pertinentibus. Opuscula. [Pavia: Damianus de Confaloneriis, 1482.] f°.

>   *Ref*: H 10773; IGI 6188; Klebs 666.1; *Duhem (Étude s)* 3me ser., 498; *Clagett (Mar)* 65–78.
>
>   *N.B*: Relates principally to the cooling of heated water.
>
>   *Mon*: CLAGETT, Marshall. *Giovanni Marliani and late medieval physics*. New York, 1941 (reviewed in *Isis* 34 1942, p. 166–168).

775   De proportione motuum in velocitate. Pavia: Damianus de Confaloneriis, 16 Dec. 1482. f°.

>   *Ref*: H 10772; IGI 6190; Klebs 665.1; *Crombie (A–G)* 267; *Sart* III 738; *Clagett (Mar)* 125–144.
>
>   *N.B*: Discusses various arguments brought against the peripatetic law of proportions; attempts to refute Bradwardine's conclusions regarding the Aristotelian rules for comparing movements; and presents Marliani's own thesis but without developing conclusive theorems in its support.

776   Quaestio de caliditate corporum humanorum. [Milan:] Antonius Zarotus, 27 Aug. 1474. f°. [LEK]

>   *Ref*: HC 10771; BMC VI 711; IGI 6189; Klebs 664.1; *Clagett (Mar)* 31, 34–36, 79; Stillwell M237; Goff M-274.
>
>   *N.B*: A study which distinguishes between heat quantity and heat intensity or temperature. Known also in an edition printed at Venice in 1501 (NLMCat 2966). [See also under NATURAL SCIENCE.]

MARSILIUS ab Inghen (Marsilius van Inghen), *c*. 1345–1396.

777   Abbreviationes libri Physicorum Aristotelis. [Pavia: Antonius Carcanus?, about 1480.] f°. [LEK]

>   *Ref*: HR 10780; Polain 2617; IGI 6198; Klebs 667.1; *Schullian (ArMed)* 306; *Sart* III 1436; *Crombie (A–G)* 1952 260; *Maier (ZG)* 279–284; *Clagett (SM)* 636–637, 639; Stillwell M244; Goff M-281.

N.B: Marsilius distinguished between rotary impetus and rectilinear impetus. Portions of his text relative to these and other aspects of impetus, and to an initial period of acceleration of a projectile, are given in Clagett, as noted above.

778 Quaestionum optimarum cursus cum textualibus expositionibus super Physicorum et ceteros naturalis philosophiae libros Aristotelis. [Cologne: Heinrich Quentell, 1489–1494.] f°. [LEK]

Ref: HC *13642; BMC I 279; BM-Ger 46[19]; Voull (K) 353; Klebs 317.1; *Clagett (SM)* 624–625; *Crombie (A–G)* 1952 258–259; Stillwell Q6; Goff Q-6.

N.B: Variously ascribed to DUNS SCOTUS, *c.* 1266–1308; often entered anonymously. The text, a nominalist denial of movement as an entity, identifies the cause of movement with the moving body. Question 7 in Book III is given in translation in Clagett (SM) 615–624 and attributed to Marsilius.

MERCATOR, Gerhard. De ratione magnetis. *See* TECHNOLOGY, *no.* 860.

MESSINUS (Masino Codronchi). *See* GAETANO di Thiene, *no.* 755*n.*

NICOLAUS de Cusa (Nicolaus Khrypffs of Cues; *called* Nicholas Krebs, Nicolaus Cusanus, Cusa), 1401–1464.

779 Idiota, libri IV. (*In volume I of his* Opuscula. [Strasbourg: Martin Flach, about 1500].) f°. [LEK]

Ref: Hain *5893(1); BMC I 157; BM-Ger 470; Oates 262; IGI 6803; Klebs 700.1; *Sart (SW)* 77, 263:1; *Clagett (SM)* 97–99*n*, 643, 644; Stillwell N80; Goff N-97.

N.B: Cardinal Cusa, a somewhat controversial figure as a man of science, seems to have been a person of ideas and theories but not generally given to clearcut statements or demonstrations. Book IV comprises his discussion *De staticis experimentis.* Book I has passing reference to impetus. An unsigned edition is assigned to about 1502 (Goff N-96). A more critical edition edited by Le Fèvre was printed at Paris in 1514.

Mon: VIETS, Henry. *De staticis experimentis of Nicolaus Cusanus* (p. 115–135 in *Annals of Medical History* IV 1922). HEINZ-MOHR, G., and W. P. ECKERT. *Das Werk des Nicolaus Cusanus, eine bibliophile Einführung.* Cologne, 1963 (Zeugnisse der Buchkunst, III).

NIFO, Agostino (Augustinus Niphus), 1473–1546.

780 De physica. (*Issued with his translation of* ARISTOTLE. Physica. Venice: Bonetus Locatellus, for heirs of Octavianus Scotus, 1508.) f°.

Ref: BM-Ital 51; *Thornd (HM)* V 72, 75; *Maier (ZG)* 296–297; *Clagett (SM)* 659.

N.B: A translation and commentary, completed in 1506, in which the author follows Thomas Aquinas, discussing air as a factor in impetus—but only as a factor.

NUNES, Pedro (*erroneously called* Nuñez), *c.* 1502–1578.

781   De crepusculis liber unus.   Lisbon: Luis Rodrigues, 1542.   4°.   [LEK]

> *Add*: ABŪ ALĪ AL-ḤASAN. De crepusculis et nubium ascensionibus.
> *Ref*: B-Port 281; Car p. 140; Manuel II (Cat) II 48.
> *N.B*: Relates to twilight and the refraction of light. Contains Nunes's Latin translation of Alhazen's treatise on the cause of twilight. Carmody enters this as a second edition and cites one from the same press in 1541.

OCKHAM, William (Occam, William of Ockham; Guillelmus de Ockham), *c.* 1300–1349.

782   Summulae in Physica Aristotelis (Ed: Marco di Benevento, *fl.* 1480). Bologna: Benedictus Hectoris, 13 Dec. 1494.   f°.   [LEK]

> *Ref*: H *11951; BMC VI 842; BM-Ital 738; IGI 6955; Klebs 706.1; *Crombie (A–G)* 1952 254, 259; *Clagett (SM)* 207, 437, 520, 589, 675; Stillwell O19; Goff O-22.
> *N.B*: In his philosophy, Ockham distinguished between dynamic and kinematic aspects of motion, a distinction to which Bradwardine and his followers gave mathematical statement. [For a brief discussion of Ockham, see p. 442–449 in the essay on *The place of John Dumbleton in the Merton school* by James A. Weisheipl, O.P. (p. 439–454 in *Isis* 50 1959.] IGI gives the printer of the *Summulae* as Benedetto Faelli.
> *Mon*: MOODY, Ernest A. *Ockham and Aegidius of Rome* (in *Franciscan Studies*, IX, 1949). SHAPIRO, H. *Motion, time, and place according to William Ockham* (p. 213–303; 319–372 in *Franciscan Studies* 16 1956). BOEHNER, P. *Ockham, philosophical writings*, Edinburgh, 1957. BRAMPTON, C. K. *Ockham and his authorship of the 'Summualae in libros Physicorum'* (p. 418–426 in *Isis* 55 1964).

ORESME, Nicole (*called* Orem; Nicolaus Horen), *c.* 1323–1382.

783   De proportionibus proportionum. (*Issued with* ALBERTUS de Saxonia, *c.* 1330–1390. Tractatus de proportionibus. Paris: for Geoffrey de Marnef [not before 1481].)   f°.   [LEK]

> *Ref*: GW 792; Pell 396; Klebs 29.9; *Maier (AG)* 289–384; *Maier (ZG)* 89–109; Clagett (SM) 331, 480–481; *Crombie (A–G)* 1961 II 92.
> *N.B*: A brilliant mathematical extension of Bradwardine's treatment in which Oresme analyzes fractional exponents. Issued by this same press on 1 Sept. 1505, in a compilation beginning with Politus's *Questio de modalibus* (BM-Ital 530).
>   [No edition is known to have been printed before 1550 of Oresme's important work—*De configurationibus qualitatum*—in which through the use of two-dimensional graphs he established a geometric method of representing and proving the hypothetical growth of a function. For text and discussion of the antecedents of Oresme's system, see CLAGETT, Marshall. *The application of two-dimensional geometry to kinematics* (p. 331–381 in his *The science of mechanics in the*

Middle Ages, Madison, 1959). See also under GIOVANNI di Casali, no. 759, whose use of graphs may have antedated that of Oresme.]

The work *De latitudinibus formarum*, attributed to Oresme in certain manuscripts and early printed books, is now, as the result of textual analysis, conceded to have been written by JACOPO da San Martino [*q.v.*]. For discussion of Oresme's theory of impetus as set forth in his commentary on Aristotle's *De caelo*—no edition of which has been found in the present survey—see Clagett (SM) 552–554.

Mon: GRANT, Edward. *Nicole Oresme and his De proportionibus proportionum* (p. 293–314 in *Isis* 51 1960). CLAGETT, Marshall. *Nicole Oresme and medieval scientific thought* (p. 298–309 in American Philosophical Society, *Proceedings* 108 1964). GRANT, Edward, *ed., tr., comm. De proportionibus proportionum . . .* Madison, 1966.

PAULUS *Venetus* (Paolo Nicoletti), *c.* 1368–*c.* 1429.

784 Expositio super Physica Aristotelis et super Commento Averrois. Venice: Gregorius de Gregoriis, 23 April 1499. f°.

> *Ref*: H*12517; Oates 1817; Polain 3016; IGI 7339; Klebs 735.1; HEHCat 2609; *Maier* (*ZG*) 273:18; *Clagett* (*SM*) 650–651, 658; Stillwell P188; Goff P-217.
>
> *N.B*: Written by a member of the new school of physics at Padua who, as was so often the case, took Aristotle's *Physica* as a point of departure for theses of his own.

PELACANI, Biagio (Blasius Parmensis; Blasius of Parma), *c.* 1377–1416.

785 Quaestiones De latitudinibus formarum Johannis Horen [Oresme]. Padua: Matthaeus Cerdonis, 12 Sept. 1482. [LEK]

> *Ref*: H 12546; Klebs 739.1; *Thornd* (*HM*) IV 65–76, 652–662; *Sart* III 1566; *Maier* (*VG*) 279–299; *Clagett* (*SM*) 346, 404–408, 646.
>
> *N.B*: Relates in part to the *De latitudinibus formarum* now attributed to JACOPO da San Martino [*q.v.*], but ascribed in fifteenth-century editions to Oresme. According to Clagett (SM) 402–408, it contains geometrical proof of the mean speed theorem derived from Giovanni di Casali and/or from Oresme's *De configurationibus qualitatum*.
>
> *Mon*: ZUBOV, V. P. *Blaise de Parme et le principe d'inertie* (p. 39–42 in *Physics* 5 1963).

PETRUS PEREGRINUS. *See* PIERRE de Maricourt.

PICCOLOMINI, Alessandro, 1508–1578.

786 In mechanicas quaestiones Aristotelis paraphrasis [with the text]. Eiusdem commentarium de certitudine mathematicarum disciplinarum. Rome: Antonio Blado, 1547. 4°. [LEK]

> *Ref*: BM-Ital 55; *Duhem* (*Études*) III 197, 208; *Clagett* (*SM*) 663.
>
> *N.B*: Written by one of a group of mid-century scholars interested in the impetus theory, whose treatises for the most part, however, were not printed until after

Piccolomini (continued)

our period. Taton in vol. II, 95, of *La science moderne, de 1450 à 1800*, Paris, 1958, cites a 1542 edition of Piccolomini.

PIERRE de Maricourt (Petrus Peregrinus; Peter the Stranger), *fl.* 1269.

787   De virtute magnetis.   Rome: Marcello Silber [not after 1520].   sm. 4°.   [LEK]

> *Ref*: *Mottelay* 46–53; *Sart* II 1030–1032; *HTech* III 524; *Crombie (A–G)* 1961 I 120–122; *Taton (A&MS)* 493.
>
> *N.B*: Written in 1269 as an *Epistola*, relative to the magnetism of iron, the geographical poles, the direction of the action exerted upon and by them, and the properties and use of lodestones. The first printed work describing floated and pivoted compasses. Formerly known in an Augsburg edition of 1558; but in a note on "The first edition of Petrus Peregrinus *De magnete*" (p. 178–179 in *Isis* 37 1947), Dr. Sarton assigns this undated edition to not after 1520 on the basis of collation with Silber's works and because of the presence of a break in the woodcut border occurring here and in Silber imprints of that period. Attributed in its label-title to Ramòn Lul; variously attributed also to Roger Bacon, a pupil of Peregrinus. Known only in a copy at the Bibliothèque Nationale, Paris, and in one purchased in 1936 by Mr. David Wheatland of Cambridge, Massachusetts. Without the section *De intentione operis*, which appears in the 1558 edition. [For further comment, see Pierre de Maricourt under TECHNOLOGY. For a partial transcript of an early manuscript copy, see Mottelay.]

PLINY *the Elder* (Plinius Secundus, Caius), 23–79 A.D.

788   Historia naturalis, libri XXXVII.   Venice: Johann von Speier, [before 18 September] 1469.   f°.   [LEK]

> *Ref*: HCR 10387; BMC V 153; BM-Ital 526; IGI 7878; Horblit 84; Klebs 786.1; *Mottelay* 11, 13; Stillwell P716; Goff P-786.
>
> *N.B*: In Book 32, chap. 1, Pliny speaks of the electrical *torpedo*, a fish which, if touched with a spear, paralyzes the muscles and feet; and in Book 36, chapter 16, discusses the magnetic quality of *lapis lyncurius*, later called by Linnaeus *lapis electricus*—the first known printed reference to the magnetic power of lodestones. [For use of magnetic needles—and for early accounts of the properties of lodestones as known to Theophrastos, Lucretius, St. Augustine, Jacobus de Vitry, Alexander of Neckam, Roger Bacon, and other writers of the centuries before the invention of printing—see Mottelay 1–63.]
>
> *Fac*: HORBLIT 84 [b].

POLITUS, Bassanus, *fl.* 1500.

789   Tractatus proportionum introductorius ad calculationes Suiset.   Venice: Bonetus Locatellus, for the heirs of Octavianus Scotus, 1505   f°.

Ref: Sart III 737; Duhem (*Études*) III, 399.

N.B: Relates to the *Opus aureum calculationum* of Richard Swineshead. Included also in a compilation issued by this same press on 1 Sept. 1505, a volume beginning with Politus' *Questio de modalibus* and including treatises by Bradwardine, Oresme, Pelacani, and Giovanni di Casali (BM-Ital 530).

POMPONAZZI, Pietro (Petrus Pomponatius), *c.* 1462-1525/26.

790 De intensione et remissione formarum. Bologna: Hieronymus de Benedictis, 10 Dec. 1514. 4°. [LEK]

Ref: BM-Ital 532; Sart III 737; Duhem (*Études*) III 120–123, 496–498.

N.B: Refutes the fourteenth-century theories of the Merton school as advanced in the *Liber calculationum* of Richard Swineshead. According to Duhem (*Physics*, in *Catholic Encyclopedia*, XII, 1911), the author was one of a sixteenth-century reactionary group of scholars supporting the theories of Aristotle as interpreted by Alexander of Aphrodisias, 193–*c.* 217.

Mon: WILSON, Curtis. *Pomponazzi's criticism of Calculator* (p. 355–362 in *Isis* 44 1953). CLAGETT, M. *Richard Swineshead and late medieval physics, I. The intension and remission of qualities* (p. 131–161 in *Osiris* 9 1950).

791 De reactione. (*Issued with his* De intensione et remissione formarum. Venice: Heirs of Octavianus Scotus, 1 Mar. 1525.)

Ref: Thornd (*HM*) V 95–96; Sart III 737.

N.B: Rejects the theories of Albertus de Saxonia, Marsilius ab Inghen, Jacopo da Forlì, and Gaetano di Thiene. Sarton mentions an edition of Bologna, 1515; not found in the present survey.

PRISCIANUS of Caesarea, *fl.* 500.

792 Carmen de ponderibus et mensuris. (*Issued in his* Opera. [Venice: Wendelin von Speier] 1470.) f°. [LEK]

Ref: H 13355; BMC V 156; BM-Ital 540; Klebs 806.1; *Moody-Clagett* (*MSW*) 37, 353; *Clagett* (*SM*) 85–91; Stillwell P877; Goff P-960.

N.B: A poem in which hydrostatic balance is described. A comparison of Priscianus and related terms in the *Etymologiae lib. XX* of Isidorus Hispalensis is given in Moody-Clagett, as noted above. The section of the poem describing the so-called "crown problem" is quoted in Clagett (SM) 86–87. [See also under TECHNOLOGY.]

REISCH, Gregor, *c.* 1465–1525. [For a note on the contents of various editions of the *Margarita philosophica*, see under TECHNOLOGY.]

SIMON de Lendenaria, *c.* 1418–1434.

793   Supra sex sophismata Hentisberi. (*Issued with* Heytesbury, William, 1310–1371. Tractatus de sensu composito. Venice: Bonetus Locatellus, for Octavianus Scotus, 27 May 1494.) f°.

    Ref: H *8437; BMC V 443; Oates 1980; IGI 4618; Klebs 514.2; *Duhem (Études)* III 408; Stillwell H51; Goff H-57.

STRODE, Ralph. *See no.* 764 *n.*

SWINESHEAD, Richard (Richardus Suiseth; *called* Calculator), *d.* 1349.

794   Opus aureum calculationum (Ed: Joannes de Cipro, *fl.* 1359). [Padua: Anonymous printer, *c.* 1477.] f°. [LEK]

    Ref: HC *15136; BMC VII 919; BM-Ital 651; Oates 2557; Klebs 943.1; *Clagett* (SM) 290–304, 440*n*, 677, *etc.*; *Sart* III 736–738; *Taton* (A&MS) 504; Stillwell S736; Goff S-830.

    N.B: An extension of Bradwardine's dynamics, attempting to relate certain kinematic theorems to variations in force and resistance; an important contribution to the concept of instantaneous velocity and the theorem of uniform acceleration as developed by the Merton School. Known also in an edition printed at Pavia in 1498 (Cen S737).

    Mon: THORNDIKE, Lynn. *Calculator and the rise of mathematical physics* (p. 370–385 in his *History of magic and experimental science* III 1934). CLAGETT, Marshall. *Richard Swineshead and late medieval physics, I. The intension and remission of qualities* (p. 131–161 in *Osiris* 9 1950).

TARTAGLIA (Nicolò Fontana, *the Stammerer*; *also called* Tartalea), *c.* 1506–1557.

795   Nuovo scienza untile per ciascuno speculativo matematico bombardiero [*Italian*]. Venice: Stefano dei Nicolini da Sabbio, 1537. 4°. [LEK]

    Ref: BM-Ital 658, 900; *Sart* III 1554; *Crombie* (A–G) 1961 II 74, 131.

    N.B: Includes discussion of various ballistic problems and experiments. The theory of three periods of impetus in the trajectory of a projectile, as it had been advanced by Albertus de Saxonia, was modified in Tartaglia's application of mathematical principles.

796   Quesiti e inventioni diverse [*Italian*]. Venice: Venturino Ruffinelli, 1546. 4°. [LEK]

    Ref: BM-Ital 658; *Wightman* (1962) II 673; *Clagett* (SM) 101.

    N.B: Books VII–VIII relate to the theory of motion and of statics. Tartaglia comments upon and paraphrases various propositions of Part I of the *Liber de ratione ponderis* attributed to Jordanus de Nemore, a work later published as *Jordani opusculum de ponderositate*, Venice, 1565. A facsimile reproduction of the 1554 edition of Tartaglia's *Quesiti* appears in the monograph noted below, which includes also a comparison of the texts of the 1546 and 1554 editions. [With regard to projectiles, see Tartaglia under TECHNOLOGY.]

Mon: *Niccolo Tartaglia: Quesiti et inventioni diverse*. With an introductory section by Arnaldo Masotti. Brescia, 1959 (Ateneo di Brescia). [Reviewed by Stillman Drake, p. 430–431 in *Isis* 52 1961.]

TARTARET, Pierre (Petrus Tarteretus), *fl.* 1490.

797 Quaestiones super philosophia et metaphysica Aristotelis. (*Issued with his* Expositio super textu logices Aristotelis. [Poitiers:] Jean Bouyer and Guillaume Bouchet, 26 Jan. 1493/94.) f°. [LEK]

Ref: H 15340; Klebs 952.1; *Clagett (SM)* 638, 640; Stillwell T29; Goff T-37.

N.B: Written by the Rector of the University of Paris, one of the few scholars of fifteenth-century France who subscribed to Buridan's theory of impetus—although overlooking Oresme and the kinematics of the earlier Merton school.

THEMO (*also called* Themon *or* Thimon *Judaei*), *fl.* 1350.

798 Quaestiones IV librorum Meteorologicorum Aristotelis. [Pavia: Antonius Carcanus, 1480/82] f°.

Ref: BMC VII 997; BM-Ital 48; Klebs 959.1; *Sart* III 1539.

N.B: Themo's theories and those of his contemporaries relative to the Aristotelian explanation are discussed by Carl B. Boyer, *The theory of the rainbow: medieval triumph and failure* (*Isis* 49, 1958, p. 378–390. See also p. 141–154 in the same volume for his *The tertiary rainbow: an historical account*). A treatise by Themo on mechanics was included in the collection edited by George Lockert [*q.v.*], printed at Paris in 1516.

THOMAS AQUINAS, *Saint, c.* 1225–1274.

799 Commentum in octo libros Physicorum Aristotelis. [Genoa?: Matthias Moravus, *c.* 1474.] f°. [LEK]

Ref: H 1525; Pell 1080; HEHCat 4131 [about 1474]; Klebs 961.1; *Clagett (SM)* 207, 516–517; Stillwell T223; Goff T-247.

N.B: Argues in favor of air as the essential instrument of motion, rejecting the theory of impressed force. The first dated edition was printed in 1480; assigned to Venice although the press has not been identified (Cen T224). For discussion of Thomas Aquinas's position on Aristotle's theory of the void, see GRANT, Edward. *Motion in the void and the principle of inertia in the Middle Ages* (p. 268–272 in his article in *Isis* 55 1964). Four fifteenth-century editions and a variant are known of the *Copulata super octo libros Physicorum Aristotelis iuxta doctrinam Thomae de*

V. Physics

Thomas Aquinas (continued)

> *Aquino* of Lambertus de Monte (Klebs 583.1–.5; Goff M-830—M-834). According to the analysis given in section C of the table preceding Goff T-160 (p. 588), Thomas Aquinas's commentary on Aristotle's *De meteorologica libri IV* is included in the Aristotelian *Opera* printed at Cologne by Heinrich Quentell, 22 Sept. 1497.
>
> *Mon*: THOMAS AQUINAS. *Commentary on Aristotle's Physics*. Tr: Blackwell, Spath, and Thirlkel. New Haven, Conn., 1963; with introduction by Vernon J. Bourke (reviewed by Edward Grant, p. 474–475 in *Isis* 56 1965).

THOME, Alvarès, of Lisbon (Alvarus Thomas), *fl.* 1509?

800 Liber de triplici motu. Paris: Guillermus Anabat [n.b. 11 Feb. 1509]. f°.

> *Ref*: BM-Fr 421; *Duhem (Études)* III 531–543; *Clagett (SM)* 657–658.
> *N.B*: Discusses the *Tria praedicamenta de motu* of Heytesbury, the *Calculationes* of Swineshead and various later tracts.

TORNI, Bernardo (Bernardus Tornius), *d.* 1500.

801 In capitulum de motu locali Hentisberi quedam annotata. Pisa: [Gregorius de Gente] 1484. 4°. [LEK]

> *Ref*: H 7351 (II); BMC VII 1096; BM-Ital 676; Klebs 978.1; *Duhem (Études)* III 501, etc.; *Clagett (SM)* 652; Stillwell T352; Goff T-386.
> *N.B*: A commentary upon the *De motu locali* of William Heytesbury [*q.v.*] of the fourteenth-century Merton school, treating of the laws of instantaneous velocity and employing arithmetical demonstrations. Also published in a compilation beginning *De sensu composito*, printed at Venice by Bonetus Locatellus, 27 May 1494 (Klebs 514.1; Cen H51).

TORRE, Giacomo della. *See* JACOPO da Forlì.

URBANO of Bologna (Urbanus, *Averroista*), *fl.* 1335.

802 Expositio commentarii Averrois super Physica Aristotelis (Ed: Defendinus Januensis and Jacobus Philippus Ferrariensis). Venice: Bernardino Stagnino, 15 Nov. 1492. f°.

> *Ref*: HC *16097; BMC V 366; BM-Ital 705; Polain 3886; Klebs 1006.1; *Sart* III 519; Goff U-65.
> *N.B*: With preface by Nicoletto Vernias da Chieti, *fl.* 1480–1490, an Italian Averroist who concerned himself with Aristotelian theory, as opposed to current interest in impetus dynamics.

SUBJECT ANALYSIS FOR
TECHNOLOGY

[1] ARCHITECTURE, ENGINEERING, and CONSTRUCTION: Alberti; Frontinus; Grapaldi; Isidorus Hispalensis; Reisch; Sagredo; Serlio; Vitruvius; Waldseemüller.——PROPORTION: Alberti; Vitruvius.——TERMS: Grapaldi.

[2] ASSAYING: Biringuccio; *Probierbüchlein.*

CARTOGRAPHY, The Beginning of: See MATHEMATICAL GEOGRAPHY: Ptolemy, Waldseemüller, Werner, *etc.*——II [no. 3]* 125.

[3] CHEMISTRY (Alchemy): Abiosi; Arnaldo de Villa Nova; Brunschwig; Fontaine; Jābir ibn Haiyān (Geber); Joannes de Rupescissa; Lul; Pantheo; Paracelsus; *Speculum alchemiae.* [For other works see THORNDIKE, L. *Alchemy to 1550* (Chapter 24 in his *History of magic and experimental science,* vol. V, New York, 1941). See also HOLMYARD, E. J. *Alchemy,* Baltimore (Penguin Books Inc.) 1957; *Chemistry to the time of Dalton,* London, 1925; and *Alchemical equipment* (p. 731-752 in vol II of *A history of technology.* Ed: Charles Singer and others. Oxford, 1956).]

[4] DYES and DYEING: Roseto; Strabo.

[5] FLYING: Riedrer.

[6] GLASS-MAKING: Agricola; Biringuccio; Pliny *the Elder*; Theophrastos. [For references to glass in early books at The Corning Museum of Glass, see: PERROT, P. N. *Special collection somewhat off the beaten track* (p. 593-597 in WILSON LIBRARY BULLETIN, Feb. 1967, vol. 41, no. 6).]

[7] INSTRUMENTS and APPLIANCES: ASTRONOMY: Andalò di Negro; Apianus, *Astronomicum, Horoscopion, Instrument Buch, Introductio, Quadrans astronomicus*; Bate; Berossos; Cellanus; Chaucer; Fine, *Protomathesis, Quadrans astrolabicus*; Leonardi; Māshā 'Allāh (Messahalla); Mercator; Nicephoros; Nunes; Pierre de Maricourt; Proclos; Ptolemy; Regiomontanus, *De compositione meteoroscopii, De torqueto, astrolabio armillari, etc*; Reisch; Robertus *Anglicus, De astrolabii compositione*; Rojas Sarmiento; Stöffler. See also under ASTRONOMY: Macrobius. [For an interesting account of the planetary equatorium, with reference to the instruments attributed to or designed by Giovanni Campano, Gerard of Sabbioneta,

Jean de Linières, Richard of Wallingford, Apianus, *etc.*, see p. 123-132 in PRICE, Derek J. *The equatorie of the planetis*, Cambridge, 1955. See also his texts on *Precision instruments to 1500* and *The manufacture of scientific instruments from c. 1500 to c. 1700* (p. 582-619 and 620-647 in *A history of technology*. Ed: Charles Singer, E. J. Holmyard, and others. Vol. III. Oxford, 1957.)]——DOMESTIC APPLIANCES: Grapaldi; Pliny *the Elder*; *Scriptores rei rusticae.*——NAVIGATION: Mercator; Pierre de Maricourt.——SURVEYING: Apianus, *Cosmographicus liber*; Reisch; Tartaglia, *Quesiti.* ——WEIGHING: Priscianus.

[8] INVENTIONS, History of: Pastrengo; Pliny *the Elder*; Tortelli; Vergilius.

[9] METALLURGY: Agricola; Biringuccio; Pantheo; Pliny *the Elder*; *Probierbüchlein*; *Stahel und Eysen kunstilich weych . . . zu machen.*

[10] MILITARY SCIENCE and EQUIPMENT: Aelianus; Ascham; Biringuccio; *Büchsenmeisterei*; Cornazzano; Dürer; Frontinus; Lirer; Machiavelli; Modestus [*pseud.* for Laetus?]; *Scriptores rei militaris*; Tartaglia; Valturio; Vegetius.

[11] MINING: Agricola; Albertus Magnus; *Bergbüchlein*; Pliny *the Elder*; Strabo.

[12] NAVIGATION: Alberti; Bartolommeo *dalli Sonetti*; Biondo; Faleiro; Fernández de Enciso; Gemma; Lul; Mercator; Nunes; Pedro de Medina; *Periplus*; Pierre de Maricourt (Peregrinus); Portolano; *Regimento do estrolabio.*

[13] PETROLEUM, Use of: Pliny *the Elder*; Strabo.

[14] PRINTING, Invention of: Balbi.

[15] SURVEYING: Apianus, *Cosmographicus liber*; Gemma; Robertus *Anglicus*; Tartaglia; Waldseemüller.

[16] TYPE-CASTING: Balbi; Biringuccio.

[17] TYPE-DESIGN: Tory.   *See also* MATHEMATICS: Dürer, no. 101.

[18] WINES and COOKERY: Apicius; Arnaldo de Villa Nova; Folz; Grapaldi; Platina; Puff von Schrick.

VI. TECHNOLOGY

ABIOSI, Giovanni Battista (Joannes Baptista Abiosus), *c.* 1470–1523.

803   Vaticinium [for 1523]. Naples: In aedibus D. Catherine de Silvestro, 12 June 1523.

> *Ref*: Thornd (*HM*) V 220–221, 541.
>
> *N.B*: In a chapter unrelated to his prognostications, the alchemist Abiosi tells of a remarkable medicine derived from elements of the fifth essence, the dissolving of precious stones and potable gold. He writes also of curing pestilential diseases by potions and plasters. Thus this in a sense antedates the works of Paracelsus on chemical medicine, as also does the publication of the work of Joannes de Rupescissa on the medicinal properties of alcohol—for which, see under MEDI-CINE. [For a brief account of alchemy during the first half of the sixteenth century, see Thornd (*HM*) V 532–549.]

AELIANUS (Aelian), *fl.* 125.

804   De instruendis aciebus tractatus (Tr: Theodoros Gaza, *fl.* 1400–1475). Rome: Eucharius Silber, 15 Feb. 1487. 4°. [LEK]

> *Ref*: GW 310; Pr 3826; BMC IV 107; Klebs 11.1; Sart I 213 *note* (g).
>
> *N.B*: A treatise on military tactics said to be derived from Asclepiodotos, *fl.* 75 B.C. Also found in the compilation of military tracts issued by this press, 29 Jan.–7 June 1487, under the title *Scriptores rei militaris* (Cen S315; Klebs 903.1). With troop formations illustrated by arrangements of type.

AGRICOLA (Georg Bauer; Georgius Agricola; *usually called* Agricola), 1491–1555.

805   De veteribus et novis metallis libri II. (*Issued with his* De ortu et causis subterraneorum. Basel: Hieronymus Froben and Nicolaus Episcopius, 1546.)

> *Ref*: BM-Ger 8; Horblit 2a; *HTech* III 28.
>
> *N.B*: A history of mining and metallurgy from ancient times, with a glossary of mineralogical terms, in Latin and German. The volume contains also *Bermannus, sive De re metallica dialogus* (see no. 562). [Agricola's work, *De re metallica*, was

Agricola (continued)

not printed until just after our period. The methods which it describes, however, and the implements it depicts, apply to our period even though the book was printed six years after its close. It repeats much of the information given in Biringuccio and contains a section on the making of glass.] See also Agricola's works under NATURAL SCIENCE.

Fac: HORBLIT 2a [2b, recto].

ALBERTI, Leone Battista, 1404–1472.

806 De re aedificatoria (Ed: Angelo Poliziano, 1454–1494). Florence: Nicolaus Laurentii, 29 Dec. 1485. f°. [LEK]

Ref: GW 579; BMC VI 630; BM-Ital 14; Oates 2336; IGI 155; Pell 266; Klebs 32.1; *HTech* III 446; Stillwell A193; Goff A-215.

N.B: Explains the geometrical construction of vaults and the strength of this construction in the erection of cathedrals and other large buildings. Another section deals with proportion in the designing of square and round towers. Still another includes a description of canal-locks, presumably those designed and constructed by Bertola in the 1450s in the waterways around Milan and Parma, the forerunners of the development of canals and inland navigation that took place in northern Europe during the coming century. In discussing the principles of architecture and engineering, the work includes reference to various appliances in use at the time. An edition edited by Geofroy Tory was issued at Paris about 1512 (LC(LJRCat) 615).

ALBERTUS MAGNUS (Albrecht von Bollstädt), *Saint, c.* 1200–1280.

807 De mineralibus (Rev: Nicolaus de Pigaciis). [Padua:] Petrus Maufer, for Antonius de Albricis, 20 Sept. 1476. f°. [LEK]

Ref: GW 686; IGI 206; Pell 336; Klebs 21.1; *Crombie (A–G)* 92–94; *Crombie (A–G)* 1961 I 123–129; *Thornd (HM)* II 545; *Holmy (Chem)* 34, 44; Stillwell A251; *Goff* A-279.

N.B: Albertus records that he visited the copper works near Paris and Cologne, where he saw things "tested by experience." As is frequently the case, he alternates between credulity and observation—the latter, however, substantiated by his phrase, *Fui et vidi, experiri*. According to Dr. Holmyard, the earliest mention of the Emerald Table, attributed to the mythical Hermes Trismegistos, occurs here in Book I, tract I, cap. 3. Issued at Pavia in 1491 and Venice in 1495 (Cen A252, A253); included in a compilation published at Strasbourg in 1541 and Venice in 1542 (NLMCat 2873n, 2873).

Mon: WYCKOFF, Dorothy. *Albertus Magnus on ore deposits* (p. 109–122 in *Isis* 1958).

ANDALÒ di Negro (Andalus de Nigro), *c.* 1270–1342.

808 Tractatus astrolabii (Ed: Pietro Buono Avogaro, *fl.* 1500). Ferrara: Johannes Picardus, de Hamell, 8 July 1475. 4°.

Ref: GW 1638; HR 967; BMC VI 608; IGI 456; Pell 621; Klebs 63.1; *Thornd (SB)* 35; Stillwell A511; Goff A-573.

Mon: THORNDIKE, L. *Andalò di Negro, Profacius Judaeus, and the Alphonsine tables* (*Isis* 10 1928, p. 52–56) treats of the author in general, although not with reference to this work on the astrolabe.

APIANUS, Petrus (Peter Bienewitz; *called* Apian), 1495–1552.

809   Astronomicum Caesareum.   Ingolstadt: In aedibus nostris, May 1540. f°.

Ref: BM-Ger 8; Van Ortroy (Apian) 112; *Price (Equatorie)* 132.
N.B: [See under ASTRONOMY.]

810   Cosmographicus liber (Ed. and Rev: Gemma Regnier [*called* Gemma *Frisius*], 1508–1555).   Antwerp: Joannes Grapheus, Feb. 1529.   4°. [LEK]

Ref: Van Ortroy (Apian) 23; *Smith (HM)* I 342; *HTech* III 528.
N.B: A cut on Fol. XVI, verso, demonstrates the use of a cross-staff in surveying. [For reproduction, from the Antwerp edition of 1539, see p. 196 in vol. II of CROMBIE, A. C. *Augustine to Galileo*. London, 1961.]

811   Horoscopion Apiani generale dignoscendis horis.   Ingolstadt: [In aedibus Apiani] 1533.   f°.

Ref: BM-Ger 37; Van Ortroy (Apian) 100.
N.B: With diagrams illustrating methods of measurement. According to Van Ortroy, the first two parts translated appeared as the *Instrument Buch*, and the third part is derived from the *Quadrans astronomicus*, 1532.

812   Instrument Buch durch Petrum Apianum erst von new beschriben [*German*].   Ingolstadt [In aedibus Apiani] 1533.   f°.   [LEK]

Ref: LC(LJRCat) 470; BM-Ger 37; Van Ortroy (Apian) 104.
N.B: Relates to day and night use of the quadrant and other instruments.

813   Introductio geographica.   Ingolstadt: [In aedibus Apiani] 1533.   f°.

Add: REGIOMONTANUS. De compositione et usu cuiusdam meteoroscopii armillaris. [A letter addressed to Cardinal Bessarion.]
Ref: BM-Ger 37; Van Ortroy (Apian) 101.
N.B: The section on the torquetum appeared in 1540 in Apian's *Astronomicum Caesareum*, with the same decorative woodcut. [See also under MATHEMATICS. For an earlier printing of the letter of Regiomontanus, see no. 880.]

814   Quadrans Apiani astronomicus.   Ingolstadt: In officina Apiani, 6 July 1532.   f°.

Ref: BM-Ger 37; Van Ortroy (Apian) 98.

APICIUS, *pseud.*

815 De re coquinaria libri X. Milan: Guillermus Le Signerre, 20 Jan. 1498.
4°. [LEK]

> *Ref*: GW 2267; H *1283; BMC VI 789; IGI 750; Klebs 75.1; Pell 907 (*var*); Sart I 340;
> Stillwell A822; Goff A-921.
>
> *N.B*: An anonymous cookbook named in honor of a 1st-century gourmet, M. Gabius
> Apicius. Of some botanical interest because of the plants mentioned in con-
> nection with cookery. Variant known with device of Johannes de Legnano,
> *publisher*. Text assigned to the third century or later. Amplified by various hands
> —see GW 2267. Issued at Basel and Lyon in 1541 (NLMCat 231, 232).
>
> *Mon*: VOLLMER, Friedrich. *Studien zu dem römischen Kochbuche von Apicius* (BAYER.
> AKAD. der WISS), 1920. MEYER, E. H. F. *Geschichte der Botanik.* vol. 2. Königs-
> berg, 1855, p. 236–249.

ARNALDO de Villa Nova (Arnoldus de Villa Nova; Arnold de Ville
Neuve), *c.* 1235–1311.

816 Opera (Ed: Thomas Murchius, *fl.* 1495). Lyon: Impendio Balthasaris
de Gabiano per Franciscum Fradin, 1504. f°. [LEK]

> *Ref*: NLMCat 305; Sart II 893–900.
>
> *N.B*: Five compilations of Arnaldo's works are cited by Sarton as issued before 1550.
> According to BM-Fr 31, the third edition (printed at Lyon by F. Fradin in 1509)
> is at the British Museum, for which edition and for those of 1505, 1520, and 1532
> revised and emended, see NLMCat 306–309.
>
> Although the majority of Arnaldo's works are of medical interest, among
> fifty-five treatises listed by Sarton as written by or attributed to him, the *Thesaurus
> thesaurorum, Rosarius philosophorum,* and several others relate to alchemy. His
> interest in alchemy and in practical chemistry is discussed in HOLMYARD, E. J.
> *Alchemy*, 1957, p. 119–123. Thorndike calls attention to the fact that, so far as the
> printing of texts is concerned, interest in alchemy did not develop until the turn
> of the century. [See *Alchemy during the first half of the sixteenth century* (p. 532–549
> in his *History of magic and experimental science.* vol. V. New York, 1941).]

817 Von Bewahrung und Bereitung der Weine [*German*:] Von bewarũg
vñ beraitũg der wein (Contributor and translator: Wilhelm von Hirnkofen, *fl.* 1478). [Esslingen: Conrad Fyner, after 2 Oct. 1478.] f°.
[LEK]

> *Ref*: GW 2537; HR 1810; BMC II 516; BM-Ger 46; Pell 1317; Osler (IM) 144; Klebs
> 101.1; *HTech* II 138; Stillwell A964; Goff A-1080.
>
> *N.B*: The story is that Arnaldo de Villa Nova wrote a treatise on the medicinal uses of
> wine while shipwrecked on the African coast. About a century and a half later,
> the text fell into the hands of Wilhelm von Hirnkofen, who turned it into a book
> on wine production and preservation. At least ten other German editions were

issued directly, and about 1500 the text was variously printed in Latin under the title, *De vinis liber*. For German editions of 1506 and 1530 (?), the latter assigned to the press of Wolffgang Meyerpeck at Zwickau, see NLMCat 313, 314. [See also under MEDICINE.]

Fac: SIGERIST, H. E., *tr.* and *ed. The earliest printed book on wine*. New York, 1943, with English translation of the text and a facsimile of the original edition.

ARRIANUS, Flavius. *See below, under* PERIPLUS.

ASCHAM, Roger, *c.* 1515–1568.

818   Toxophilus or the Schole of shootynge.   London: Edward Whyt-church, 1545.   4°.   [LEK]

Ref: STC 837; HTech III 351; Sart (SW) 10.
N.B: A well-known book on archery, a skill in fighting which continued in use throughout the sixteenth century and is here advocated as a sport.

ASTROLABIUM.

819   Astrolabii canones.   [Venice: Paganinus de Paganinis, 1497/98.]   4°.

Ref: GW 2759; H *1898; BMC V 458; IGI 929; Klebs 119.1; Stillwell A1038; Goff A-1171.
Mon: NEUGEBAUER, O. *The early history of the astrolabe* (p. 240–256 in *Isis* 40 1949); MICHEL, H. *Traité de l'astrolabe*, Paris, 1947 (reviewed by G. Van Biesbroeck— *Isis* 39 1948).

BACON, Roger, *c.* 1214–1294.

820   Speculum alchemiae.   Nuremberg: Johannes Petreius, 1541.

Ref: *Thornd* (*HM*) V 537; Sart II 963.
N.B: Ascription sometimes questioned. Possibly published as part of a compilation, the imprint of which—Nuremberg: Johannes Petreius, 1541—is noted by Thorndike but without its title; possibly the compilation entered by BM-Ger 434 as "Jābir ibn Ḥaiyān. De alchemia [*and other works*]," which bears the same imprint.

BALBI, Giovanni (Johannes Balbus), *d.* 1298.

821   Catholicon.   Mainz: [Eponymous press (Johann Gutenberg?)] 1460. f°.

Ref: GW 3182; HC *2254; BMC I 39; Oates 47; DeR (M) 90; Stillwell B19; Goff B-20.

Balbi (continued)

> *N.B*: A Latin glossary which includes, in the colophon of this its first printed edition, a poetic reference to its anonymous printer, the interpretation of which has long been a factor in the Gutenberg controversy. The colophon contains also a statement regarding the process of printing that reads as follows: "... this excellent book, Catholicon, has been printed in the goodly city of Mainz ... and ... brought to completion in the year of our Lord's incarnation, 1460—not by means of reed, stylus, or quill, but with the miraculous and harmonious concurrence of punches and types cast in moulds." The book stands as the first to name its place of printing and also as containing the first printed statement regarding the process.
>
> *Mon*: STILLWELL, M. B. *Gutenberg and the Catholicon*, New York, 1936. GELDNER, Ferdinand. *Das "Catholicon" des Johannes Balbus in ältesten Buchdruck* (p. 90–98 in OHLY, K. and W. KRIEG, ed. *Aus der Welt des Bibliothekars: Festschrift für Rudolf Juchoff*. Cologne [1961]).

BARTOLOMEO *dalli Sonetti, fl.* 1480 [?].

822 Isolario [*Italian, verse*]. [Venice: Guglielmo Anima Mia (da Trino), 1485/86.]   4°. [LEK]

> *Ref*: HCR 2538; BMC V 410; BM-Ital 74; IGI 1278; Klebs 158.1; LC(LJRCat) 218; *Haraszti (MB)* 1943, 108–111; Stillwell B166; Goff B-183.
>
> *N.B*: The first book to contain printed nautical charts. Known in two states. Contains forty-eight woodcut charts showing the relative locations of the islands of the Aegean Sea, each group projected upon a wind-rose marked with compass bearings. The islands are described in verse. The attribution of authorship to Bartolommeo Zamberti or to Bartolommeo Turco has been questioned.
>
> *Mon*: BÜHLER, C. F. *Variants in the first atlas of the Mediterranean* (p. 94–97 in *Gutenberg Jahrbuch*, 1957). WALTERS ART GALLERY, Baltimore, *The World encompassed*, 1952, no. 82. NORDENSKIÖLD, A. E. *Periplus. An essay on the early history of charts and sailing-directions* (Tr: F. A. Bather), Stockholm, 1897. DESTOMBES, Marcel, *Catalogue des cartes gravées au XVe siècle* (p. 77–78 in UNION GÉOGRAPHIQUE INTERNATIONALE. *Rapport*, fasc. II., 1952).

BATE, Henri (Henry of Malines), *c.* 1246–1310.

823 Magistralis compositio astrolabii. Descriptio instrumenti pro equatione planetarum. (*Issued with* ABRĀHĀM ben-'Ezrā. De nativitatibus. Venice: Erhard Ratdolt, 24 Dec. 1484 ("M.cccc.lxxxv. nonas kalendas Ianuarij").   4°.

> *Ref*: GW 113; HC *21; BMC V 291; BM-Ital 2; Schullian (ArMed) 2; Klebs 4.1; Stillwell A6; Goff A-7.
>
> *Mon*: BIRKENMAJER, A. *Henri Bate of Malines*. Cracow, 1923.

BERGBÜCHLEIN.

824 Bergbüchlein (*also called* Bergwerkbüchlein).   Augsburg: Erhard Ratdolt, 1505. [LEK]

> *Ref*: *Sart (SW)* 121–122; *Hoover (Agricola)* 610–614.
> *N.B*: The first work on mining-geology to be printed. Attributed to Ulrich Rühlein von Kalbe, *d.* 1523; also known as Calbus of Freiberg. The first dated edition on record—a statement made advisedly since it is possible that an undated edition somewhat variant from this may have been printed earlier. [See also under NATURAL SCIENCE.]
> *Mon*: SISCO, Anneliese G. *How old is the Bergwerkbüchlein?* (p. 337–343 in *Isis* 43 1952). GUELPA, P. M. *Le plus ancien livre sur les gites minéraux, Le bergbüchlein* (p. 187–191 in *La Nature*, June 1951). SISCO, Anneliese G. and Cyril S. SMITH, tr. *Bergwerk- und Probierbüchlein*. New York, 1949 (reviewed in *Isis* 42 1951, p. 54–56). PIEPER, Wilhelm. *Ulrich Rühlein von Calw und sein Bergbüchlein*. Berlin, 1955 (Freiberger Forschungshefte. Reihe D. Kultur und Technik, 7).

BEROSSOS, *erroneous attribution.*

825 Hemicyclium [*sundial*]. (*In* ZIEGLER, J. ed., Sphaera atque astrorum coelestium ratio, natura, et motus [*Greek and Latin*]. Basel: Johann Walder, 1536.)

> *Ref*: *Smith (HM)* I 146, II 670; *Wightman* (1962) II 752.
> *N.B*: According to Vitruvius IX 4, X 7, 9, Berossos invented the hemispherical sundial. The present work, however, is believed to be spurious.

BIONDO, Michel-Angelo, 1497–1565.

826 De ventis et navigatione libellus in quo navigationis utilissima continetur doctrina cum pixide novo.   Venice: Comin da Trino, 1546.   4°.

> *Ref*: BM-Ital 105; Harrisse (BAV) 274.

BIRINGUCCIO, Vannoccio, 1480–1539.

827 De la pirotechnia libri X.   Venice: Venturino Ruffinelli, 1540.   4°. [LEK]

> *Ref*: BM-Ital 106; *Sart (SW)* 119–121; *HTech* III 27, 44, 364, *etc.*
> *N.B*: The first printed book to cover all aspects of metallurgy. The earliest of the four great classics on the subject. Written by the engineer and military adviser to the Este and Farnese families. It describes also the making of glass and commends especially the skill, beauty, and color of that produced at Murano.
>   Contains a description of a reverberatory furnace, includes sections on mining, smelting, liquation, and amalgamation, and gives an account of the alloys used in bronze, brass, and the casting of type. For type it gives the recipe as 3 parts of

fine tin; ⅛ part, black lead; ⅛ part, fused marcasite of antimony. The method of casting cannon in bronze is described in Book VI.

Mon: SMITH, Cyril Stanley and Martha Teach GNUDI, *tr.* and *ed. The Pirotechnia of Vannoccio Biringuccio.* New York: The American Institute of Mining and Metallurgical Engineers, 1943 (reviewed in *Isis* 34 1942, p. 514–516). Published also as no. 48 in the Massachusetts Institute of Technology Paperback Series. [Re-edited by Derek J. Price for *The Collector's Series in Science* and published by Basic Books, Inc., New York, 1959.]

BRUNSCHWIG, Hieronymus (Jeronimo Brunschweick; Hieronymus von Brawnschweig), *c.* 1450–1512.

828   Liber de arte distillandi de compositis (*the so-called* Grosses Distillierbuch) [*German*]. Strasbourg: Johann (Reinhard) Grüninger, 1512. 364 fol. f°. [LEK]

Ref: NLMCat 748; H*Tech* II 143, *fac*; Hunt (Quinby) I 84, *note*; Wightman (1962) II 101, *fac. of titlepage*.

N.B: The page-facsimile noted above under *HTech* shows a botanical garden equipped with apparatus for the distilling of alcohol. That of the titlepage shows an air- and water-cooled stillhead in operation. The various editions of Brunschwig's texts present bibliographical and textual problems not yet solved. [For the considerable collection of Brunschwig titles and editions which are at the National Library of Medicine, see Schullian (ArMed) 130 and NLMCat 739–765.]

829   Liber de arte distillandi de simplicibus (*the so-called* Kleines Distillierbuch) [*German*]. Strasbourg: Johann (Reinhard) Grüninger, 8 May 1500. 230 fol. f°. [LEK]

Ref: GW 5595; HC *4021; BMC I 114; BM-Ger 148; LC(LJRCat) 182; Nissen 262; Klebs 227.1; Sart (*SW*) 105; Stillwell B1089; Goff B-1227.

N.B: Although printed in German, the text begins with a Latin incipit. As translated by Laurence Andrew and printed at London in 1527, the book appeared as *The vertuose boke of distyllacyon of the waters of herbes, with the fygures of the styllatoryes* (NLMCat 759; *see also* LC(LJRCat) 697). For discussion of the subject see FORBES, R. J. *Short history of the art of distillation*, Leiden, 1948. [See also under MEDICINE.]

BUCHSENMEISTEREI.

830   Buchsenmeisterei [*German*]. Augsburg, 1529. [LEK]

Ref: Wightman (1962) I 179.

N.B: Believed to be the first printed book on gunpowder, its text derived from the so-called *Feuerwerkbuch* known in manuscripts of about 1420.

VI. *Technology*

CATO, Marcus Porcius, 234–149 B.C.

De re rustica. *See under* SCRIPTORES REI RUSTICAE.

CELLANUS, Franciscus Sarzosius, of Aragon.

831 In aequatorem planetarum libri duo. Paris: Simon de Colines, 1526.
f°. [LEK]

> *Ref*: *Price* (*Equatorie*) 132; Renouard (Colines) 91.
> *N.B*: With tables, diagrams, and a volvelle.

CHAUCER, Geoffrey, *c.* 1340–1400.

832 Tretis of the astrolabie. (*Included in* The workes of Geoffray Chaucer.
(Ed. William Thynne, *d.* 1546.) London: Thomas Godfray, 1532.)
[LEK]

> *Ref*: STC 5068; *Sart* III 1421, 1424; *Price* (*Equatorie*) 156–159.
> *N.B*: Written as a textbook for a young boy, but in spite of its elementary character,
> a valid and exceptional treatise on the astrolabe. Assigned to 1391/92. Formerly
> ascribed to Simon Bredon, *c.* 1330–1368. [Chaucer's relation to alchemy is
> discussed by Gareth W. Dunleavy in *Ambix*, vol. XIII, no. 1, Feb. 1965.] See
> also Chaucer's works printed by Richard Pynson at London in 1526.
> *Mon*: GUNTHER, Robert T. *Chaucer and Messahalla on the astrolabe*. London, 1929, 1932
> [revised]. With texts and translations (reviewed in *Isis* 14 233–235).

COLUMELLA, Lucius Junius Moderatus, *1st century A.D.*

833 De cultu hortorum carmen. [Rome: Printer of Silius Italicus, *c.* 1471.]
4°. [LEK]

> *Ref*: GW 7180; Oates 1386; Klebs 287.1; *Nordenskiöld* (HB) 53.
> *N.B*: Book X of Columella's *De re rustica*, which was issued in the collection known as
> *Scriptores rei rusticae* and printed at Venice by Nicolaus Jenson in 1472 [*no.* 889].
> Seven early printed editions are recorded in Klebs 287. Three unsigned editions
> of an anonymous commentary are assigned to Rome, 1472, 1485, and 1490
> (GW 7187–7189; Cen C698).

CORNAZZANO, Antonio, 1429–1484.

834 Dell' arte militare [*Italian*]. Venice: Christophorus de Pensis, de Mandello, for Petrus Benalius, 1493/94. f°.

> *Ref*: GW 7548; HR 5730; BMC V 468; IGI 3197; Klebs 306.1; Stillwell C811; Goff
> C-911.
> *N.B*: A poem written by a poet who was at the Court of Francesco Sforza at Milan
> until 1466 and then in the service of the Colleoni and Este families. With the
> Privilege dated Jan. 1493 [*i.e.*, 1494] and the colophon 8 Nov. 1493.

DÜRER, Albrecht, 1471–1528.

835 Etliche vnderricht zu befestigung der Stett, Schloss vnd Flecken [*German*]. [Nuremberg: Hieronymus (Andreae) *Formschneider*, 1527]. f°. [LEK]

> *Ref*: BM-Ger 256; LC(LJRCat) 465, 465A; *Smith* (*HM*) I 326.
> *N.B*: A treatise on the fortification of city, castle, and market-place. Known in issues with an errata-list inserted and with corrections incorporated. [For various editions of Dürer's treatise on the symmetry and artistic proportions of the human body, see NATURAL SCIENCE: Dürer. See also under MATHEMATICS: Dürer.]

FALEIRO, Francisco (*called* Falero).

836 Tratado del esphera y del arte del marear. Sevilla: 1535.

> *Ref*: Sart (*SW*) 92.
> *N.B*: The first discussion of declination to be printed and one of the rarest of the early books on navigation.
> *Mon*: HARRADON, H. D. *Treatise on the sphere and the art of navigation, Francisco Falero* (p. 79–91 in *Terrestrial Magnetism*, June 1943).
> *Fac*: HELLMAN, G. *Neudrucke*, 1898 (no. 10).

FERNÁNDEZ De Enciso, Martín.

837 Suma de geographia que trata . . . largamente del arte del marear . . . Sevilla: Jacob Cromberger, 1519. f°. [LEK]

> *Ref*: Harrisse (BAV) 97; Church 42.
> *N.B*: The first navigation manual issued in Spain. Contains tables for determining a ship's position from the stars. Certain errors in computation were corrected in subsequent editions.

FINE, Oronce (Orontius Finaeus), 1494–1555.

838 Protomathesis. Paris: For Gerardus Morrhius and Joannes Petrius, 1532. f°. [LEK]

> *Ref*: RA 160; 161, 162 *facs* [showing the contemporary use of the quadrans].
> *N.B*: The present volume relates to horography as well as to arithmetic, geometry, and cosmography. It contains designs by the author and a self portrait, in an initial O. He was an illustrator as well as a professor and a writer on mathematical subjects.

839 Quadrans astrolabicus. Paris: Simon de Colines, 1534. f°.

> *Ref*: Renouard (Colines) 229.
> *N.B*: Possibly first printed in 1527.

FOLZ, Hans, *fl.* 1460–1490.

840   Wem der geprant Wein nutz sey oder schad, un wie er gerecht oder falschlich gemacht sey [*German*].   Bamberg: Marcus Ayrer and Hans Bernecker, 1493.

> *Ref*: Klebs 417.1 (?); *HTech* II 144, 146.
> *N.B*: The opening phrase of a small pamphlet on wine, whose text warns the reader not to over-indulge. The author's *Liber collationum* issued in German verse in 1485 and assigned to the press of Johann Sensenschmidt at Nuremberg (Cen F216) was followed by an unsigned edition possibly printed by Peter Wagner at Nuremberg about 1495 (Sudhoff 177, 178; Klebs 415.1–.2).

FONTAINE, Jean de la, *fl.* 1413.

841   La fontaine des amoureux de science [*French*].   [Paris: Antoine Vérard, 1505?]   4°.   [LEK]

> *Ref*: BM-Fr 168.
> *N.B*: An alchemical poem. Also known as the *Pleasant fountain of knowledge*, which according to a seventeenth-century translation was 'First written in French Año 1413 by John de la Fonteine of Valencia in Henault'—*Ambix*, IV, Dec. 1949, p. 27.

FRONTINUS, Sextus Julius, *c.* 40–103.

842   De aquaeductibus urbis Romae (Ed: Pomponius Laetus, 1425–1497, and Joannes Sulpicius, *fl.* 1460–1490?).   [Rome: Eucharius Silber, 1483–90.]   f°.   [LEK]

> *Ref*: H 7389; BMC IV 123, VII 1132; IGI 4104; Klebs 422.1; Stillwell F290; Goff F-324.
> *N.B*: The most important ancient work on aqueducts. Re-issued in 1495 in a compilation containing the works of Vitruvius Pollio and Politianus, and in 1497 in another compilation containing also the *Harmonicum introductorium* of Cleonides, both issued in Venice (Cen V276, C677 respectively). Included also in a compilation issued at Strasbourg in 1543 (NLMCat 4651).
> *Mon*: DRACHMANN, A. G. *The mechanical technology of Greek and Roman antiquity.* Copenhagen, 1963.

843   Strategematicon.   Rome: Eucharius Silber, 1 June 1487.   4°.   [LEK]

> *Ref*: C 2593; Voull (B) 3482; Klebs 423.1; Sart I 255.
> *N.B*: A treatise on military stratagems. Also found in various editions of the compilation of military tracts commonly called *Scriptores rei militaris* (Cen S315; Klebs 903.1). According to GW 6647, one of the works used as the basis for the *Faits d'armes et de chevalerie* of Christine de Pisan, printed at Paris for Antoine Vérard in 1488 (Cen C425).

GEBER or *Liber Geber*. *See* JĀBIR ibn Ḥaiyān.

GEMMA (Gemma Regnier, of Frisia; *called* Gemma; Gemma Frisius), 1508–1555.

844 Libellus de locorum describendorum ratione. (*Issued with his edition of* APIANUS, Petrus, 1495–1552. Cosmographicus liber. Antwerp: Joannes Grapheus, Feb. 1533). [LEK]

> *Ref*: Van Ortroy (Apian) 26, 27 (*var*); *Crombie (A–G)* 346; *HTech* III 539–540.
> *N.B*: Suggests a method in triangulation valuable in surveying and in mapping. A cut demonstrating the use of a cross-staff in surveying is shown in Gemma's revision of the *Cosmographicus liber* of Apianus, Antwerp, 1529.
> *Mon*: VAN ORTROY, F. *Bio-bibliographie de Gemma Frisius fondateur de l'école belge de géographie* (ACADÉMIE ROYALE de BELGIQUE. Mémoires. Classe des lettres, collection in-8°. 2me série, tome XI. Bruxelles, Dec. 1920). POGO, Alexander. *Gemma Frisius, his method of determining differences of longitude by transporting timepieces* (1530), *and his treatise on triangulation* (1533) [p. 469–504 in *Isis* 22 1934–35].
> *Fac*: *Isis* 22 1934–35, pl. 18.

845 De principiis astronomiae & cosmographici, deque usu globi ab eodem editi.   Antwerp: Joannes Grapheus, Oct. 1530.   [LEK]

> *Ref*: Harrisse (BAV) 156, *add* 92.
> *N.B*: A work that marks the beginning of mathematical navigation. Chapter XVIII in the section *De usu globi*, under the heading *De novo modo inveniendi longitudinem*, introduces the method of employing differences in time for obtaining longitude, a principle still used today. Variant imprints known.
> *Mon*: [See Van Ortroy and Pogo as noted in the preceding entry.]
> *Fac*: *Isis* 22 1934–35, pl. 17, 19.

GRAPALDI, Francesco Mario (Franciscus Marius Grapaldus), 1465–1515.

846 De partibus aedium. [Parma:] Angelus Ugoletus [*c*. 1494].   4°. [LEK]

> *Ref*: HCR 7868; BMC VII 945; IGI 4781; Schullian (ArMed) 215; Klebs 471.1; Stillwell G312; Goff G-349.
> *N.B*: Contains a glossary of terms used in building, gardening, and domestic crafts; and includes an interesting tour of a house, its nursery and library, its fishpond, aviary, and stables. Relates also to architecture and gastronomy. The date assignment is derived from the preface in an edition of 1501. The Parma edition of 1516 is collated as having 130 ff. devoted to definitions of terms. NLMCat 2148 and 2149 record editions printed at Paris in 1517 and Lyon in 1535, the latter entitled *Lexicon de partibus aedium*.

847–849 Cancelled.

VI. *Technology*

ISIDORUS Hispalensis (Isidore, *Bishop of Sevilla*), Saint, *c.* 570–636.

850 Etymologiae libri XX. [Augsburg:] Günther Zainer, 19 Nov. 1472.
f°. [LEK]

> *Ref:* H *9273; BMC II 317; BM-Ger 432; Schullian (ArMed) 250; *Clagett (GSA)*
> 158–159; *Sart* I 471–472; Stillwell I153; Goff I-181.
>
> *N.B:* An encyclopaedia of world-knowledge, the first to be printed. Book XIX relates
> to ship-building, architecture, and other technological subjects. The work con-
> tains the earliest printed map of the world, a schematic "T-map" with areas
> marked as Asia, Europe, and Africa, the whole surrounded by a circle of water,
> with inland waterways between the continents—that between Europe and
> Africa [the stem of the T] being marked as the Mediterranean.
>
> *Mon:* UHDEN, Richard. *Die Weltkarte des Isidorus von Sevilla* (p. 1–28 in *Mnemosyne.*
> Ser. III, vol. 3, 1936).

JĀBIR ibn Ḥaiyān (*called* Geber), *fl.* 775.

851 Flos naturarum. [Rome: Johannes Schurener?] 2 Aug. 1473.

> *Ref:* Hain 7504; Klebs 440.1; *Thornd (HM)* V 536; *Sart* I 532–533.
>
> *N.B:* Authorship questioned. According to *Osiris* 5, p. 106, apparently following
> Darmstaedter's analysis, this text does not relate to alchemy *per se* but is "an
> account of organotherapeutic superstitions."
>
> *Mon:* DARMSTAEDTER, E. *Die Geber-Inkunabel Hain 7504* (p. 214–217 in *Archiv für Ge-
> schichte der Medizin* XVI 1925).

852 Summa perfectionis magisterii, sive liber Geber, libri II [*and other works*].
[Rome: Eucharius Silber, 1483–90.] 4°. [LEK]

> *Ref:* HC *7505; BMC IV 124; BM-Ital 343; IGI 4185 [*c.* 1500]; Klebs 441.1; *Sart* II
> 1043–45; *Thornd (HM)* V 536–537; *Holmy (Alch)* 66–80, 131–137; *Holmy (Chem)*
> 39–42; *HTech* II 736, 738, 739; Stillwell G102; Goff G-112.
>
> *N.B:* An important treatise on alchemical theory and practice. Authenticity ques-
> tioned. The earliest known manuscript, at Munich, is of the late thirteenth
> century. For a summary of the text, see Holmy (Chem) 39–44. Thorndike cites
> a 1541 Nuremberg edition of Jābir's alchemical treatises, printed by Joannes
> Petreius, which also includes the *Speculum alchemiae* attributed to Roger Bacon,
> and other works. Sarton cites six editions printed in the first half of the sixteenth
> century. Jābir himself may be accredited as the first chemist to whom the term
> may properly be applied.
>
> *Mon:* DARMSTAEDTER, Ernest. *Die Alchemie des Geber übersetzt und erklärt.* Berlin, 1922
> (reviewed in *Isis* 5 451–455).
>
> *Fac:* *Osiris* 5 1938, *fig.* 15.

JOANNES de Rupescissa (Juan de Peratallada; *called* Rupescissa), *fl.* 1350.

853 De consideratione quintae essentiae. (*Issued with* FERRARI, Gianmatteo,
da Gradi. Consiliorum utile repertorium. Venice: Georgius Arrivabenus
for the heirs of Octavianus Scotus, 1514.)

Joannes de Rupescissa (continued)

    Ref: NLMCat 1499; BM-Ital 247.

    N.B: A treatise relating to alchemy and the medicinal properties of alcohol. [With regard to Rupescissa's claim to the founding of medical chemistry, antedating that of Paracelsus (1493–1541), and the relation of this work to the writings of Ramòn Lul (*c.* 1235–1315) to whom it is sometimes credited, *see* MEDICINE: Joannes de Rupescissa.] Re-issued in 1521, 1535, 1541, and 1542—*see* NLMCat 2873, 2873*n*.

LEONARDI, Camillo, of Pesaro, *fl.* 1480.

854   Liber desideratus canonum aequatorii coelestium motuum sine calculo. Venice: Georgius Arrivabenus, 21 July 1496. 4°.

    Ref: HR 4283; IGI 5730; Pell 3178; Klebs 597.1; Stillwell L117; Goff L-139.

    N.B: For an account of the early history of the equatorium and of its adaptation in printed books, see p. 119–133 in PRICE, Derek J. *The equatorie of the planetis.* Cambridge, 1955.

LIRER, Thomas.

855   Chronik von allen Königen und Kaisern [*German*]. [Ulm: Conrad Dinckmut, 1484/88.] f°. [LEK]

    Ref: HC *10116; BMC II 537; BM-Ger 504; Stillwell L197; Goff L-225.

    N.B: An illustrated chronicle, with a woodcut showing cannon in action. [An earlier cut of a cannon appears in the "Destruction of Babylon," in the Dutch version of Rolewinck's *Fasciculus temporum.* Utrecht, 1480.] The first signed edition of the Lirer was printed at Ulm by Dinckmut in 1486.

LUL, Ramòn (Raymond Lull; Raymundus Lullus), *c.* 1235–1315.

856   Arbor scientiae. Barcelona: Pedro Posa, 22 Aug. 1482. f°.

    Ref: BM-Sp 55; IGI 5898; Polain 3309; Schullian (ArMed) 287; Klebs 629.1; Stillwell L344; Goff L-383.

    N.B: According to Professor E. G. R. Taylor (p. 526 in *A History of technology.* Ed: Charles Singer, *etc.*, III. 1957), question no. 192 in the *Arbor scientiae* relates to returning to course after a ship has been forced to tack.

857   De secretis naturae. (*Issued with* FERRARI, Gianmatteo, da Grado. Consiliorum utile repertorium. Venice: Georgius Arrivabenus for the heirs of Octavianus Scotus, 1514.) f°. [LEK]

    Ref: NLMCat 1499; BM-Ital 247; *Thornd (HM)* V 536; *Sart* II 909.

    N.B: The opening portion of an alchemical work on the fifth essence, which here appears together with a confused version of JOANNES de Rupescissa's treatise on the fifth essence [*q.v. See also* NLMCat 2873*n*]. Attribution seriously questioned. For a list of sixty or more alchemical works ascribed to Lul by Nazari in a treatise printed at Brescia in 1572, see Thornd (HM) V 691–693. At least seven other editions of the *De secretis naturae* were issued before the end of our period.

Mon: THORNDIKE, Lynn. *The Lullian alchemical collection* (p. 3–64 in vol. 4 of his *History of magic and experimental science*, New York, 1934).

MACHIAVELLI, Nicolò, 1469–1527.

858   Libro della arte della guerra [*Italian*].   Florence: For the heirs of Filippo Giunta, 1521.   8°.   [LEK]

Ref: BM-Ital 400; *Hall (SR)* 9.

N.B: The earliest edition found in the present survey. Re-issued in at least six editions during our period. An English version by Peter [Withorne] Whitehorne was printed at [London] in 1573—LC(LJRCat) 713.

MĀSHĀ 'ALLĀH (Mīshā; *called* Messahalla, Messehalath), d. 815.

859   Tractatus de compositione astrolabii Messehalath. (*Issued with* REISCH, Gregor, *d.* 1525. Margarita philosophica nova. Strasbourg: Johann Grüninger, 1512.)   4°.   [LEK]

Ref: NLMCat 3850; BM-Ger 731; Car p. 24; Zinner (ALD) 967; Eames (Sabin) 69127.

N.B: With a woodcut of an astrolabe and various diagrams. According to Sarton, this work appeared in the 1503 Freiburg edition of Reisch (LC(LJRCat) 429). Māshā 'Allāh is reputed to have taken part in surveying the site for the founding of Baghdād in 762–763—HTech III 529.

Mon: GUNTHER, Robert T. *Chaucer and Messahalla on the astrolabe*. London, 1929, 1932 [revised]. With texts and translations (reviewed in *Isis* 14 233–235).

MERCATOR, Gerhard, 1512–1594.

860   De ratione magnetis circa navigationem.   Louvain, 1546.

Ref: *Sart (SW)* 93, 271:72.

N.B: Relates to the magnetic pole, which he believed different from the geographical pole. [Mercator's projection for marine charts was invented after our period, in 1569.]

Mon: HARRADON, H. D. *Mercator to Antonius Perrenotus* (p. 200–202 in *Terrestrial Magnetism*, Dec. 1943).

MODESTUS, *pseudonym* (?).

861   De re militari.   [Venice:] Bartholomaeus Cremonensis [and Bartholomaeus de Carlo], 27 May 1474.   4°.   [LEK]

Modestus (continued)

    Add: Laetus, Pomponius: De magistratibus urbis; De sacerdotiis; De legibus. Suetonius. De grammaticis et rhetoribus.

    Ref: HC *11443, (Add) 11443; BMC V 209 (1A 20027, 20028); BM-Ital 442; IGI 6656 [*var*]; Klebs 685.2 and .2[*var*]; Stillwell M627; Goff M-737.

    N.B: According to BMC VII xix and xxxiv, the work is believed to be a falsification by Pomponius Laetus, 1425–1497. In fact, a *De re militari* ascribed to Laetus appears in the 1471 Venetian edition of Cicero's *De natura deorum, etc.* (GW 6902.4; Cen C516). Variants of the present edition are known: one naming Venice and both printers in the colophon; the other, naming the first printer only. Both issues bear the same date. Another edition is assigned to the press of Johannes Schurener at Rome about 1475 (Cen M628). Issued also in various editions of the collection commonly called *Scriptores rei militaris* (Cen S315; Klebs 903.1).

NICEPHOROS GREGORAS, 1295–1359.

862   De astrolabo. (*In* Valla, Giorgio, 1447–1499. Collectio. Venice: Simon Bevilaqua, 30 Sept. 1498.) f°.

    Ref: HC *11748; BMC V 523; IGI 6792; Klebs 1012.1; Schullian (ArMed) 477; Sart III 949–953; Stillwell N33; Goff N-44.

    Mon: Mogenet, T. *Les deux traités sur l'astrolabe de Nicéphore Grégoras* (IIIe Congrès National des Sciences. Bruxelles, 1950, p. 25, 26).

NUNES, Pedro (*erroneously called* Nuñez), *c.* 1502–1578.

863   De crepusculis liber unus. Lisbon: Luis Rodriguez, 1542. 4°.

    Ref: BM-Port 281–282; *Smith* (HM) I 349.

    N.B: Describes a graduating instrument for measuring small angles, invented by Nunes and named for him, the "nonius"; later developed into the vernier. Carmody p. 140 enters this as a second edition and cites one from the same press in 1541.

864   Tratado sobre certas duvidas da navegação. Tratado em defensam da carta de marear [*Portuguese*]. (*Issued with* Joannes de Sacro Bosco. Tratado da sphera [*Portuguese*]. Lisbon: Germão Galharde, 1537.) s.m. f°.

    Ref: Harrisse (BAV) 222; Manoel II (Cat) 36; Church 76; Horblit 80; LC(LJRCat) 782; *HTech* III 548.

    N.B: The first scientific treatise on navigation. Compiled by a mathematician, who was also a critical scholar. Although "great-circle sailing" had been practiced before this time, this volume was the first to be printed containing a description of the method. It introduced the basic theory of rhumb-lines or loxodromes. In addition, the volume contains the *Tratado da sphera*, comprising Nunes's annotations and translation of the *Sphaera mundi* of Joannes de Sacro Bosco; and Nunes's translations of part of the *Theoricae novae planetarum* of Georg Peurbach and of Book I of Ptolemy's *Geographia*.

Mon: Pereira da Silva, Luciano. *A primeira edição dos tratados sobre a arte de navegar, de Pedro Nunes* (*Anais des bibliotecas*. 2nd ser., II, 98–101, 1921).

Fac: Manoel II, *King of Portugal. Early Portuguese books, 1489–1600*. Cambridge, 1929, I, p. 561–564. Horblit 80 [b].

NOVUS ORBIS REGIONUM.

865 Novus orbis regionum ac insularum veteribus incognitarum, una cum tabula cosmographica, & aliquot alijs consimilis argumenti libellis (Comp: Johann Huttich). Basel: Apud Johannem Hervagium, 1532. f°.

Ref: LC (LJRCat) 770.

N.B: An example of collected accounts of exploration as published after the discoveries of Columbus, Vespuccius, Magellan, *etc*. [For contents see LC, as cited above.] With map engraved by Hans Holbein the younger, known in two states—Harrisse (BAV) 171.

PALLADIUS, Rutilius Taurus Aemilianus, *fl*. 340.

De re rustica libri XIV. *See under* Scriptores Rei Rusticae.

PANTEO, Giovanni Agostino (Joannes Augustinus Pantheus), *fl*. 1520.

866 Ars transmutationis metallicae. Venice: In aedibus Joannis Tacuini, 30 Dec. 1518. 4°. [LEK]

Ref: BM-Ital 488; *Thornd* (*HM*) V 537–540.

N.B: Published with consent of the Council of Ten and under an edict of Pope Leo X, who looked with favor upon alchemy—for which reason, it is believed, the 15th-century prohibitions of the practice of alchemy were ignored.

867 Voarchadumia contra alchimiam. Venice: [Joannes Tacuinus]1530. 4°.

Ref: NLMCat 3440; LC(LJRCat) 561; BM-Ital 488; *Thornd* (*HM*) V 539; *HTech* III 27, 29, 48.

N.B: Although purporting to be against the study of alchemy, this work was issued without the printer's signature; and in its discussion of the metallurgy of precious metals, the use of sulphides, the making of unbreakable mirrors, *etc*., it repeats much of the text of Panteo's *Ars transmutationis metallicae* (no. 866).

PARACELSUS (Philippus Aureolus Theophrastus Bombastus Paracelsus von Hohenheim. *Variously called* Paracelsus, Theophrastus, *or* Bombast), 1493–1541.

868 Grosse Wund Artzney [*German*].   Ulm: Hans Varnier, 1536.   f°. [LEK]

> *Ref*: NLMCat 3447; Sudhoff (Bibl P) 14; *Castiglioni* (1947) 444–450.
>
> *N.B*: Also issued in 1536 in two other editions, printed at Augsburg by Heinrich Steiner. Re-issued at Augsburg (2) in 1537 and at Frankfurt-am-Main (1) in 1549. Among its many topics, the text suggests thunder and lightning as comprising aerial niter and sulphur. [With regard to Paracelsus and medicinal chemistry, see nos. 433, 467, 803, 853.]
>
> *Mon*: DEBUS, Allen G. *The Paracelsian aerial niter* (p. 43–61 in *Isis* 55 1964). [For other monographs on the works of Paracelsus, see no. 467.]

PASTRENGO (Guglielmo da Pastrengo), *c*. 1290–1363.

868a De originibus rerum libellus . . . in quo agitur de scriptoris virorum illustrium . . . De inventoribus rerum . . . (Ed: Michaelangelo Blondo [Biondo]).   Venice: Nicolo de Bascarini, 1547.

> *Ref*: Sart III 921.
>
> *N.B*: According to Graesse, "C'est le premiere essai d'un dictionaire historique bibliographique et geographique, d'ailleurs ce n'est que la seconde partie de l'ouvrage que se conserve en manuscr. en 2 vol. in fol. dans la Biblioth. de Saint-Jean et Saint-Paul à Venise." A similar note, somewhat expanded, is given in Brunet.
>
>   The *Explicit* from which the above imprint is cited occurs on the penultimate page. The final page, relating to a Privilege, bears the caption: *Michaelangelo Blondus Bibliopolis & Typographis* and ends with the statement: *Dat. Venetijs Anno 1547. Ex Tugurio Blondi. Apud Scipionem Blondum sub Apolline.*

PEDRO DE Medina, 1493?–1567?

869 Arte de navegar [*Spanish*].   Valladolid: Francisco Fernandez de Cordova, 1 Oct. 1545.   f°.   [LEK]

> *Ref*: LC(LJRCat) 763; Harrisse (BAV) 266; Sart (SW) 93, 271:70.
>
> *N.B*: A popular book on navigation, long used by captains sailing the Spanish Main; re-issued in French, Italian, Flemish, and Spanish.

PEREGRINUS, Petrus. *See* PIERRE de Maricourt.

PERIPLUS.

870 Arriani et Hannonis periplus [*Greek*] (Ed: Sigmund Gelenius).   Basel: [Hieronymus Froben and Nicolaus Episcopius], 1533.   4°.

Ref: BM-Ger 47; *Sart* I 257, 284, 103.

N.B: A manual for navigating the Indian Ocean. Possibly written in the first century or earlier.

Mon: SCHOFF, Wilfred H. *The periplus of the Erythrean Sea.* London, 1912 [with English translation]; *The date of the periplus* (p. 827–830 in *Royal Asiatic Society Journal.* 1917).

PIERRE de Maricourt (Petrus Peregrinus; Peter the Stranger), *fl.* 1269.

871 De virtute magnetis. Rome: Marcello Silber [not after 1520]. sm. 4°. [LEK]

Ref: *Sart* II 1030; *Mottelay* 46–53; *HTech* III 524; *Crombie* (A–G) 1961, 120–122.

N.B: The author, a Crusader and the teacher of Roger Bacon, was an advocate of experimental science. Erroneously attributed to Ramòn Lul in this edition, but issued under the author's name, at Augsburg in 1558. This work, written in 1269 and a forerunner of the work of William Gilbert (1600), gives the first technical description of the compass; for analysis, see Sart II 1030–1032.

Mon: THOMPSON, Silvanus P. *Peregrinus and his epistola*, London, 1907. SCHLUND, Erhard. *Peregrinus, sein Leben und seine Schriften* (in *Archivum franciscanum historicum*, v. 4, 1911; v. 5, 1912). S[ARTON], G. *The first edition of Petrus Peregrinus* (in *Notes & Correspondence*, p. 178–179 in *Isis* 37 1947).

Fac: *Isis* 37 1947, p. 178.

PLATINA (Bartolomeo de' Sacchi, di Piadena; Bertholomaeus Sacchi, de Platina; *called* Platina), 1421–1481.

872 De honesta voluptate et valetudine. [Rome: Ulrich Han, about 1475.] 4°. [LEK]

Ref: HC(Add)R 13049; Pr 3380; IGI 7847–7856; Klebs 783.1; Schullian (ArMed) 368; Stillwell P692; Goff P-761.

N.B: A gourmet's cookbook written by a Papal Secretary and Librarian. The first dated edition was issued at Venice by Laurentius de Aquila and Sibyllinus Umber on 13 June 1475 (Cen P693). Known in at least ten fifteenth-century editions or variants, two of which are in Italian (Klebs 783.1–.6 *var.*, 784.1–.2; Cen P692–P698). NLMCat (3680–3682) lists editions printed in 1517 and 1530, a German version issued at Strasbourg in 1530; and (231, 232) two instances of the printing of the text with Apicius's *De re culinaria libri X*, at Basel and Lyon in 1541.

PLINY *the Elder* (Plinius Secundus, Gaius), 23–79 A.D.

873 Historia naturalis, libri XXXVII. Venice: Johann von Speier, [before 18 Sept.] 1469. f°. [LEK]

Ref: HC(+Add)R 13087; BMC V 153; BM-Ital 526; Osler (IM) 3; Horblit 84; Klebs 786.1; *HTech* I 254, *etc.*, II 105, *etc.*; *Sart* I 249; Stillwell P716; Goff P-786.

Pliny (continued)

N.B: A scientific encyclopaedia including some matters of technological interest. For instance, it describes methods of ventilating mines, of employing water to crack rocks. It tells of the origin of glass, of the method by which it is produced, and the manner in which it is used. It refers to the production of steel and gives recipes for lead and tin solders. It discusses the use of bitumen seepage [a form of petroleum] along the Red Sea, in the making of pitch. It describes the process of milling flour and tells of the use of the foam on beer as leavening for bread. It describes a reaping machine in detail and also the construction of four different kinds of presses for olives and grapes.

The date of this first edition is derived from the fact that a Cicero and this Pliny are mentioned as already published, in the five-year privilege granted Johann von Speier on 18 September 1469, by the Signoria of Venice. [Klebs lists eighteen editions before 1500, three of which are in Italian (Goff P-786—P-803). NLMCat (3695, 3696) lists two Italian versions printed in 1543 and 1548 at Venice; and (NLMCat 3686–3691) six Latin editions issued during 1507–1548 at Venice (2), Paris (1), Cologne (1), Basel (1) and Lyon (1).]

Fac: HORBLIT 84 [b].

PORTOLANO.

874 Portolano per tutti i navichanti [*Italian*].   Venice: Bernardino Rizo, 6 Nov. 1490.   4°.

Ref: HCR 13302; BMC V 402; BM-Ital 537; IGI 8034; Klebs 803.1; *Haraszti (MB)* 1943, 110–114; Stillwell P863; Goff P-945.

N.B: The volume comprises calculations and distances between ports and islands, and was intended to supplement the sea-charts used by mariners, which merely indicated ports on the coastline. The earliest printed book of sailing directions to give distances; the so-called "Portolano Rizo," its contemporary use resulting in present rarity. Its first part covers ports along the English Channel and *en route* from Flanders to Ireland; its second, ports from Venice to Constantinople and Alexandria. Variously attributed to Luigi da Cada Mosto.

PRISCIANUS of Caesarea, *fl.* 500.

875 Carmen de ponderibus et mensuris. (*Issued in his* Opera. [Venice: Wendelin von Speier] 1470.)   f°.   [LEK]

Ref: H 13355; BMC V 156; BM-Ital 540; IGI 8045; Klebs 806.1; *Clagett (SM)* 85–91; Stillwell P877; Goff P-960.

N.B: Describes a trutina, a type of balance used in weighing precious metals; a hydrometer; and two methods of determining the relative content of gold with a silver alloy. Clagett, as cited above, gives the Latin text and translation of the sections describing the two methods—hydrostatic and volumetric—of determining the gold and silver content in the so-called crown-problem. [Moody and Clagett (MSW) 353 describes a trutina and the Roman system of weights.]

VI. *Technology*

PROBIERBÜCHLEIN.

876 Probierbüchlein. Magdeburg, 1524. 8°. [LEK]

> *Ref*: *HTech* III 27; *Sart* (*SW*) 122; *Hoover* (*Agricola*) 612–613, *fac*.
>
> *N.B*: A popular manual on assaying and metallurgy. Issued in several undated editions not identified but possibly prior to this, the earliest dated edition.
>
> *Mon*: SISCO, A. G. and C. S. SMITH, *tr. Bergwerk- und Probierbüchlein*. New York, 1949.

PROCLOS (Proklos; Proclus), *c*. 412–485.

877 De fabrica usuque astrolabii. (*In* VALLA, Giorgio, 1447–1499. Collectio. Venice: Simon Bevilaqua, 30 Sept. 1498.) f°.

> *Ref*: HC *11748; BMC V 523; Klebs 1012.1; Schullian (ArMed) 477; Stillwell N33; Goff N-44.

PTOLEMY (Ptolemaios; Claudius Ptolemaeus), *fl.* 150.

Syntaxis mathematika (*usually called the* Almagest). Venice: Petrus Liechtenstein, 10 Jan. 1515.

> *N.B*: [For a note on various astronomical instruments mentioned in the text of the *Almagest*, see entry under ASTRONOMY.]

PUFF von Schrick, Michael (Michael Puff; Michael Schrick), *d*. 1472/73.

878 Von den ausgebrannten Wassern [*German*]. Augsburg: Johann Bämler, 25 Oct. [14]77. f°. [LEK]

> *Ref*: BMC II 336; BM-Ger 796 [misprint, 1447]; Goff (DGI) 53; Klebs 895.1; Stillwell S299; Goff S-325.
>
> *N.B*: A book on brandy that was issued in many editions, at least twenty-four within our period. Klebs lists twenty-one editions and a variant issued in Germany during the years 1477–1500. NLMCat lists two editions assigned to Nuremberg, 1523 and 1530 (4145, 4146); four instances (p. 534) of the inclusion of the text with other tracts in 1529 and 1535; and a unique copy of an edition (4144) assigned to the press of Hans Hochspring at Ulm in 1501 (*cf*. R. J. and M. Durling, p. 55–57 in *The Library*, 5 ser, v. 20, 1965).

REGIMENTO.

879 Regimento do estrolabio e do quadrante [*Portuguese*]. (*Issued with* JOAN-NES de Sacro Bosco. Tractado da spera do mundo [*Portuguese*]. [Lisbon, *c*. 1509])

> *Ref*: Klebs 875.1; *HTech* III 547–548.
>
> *N.B*: The earliest printed manual on navigation extant. Known only in a copy at Munich. Comprises tables and rules for finding latitude at various positions and

Regimento (continued)

for raising or dropping degrees according to direction and the distance travelled, together with a list of latitudes from Cape Finisterre to the equator.

Fac: BENSAUDE, J. *Regimento do estrolabio*. Munich, 1914.

REGIOMONTANUS (Johann Müller of Königsberg; Joannes de Monteregio), 1436–1476.

880 De compositione et usu cuiusdam meteoroscopii armillaris. (*Issued with* PTOLEMY, *fl.* 150. Geographia, liber I [Tr: Johann Werner]. Nuremberg: Johann Stüchs, 4 Nov. 1514.)

Ref: Eames (Sabin) 66479; BM-Ger 719:[14]; Pr 11095; Zinner (ALD) 1019.

N.B: A letter addressed to Cardinal Bessarion. Also issued in the *Introductio geographica* of Apianus, printed at Ingolstadt in 1533.

881 Scripta de torqueto, astrolabio armillari, regula magna Ptolemaica, baculoque astronomico et observationibus cometarum (Ed: and Add: Johann Schöner, 1477–1547). Nuremberg: Apud Joannem Montanum et Ulricum Neuberum, 1544.

Add: PEURBACH, Georg von, 1423–1461. De quadrato geometrico [*first printed in 1516*].

Ref: BM-Ger 632; *Thornd* (*HM*) V 365; *HTech* III 614.

N.B: For the earliest use of a volvelle in a printed book, a device known since the thirteenth century, see his *Calendarium* [Nuremberg, 1474]—under ASTRONOMY.

Fac: For a reproduction of a torquetum, see *Osiris*. Vol. I, 1936, p. 388.

REGNIER, Gemma, of Frisia. *See* GEMMA.

REISCH, Gregor, *c.* 1465–1525.

882 Margarita philosophica. Freiburg [im Breisgau]: Johann Schott, *citra festum Margarethe* (before 19 July) 1503. 4°. [LEK]

Ref: BM-Ger 731; Pr 11717; Eames (Sabin) 69122; LC(LJRCat) 429; *HTech* III 538; *Hall* (*SR*) 11, 22, 23.

N.B: An encyclopaedic work printed in at least nine editions during the years 1503–1535, *i.e.*, four by Johann Schott; four by Johann Grüninger, including his pirated edition printed at Strasbourg in February 1504; and in 1535 a revision by Oronce Fine. No fifteenth-century edition is known, the occasional reference to an edition of 1496 being an error stemming from a dated poem addressed to Reisch, which appears in the March edition of 1504. Additional text and woodcuts appear in succeeding editions, the editions of 1512, 1515, and 1517 being perhaps the most important of the series. The 1512 edition printed at Strasbourg by Johann Grüninger, in addition to the section on "Architecturae et perspectivae rudimenta" [which had appeared in the 1508 edition] and the polimetrum, Fi *recto*, ascribed to Martin Waldseemüller, contains also the "De compositione astrolabii Messahalath (Māshā'Allāh)," and the "Formatio torqueti," with wood-cuts of the astrolabe and torquetum. The edition of 1515 omits the original section on music and adds sections on the quadrature of the circle, the cubation of the sphere, the rudiments of perspective and a diagram on map-projecting entitled "Sphera in plano." The world map appearing in each edition is somewhat indic-ative of the advance of geographical knowledge, that of 1515, for instance, showing two islands in the Caribbean and a section of the American coast-line, whereas in that of the 1503 edition an apparent landmass, showing in a narrow strip at the base of the map and joining Africa and Asia, bears the legend, "Hic non terra sed mare est: in quo mire magnitudinis Insule, sed Ptolemeo fuerūt incognite." [For editions of 1504, 1508, 1508 enlarged, and 1512 printed at or assigned to Freiburg-i.-B., Basel, and Strasbourg (2), see NLMCat 3847–3850; Sabin 69124–69127.]

Mon: FERGUSON, J. *Bibliography of the Margarita philosophica of Gregorius Reisch* (p. 194–216 in *The Library*, 4th Ser., X, no. 2, 1929).

Fac: HTech III 538, Waldseemüller's polimetrum, *reduced*.

RIEDRER, Friedrich, *fl.* 1495.

883   Spiegel der wahren Rhetorik [*German*].   Freiburg im Breisgau: Fried-rich Riedrer, 11 Dec. 1493.   f°.   [LEK]

Ref: HC 13914; BMC III 696; BM-Ger 740; Oates 1340; Stillwell R191; Goff R-197.

N.B: Written by a schoolmaster-printer. Contains the first reference in a printed book to man's desire to fly. [Unfortunately, no mention of the design for a flying-machine made by Leonardo da Vinci, 1452–1519, has been found in the books of his time.]

ROBERTUS *Anglicus*, *fl.* 1271.

884   De astrolabio canones; De astrolabii compositione. (Ed: Ulysses Lan-ciarinus).   Perugia [Anonymous press, 1477/78]   4°.   [LEK]

Ref: Pr 7183; BMC VI 879; BM-Ital 557; Klebs 850.1; Sart II 993; HTech III 537; Stillwell R197; Goff R-203.

N.B: Contains a treatise on mensuration, a method applicable to the measuring of heights, depths, or distances. Perugia is cited in the dedicatory letter as the place of printing. Regarding the identification of the author, see THORNDIKE, L. *Robertus Anglicus* (p. 467–469 in *Isis* 34 1942). Assigned in IGI 8386 to the press of Robertus *Anglicus*.

ROJAS SARMIENTO, Juan de, *fl.* 1530.

885   Commentariorum in astrolabium quod planisphaerium vocant libri VI. Paris: Apud Vascosanum, 1550.   4°.   [LEK]

Rojas Sarmiento (continued)

    Ref: BM-Fr 378; *Crombie (A–G)* 1961 I 95.
    N.B: A treatise on the planisphere, combined with an annotated text of the first six chapters of GEMMA's *Libellus*.

ROSETO, Giovanni Ventura.

886   Plictho. Dell' arte de' tentori [*Italian*].   Venice: Francesco Rampazetto, 1540. 4°.

    Ref: BM-Ital 588; *HTech* III 699, 707.
    N.B: The first printed textbook on dyeing.

RULEIN von Calw, Ulrich (Calbus, of Freiburg), *d.* 1523. *See under* BERGBÜCHLEIN.

SAGREDO, Diego de.

887   Medidas d'l Romanos. Lisbon: Luis Rodriguez, 1542. 4°.

    Ref: BM-Port 285.
    N.B: A work based on the architectural treatise of Vitruvius. Presumably the text that was translated from Spanish into French, and printed at Paris by Simon de Colines in 1539, 1543, and in an undated edition about 1535—Renouard (Colines) 316, 422.

SCHRICK, Michael. *See* PUFF von Schrick.

SCRIPTORES REI MILITARIS.

888   Scriptores rei militaris (Ed: Joannes Sulpicius, *fl.* 1460–1490?). Rome: Eucharius Silber, 29 Jan.—7 June 1487. 4°. [LEK]

    Ref: HC *15913; BMC IV 107–108; BM-Ital 713; Klebs 903.1; Stillwell S315; Goff S-343.
    N.B: A compilation of military tracts, separately dated; without signatures. Presumably also issued as separates. Contains the first known printing of the *Strategematicon* of Sextus Julius FRONTINUS (*c.* 40–103); includes also the *De instruendis aciebus* of AELIANUS (*see no.* 804); the *De vocabulis rei militaris* ascribed to MODESTUS, pseudonym? (*no* 861); and the *De re militari* of VEGETIUS (*no.* 898). The *De optimo imperatore* of ONOSANDROS, in the translation of Nicolaus Sagundinus, was added to the compilation in Silber's second edition issued with continuous signaturing at Rome in 1494 (Cen S316). Issued under the editorship of Philippus Beroaldus at Bologna in 1495/96 (Cen S317); with continuous signaturing but without the Onosandros.

VI. *Technology*

SCRIPTORES REI RUSTICAE.

889 Scriptores rei rusticae. Venice: Nicolaus Jenson, 1472. f°. [LEK]

> *Ref*: H *14564; BMC V 173; Klebs 902.1; *HTech* II 86, 111, 114, *etc.*; Stillwell S318; Goff S-346.
>
> *N.B*: A compilation of four works written by Marcus Porcius CATO (234–149 B.C.); Marcus Terentius VARRO (116–27 B.C.); Lucius Junius Moderatus COLUMELLA (*fl.* 50); and Rutilius Taurus Aemilianus PALLADIUS (*fl.* 340), respectively.
>
> Although relating primarily to agriculture, these early texts give occasional glimpses of customs and technological factors as known in ancient times. Cato, for instance, mentions detachable plough-shares. He tells of a flour-mill worked by donkeys. He describes a beam-press for squeezing grapes and olives, and like Columella and Varro, gives details of wine-growing. Palladius mentions water-mills. The treatise by Columella, however, had already been issued, as a separate assignable to a Roman press about 1471 [*no.* 833].

SERLIO, Sebastiano, 1475–1554.

890 Regole generali di architetura sopra le cinque maniere de gliedifici, cioe, thoscano, dorico, ionico, corinthio, et composito, . . . concordano con la dottrina di Vitruvio [*Italian*]. Venice: Francesco Marcolini, 1537. f°.

> *Ref*: BM-Ital 623.
>
> *N.B*: Book IV of his treatise on architecture, which was published in full at Venice by Melchiorre Sessa in 1551.
>
> *Fac*: *A history of the printed book. The Dolphin*, no. III. New York, 1938 (The Limited Editions Club), *figure 40*.

STAHEL und Eysen.

891 Stahel und Eysen kunstilich weych und hart zu machen [*German*]. Mainz, 1532. [LEK]

> *Ref*: *HTech* III 35, 71.
>
> *N.B*: Relates to the production and hardening of steel.
>
> *Mon*: Translation of a later edition, by H. W. Williams (*Tech. Stud. Fine Arts*. IV 64 1935).

STÖFFLER, Johann, 1452–1531.

892 Elucidatio fabricae ususque astrolabii. Oppenheim: Jacob Köbel, 1512/ 13. f°. [LEK]

> *Ref*: BM-Ger 834; Pr 11922; AmBCat 192; *HTech* III 536.
>
> *N.B*: With diagrams illustrating problems in perspective. Although the colophon gives the date 1512, the titlepage is dated 1513. (Stöffler recognized that, in

Stöffler (continued)

mapping, computation of the distance between two places whose latitude and longitude were known failed to take into account the convergence of the meridians.) For his tract *Von künstlicher Abmessung aller Grösse, Ebene, oder Nidere ... mit eim Astrolabio und Quadranten, oder Messleiter ...* Franckfurt: C. Egenolph, 1536, see LC(LJRCat) 476. [See also under ASTRONOMY.]

STRABO (Strabon), *c.* 63 B.C.–20 A.D.

893   De situ orbis libri XVI (Tr: Guarino da Verona, *c.* 1370–1460, and Gregorios Tifernas, *fl.* 1458. Ed: Giovanni D'Andrea de' Bossi, *Bp. of Aleria, Papal Librarian, c.* 1430–1472). Rome: Conradus Sweynheim and Arnoldus Pannartz [1469]. f°. [LEK]

Ref: H 15086; BMC IV 8; Oates 1360; Klebs 935.1; *HTech* I–II *index*; Stillwell S704; Goff S-793.

N.B: A geographical encyclopaedia written for the information of governmental officials and travellers and containing much regarding the customs and usages of various countries that is of technological interest. For instance, it describes the marble quarries of Carrara, the mining of vermilion in Spain, and the use of rock salt deposits there. It mentions the raising of water by means of Archimedean screws. It describes the use of asphalt for building-blocks and in liquid form as a water-proofing agent—a product made from a bitumen seepage in Babylonia. It speaks of trade in bitumen, a product of the petroleum family, and discusses dyes, use of pitch in sealing the cracks in Celtic beer barrels, and the fact that Spanish wine will keep. An edition of exceptionally fine typography. Known in five other editions before 1496.

TARTAGLIA (Nicolò Fontana, *the Stammerer; also called* Tartalea), *c.* 1506–1557.

894   Nuova scienza utile per ciascuno speculativo matematico bombardiero [*Italian*]. Venice: Stefano dei Nicolini da Sabbio, 1537. 4°. [LEK]

Ref: BM-Ital 658, 900; *Sart* III 1554.

N.B: Includes discussion of various ballistic problems and experiments. [For an evaluation of Tartaglia's status and that of his contemporaries, see Ore, Oystein. *The battle of the scholars* (p. 53–107 in his *Cardano, the gambling scholar*. Princeton University Press, 1953).]

895   Quesiti et inventioni diverse [*Italian*]. Venice: Venturino Ruffinelli, 1546. 4°. [LEK]

Ref: BM-Ital 658; *Sart (SW)* 82; *Wightman* (1962) II 673.

N.B: Relates to experiments in ballistics and the manufacture of guns, gunpowder, and bombs. It discusses also the curve of a projectile as influenced by air, gravity, and impetus, and notes experiments regarding the length and caliber of a gun and the weight and size of the missile. A section on surveying describes two compass-like instruments for use in taking horizontal angles of position—HTech III 539, *illus.*

THEOPHRASTOS. *See no. 701.*

TORTELLI, Giovanni (Johannes Tortellius), 1400–*c.* 1466.

895a Orthographia. Venice: Nicolaus Jenson, 1471. f°. [LEK]

> *Ref:* HC *15564; BMC V 170; LC (LJRCat) 195; Stillwell T360; Goff T-395.
> *N.B:* A section entitled *Horologium* appears on Fol. 161a–162a. At least eleven other editions were issued during the fifteenth century, including one printed at Rome [after 10 August] 1471 (Goff T-394), in which the *Horologium* appears on Fol. 160a–161b.

TORY, Geofroy, 1480–1533.

896 Champ Fleury. Au quel est contenu Lart & Science de la . . . vraye Proportiõ des Lettres Attiques, quõ dit . . . vulgairement Lettres Romaines . . . [Paris] For Geofroy Tory de Bourges, 28 April 1529. 4°. [LEK]

> *Ref:* LC(LJRCat) 637.
> *N.B:* Written by Geofroy Tory—philologist and decorative designer—who together with his famous pupil, Claude Garamond, introduced a modified roman letter which in general, in France and various neighboring countries, superseded gothic characters in type-design and influenced fine printing for more than two centuries. Re-issued in 1549 under the title, *L'art & science de la vraye proportion des lettres . . . antiques autremẽt dictes, romaines . . . avec l'instructiõ & maniere de faire chiffres . . .* (LC(LJRCat) 666).
> *Mon:* TORY, Geofroy. *Champ fleury . . . translated into English and annotated by George B. Ives.* New York, The Grolier Club, 1927.

VALTURIO, Roberto, *c.* 1405–1484.

897 De arithmetica et militari geometria (Bk. II in his *De re militari.* [Verona:] Giovanni Nicolai da Verona, 1472.) f°. [LEK]

> *Ref:* HC *15847; BMC VII 948; BM-Ital 710; Oates 2593; Klebs 1014.1; LC(LJRCat) 197; *HTech* II 620; *Sart* III 1552; Stillwell V80; Goff V-88.
> *N.B:* Written by the technical adviser and engineer to Sigismondo Pandolfo Malatesta of Rimini. Possibly the earliest technical work printed. An Italian translation by Paolo Ramusio, *c.* 1443–1506, was issued at Verona in 1483 (Cen V82); also a Latin edition in 1483 by the same press, that of Boninus de Boninis (Cen V81). The *De re militari libri XII* was issued by Christian Wechel at Paris in 1532 (NLM 4527; LC(LJRCat) 645).

VARRO, Marcus Terentius, 116–27 B.C. *See under* SCRIPTORES REI RUSTICAE.

VEGETIUS, Flavius Renatus, *fl.* 380–395.

898 De re militari. [Utrecht: Nicolaus Ketelaer and Gerardus de Leempt, *c.* 1473–74.] f°. [LEK]

> *Ref:* HC 15910; BMC IX 10; Kron 1706; Klebs 1019.2; Sart I 368; Stillwell V93; Goff V-104.
>
> *N.B:* Two other editions are assigned to Paris and Cologne about 1475 (Goff V-105, V-106). Subsequently issued in whole or in part in German, French, and English (Cen V95, C425, C426 respectively). According to a note in Sarton, the cuts of the war-machine occurring in the text of the 1472 Valturio printed at Verona appeared in the German version of Vegetius (Cen V95) and remained unique in Germany for a period of eighty years. A text later included in a compilation known as the *Scriptores rei militaris.*
>
> *Mon:* BÜHLER, C. F. *The earliest appearances in print of Vegetius* (p. 91–93 in *Gutenberg Jahrbuch*, 1956).

VERGILIUS, Polydorus (Polidoro Vergilio), *c.* 1470–1555.

898a De inventoribus rerum. Venice: Christophorus de Pensis, de Mandello, 31 Aug. 1499. 4°. [LEK]

> *Ref:* H*16008; BMC V 473; Klebs 1025.1; *Hay* 60, 180; Stillwell V130; Goff V-146.
>
> *N.B:* A popular medley of information, frequently reprinted. Relates to inventors and covers a wide variety of topics, among them books, military science, weapons, glass, architecture, tools and maritime navigation. Notable because the author's sources are cited. For an edition printed at Strasbourg by Matthias Schürer about 1515, see NML 4572. The Strasbourg edition of 1606 and the Elzivir of 1671 are cited by Hay, p. 181, as containing an alphabetical list of inventors and their inventions.
>
> *Mon:* FERGUSON, John. *Notes on the work of Polydore Vergil, De inventoribus rerum* (p. 17–93 in *Isis* 7 1932). FULTON, John and Charlotte H. PETERS. *Hand list of editions of Polydore Vergil's De inuentoribus rerum* (Historical Library of the Yale University School of Medicine, 1944). HAY, Denys. *Polydore Vergil, Renaissance historian and man of letters.* Oxford, 1952.
>
> *Fac:* *Osiris* 5 1938, p. 122, 178.

VITRUVIUS POLLIO, Marcus, *fl.* 27 B.C.

899 De architectura libri X (Ed: Joannes Sulpicius, *fl.* 1460–1490?). [Rome: Eucharius Silber, 1483–95.] f°. [LEK]

> *Ref:* CR 6268; BMC IV 124; BM-Ital 735 [1495?]; Klebs 1044.1; Sart (HS) II 350–357; Sart (Appr) 8; Stillwell V275; Goff V-306.

VI. *Technology*

N.B: Vitruvius conceived of the architect as being also an engineer and a technologist. His book, therefore, deals with materials, construction problems, and the canons of symmetry and proportion, in addition to presenting a history of architecture. Its ten parts comprise 1) architectural principles and city planning; 2) history of architecture and of materials; 3–4) the construction of temples; 5) of public buildings; 6) of town and country houses; 7) interior decoration; 8) water supply; 9) horology; and 10) practical mechanics and machinery for architectural construction and military engineering, the latter discussing catapults, siege engines, battering rams, and various defensive methods. Variant known. The first of the beautifully illustrated editions was printed by Joannes Tacuinus at Venice in 1511. Issued at Como in 1521—LC(LJRCat) 552. Included in compilations published at Venice in 1495 and 1497 (Cen V276, C677), and at Strasbourg in 1543 (NLMCat 4651). A German version was issued at Nuremberg in 1548 and a French version at Paris in 1547—LC(LJRCat) 486, 662, respectively.

Mon: VITRUVIUS. *The ten books on architecture* (Tr: M. H. Morgan). Cambridge, Mass., 1926.

WALDSEEMÜLLER, Martin (*called* Ilacomilus; Hylacomylus), *c.* 1475–1516, *attributed.*

900 Tabula nova [*with regional maps of Alsace and the Rhineland*]. (*Issued with* PTOLEMY. Cosmographia. Strasbourg: Johann Schott, 12 Mar. 1513.) f°.

Ref: Eames (Sabin) 66478; BM-Ger 719:[3]; Pr 10271; Harrisse (BAV) 74; *HTech* III 538.

N.B: It is noteworthy that regional maps of the Rhine valley and of Alsace included in this edition of Ptolemy are apparently based upon actual field-survey. They appear in a section of "Tabula nova" added as a supplement, and attributable to Martin Waldseemüller, the cartographer of the great world-map of 1507. [For a note on his world-map and in 1507 his naming of the newly found land "America," see above under MATHEMATICS: Mathematical Geography (Waldseemüller, no. 250).]

Waldseemüller's *Architecturae et perspectivae rudimenta* is included with his prefatory letter to Matthias Ringmann in the 1508 Strasbourg edition of the *Margarita philosophica* of Gregor Reisch; without the prefatory letter, in the Strasbourg edition of 1512 (NLMCat 3849, 3850).

Mon: For an account of early methods and instruments of surveying, see TAYLOR, E. G. R. *Cartography, survey, and navigation, 1400–1750* (p. 530–549 in *A history of technology* [Ed: Charles Singer, *and others*]. III. Oxford, 1957).

PART II

A: 1 Commentators

The following list relates to the commentators of the works cited in the present volume. A name enclosed in square brackets indicates a variant form of the commentator's name. Words in italics and enclosed in parentheses indicate the name of the author or the title of the work discussed. A dash followed by a colon and title refers to the name of the preceding author.

Roman numerals indicate the six categories to which the present volume relates. Arabic numbers refer to the numbered entries. A dash following a period is used to separate the works or categories from one another. Accents on Arabic names are omitted.

Achillini: IV 559 (*Mondino*).

Aegidius Romanus [Colonna]: V 733*n* (*Aristotle: De generatione et corruptione*); V 719 (——: *Physica*).

Al-Battani: I 10 ("*Planetary hypotheses*").

Al-Farghana: I 13 ("*Planetary hypotheses*").

Albertus de Saxonia: I 11; V 723 (*Aristotle: De caelo*).—V 724 (——: *Physica*).

Alexander of Aphrodisias: V 726 (*Aristotle: Physica*).

Ali ibn Ridwan: III 280*n* (*Galen: Tegni*).

[Anon.] *Aliud commentum*: V 769*n* (*Jordanus de Nemore*).

Arcolani: III 271*n* (*Rhasis*).

Averroës: IV 572 (*Aristotle: De anima*).—I 25, V 733 (——: *De caelo*).—III 289, IV 590 (——: *Cantica*).—IV 576, V 733 (——: *De generatione et corruptione*).—I 26 (——: *Metaphysica*).—IV 577, V 735 (——: *Meteorologica, liber 4*).—IV 580 (——: *Parva naturalia*).—V 736, 737 (——: *Physica*).

Barbaro: IV 592 (*Pliny the Elder*).

Barzizza: III 295*n* (*Rhasis*).

Benzi: III 305 (*Galen: Tegni*).—III 308 (——: *Aphorismi*).—III 308 (*Hippocrates: Aphorismi*).

Berengario da Carpi: III 310, IV 598 (*Mondino*).

Brasavola: III 318 (*Hippocrates, Galen: De ratione victus*).

Bricot: V 741 (*Aristotle: Metaphysica, Physica*).

Brudzewo: I 33 (*Peurbach*).

Buridan: V 742 (*Aristotle: Physica*).

Burley: V 743 (*Aristotle: Physica*).

Celaya: V 733*n* (*Aristotle: De generatione et corruptione*).—V 746 (——: *Physica*).

Collenuccio: III 344 (*Leonicenus*).

Colonna, Egidio. SEE Aegidius Romanus.

Danck [Johann de Saxonia]: I 1*n* (*Alchabitius*. —I 48 (*Alfonso X*).

Desparts, Jacques. SEE Jacobus de Partibus.

Dino del Garbo: III 351; IV 666*n* (*Avicenna*).

Dullaert: V 748 (*Aristotle: Physica*).

Duns Scotus: V 778 (*Aristotle: Physica*).

Eutocios: II 140; V 731 (*Archimedes*).

Ferrari: III 365 (*Rhasis*).

François de Meyronnes: I 58 (*Petrus Lombardus*).

Fuchs: III 411*n* (*Hippocrates: Epidemiarum libri VII*).

Gaetano: V 735 (*Aristotle: Meteorologica*).— V 758 (——: *Physica*).—V 755 (*Heytesbury*).

Galen: III 280*n*, 376 (3, 4, 10), 377 (3, 5, 8-16, 28, 39); IV 644 (6, 7) (*Hippocrates*).

Gentile da Foligno: III 391, IV 648 (*Gilles of Corbeil*).

Georges de Bruxelles: V 759 (*Aristotle: Physica*).

Grosseteste: V 761 (*Aristotle: Physica*).

Jabir ibn Aflah: I 68 (*Ptolemy: Almagest*).

Jacobus de Partibus [Jacques Desparts]: III 265 (*Alexander of Tralles*).

Jacopo da Forlì: III 430, IV 666 (*Avicenna*).— III 431 (*Galen: Tegni*).—III 429 (*Hippocrates: Aphorismi*).

Jean de Jandun: V 768*n* (*Aristotle: Physica*).

Jean de Tournemire: III 432 (*Rhasis*).

Joannes Alexandrinus: III 411 (*Hippocrates: Epidemiarum . . .*).

Joannes Canonicus: V 768 (*Aristotle: Physica*).

Johannes of Amersfordia: V 735n (*Aristotle: Meteorologica*).

Le Fèvre d'Étaples: V 770 (*Aristotle: Physica*).—II 187 (*Jordanus de Nemore*).

Leonicenus, III 441n: IV 671 (*Pliny the Elder*).

Leonico Tomeo. SEE *Tomeo*.

Macrobius, I 74 (*Cicero*).

Maimonides: III 444, IV 674 (*Galen: Aphorismi*).

Manardi: III 446n (*Mesuë the Younger*).

Marliani: V 775n (*Bradwardine*).

Marsiglio da Santa Sofia: III 448 (*Hippocrates: Aphorismi* III & VII).

Marsilius ab Inghen: V 733n (*Aristotle: De generatione et corruptione*).—V 777, 778 (———: *Physica*).

Mattioli, Pierandrea: IV 618n, 677 (*Dioskorides*).

Monte: III 456 (*Galen: Ars parva*).

Montuus [Monteux]: IV 639n (*Fuchs*).

Nifo: V 733n (*Aristotle: De generatione et corruptione*).—V 780 (———: *Physica*).

Ockham: V 782 (*Aristotle: Physica*).

Oreibasios: III 462 (*Hippocrates: Aphorismi*).

Pappos: I 97n (*Ptolemy: Almagest*).

Paulus Venetus: IV 681, V 733 (*Aristotle: De generatione et corruptione*).—V 784 (———: *Physica*).—V 784 (*Averroës*).

Peurbach: I 85 (*Ptolemy: Almagest*).—II 208 (———: *De sinibus et chordis*).

Philoponus: V 733n (*Aristotle: De generatione et corruptione*).

Piccolomini: V 786 (*Aristotle, spurious: Mechanica*).

Pietro d'Abano: III 354, IV 618 (*Dioskorides*).

Proclos: II 210 (*Euclid*).—I 97n (*Ptolemy: Almagest*).

Regiomontanus [Johann Müller]: I 101 Gherardo da Sabbioneta). [See also INDEX under CORRECTORS.]

Scaliger: IV 582n (*Aristotle, spurious: De plantis*).—III 413 (*Hippocrates: De insomniis liber*).

Sermoneta: III 521 (*Galen: Tegni*), (*Hippocrates: Aphorismi*).

Simon de Lendenaria: V 762n (*Heytesbury*).

Simon of Genoa: III 265 (*Alexander of Tralles*).

Syllanus de Nigris: III 502 (*Rhasis*).

Tartaglia: V 796 (*Jordanus de Nemore*).

Tartaret: V 797 (*Aristotle: Metaphysica*).

Thabit ibn Qurra: I 117n (*Ptolemy[?]: Planetary hypotheses*).

Themo: V 798 (*Aristotle: Meteorologica*).

Theōn of Alexandria: I 23n, 124n, V 730n (*Aratos*).—I 97n, 118 (*Ptolemy: Almagest*). [See also INDEX under REVISERS.]

Thomas Aquinas: V 733 (*Aristotle: De generatione et corruptione*).—V 799 (———: *Physica*).

Thome: V 800n (*Heytesbury; Swineshead*).

Tomeo: IV 579n (*Aristotle: De motu animalium*).—V 734n (*Mechanica*).

Torrigiani: III 538 (*Galen: Microtegni*).

Urbano of Bologna: V 802 (*Averroës: Physica*).

[See also INDEX: CORRECTORS.]

A: 2 Editors

The following list refers to the editors of works cited in the present volume. A name in square brackets indicates a variant form of the editor's name. A name or title in italics and enclosed in parentheses relates to the work edited. A dash is used to separate the works in instances where an editor produced more than one.

Roman numerals indicate the six categories to which the present volume relates. Arabic numerals refer to the numbered entries.

Achillini, Philotheus: IV 559 (*Antonio Achillini*).

Aegidius Viterbiensis: V 719 (*Aegidius Romanus*).

Alouisius, Jacobus Baptista: IV 681 (*Paulus Venetus*).

Althamer, Andreas, of Brenz. *See* Brentius, A.

Andreae, Joannes [Giovanni D'Andrea de' Bossi]: VI 893 (*Strabo*).

Angelus, Joannes [Johann Engel?]: I 9 (*Albumasar*).—I 31 (*Bonatti*).—II 217 (*Regiomontanus*).

Apianus, Petrus [Bienewitz]: V 769 (*Jordanus de Nemore*).—II 254 (*Witelo*).

Argilagnes, Franciscus de: III 411 (*Hippocrates*).

Asulanus, Andreas. SEE Torresani, Andrea.

Asulanus, Franciscus. SEE Torresani, Francesco.

Avogaro, Pietro Buono: VI 808 (*Andalo di Negro*).

Barnabas Picardus: II 212 (*Ptolemy: Geographia*).

Bartholomaeus de Alten: I 6 (*Albohazen*).

Bassinis, Joannes Antonius de: III 361 (*Falcucci*).

Benevento, Marco di: V 782 (*Ockham*).

Benivieni, Girolamo: III 299; IV 597 (*Antonio Beniviene*).

Beroaldus, Philippus: IV 611 (*Censorinus*).

Bienewitz, Peter. SEE Apianus.

Biondo, Michelangelo [Blondo]: VI 868 b (*Pastrengo*).

Bodianus, Franciscus Vitalis: I 77 (*Martianus Capella*).

Boius, Andreas Stiborius: II 176 (*Grosseteste*).

Bonardus, Diomedes: III 375; IV 642 (*Galen: Opera*).

Brentius, Andreas [Althamer]: III 407 (*Hippocrates: Opera parva*).

Brunfels, Otto: IV 618n (*Dioskorides*).

Bugatus, Joannes: III 501 (*Rhasis*).

Caesar de Landulfis: III 361 (*Falcucci*).

Caius, Joannes: III 374n (*Galen*).

Camerarius, Joachim: III 374n (*Galen*).—I 97n (*Ptolemy: Almagest* [*Grk, v.* II]).

Campano da Novara, Giovanni: II 163 (*Euclid*).

Capella, Michael de. SEE Michael de Capella.

Cardano, Facio: II 205 (*Peckham*).

Catone de Sepino, Angelo: III 522 (*Silvatico*).

Cipelli, Giovanni Battista: IV 593 (*Barbaro*).

Cittadino, Antonio: III 303 (*Benzi*).

Clichtove, Josse: V 770 (*Le Fèvre d'Étaples*).

Collimitius, *pseud.* SEE Tanstetter, Georg.

Comes, Heremannus: III 532 (*Theodorus Priscianus*).

Cornarius, Janus: III 377:39 (*Galen*).—III 405n, 407n; IV 656n, 657n, 658n (*Hippocrates*).

D'Andrea de' Bossi, Giovanni. SEE Andreae, Joannes.

De la Porta, Joannes Petrus: V 764 (*Heytesbury*).

Defendinus Januensis: V 802 (*Urbano of Bologna*).

Dullaert, Jean: V 742 (*Buridan*).

Egnatius, Joannes Baptista, *pseud.* SEE Cipelli, Giovanni Battista.

Engel, Johann. SEE Angelus, Joannes.

Erasmus, Desiderius: IV 570*n* (*Aristotle*).

Faber Stapulensis, Jacobus. SEE Le Fèvre d'Étaples.

Fernandus Cordubiensis: IV 566 (*Albertus Magnus*).

Fine, Oronce: IV 591 (*Bacon*).

Fontana, Nicolo. SEE Tartaglia.

Fonti, Bartolomeo: III 331; IV 610 (*Celsus*).

Franciscus Asulanus. SEE Torresani, Francesco.

Fuchs, Leonhart: III 374*n* (*Galen*).

Gaurico, Luca: II 170.

Gelenius, Sigmund: VI 870 (*Periplus*).

Gemma Frisius [Regnier]: II 136*n*; VI 810 (*Apianus*).

Gemusaeus, Hieronymus: III 374*n* (*Galen*).

Geschauff, Thomas: II 140; V 731 (*Archimedes*).

Giovanni D'Andreae de' Bossi. SEE Andreae, Joannes.

Gondisalvus de Toledo: III 378 (*Ganivet*).

Granellus, Bernardus: V 719 (*Aegidius Romanus*).

Grynaeus, Simon [Gryne]: III 346*n* (*Constantinos VII*).—II 163*n*, 210*n* (*Euclid*).—I 97 (*Ptolemy: Almagest* [*Grk, v.* I]).

Günther, Johann: III 526 (*Soranos*).

Huttich, Johann: VI 865 (*Novus orbis regionum*).

Jacobus de Vitalibus: III 455 (*Montagnana*).

Jacobus Philippus Ferrariensis: V 802 (*Urbano of Bologna*).

Joannes de Cipro: V 794 (*Swineshead*).

Kraut, Georg: III 539 (*Trotula*).

Laeto, Giulio Pomponio [Pomponius Laetus]: VI 842 (*Frontinus*).

Laurentius de Gozadinis: III 300 (*Benzi*).

Le Fèvre d'Étaples: V 779 (*Nicolaus de Cusa*).

Leennius, Andreas: III 490 (*Psellus*).

Lockert, Jean: V 772.

Luceus, Antonius: III 319 (*Brissot*).

Marsilius ab Inghen: V 777 (*Aristotle: Physica*).

Melanchthon, Philipp: V 750 (*Euclid*).—I 69 (*Joannes de Sacro Bosco*).

Merula, Giorgio: IV 613 (*Columella*).—III 533, IV 702 (*Theophrastos*).

Michael de Capella: IV 602 (*Bertuccio*).

Montanus, J. B.: III 377 [5, 11–13, 19, 33]; IV 644 [6, 18] (*Galen*).

Moretus, Matthaeus: III 481 (*Pietro d'Argellata*).—III 522*n* (*Silvatico*).

Murchius, Thomas: VI 816 (*Arnaldo de Villa Nova*).

Mutius, Venantius: III 391; IV 648 (*Gilles of Corbeil*).

Nicolaus de Landa: III 313 (*Bertuccio*).

Opizo, Giovanni Battista: III 374; IV 641 (*Galen: Opera* [*Grk*]).

Oporinus, Joannes: IV 592 (*Barbaro*).

Panis, Nicolaus: III 398; IV 650 (*Guy de Chauliac*).

Peregrinus Cavalcabovis: III 533 (*Mesuë the Younger*).

Philippus, Jacobus. SEE Jacobus Philippus Ferrariensis.

Pico della Mirandola, Giovanni Francesco: I 87 (*Pico della Mirandola, Giovanni*).

Pirkheimer, Willibald: IV 622 (*Dürer*).

Pitatus, Petrus: I 113 (*Stöffler*).

Podocatharus, Ludovicus: IV 573 (*Aristotle: De animalibus*).

Politus, Bassianus: IV 666*n* (*Jacopo da Forlì*).

Poliziano, Angelo: VI 806 (*Alberti*).—V 726 (*Alexander of Aphrodisias*).

Ramusio, Giovanni Battista: IV 686*n* (*Marco Polo*).

Regnier, Gemma, *Frisius.* SEE Gemma.

Rheticus, Georg Joachim: II 160 (*Copernicus*).

Rosati, Giovanni: IV 597 (*Benivieni, A.*).

Rusticus Placentinus: III 377 [35, 36]; IV 644 [1, 2, 11, 12, 17] (*Galen*).

Santritter, Johannes Lucilius: I 102*n* (*Regiomontanus*).

Schöner, Johann: I 17 (*Al-Zarqali*).—II 218, VI 881*n* (*Regiomontanus*).—I 17 (*Toledo Tables*).

Sichardt, Johannes: III 528 (*Soranos*).

Simon of Genoa [Januensis]: III 256 (*Abulcasis*).

Sulpicius, Joannes: VI 842 (*Frontinus*).—VI 888 (*Scriptores rei militaris*).—VI 899 (*Vitruvius*).

Tanstetter, Georg [Collimitius]: I 105 (*Regiomontanus*).—II 254 (*Witelo*).

Tartaglia [N. Fontana]: II 141; V 732 (*Archimedes*).

Thorer, Alban [Torinus]: III 535 (*Collectio*). —III 487n (*Pliny the Elder*).—III 527 (*Soranos*).

Thynne, William: VI 832 (*Chaucer*).

Torinus, Albanus. SEE Thorer, Alban.

Torresani, Andrea [Asulanus]: III 374; IV 641 (*Galen: Opera* [*Grk*]).

Torresani, Francesco [Asulanus]: III 405; IV 656 (*Hippocrates: Opera* [*Grk*]).

Vadius, Angelus: II 212 (*Ptolemy: Geographia*).

Valla, Giorgio (? *tr. & ed.*): II 141n (*Archimedes*).—I 24 (*Aristarchos*).—I 28; II 145 (*Autolycos*).—II 162, 164 (*Euclid*).—VI 862 (*Nicephoros Gregoras*).—VI 877 (*Proclos*). *See also under* A:5 TRANSLATORS.

Ventorius, *pseud.* SEE Geschauff, Thomas.

Vitalis, Antonius: III 400; IV 653 (*Haly Abbas*).

Vitalis, Franciscus. SEE Bodianus.

Vögelin, Johann: II 243n (*Theodosios of Bithynia*).

Wonnecke von Cube, Johann: III 379 (*Gart der Gesundheit*).

Ziegler, Jakob: I 124 (*Sphaerae . . . ratio*).

[*See also* INDEX: REVISERS.]

A: 3   Places of Printing

The following list relates to first editions as noted in the main entries of the present volume. Excepting in questions of priority due to the issuing of other editions within the given year, such other editions as are mentioned in the notes under the main entries are not included.

Reference to the entries cited will show that in various instances the first printing of a text was presented in combination with other texts, rather than as a separate issue.

Dashes are used as a means of keeping the categories I–VI distinct from one another.

Alcalà: I 41.—III 268.

Alost (?): III 258.

Antwerp: I 61.—II 171, 172, 173, 246.—III 377.32, 506.—IV 692.—VI 810, 844, 845, 868n.

Augsburg: I 7, 8, 9, 31, 51, 71, 88.—II 148, 180, 190, 217, 228.—III 257, 263, 345, 350, 395, 412, 435, 452, 467n, 492, 495, 519, 541.—IV 601, 614, 615, 652, 665.—V 771.—VI 824, 830, 850, 868, 878.

Bamberg: I 50, 110n.—II 249.—VI 840.

Barcelona: II 229.—III 546.—IV 706.—VI 856.

Basel: I 32, 34, 107, 118, 124.—II 140, 165, 175, 210, 230, 231.—III 259, 316, 323, 346, 372, 373, 377.18, 377.21, 377.22, 377.24, 377.27, 377.29, 377.39, 389, 459, 463, 465, 473n, 474, 490, 527, 528, 535, 547.—IV 561, 562, 563, 564, 565, 595, 640, 644.5, 644.23, 644.24, 649n, 709, 710, 711.—V 726, 731, 750, 751.—VI 805, 825, 865, 870.

Beromünster: I 44.

Besançon: III 269.

Bologna: I 87.—III 296, 297, 300, 301, 310, 311, 444, 447, 457, 505, 513, 515, 517, 524, 538.—IV 559, 560, 598, 599, 600, 611, 644.3, 674, 691, 703.—V 718, 730, 782, 790.

Brescia: I 43.—III 334, 501.—IV 672.—V 773.

Brussels: II 179n.

Chambéry: IV 654.

Colle di Valdelsa: III 354, 514.—IV 618, 680.

Cologne: I 62, 119.—II 133, 178, 200.—III 262, 347, 388, 498.—IV 581, 584, 704.—V 778, 779n.

Cracow: II 186.

Cremona: I 122.

Danzig: I 106.

Delft: III 399.—IV 651.

Erfurt: II 222, 223.—III 477.

Esslingen: III 279, 476.—VI 817.

Ferrara: I 13, 63, 67.—III 261, 270, 285, 303, 308, 312, 344, 351, 390, 392, 441, 446, 512.—IV 587, 608, 671, 697n.—VI 808.

Florence: I 91, 108.—II 147, 150, 154, 157, 174.—III 299, 331, 366, 445, 486.—IV 597, 610.—VI 806, 858.

Frankfort-am-Main: III 470.

Freiburg im Breisgau: II 219.—IV 688.—VI 882, 883.

Geneva: I 36.—III 282, 497.

Genoa: V 799.

Hagenau: III 371.—IV 639.

Heidelberg: III 518.

Ingolstadt: I 19.—II 135, 137, 138.—VI 809, 811, 812, 813, 814.

Landshut: I 22.—II 136.

Leipzig: I 45, 46, 49, 53, 54, 55.—II 129, 130, 131, 132, 194, 220, 221, 232, 253.—III 275, 278, 281, 484, 496.—IV 664, 682.

Leiria: I 123.

Lisbon: II 197.—IV 644.22.—V 717, 781.—VI 863, 864, 879, 887.

London: II 216, 245.—III 292, 377.31.—IV 624, 637, 644.10, 645, 705, 713.—VI 818, 832, 860.

Louvain: I 89.—II 125.—III 438, 443.

Venice (continued)

400, 403, 405, 411, 414, 415, 419, 426, 429, 433, 436, 440, 449, 450, 453, 454, 456, 460, 461, 472, 481, 482, 487, 488, 503, 504, 508, 509, 516, 525, 534, 553, 555, 557 —IV 568, 570, 571, 573, 575, 579, 582, 586, 588, 590, 593, 596, 603, 612, 616, 617, 641, 642, 644.6, 644.8, 644.18, 644.19, 647, 653, 656, 659, 667, 670, 676, 677, 678, 681, 684, 685, 690, 694, 695, 701, 707, 708, 716.—V 720, 722, 724, 728, 732, 734, 744, 749, 753, 754, 755, 756, 757, 760, 761, 780, 784, 788, 789, 791, 792, 793, 795, 796, 802.—VI 819, 822, 823,

826, 827, 834, 853, 854, 857, 861, 862, 866, 867, 868a, 873, 874, 875, 877, 886, 889, 890, 894, 895, 895a, 898a.

Verona: III 369.—VI 897.

Vicenza: I 77.—II 212.

Vienna: I 83, 84, 105.—II 183, 184, 207, 227.—III 529.—IV 698.

Vienne: III 359.

Westminster: II 143.

Wittenberg: I 69, 80.—II 160, 238.

Zurich: II 82.—III 469.—IV 646.

Zwolle: II 186*b*.

A:4   Printers and Publishers

The place of printing and dates of the earliest and latest imprints cited under the main entries of the present volume are given in parentheses, following the name of the printer or publisher. The latter may be recognized by the term *publ.*

Roman numbers refer to the six categories or sections into which the volume is divided, as I) Astronomy; II) Mathematics; III) Medicine; IV) Natural Science; V) Physics; VI) Technology. Dashes are used to keep the categories distinct from one another. Arabic numerals refer to the numbered entries in the main text. A long dash at the beginning of an entry, however, refers to the last printer or publisher cited above.

Achates, Leonardus (*Padua*, 1473): III 273.

Alantsee, Lucas, *publ.* (*Nuremberg*, 1518): II 233.

Albricis, Antonius de, *publ.* (*Padua*, 1476): IV 567.—VI 807.

Alopa, Laurentius de (*Florence, c.* 1484): I 91. —III 486.

Amsterdam, Martinus de. SEE Martinus de Amsterdam.

Anabat, Guillermus (*Paris*, 1509): V 800.

Andreae, Hieronymus, *Formschneider* (*Nuremberg*, 1525, 1528): II 161.—IV 622.— VI 835.

Andreas Asulanus. SEE Torresanus, Andreas, de Asula.

Anima Mia, Guglielmo (*Venice, c.* 1485): VI 822.

Anselm, Thomas (*Tübingen*, 1512, 1514): I 144.—III 418.

Antonius de Albricis, *publ.* (*Padua*, 1476): IV 567.—VI 807.

Apianus, Petrus, *and others.*
   Georgius Apianus (*Ingoldstadt*, 1527): II 137.   In aedibus Apiani (*Ingoldstadt*, 1531, 1533): II 135, 138.—VI 811, 812, 813.   In aedibus nostris (*Ingoldstadt*, 1540): I 19.— VI 809. In officina Apiani (*Ingoldstadt*, 1532): VI 814.

Arrivabenus, Georgius (*Venice*, 1496, 1514): III 353, 433.—VI 853, 854, 857.

Ascensius. SEE Badius Ascensius, Jodocus.

Asula, Thomas de (*Padua*, 1476): V 743.

Aurelianus, Johannes Philippus, et fratres, *publ.* (*Padua*, 1472, 1474): I 25, 26.—IV 572, 576, 577.—V 733, 735.

Ayrer, Marcus (*Bamberg*, 1493): VI 840.

Badius Ascensius, Jodocus (*Paris*, 1512, 1526): III 343n, 377[29].—V 739, 772.

Bämler, Johann (*Augsburg*, 1472, 1477): III 345, 495.—IV 614, 878.

Banckes, Rycharde, *publ.* (*London*, 1525): III 292.

Barbari, Luigi and Francesco (*Venice*, 1516): III 294.—IV 593.

Barbaro, Daniele, *publ.* (*Venice, c.* 1493): IV 592n.

Bartholomaeus Cremonensis (*Venice*, 1473, 1474): III 429.—VI 861.

Bartholomaeus, Joannes, Astensis (*Venice*, 1516): III 294.—IV 593.

Bascarini, Nicolò de (*Venice*, 1544, 1549): III 450.—IV 677.—V 720.—VI 868a.

Baumeister, Johannes (*Mantua*, 1473): III 479.

Bebel, Johann (*Basel*, 1532, 1533): III 377 [27], 473n, 474.

Belfortis, Andreas (*Ferrara*, 1472, 1493): I 13, 63.—III 270, 303, 312n, 344, 351, 512.

Bellot, Jean (*Genève*, 1500): III 282.

Benalius, Petrus, *publ.* (Venice, 1493/94): VI 834.

Benedetti, Giovanni Antonio (*Bologna*, 1503, 1504): III 505, 560.—IV 691.

Benedetti, Girolamo [Hieronymus de Benedictiis] (*Bologna*, 1514, 1521): III 310, 311. —IV 559, 598, 600.—V 790.

Benedictis, Franciscus (Plato) de (*Bologna*, 1489): III 296, 444.—IV 674.

Benedictis, Nicolaus de (*Turin*, 1492): II 206.

Benedictus Genuensis (*Venice*, 1480): III 481.

Berg, Johann vom. SEE Montanus, Joannes .

Bergmann, Johann, de Olpe (*Basel*, 1492, 1496): I 32.—III 316

Bernecker, Hans (*Bamberg*, 1493): VI 840

Bertochus, Dionysius (*Bologna*, 1487): III 513

Bertochus, Doninus (*Bologna*, 1474): I 23.— V 730.

Berwalt, Jacob (*Leipzig*, 1550): II 221.

Besicken, Johann (*Rome*, c. 1500): III 434, 536.

Bevilaqua, Simon (*Venice*, 1495, 1498): I 29, 56.—III 376[7-9], 504.—VI 862, 867.

Bindoni, Alessandro (*Venice*, 1522): III 403.

Bindoni, Bernardino (*Venice*, 1537, 1538): II 139.—III 377[38].

Bindoni, Francesco, di Alessandro (*Venice*, 1526, 1536): II 167.—III 449.—IV 676.

Bischof. SEE Episcopius.

Blado, Antonio, de Asula (*Rome*, 1535, 1547): III 317.—IV 644[14].—V 786.

Blanchard, Antoine (*Lyon*, 1528): IV 578, 585.

Blaublom, Louis (*Paris*, 1530): III 346.

Blum, Michael (*Leipzig*, 1545): II 232.

Boettiger, Gregor (*Leipzig*, n.a. 1494): I 46.

Bolanus, Franciscus, *publ* (*Venice*, 1489): I 52.—III 360.—V 749.

Bonetis, Andreas (*Venice*, 1483): V 755.

Bononia, Thomas de (*Bologna*, 1478): III 524.

Bontius, Georgius (*Antwerp*, 1540): II 171.

Bonus Gallus. SEE Gallus, Bonus, de Francia.

Boscho, Joannes Andreas (*Pavia*, 1496, 1498): III 304, 520.

Bottis, Christophorus de (*Venice*, 1496): III 525.

Bouchet, Guillaume (*Poitiers*, 1493/94): V 797.

Bouyer, Jean (*Poitiers*, 1493/94): V 797.

Braem, Conrad (*Louvain*, 1481): III 438.

Brandis, Lucas (*Lübeck*, c. 1475, c. 1478): I 72, 93.

Brandis, Marcus (*Leipzig*, c. 1481): I 54.

Britannicus, Jacobus (*Brescia*, 1486): III 501.

Brocar, Arnão Guillen de (*Alcalá de Henares*, 1521): I 41.

Bruxella, Arnaldus de (*Naples*, 1477): III 442.

Burgofranco, Jacobus de (*Pavia*, 1515/16): III 377[35, 36].—IV 644[1, 2, 11, 12, 17].

Buyer, Barthélemy, *publ.* (*Lyon*, 1478): III 398.—IV 650.

Byddellus, Joannes (*London*, 1538): IV 705.

Caesarus, Martinus, *Widow of* (*Antwerp*, 1536): III 506.—IV 692.

Calcar, J. S., *publ.* (*Venice*, 1538): IV 708n.

Calvo, Francesco Minizio (*Rome*, 1525): III 406.—IV 657.

Campis, Jannot de (*Lyon*, 1506): III 340.

Canibus, Christophorus de (*Pavia*, 1488): III 307.

Canozius, Laurentius, de Lendenaria (*Padua*, c. 1472-1475): I 25, 26.—III 382.—IV 572, 576, 577, 580.—V 733, 735, 736, 737, 738.

Carcanus, Antonius (*Pavia*, 1479, 1496): I 11.—III 295, 305, 381.—IV 666.—V 723, 729, 762, 764, 765, 777, 798.

Carlo, Bartolomaeus de (*Venice*, 1474): VI 861.

Carlo, Gianstephano di (*Florence*, 1517): II 150.

Carnerius, Augustinus (*Ferrara*, 1475): I 67.

Cartolari, Girolama (*Rome*, 1544): I 30.—III 314.

Castiglione, Giovanni Antonino de (*Milan*, 1539): II 156.

Caxton, William (*Westminster*, c. 1481): II 143.

Cerdonis, Matthaeus (*Padua*, 1482, 1487): I 3.—II 146, 182.—III 356, 391, 416, 427.— IV 648.—V 725n, 767, 785.

Cervicornus, Eucharius (*Marburg*, 1536, 1537): III 356.—IV 619, 621.

Chardella, Simon Nicolai (*Rome*, 1478): IV 566.

Chevallon, Claude (*Paris*, 1526): III 409.— IV 661, 662.

Christophorus de Pensis, de Mandello (*Venice*, 1499): VI 898a.

Clemens *Patavinus* (*Venice*, c. 1471): III 553.

Cock, Symon (*Antwerp*, 1537): II 246.

Colines, Simon de (*Paris*, 1525, 1545): II 168, 169.—III 319, 346, 374n, 377[2, 4, 7, 8, 10, 15, 26, 32, 37n], 462, 473, 526.—IV 591, 626, 628, 636, 644[4, 13, 15, 16, 20, 21, 23, 24], 649, 693, 696.—VI 831, 839.

Colonia, Henricus de (*Brescia*, 1474, 1476): III 334.

Colonia, Johannes de (*Venice*, 1476): III 393. —IV 573.

Confaloneriis, Damianus de (*Pavia*, c. 1478,

1482): III 306, 361, 364.—IV 633.—V 774, 775.

Confalonerius, Bartholomaeus (*Treviso*, 1483): III 533.—IV 703.

Contugo, Nicolaus de (*Venice*, 1483): III 289. —IV 590.

Corneno, Petrus de (*Milan*, 1481, *c*. 1482): II 205.—III 309.

Cratander, Andreas (*Basel*, 1520, *c*. 1536): III 377[18, 22, 24, 27], 459, 465, 473*n*, 474, 490, 527, 535.—IV 644[5, 23, 24].—V 726.

Cremonensis. SEE Bartholomaeus Cremonensis.

Crespin, Jean (*Lyon*, 1532): III 337.

Creussner, Friedrich (*Nuremberg*, 1477): IV 686.

Cromberger, Jacob (*Sevilla*, 1512, 1519): II 188.—VI 837.

Darlerius, Carolus (*Cremona*, 1494/95): I 122.

Davost, Claude (*Lyon*, 1509): III 313.—IV 602.

De Pratis, Nicolas. SEE Des Prez, Nicolas.

Des Prez, Nicolas [Nicolaus Pratensis; Nicolas De Pratis] (*Paris*, 1506): V 748.

Dinckmut, Conrad (*Ulm*, *c*. 1484): VI 855.

Dino, Francesco di (*Florence*, 1481): II 157.

Dortas, Abraham (*Leiria*, 1496): I 123.

Du Bois, Simon [Sylvius] (*Paris*, *c*. 1505, 1529): II 201.—III 377[6, 34].

Dürer, Albrecht, *Widow of, publ.* (*Nuremberg*, 1528): IV 622.

Du Jardin (*Lyon*, *b*. 1476): III 493.

Du Pré, Jean (*Paris*, 1517): V 746.

Durantibus, Hieronymus de (*Padua*, 1493): V 719.

—— (*Pavia*, 1488): III 307.—V 755*n*.

Du Ry, Antoine (*Lyon*, 1523): IV 569.

Egenolff, Christian (*Marburg*, 1541): IV 620.

—— (*Strasbourg*, 1529): II 248.

Eggestein, Heinrich (*Strasbourg*, *c*. 1475): III 476*n*.—IV 673.

Episcopius, Nicolaus, *the Elder* (Bischof) (*Basel*, 1533, 1549): I 34.—III 323, 377[39], 389.—IV 561, 563, 564, 565.—VI 805, 870.

Eponymous press, *i.e.*, the producer of an anonymously issued item around which, as the result of typographical and bibliographical identification, other anonymously issued items are grouped as a means of tentative classification. For a list

of items thus designated in the present volume, see EPONYMOUS PRESSES, at the end of this section.

Estienne, François [*Franciscus Stephanus*] (*Paris*, 1537, 1543): IV 625, 628, 631, 632.

Estienne, Henri [Henricus Stephanus] (*Paris*, 1510, 1513): II 159.—III 422, 475.

Estienne, Robert [Robertus Stephanus] (*Paris*, 1535, 1536): IV 627, 629, 630.

Faber, Johann (*Basel*, 1527): II 175.

Faelli [Phaelli], Giovanni Battista (*Bologna*, 1529): IV 644[3].

Farri, Giovanni de (*Venice*, 1541): IV 644 [19].

Fernández, Francisco, de Córdoba (*Valladolid*, 1545): VI 869.

Ferrandus, Thomas (*Brescia*, *c*. 1473): IV 672. —V 773.

Ferratis, Joannes Petrus de (*Piacenza*, 1476): III 511.

Fezandat, Michel (*Paris*, 1550): III 329.—IV 609.—V 745.

Fiviz(z)ano, Jacobus de (*Venice*, 1477): III 453.—IV 678.

Flach, Martin (*Strasbourg*, *c*. 1500, 1513): I 81.—II 198.—III 507.—V 779.

Florentius de Argentina (*Venice*, *c*. 1472): I 70.

Fontana, Benedictus, *publ.* (*Venice*, 1496): IV 586.

Fradin, François (*Lyon*, *after* 1500, 1504/05): III 265, 276, 286, 293.—VI 816.

Frellon, Jean and François (*Lyon*, 1542): III 389*n*.

Friedberg, Peter von (*Mainz*, *c*. 1491): I 65.

Froben: *In aedibus Frobenianis* (*Basel*, 1530, 1533): IV 562.—V 721*n*.

Froben, Hieronymus (*Basel*, 1533, 1549): I 34.—III 323, 377[39].—IV 561, 563, 564, 565.—VI 805, 870.

Froben, Johann (*Basel*, 1526): III 377 [21, 29].

Froben, Johann (Johann Erasmus Froben?) (*Basel*, 1543): III 389.

Froschauer, Christoph (*Zürich*, 1542): IV 646.

Froschauer, Johann (*Augsburg*, *c*. 1495–1500): III 412, 541.

Furter, Michael (*Basel*, 1492): I 32.

Fyner, Conrad (*Esslingen*, *c*. 1475, *c*. 1478): III 279, 476.—VI 817.

Gabiano, Baldassarre de, *publ.* (*Lyon*, 1504): VI 816.

Galharde, Germão (*Lisbon*, 1519, 1537): II 197.—VI 864.

Gallicus, Statius (*Brescia*, 1474): VI 848.

Gallus, Bonus, de Francia (*Colle di Valdelsa*, 1478, 1479): III 514.—IV 680.

—— (*Padua*, 1475, 1476): V 743, 768.

Gasellus, Jacobus (*Paris*, 1542): III 357.

Gaultier (Galterius), Pierre (*Paris*, 1544): III 397.

Gaulterot, Vivant (*Paris*, 1545): III 471.

Gente, Gregorius de (*Pisa*, 1484): V 801.

Gering, Ulrich (*Paris*, c. 1480): III 494.

Gerla, Leonardus (*Pavia*, c. 1496): III 302.

Girardengus, Nicolaus (*Pavia*, 1483): V 763.

Giunta, Filippo (*Florence*, 1507): III 299.—IV 597.

——, *Heirs of, publ.* (*Florence*, 1521): VI 858.

Giunta, Luc' Antonio (*Venice*, 1518, 1531): I 12.—II 214.

——, *Heirs of* (*Venice*, 1541/42, 1550): I 79.—III 318n, 368, 377[5, 11–13, 17, 19, 30, 33], 456.—IV 644[6, 8, 18].

Giunta family (*Venice*, c. 1546): III 456.

Godfray, Thomas (*London*, 1532): VI 832.

Götz, Nicolaus (*Cologne*, c. 1475): III 262.

Granjon, Robert (*Paris*, 1550): III 329.—IV 609.—V 745.

Grapheus, Joannes (*Antwerp*, 1529, 1533): I 61.—II 172, 173.—III 377[32].—VI 810, 844, 845.

Grassis, Andreas de, de Castronovo (*Ferrara*, 1492, 1493): III 308, 441.—IV 671.

Gregoriis, Gregorius de (*Venice*, 1491, 1499): V 784.

Gregoriis, Joannes and Gregorius, de Forlivio (*Venice*, 1488, c. 1500): II 149.—III 284, 298, 436.—IV 586, 588, 667.—V 722, 756, 757.

Greif, Michael (*Reutlingen*, 1503 or later): III 394.

Grim, Sigismund (*Augsburg*, 1518, 1519): III 257, 492, 519.

Grüninger, Johann [Reinhard] (*Strasbourg*, 1497, 1526): II 250n.—III 320, 321, 322, 544, 551.—IV 607, 638.—VI 828, 829, 859.

Gutenberg, Johann (?), (*Mainz*, 1460): VI 821.

Guerraldus, Bernardinus (*Venice*, 1502): IV 596.

Guillery, Étienne (*Rome*, 1514): III 548.

Gymnich, Johann [Gymnicus] (*Cologne*, 1534, 1544): III 347.—IV 704.

Hamman, Johannes (*Venice*, 1496): I 103.

Han, Ulrich (*Rome*, c. 1475): III 326, 485.—VI 872.

Harlem, Henricus de (*Bologna*, 1482, 1487): III 300, 301, 515.

Harlem, Nicolaus Petri de. SEE Petri, Nicolaus, de Harlem.

Hassia, Joannes de (*Treviso*, c. 1476): V 758.

Hectoris, Benedictus (*Bologna*, 1495, 1522): I 87.—III 517.—IV 599, 611, 703.—V 718, 782.

——, *publ.* (*Bologna*, 1489): III 444.—IV 674.

Heliae, Helias (*Beromünster*, c. 1472): I 44.

Henricus de Harlem. SEE Harlem, Henricus de.

Herbort, Johannes (*Padua*, 1475, 1476): III 290, 431.—V 725, 766.

Herbster, Hans. SEE Oporinus, Johannes, *pseud.*

Herford, John (*Saint Albans*, 1537): II 179.—(*London*, 1545): IV 645.

Herwagen, Johann (*Basel*, 1532, 1550): II 140, 165, 210, 230.—V 731, 750, 751.—VI 865.

Higman, Johann (*Paris*, 1492, 1496): II 187, 192, 193.—V 770.

Hochfeder, Caspar (*Nuremberg*, c. 1493, c. 1496): I 66.—III 542.

Hohenstein, Jodocus (*Naples*, 1475/76): III 333.

Hopyl, Wolfgang (*Paris*, 1496): II 187, 192, 193.

Huss, Mathias (*Lyon*, n.b. 1480): III 499.

Huyon, Guillaume (*Lyon*, 1520): II 224.

Hylacomylus. SEE Waldseemüller, Martin.

Ilacomilus. SEE Waldseemüller, Martin.

Isengrin, Michel (*Basel*, 1542): III 372.—IV 640.

Jenson, Nicolaus (*Venice*, 1471, 1472): I 74.—III 256, 461.—IV 695.—VI 889, 895a.

Johann von Speier (*Venice*, 1469): III 487.—IV 684.—V 788.—VI 873.

Kachelofen, Conrad (*Leipzig*, 1489, c. 1500): II 253.—III 484, 496.

Kempen, Arnoldus (*Zwolle*, 1502): II 186b.

Ketelaer, Nicolaus (*Utrecht*, 1473/74): VI 898.

Khol, Paulus (*Regensburg*, c. 1522): I 20.

Morhart, Ulrich (*Tübingen*, 1548): I 113.

Morrhy, Gérard [Gerardus Morrhuis] (*Paris*, *c.* 1531, 1532): III 377[9, 14].—IV 644[7]. —VI 838.

Müller, Johann, of Königsberg [Regiomontanus] (*Nuremberg, c.* 1473, *c.* 1475): I 75, 85, 98, 99, 101, 102.

Nebiis, Franciscus de, *publ.* (*Pavia, c.* 1496, 1498): III 302, 304.

Neuber, Ulrich (*Nuremberg*, 1544): VI 881.

Neyret, Antoine (*Chambéry*, 1486): IV 654.

Nicolai da Verona, Giovanni (*Verona*, 1472): VI 897.

Nicolas de Pratis. SEE Des Pres, Nicolas.

Nicolini da Sabbio, Stefano dei (*Venice*, 1537): V 795.—VI 894.

—— (*Verona*, 1530): III 369.

Nigro, Joannes de, *publ.* (*Venice*, 1492): III 400.—IV 653.

Nördlingen, Johann de (*Bologna*, 1482): III 300, 301.

Noot, Thomas van der (*Brussels*, 1508): II 179n.

Novimagio, Reynaldus (*Venice*, 1479): III 555.

Odonino, Bernardinus de (*Ferrara*, 1521): III 446.

Oeglin, Erhart (*Augsburg*, 1514): II 190.

Oporinus, Joannes [Hans Herbster], *publ.* (*Basel*, 1543, 1549): II 231.—III 547.—IV 709, 710, 711.

Orta, Alfonso de (*Valencia, c.* 1496): I 120.

Pachel, Leonardus (*Milan*, 1481, *c.* 1484): III 376[5, 6], 410, 417, 421, 500, 552.—IV 658, 660, 689.

Padavano, Giovanni. SEE Patavinus, Joannes.

Paderborn, Conradus de (*Padua, c.* 1473): III 396.

Paderborn, Johann de (*Alost?, c.* 1473): III 258.

—— (*Louvain*, 1482, *c.* 1483): I 89.—III 443.

Paganinis, Paganinus de (*Venice*, 1494, 1509): II 202, 203.—VI 819.

Pannartz, Arnoldus (*Rome, c.* 1469, 1471): IV 612n.—VI 893.

Parcus, Jacobus [Jakob Kündig] (*Basel*, 1549): II 231.

Pasini, Maffeo (*Venice*, 1526, 1536): III 167, 449.—IV 676.

Pasqualibus, Peregrinus de (*Venice*, 1489): III 454.

Patavinus, Joannes [Giovanni Padavano] (*Venice*, 1535, 1536): I 18.—III 377[25, 37], 488.

Pencio da Lecco, Jacopo [Jacobus Pentius, de Leucho] (*Venice, c.* 1504): V 724.

Pensis, Christophorus de (*Venice*, 1493, 1499): III 557.—IV 707.—VI 834, 898a.

Petit, Jean (*Paris*, 1512): V 739n.

Petras, Remon de (*Toledo*, 1526): IV 634.

Petreius, Johann (*Nuremberg*, 1533, 1546): I 10, 21, 47, 59, 68, 109, 110.—II 126, 155, 181, 208, 218, 236, 237, 254.—III 349.— V 769.—VI 820.

Petri, Johann (*Florence*, 1491/92): II 154.

Petri, Nicolaus, de Harlem (*Padua, c.* 1476): III 280, 376[1, 3, 4, 10], 385, 408, 420, 425. —IV 700.—VI 838.

Petrius, Joannes [Jean Petit?], *publ.* (*Paris*, 1532): VI 838.

Petzensteiner, Heinrich (*Bamberg*, 1482): II 249.

Peypus, Friedrich (*Nuremberg*, 1522, 1529): II 251.—III 468.

Philovallus, Hieronymus (*Vienna*, 1510): IV 698.

Picardus, Johannes, de Hamell (*Ferrara*, 1475): VI 808.

Pietro, Filippo di (*Venice*, 1474, 1482): III 509.—IV 571, 575, 579, 582, 694.

Pietro, Gabriel di (*Venice, c.* 1478): III 503.

Pincio, Filippo (*Venice*, 1490): III 375.—IV 642.

Plannck, Stephan (*Rome, c.* 1482): II 235.

Platter, Thomas (*Basel*, 1536): IV 649n.

Posa, Pedro (*Barcelona*, 1482, 1484): II 229. —III 546.—IV 706.—VI 856.

Prüss, Johann (*Strasbourg*, 1488): II 134, 185.

Pynson, Richard (*London*, 1522, *c.* 1523): II 245.—III 377[31].—IV 637, 644[10].

Quarengiis, Petrus de (*Venice*, [1493], 1500): III 508.—V 761.

Quentell, Heinrich (*Cologne, c.* 1489, 1497): V 778, 799n.

—— In officina felicis memorie honesti viri Heinrich Quentell (*Cologne*, 1501): II 178.

R-Printer. SEE Rusch, Adolf.

Rampazetto, Francesco (*Venice*, 1540): VI 886.

Ratdolt, Erhard (*Augsburg*, 1488, 1505): I 7, 8, 9, 31, 51, 71, 88.—II 148, 217.—IV 601. —V 771.—VI 824.

—— (*Venice*, 1476, 1485): I 4, 6, 14, 48, 96, 100.—II 151, 163.—V 753.—VI 823.

Reger, Johann (*Ulm*, 1490, 1499): I 104, 115.—IV 574.

Reinhard, Johann. SEE Grüninger.

Reno, Joannes de (*Padua*, 1473): III 330, 380, 386.

Resch, Conradus (*Paris*, 1516): V 772.

Reuwich, Erhard (*Mainz*, 1486): IV 605.

Rhode, Franciscus (*Marburg*, 1529): III 348.

—— (?) (*Danzig*, 1540): I 106.

Riedrer, Friedrich (*Freiburg-im-B.*, 1493): VI 883.

Riessinger, Sixtus (*Naples*, c. 1472): I 40.

Rihel, Wendelin (*Strasbourg*, 1539): IV 604.

Ripoli Press. SEE Santo Jacopo di Ripoli.

Rizo, Bernardino (*Venice*, 1490, 1492): III 400.—IV 653.—VI 874.

Roce, Denys, *publ.* (*Paris*, 1509): V 742.

Rodriguez, Luis, *publ.* (*Lisbon*, 1540, 1542): IV 644[22].—V 717, 781.—VI 863, 887.

Romanus, Aldus. SEE Manutius, Aldus, *Romanus*.

Rossi, Francesco (*Ferrara*, c. 1543): IV 608.

Rottweil, Adam von (*Venice*, c. 1476): II 128.

Roville, Guillaume (*Lyon*, 1547, 1550): III 377[3].—IV 644[9, 25].

Rubeis, Laurentius de (*Ferrara*, 1482, *n.b.* 1497): III 285, 308, 390, 441.—IV 587, 671.

Ruberia, Giustiniano de (*Bologna*, 1497?): III 457.

Ruffinelli, Venturino (*Venice*, 1535, 1546): I 18.—II 141, 241.—III 377[25, 37], 488.—V 732, 796.—VI 827, 895.

Rugerius, Ugo (*Bologna*, 1474, 1489): I 23.—III 538.—V 730.

Ruppel, Berthold (*Basel*, 1471/72): III 259.—IV 595.

Rusch, Adolf [the R-Printer] (*Strasbourg*, c. 1467, c 1477): III 355, 491, 550.—IV 687, 712

Sainct Denys, I (*Paris*, 1530): III 439.

Sancta Lucia, Alovisius de (*Venice*, 1492): I 5.

Sancto Nazario, Jacobus de, de Ripa (*Milan*, 1494): III 363.

Sancto Petro, Jacobus de (*Pavia*, 1479): III 384.

Sancto Ursio, Henricus de (*Vicenza*, 1499): I 77.

Santo Jacopo di Ripoli, *Dominican convent* (*Florence*, 1481): III 366, 445.

Santritter, Johannes Lucilius (*Venice*, 1489): I 52.—III 360.—V 749.

Schauer, Johann (*Augsburg*, 1496 or later): III 395.

Schenck, Peter (*Vienne*, b. 1485): III 359.

Schoeffer, Johann (*Mainz*, 1519, 1530): III 377[1], 540.

Schoeffer, Peter (*Mainz*, 1484, 1485): III 379, 402.—IV 605

Schönsperger, Johann (*Augsburg*, 1494): III 435.

Schoolmaster Printer, The (*St. Albans*, 1486): IV 594.

Schott, Johann (*Freiburg-im-Breisgau*, 1503): II 219.—IV 688.—VI 882.

—— (*Strasbourg*, 1513, 1544): III 266, 370, 387, 404, 423, 464, 531, 532, 539.—IV 606, 655.—V 727.—VI 900.

Schriber, Johannes, de Annunciata (*Bologna*, 1478): III 297, 447, 524.

Schüssler, Johann (*Augsburg*, 1471): III 350.—IV 615.

Schurener, Johannes (*Rome*, 1473): III 428.—VI 851.

Scinzenzeler, Uldericus (*Milan*, 1481, 1494): I 33.—III 376[5, 6], 410, 417, 421, 521, 552, 660.—IV 658, 689.

Scoto, Girolamo [Hieronymus Scotus] (*Venice*, 1545, 1546): III 318, 327.

Scoto, Ottaviano [Octavianus Scotus], *publ.* (*Venice*, 1494, 1498): III 283, 295, 352, 516.—IV 681, 690.—V 744, 793.

—— *Heirs of, publ.* (*Venice*, 1500/01, 1525): I 39.—III 255, 353, 433.—IV 716.—V 760, 780, 789, 791.—VI 853, 857.

—— Apud Octavianum Scotum (*Venice*, 1536, 1537?): III 328, 419.

Secerius, Johannes. SEE Setzer, Johann.

Sensenschmidt, Johann (*Bamberg*, c. 1483): I 50.

Septem Arboribus, Martinus de (*Padua*, 1472): III 291.

Septemcastrensis, Thomas (*Mantua*, 1472): III 478, 480.

Servius, Oliverius (*Rome*, c. 1481): III 413.

Sessa, Giovanni Battista (*Venice*, 1502, 1503): II 142, 170.—IV 670.

Sessa, Melchiorre (*Venice*, 1541): IV 647.

Setzer, Johann [Johannes Secerius] (*Hagenau*, 1530, 1531): III 371.—IV 639.

Severinus Ferrariensis (*Ferrara*, 1474, *c.* 1477): III 261, 392.

Seybold, Heinrich (*Strasbourg*, 1528): III 377 [28].

Sidriano, Joannes de (*Pavia*, 1472/73): III 365*n*, 502*n*.

Silber, Eucharius (*Rome*, *c.* 1483, 1494): III 407, 558.—IV 592.—VI 804, 842, 843, 852, 888, 899.

Silber, Marcello (*Rome*, *n.a.* 1520): V 787.— VI 871.

Silvestro, In aedibus D. Catharine de (*Naples*, 1523): VI 803.

Singriener, Johann (*Vienna*, 1515, 1526): II 183, 184.—II 227.

Sorg, Anton (*Augsburg*, *c.* 1480, *c.* 1485): III 263.—IV 652.

Speier, Johann von [Speyer; Spira]. SEE Johann von Speier.

Speier, Wendelin von [Speyer; Spira]. SEE Wendelin von Speier.

Spindeler, Nicolaus (*Valencia*, *c.* 1490, 1495): III 264, 272.

Spörer, Hans (*Erfurt*, 1500): III 477.

Stagnino, Bernardino (*Venice*, 1492): V 802.

Stayner, Heinrich. SEE Steiner, Heinrich.

Steelsius, Joannes, *publ.* (*Antwerp*, 1533): III 377[32].

Steiner, Heinrich (*Augsburg*, 1530, 1536): II 228.—III 467*n*.—VI 868*n*.

Steinschaber, Adam (*Geneva*, 1479): I 36.— III 497.

Stendal, Albertus de (*Padua*, 1475): V 768.

Stephanus. SEE Estienne.

Stephanus Calcarensis, Joannes, *publ.* (*Venice*, 1538): IV 708.

Steynschaber. SEE Steinschaber.

Stöckel, Wolfgang (*Leipzig*, 1501, 1511): III 275.—IV 664.

Strata, Antonius de (*Venice*, 1488?): I 24.

Stüchs, Johann (*Nuremberg*, 1514, 1518): II 233, 252.—VI 880.

Suigus, Jacobinus, de Suico (*Turin*, 1492): II 206.

Sweynheim, Conradus (*Rome*, *c.* 1469, 1471): IV 612*n*.—VI 893.

Sylvius, Simon. SEE DuBois, Simon.

Tacuinus, Joannes (*Venice*, 1505, 1530): II 244.—VI 866, 867.

Thedesco da Maganza, Giovanni (*Florence*, 1491/92): II 154*n*.

Ther Hoernen, Arnold (*Cologne*, *c.* 1472): IV 581, 584.

Torresani, Andrea [Andreas Torresanus, *Asulanus*] (*Venice*, 1498, 1534): I 94.—III 260, 374, 405, 426, 472.—IV 568, 641, 656.

Tory, Geofroy, *publ.* (*Paris*, 1529): VI 896.

Trechsel, Johann (*Lyon*, 1490, 1496): III 378, 432.

Trechsel, Melchior and Gaspar (*Lyon*, 1533, 1535): III 338.—IV 644[14].

Trino, Comin da (*Venice*, 1546): VI 826.

Trot, Barthélemi, *publ.* (*Lyon*, 1509): III 313. —IV 602.

Tuppo, Francesco del (*Naples*, 1480, *c.* 1485): I 64.—III 312.

Turre, Petrus de (*Rome*, 1497): III 537.

Ugoleto, Angelo (*Parma*, *c.* 1494): VI 846.

Unglerius, Florianus (*Cracow*, 1512): II 186.

Valdarfer, Christophorus (*Milan*, 1475, 1483): III 274, 332.

Valdezoccho, Bartholomaeus de (*Padua*, 1472): III 291.

Valla, Joannes Petrus, *publ.* (*Venice*, 1501): II 162.

Varnier, Hans (*Ulm*, 1536): III 467.—VI 868.

Vascosan, Michel (*Paris*, 1550): II 225.—VI 885.

Vérard, Antoine, *publ.* (*Paris*, 1492, *c.* 1505): IV 669, 699.—VI 841.

Verona, Joannes Nicolaus de. SEE Nicolai, Giovanni, da Verona.

Vietor, Hieronymus (*Vienna*, *c.* 1530/31): I 83.

Vincent, Simon, *publ.* (*Lyon*, *c.* 1509?, *n.a.* 1515): III 341, 342, 377[20].

—— [For the heirs of Simon Vincent?] (*Lyon*, 1535): IV 644[14].

Vitali, Bernardino dei (*Rome*, 1507): II 213.

—— (*Venice*, 1501, 1538): I 27.—IV 708.

Vurster, Johann (*Mantua*, 1472, 1473): I 11.— III 273*n*, 478, 479, 480.—IV 583.

—— (*Modena*, 1475): III 554.

Walbeck, Johannes (*Bologna*, 1487): III 515.

Walder, Johann (*Basel*, 1536, 1538): I 118, 124.—VI 825.

Waldseemüller, Martin (Ilacomilus *pseud.*; Lud and Ilacomilus) *publ.*? (*St. Dié*, 1507): II 250.

Wechel, Chrétien (*Paris*, 1528, 1548): II 199.
—III 358, 362, 377[6, 16, 23, 34], 483.—IV
635, 644[14].—V 721.
Weissenburger, Johann (*Landshut, c.* 1521,
1524): I 22, 136.
—— (*Nuremberg*, 1503, 1504): I 78.—II 176.
Wendelin von Speier (*Venice*, 1470, 1473):
IV 603, 612, 616.—V 792.—VI 875.
Whytchurch, Edward (*London*, 1545): VI
818.
Winter, Robert (*Basel*, 1539): III 373.
Winterberger, Johann (*Vienna*, 1495, 1514):
I 84, 105.—II 207.—III 529.
Winters, Conrad, de Homborch (*Cologne, c.*
1480): III 498.
Wirsung, Marcus, *publ.* (*Augsburg*, 1518,
1519): III 257, 492, 519.
Wirzburg, Heinrich [Wircburg, Henricus]
(*Geneva*, 1479): I 36.—III 497.
Wolf(e), Reginalde (*London*, 1542): II 216.
Worde, Wynkyn de (*London, c.* 1510): IV
713.
Zainer, Günther (*Augsburg*, 1472, *c.* 1473): II
180.—III 452.—IV 665.—VI 850.
Zainer, Johann, de Reutlingen (*Ulm*, 1473,
1488 *or later*): I 73, 86.—III 530.
Zarotus, Antonius (*Milan*, 1473, 1492): III
376[11], 458, 523, 556.—IV 643, 675, 714.
—V 776.
Zel, Ulrich (*Cologne, c.* 1466, *c.* 1472): I 62.
— II 200.—III 388.
Zeninger, Conrad (*Venice*, 1486): I 37.
Zierkzee, Cornelis de (*Cologne, c.* 1500): II
133.
Zoppino, Nicolò, d'Aristotile (*Venice*, 1517/
18, 1534): II 166, 234.

Eponymous Presses

Texts printed anonymously but identified typo-
graphically with presses designated as:

[Printer of Antonius Nebrissensis, 'Introduc-
tiones'] (*Salamanca*, 1485): I 121.
[Printer of Capotius (Martin Landsberg?)]
(*Leipzig, c.* 1487/88): I 45.
[Printer of 'Catholicon' (Johann Guten-
berg?)] (*Mainz*, 1460): VI 821.
[Printer of 'Dictys'] (*Cologne, c.* 1470): I 119.
[Printer of Jacopo da Forlì, 'Expositio'] (*Up-
per Italy?, c.* 1475): III 335.
[Printer of Silius Italicus] (*Rome, c.* 1471): IV
613.—VI 833.
[Printer of the 36-line Bible. Unlocalized
(Bamberg?), 1459/60, not after 1461]: I
35, 42, 76, 90.—III 324.
[Printer of Valasco de Taranta, 'De epide-
mia'] (*France* or *Italy, c.* 1474?): III 277.

Monographs

Von RATH, Erich. *The spread of printing in the*
fifteenth century ... Translated by Aileen Calder-
wood; JOHNSON, A. F. *The sixteenth century* (p.
59-119 and 121-156, respectively, in *A his-*
tory of the printed book, New York, Limited
Editions Club, 1938 [The Dolphin, no. 3]).
STILLWELL, Margaret Bingham. *Bibliographi-*
cal survey: Printing in the 15th and 16th centuries
as represented in the Hunt Collection (p. xlix-
lxvii in volume I of the *Catalogue of botanical*
books, Pittsburgh, The Hunt Botanical Library, 1958).

A: 5   Translators

The following list relates to the translators of works cited in the present volume. A name enclosed in square brackets indicates a variant form of the translator's name. A name or title in italics and enclosed in parentheses denotes the work translated. When more than one work is listed under a translator's name, a dash is used to separate the translations from one another.

Roman numerals indicate the six categories to which the present volume relates. Arabic numbers refer to the numbered entries. Accents on Arabic names are omitted.

Abraham *Judaeus* [Abraham ben Shemtob, of Tortosa]: III 256 (*Abu ab Kasim*).—III 556; IV 714 (*Yuhanna ibn Sarabiyun* [Serapion *the Younger*]).
Accursius of Pistoia [Accursio]: III 375[17] (*Galen*).
Adelhard of Bath (?): II 163 (*Euclid*).
Aegidius de Tebaldis: I 6 (*Abu-l-Hasan*).
Al-Hajjaj: I 97n (*Ptolemy*).
Alexandrinus, Julius: III 377[5] (*Galen*).
Alfredus *Anglicus*: IV 578 (*Aristotle*).
Alpago, Andrea: IV 589n (*Avicenna*).
Althamer, Andreas, of Brenz [*Brentius*]: III 406n, 407, 413; IV 657n, 660n (*Hippocrates*).
Andrew, Lawrence: VI 829n (*Brunschwig*).
Angelo da Scarperia, Giacomo d': II 212 (*Ptolemy*).
Argyropylus, Johannes: V 736n (*Aristotle*).
Armengand of Monte Pessulano: III 289 (*Avicenna*).
Arnaldo de Villa Nova: III 290 (*Avicenna*).—III 415 (*Hippocrates*).
Ayora, Gundisalvus: III 458 (*Montis*).
Barbaro, Ermolao: IV 593n, 618n (*Dioskorides*).
Barlandus, Hubertus: III 377[32] (*Galen*).
Bartholomaeus de Messana (?): IV 585 (*Aristotle*).
Bartolomeo da Messina: IV 659 (*Hippocrates*).
Beccaria, Antonio: IV 617 (*Dionysios Periegetes*).
Boninus de Boninis: I 122 (*Willem Gilliszoon*).
Brentius, Andreas: SEE Althamer, Andreas, of Brenz.

Bruno, Gabriele: III 508 (*Ruffo*).
Burgundio of Pisa: III 375[16, 39]; IV 642 [8, 11] (*Galen*).
Caelius Aurelianus: III 526, 528 (*Soranos*).
Caesar, Germanicus: I 23; V 730 (*Aratos*).
Calcagnini, Celio: IV 575n (*Aristotle*).
Calonymos, Calo [Qalonymos ben David]: I 12 (*Al-Bitruji*).
Calvus, Marcus Fabius: III 406, 409; IV 600n, 657, 662 (*Hippocrates*).
Camerarius, Joachim: IV 622n (*Dürer*).—III 374n (*Galen*).
Chalcondylas, Demetrius: III 377[20]; IV 644[3] (*Galen*).
Commandino, Federigo: V 731n, 732n (*Archimedes*).
Constantinus *Africanus*: III 354 (*Dioskorides*). —III 376[3, 4]; IV 642[18], 644[12] (*Galen*). —IV 653n (*Haly Abbas*).—III 280n (*Hippocrates*).—III 427 (*Ishaq al Isra 'Ili*).
Copus, Gulielmus [Copp]: III 406n, 422; IV 657n (*Hippocrates*).—III 475 (*Paulos of Aigina*).
Cornarius, Janus [Hagenbut, Haynpol]: III 377[39] (*Galen*).
Crassus, Junius Paulus: III 377[11, 33, 38] (*Galen*).—III 419 (*Hippocrates*).
Cruserius, Hermannus [Croeser]: III 377[9, 10, 14]; IV 644[7, 15, 16] (*Galen*).
Dalmata, Hermann: I 8 (*Abu Ma'shar Ga'far* [*Albumasar*]).
Danz von Ast, J.: III 354n (*Dioskorides*).
Drummond, Jonas: III 275 (*Arnaldo de Villa Nova*).
Erasmus, Desiderius: III 377[21] (*Galen*).
Faraj ben Salim: III 501 (*Rhasis*).

312

Fausto, Sebastiano: III 354n (*Dioskorides*).

Felicianus, Johannes Bernardus [Regazzola]: III 377[12, 13]; IV 644[5, 6] (*Galen*).—III 474 (*Paulos of Aigina*).

Fichardus, Johannes: III 377[18, 22, 24] (*Galen*).

Ficino, Marsilio: I 91; III 486 (*Plato*).

Fortolus, Andreas: IV 644[4, 13] (*Galen*).

Fuchs, Leonhart: III 374n (*Galen*).—III 411n (*Hippocrates*).

Gadaldinus, Augustus: IV 644[9, 24] (*Galen*).

Gaza, Theodoros: VI 804 (*Aelianus*).—IV 573, 583 (*Aristotle*).—III 429n (*Hippocrates*).—III 533; IV 702 (*Theophrastos*).

Gemusaeus, Hieronymus: III 374n (*Galen*).

George "of Trebizond" [Trapezuntinus]: I 97n (*Ptolemy*).

Gherardo da Cremona [Gerard of Cremona]: V 717 (*Abu Ali al-Hasan*).—III 287, 288; IV 589 (*Avicenna*).—III 375[23, 24], 376[1], 431n; IV 642[19] (*Galen*).—I 68; II 181 (*Jabir ibn Aflah*).—I 78n (*Masha 'Allah*).—I 97; II 215 (*Ptolemy*).—I 117; II 242 (*Thabit ibn Qurra*).—III 555 (*Yuhanna ibn Sarabiyun* [Serapion *the Elder*]).

Grosseteste, Robert (?): IV 713 (*Walter of Henley*).

Guarino da Verona: VI 893 (*Strabo*).

Gulielmus de Moerbeke. SEE William of Moerbeke.

Günther, Johann [Philogus, *pseud.* (?)]: III 377[2, 4, 7 (?), 8, 16, 23, 26, 32]; IV 644[24] (*Galen*).—III 462 (*Oreibasios*).—III 473 (*Paulos of Aigina*).

Hermann of Carinthia: II 213 (*Ptolemy*).

Heyll, Christopher [Soter]: III 377[1] (*Galen*).

Hirnkofen, Wilhelm von. SEE Wilhelm von Hirnkofen.

Hunain ibn Ishaq [Johannitius]: III 425n (*Galen, etc.*).

Jacobus *Hebraeus*: III 284 (*Avenzohar*).

Jacopo da Cremona: II 140; V 731 (*Archimedes*).

Joannes Hispalensis: I 1 (*Abd-al-'Aziz ibn 'Uthman ibn Ali al-Qabisi* [*Alchabitius*]).—I 13 (*Al-Farghani*).—I 96n (*Masha 'Allah*).

Laurentianus, Laurentius [Laurenziani]: III 408n, 431n (*Galen*).

Leonicenus, Nicolaus: III 431n; IV 644[10]

(*Galen*).—III 406n, 429n; IV 657n (*Hippocrates*).—I 94 (*Ptolemy*).

Linacre, Thomas: II 211 (*Proclos*).

Lippius, Laurentius: IV 680 (*Oppianos*).

Longolius, Gilbertus: III 377[3] (*Galen*).

Ludovicus, Antonius: IV 644[22] (*Galen*).

Maignan, Eloy de: III 372; IV 640 (*Fuchs*).

Manente, Giovanni: IV 581n (*Aristotle*).

Manilius, Sebastian: IV 667 (*Ketham*).

Marc of Toledo: IV 642[5], 644[17] (*Galen*).

Maslama: II 213 (*Ptolemy*).

Mattioli, Pierandrea: III 354n, 450; IV 618n, 677 (*Dioskorides*).

Memo, Giovanni Battista: II 139 (*Apollōnios*).

Michael *Scotus*: I 12n (*Al-Bitruji*).—IV 588 (*Avicenna*).

Montigiano, Marcantonio: III 354n (*Dioskorides*).

Nicolò da Lonigo. SEE Leonicenus.

Nicolò da Regio: III 375[3, 4, 5, 7, 9, 10, 12, 14, 19, 25, 28–31, 33, 35, 36, 38, 40 (?), 44–48, 49 (?), 50, 376[11], 377[35]; IV 642[1, 2, 4, 7, 12, 13, 14 (?), 16, 22], 643, 644[20] (*Galen*).

Nunes, Pedro: I 70n; VI 864n (*Joannes de Sacro Bosco*).—VI 864n (*Peurbach*).—VI 864n (*Ptolemy*).

Patavinus, *Magister*: III 284n (*Avenzoar*).

Perottus, Nicolaus: IV 611n (*Basilius Magnus*).

Philippus *Tripolitanus*: IV 584 (*Aristotle*).

Philogus, Johannes, *pseud.* SEE (?) Günther, Johann.

Pietro d'Abano: I 2 (*Abraham ben-'Ezra*).—III 375[32]; IV 642[3, 14 (?)] (*Galen*).

Platin, Claude: II 188n (*Juan de Ortega*).

Plato *Tiburtinus* [Plato of Tivoli]: I 10; II 126 (*Al-Battani*).

Poliziano, Angelo: V 726 (*Alexander of Aphrodisias*).

Polltus, Johannes: III 377[27] (*Galen*).

Priscianus: IV 617 (*Dionysios Periegetes*).

Qalonymos ben David. SEE Calonymos, Calo.

Ramusio, Paolo: VI 897n (*Valturio*).

Regazzola, Giovanni Bernardo. SEE Felicianus, Johannes Bernardus.

Reuchlin, Johann: III 418 (*Hippocrates*).

Riccius, Augusta, of Lucca: IV 644[19] (*Galen*).

Rota, Julianus Martianus: III 377[19] (*Galen*).

Ruelle, Jean de la: III 354n; IV 618n (*Dioskorides*).—III 346; IV 693n (*Veterinariae medicinae libri II* [*Hippiatrica*]).

Sagundinus, Nicolaus: VI 888n (*Onasandros*).

Sichardt, Johannes: III 463 (*Oreibasios*).

Simon of Genoa: III 256 (*Abu al-Kasim*).—III 556; IV 714 (*Yuhanna ibn Sarabiyun* [Serapion, *the Younger*]).

Stephanus of Antioch: III 400; IV 653 (*Haly Abbas*).

Struthius, Josephus: III 377[25, 37] (*Galen*).

Tectander, Josephus [Zimmermann]: IV 644 [23] (*Galen*).

Theodorus, Matthias: IV 644[22] (*Galen*).

Thorer, Alban [Albanus Torinus]: III 473n (*Paulos of Aigina*).—III 504n (*Rhasis*).—IV 711n (*Vesalius*).

Tifernas, Gregorios: VI 893 (*Strabo*).

Trapezuntinus, Georgius. SEE George "of Trebizond."

Trevisa, John: IV 595 (*Bartholomaeus Anglicus*).

Trincavellius, Victor: IV 644[8] (*Galen*).

Valgulius, Carolus: I 43 (*Cleomedes*).

Valla, Giorgio: III 376[5, 7–9], 377[36] (*Galen*).—III 490 (*Psellus*). [*See also under* A:2 EDITORS.]

Valla, Giovanni Pietro: III 376[9] (*Galen*).

Vassaeus, Johannes: III 377[15] (*Galen*).

Vergerius, Petrus Paulus: III 414 (*Hippocrates*).

Vincente de Burgos: IV 595 (*Bartholomaeus Anglicus*).

Vizinus, Josephus: I 123 (*Zacuto*).

Werner, Johann: II 138n, 252 (*Ptolemy*).

Wilhelm von Hirnkofen: III 279; IV 817 (*Arnaldo de Villa Nova*).

William of Moerbeke (Gulielmus de Moerbeke): II 141; V 732 (*Archimedes*).—V 736n (*Aristotle*).—III 375[2] (*Galen*).

Zamberti, Bartolomeo: II 162n, 163n, 164n (*Euclid*).

B: 1   Authors By Periods

The purpose of this list is to indicate the general periods in which the texts of the first printed books of scientific interest were originally written or known.

The Roman numerals, separated from the entries by a dash, refer to the main categories under which the authors are entered alphabetically in the present volume, as—I, Astronomy; II, Mathematics; III, Medicine; IV, Natural Science; V, Physics; VI, Technology.

BEFORE THE CHRISTIAN ERA

Apollōnios of Perga, *d.* 190 B.C.—II.
Aratos of Soli, *fl.* 275 B.C.—I, V.
Archimedes of Syracuse, *d.* 212 B.C.—II, V.
Aristarchos, *d.* 230 B.C.—I.
Aristotle, *d.* 322 B.C.—I, IV, V.
Autolycos of Pitane, *fl.* 300 B.C.—I, II.
Cato, Marcus Porcius, *d.* 149 B.C.—IV.
Cicero, Marcus Tullius, *d.* 43 B.C.—IV.
Euclid, *fl.* 300 B.C.—II, V.
Geminos of Rhodes, *fl.* 70 B.C.—I.
Hippocrates, *d.* 375 B.C.—III, IV.
Hyginus, Caius Julius, *fl.* 25 B.C.—I.
Hypsicles of Alexandria, *2nd century* B.C.—II.
Lucretius Carus, Titus, *1st century* B.C.—IV, V.
Musa, Antonius, *1st century* B.C.—III.
Nicandros [Nicander], *3rd century* B.C.—III.
Plato, *d.* 347 B.C.—I, III.
Theodosios of Bithynia, *1st century* B.C.—II.
Theophrastos, *d.* 286 B.C. (?)—III, IV.
Vitruvius Pollio, Marcus, *1st century* B.C.—VI.

DURING THE CHRISTIAN ERA

In instances where the life of an author extended twenty years or more into the century following that of his birth, his name is here entered under the later century, as presumably the more productive period of his life. Authors contemporary with the first century of printing, however, are assigned to the century in which one or more works were first printed.

1ST CENTURY:
Celsus, Aulus Cornelius—III, IV.
Columella, Lucius Junius Moderatus—IV, VI.

Curtius Rufus, Quintus—IV.
Dionysios Periegetes—IV.
Dioskorides, Pedanios—III, IV.
Frontinus, Sextus Julius—VI.
Manilius, Marcus—I.
Menelaos of Alexandria—II.
Nicomachos of Gerasa—II.
Onosandros—VI.
Pliny *the Elder*—III, IV, V, VI.
Strabo [Strabon]—VI.

2ND CENTURY:
Aelianus, *a tactician*—VI.
Cleomedes [SEE *no.* 43, *note*]—I.
Galen—III, IV.
Herodianos—II.
Oppianos—IV.
Pollux—IV.
Ptolemy—I, II.
Soranos of Ephesos—III.

3RD CENTURY:
Alexander of Aphrodisias—V.
Censorinus—IV.

4TH CENTURY:
Firmicus Maternus—I.
Oreibasios—III.
Theodorus Priscianus—III.
Theōn of Alexandria—I, II.
Vegetius, Flavius Renatus—VI.

5TH CENTURY:
Macrobius, Ambrosius Theodosius—I.
Martianus Capella—I.
Proclos—II, VI.

6TH CENTURY:

Aëtius—III.
Alexander of Tralles—III.
Boethius, Anicius Manlius Severinus—II.
Eutocios of Ascalon—II, V.
Gregorius I—III.
Priscianus of Caesarea—V, VI.

7TH CENTURY:

Isidorus Hispalensis—II, IV, VI.
Paulos of Aigina—III.
Theophilos—IV.

8TH CENTURY:

Jābir ibn Ḥaiyān (*Geber*)—III, VI.
Māshā 'Allāh [*Messahalah*]—I, VI.

9TH CENTURY:

Abū Bakr al-Ḥasan [*Albubather*]—I.
Abū-Ma'shar Gā'far [*Albumasar*]—I.
Al-Farghānī [*Alfraganus*]—I.
Al-Kindī—I, III, V.
Ḥunain ibn Isḥāq [*Johannitius*]—III.
Rabanus Maurus [*Hrabanus*]—III, IV.
Strabo, Walafrid—IV.
Thābit ibn Qurra—I, II.
Yūḥannā ibn Masawaih [Mesuë *the Elder*]—III.
Yūḥannā ibn Sarābiyūn [Serapion *the Elder*]—III.

10TH CENTURY:

'Abd-al-'Azīz ibn 'Uthmān ibn 'Alī al-Qabīsī [*Alchabitius*]—I.
Al-Battāni (*Albetegnius*)—I, II.
Constantinos VII, Porphyrogennetos—III.
Haly Abbas ['Alī ibn 'Abbās]—III, IV.
Isḥaq al Isrā 'Īlī [Isaac *Judaeus*]—III.
Rhasis [Abū Bakr Muḥammad ibn Zakarīyā al-Rāzī]—III, IV.
Yūḥannā ibn Masawaih al-Mardini [Mesuë *the Younger*]—III.

11TH CENTURY:

Abū al-Kāsim [*Abulcasis*]—III.
Abū Alī al-Ḥasan ibn al-Haitham [*Alhazen*]—II, V.
Abū-l-Ḥasan 'Alī ibn Abī-l-Rijāl[*Albohazen*]—I.
Al-Zarqālī [*Arzachel*]—I.

'Alī ibn Ridwān—III.
Avicenna [Abū 'Ali al-Ḥusain ibn 'Abdallah ibn Sina]—III, IV.
'Isā ibn 'Alī[*Jesu Haly*]—III.
Psellus—III.
Yūḥannā ibn Sarābiyūn [Serapion *the Younger*]—III, IV.

12TH CENTURY:

Abrāhām ben-'Ezrā [*Avenezra*]—I.
Al-Biṭrūjī [*Alpetragius*]—I.
Avenzohar [Abū Marwān ibn Zohr]—III.
Averroës [Abū-l-Walīd Muḥammad ibn Aḥmad ibn Muḥammad ibn Rushd]—III, IV, V.
Hildegard of Bingen, *Saint*—III, IV.
Jābir ibn Aflah—I, II.
Maimonides [Abū 'Imrām Mūsā ibn Maimūn]—III, IV.

13TH CENTURY:

Aegidius *Romanus* [Giles of Rome]—V.
Albertus Magnus [Albrecht von Bollstädt] *Saint*—III, IV, V, VI.
Alfonso *the Tenth*—I.
Arnaldo de Villa Nova—I, III, VI.
Bacon, Roger—IV, VI.
Balbi, Giovanni—VI.
Bate, Henri—VI.
Bartholomaeus *Anglicus*—IV.
Bernardus de Gordonio—III.
Bonatti, Guido—I.
Campano, Giovanni—I, II.
Gherardo da Sabbioneta—I.
Gilles of Corbeil—III, IV.
Grassus, Benvenutus—III.
Grosseteste, Robert [Robertus Lincolniensis]—II, V.
Joannes de Sacro Bosco—I, II.
Jordanus de Nemore—II, V.
Lanfranchi, Guido—III.
Leopoldus, *Dux Austriae*—I, V.
Lul, Ramòn—VI.
Michael *Scotus*—III, IV.
Peckham, John de—II.
Pierre de Maricourt [Petrus Peregrinus]—V, VI.
Pietro d'Abano—III, IV.
Robertus *Anglicus*—VI.
Ruffo, Giordano.—III.
Saliceto, Guglielmo [Saliceti]—III, IV.

Thomas Aquinas, *Saint*—I, V.
Vincent de Beauvais—III, IV.
Walter of Henley—IV.
Witelo—II.

14TH CENTURY:

Albertus de Saxonia [Ricmestorp]—I, V.
Andalò di Negro—VI.
Angelo da Fossombrone—V.
Barnes, Juliana [Berners]—IV.
Bertuccio, Nicolò—III, IV.
Boccaccio, Giovanni—IV.
Bonaventura de' Castelli [Tura de' Castelli]
  —III.
Bradwardine, Thomas—II, V.
Buridan, Jean—V.
Burley, Walter—V.
Casini, Francesco—III.
Chaucer, Geoffrey—VI.
Conrad von Megenberg—III, IV.
Crescenzi, Pier de'—III, IV.
Danck, Johann, de Saxonia—I.
Dino del Garbo—III.
Dondis, Jacobus de—III.
Estwood, John [Eschuid]—I, III, V.
Falcucci, Nicolò—III, IV.
Firmin de Beauval—V.
Fontaine, Jean de la—VI.
François de Meyronnes—I.
Gentile da Foligno—III.
Giovanni di Casali—V.
Guy de Chauliac—III, IV.
Henri de Ferrières—IV.
Heytesbury, William—V.
Jacopo da Forlì [Giacomo delle Torre]—III,
  IV, V.
Jacopo da San Martino—V.
Jean de Linières [de Lignières]—II.
Jean de Meurs—II.
Jean de Tournemire—III.
Joannes *Canonicus*—V.
Joannes de Rupescissa—III, VI.
Ludolf von Suchen—IV.
Magninus Mediolanensis [Mayno de' May-
  neri]—III.
Marsiglio da Santa Sofia—III.
Marsilius ab Inghen—V.
Mondino [Raimondo de' Luzzi]—III, IV.
Nicephoros Gregoras—VI.
Ockham, William—V.
Oresme, Nicole—II, V.

Pastrengo, Guglielmo da—VI.
Pelacani, Biagio—V.
Petrarca, Francesco—III.
Pietro da Tossignano—III.
Polo, Marco—IV.
Silvatico, Matteo—III, IV.
Simon of Genoa—III.
Strode, Ralph—V.
Swineshead, Richard [Suiseth]—V.
Themo [Themon]—V.
Torrigiani, Torrigiano dei—III.
Urbano of Bologna—V.
Valasco de Taranta—III, IV.

15TH CENTURY:

Achillini, Alessandro—IV, V.
Alberti, Leone Battista—VI.
Alcañiz, Luis—III.
Arcolani, Giovanni—III.
Augustone, Giovanni Basilio—III.
Barbaro, Ermolao—III, IV.
Bartolommeo *dalli Sonetti*—VI.
Barzizza, Cristoforo—III.
Bavarii, Baverio de—III.
Beldamandis, Prosdocimo de—II.
Benedetti, Alessandro—III, IV.
Benivieni, Antonio—III, IV.
Benzi, Ugo—III.
Berlinghieri, Francesco—II.
Bianchini, Giovanni [Blanchinus]—I.
Borghi, Pietro—II.
Breydenbach, Bernhard von—IV.
Bricot, Thomas—V.
Brudzewo, Albertus de—I.
Brunschwig, Hieronymus—III, IV, VI.
Calandri, Filippo—II.
Capelluti, Rolando—III.
Celaya, Juan—V.
Cepolla, Bartolommeo—III.
Cermisone, Antonio—III.
Chiarini, Giorgio—II.
Cornazzano, Antonio—VI.
Coronel, Luiz—V.
Dullaert, Jean—V.
Eck, Paulus—I.
Engel, Johann [Johannes Angeli]—I.
Faber von Budweis, Wenzel—I.
Ferrari, Gianmatteo—III.
Ficino, Marsilio—III.
Folz, Hans—VI.

15TH CENTURY (*continued*):

Gaetano di Thiene—V.
Ganivet, Jean—III.
Georges de Bruxelles—V.
Gersdorff, Hans von—III.
Gerson, Jean Charlier de—I, III.
Gilino, Corradino—III.
Grapaldi, Francesco Mario—VI.
Grünpeck, Joseph—III.
Guaineri, Antonio—III.
Hernsheimer, Peter—I.
Honiger, Jakob—I.
Hundt, Magnus, *the Elder*—IV.
Huswirt, Johann—II.
Joannes de Gmunden—II.
Joannes de Stobniza—II.
Ketham, Johannes de—III, IV.
Leonardi, Camillo—IV, VI.
Licht, Balthasar—II.
Lichtenberger, Johannes—I.
Manfredi, Girolamo di—III.
Marliani, Giovanni—IV, V.
Montagnana, Bartolommeo—III.
Montesauro, Natale—III.
Montis, Petrus de—III.
Nicolas, Gaspar—II.
Nicolaus de Cusa [Khrypffs]—I, II, V.
Nider, Johann—II.
Pacioli, Luca da—II.
Pasi, Bartolommeo di—II.
Paulus Venetus—IV, V.
Pellos, Francesco—II.
Peurbach, Georg von—I, II.
Pflaum, Jakob—I.
Pico della Mirandola, Giovanni—I.
Pierre d'Ailly—I.
Pietro d'Argellata—III.
Platea, Francesco de—II.
Platina [Bartolomeo de' Sacchi]—III, VI.
Politus, Bassanus—V.
Puff von Schrick, Michael—VI.
Regiomontanus [Johann Müller of Königsberg]—I, II, VI.
Riedrer, Friedrich—VI.
Rocca, Bartolommeo delle [Cocles]—III, IV.
Roche, Estienne de la—II.
Röslin, Eucharius—III.
Savonarola, Giovanni Michele—III.
Savonarola, Girolamo Maria Francesco Matteo—I.

Scanaroli, Antonio—III.
Schellig, Konrad—III.
Schmaus, Leonard—III.
Schreiber, Heinrich—II.
Scillacio, Nicolò—III.
Sermoneta, Giovanni—III.
Sherwood, John—II.
Simon de Lendenaria—V.
Soldi, Jacopo—III.
Sommariva, Giorgio—III.
Steinhöwel, Heinrich—III.
Tardif, Guillaume—IV.
Tartaret, Pierre—V.
Thome, Alvarès—V.
Tiberti, Antiocho—IV.
Torni, Bernardo—V.
Torrella, Gaspare—III.
Torrella, Girolamo—I.
Tortelli, Giovanni—VI.
Ulsen, Dietrich—III.
Valturio, Roberto—VI.
Vergilius, Polydorus [Polidoro Vergilio]—IV, VI.
Wagner, Ulrich—II.
Waldseemüller, Martin—II, VI.
Willem Gilliszoon—I.
Zacuto, Abraham Ben Śemŭ'ēl—I.
Zerbis, Gabriele—III, IV.

16TH CENTURY:

Abiosi, Giovanni Battista—VI.
Affaitatus, Fortunius [?]—V.
Agricola [Georg Bauer]—IV, V, VI.
Amico, Giovanni Battista—I.
Antonius Cartaginensis—III.
Apianus, Petrus [Bienewitz]—I, II, VI.
Ascham, Roger—VI.
Berengario da Carpi, Jacopo—III, IV.
Biondo, Michel-Angelo—I, III, VI.
Biringuccio, Vannoccio—VI.
Bock, Hieronymus—IV.
Bonini, Pietro Maria—II.
Bouelles, Charles de—V.
Brant, Sebastian—I, III.
Brasavola, Antonio Musa—III.
Brissot, Pierre—III.
Brunfels, Otto—IV.
Caius, John—III.
Calcagnine, Celio—I.
Canano, Giovanni Battista—IV.
Cardano, Girolamo [Cardan]—II, III, IV, V.

Champier, Symphorien—III.
Ciruelo, Pedro Sánchez [Cirvellus]—I, II.
Clichtove, Josse—II.
Copernicus, Nicolaus [Koppernigk]—I, II.
Cordus, Euricius—III.
Cordus, Valerius—III.
Dryander, Johannes [Eichmann]—III, IV.
Dubois, Jacques [Sylvius]—III.
Dürer, Albrecht—II, IV, VI.
Estienne, Charles [Stephanus]—IV.
Feliciano, Francesco—II.
Fernández de Oviedo y Valdés, Gonzalo—
    IV.
Fernel, Jean—II, III, IV.
Fine, Oronce—II, VI.
Fitzherbert, John—IV.
Fracastoro, Girolamo—I, III.
Fries, Lourenz—IV.
Fuchs, Leonhart—III, IV.
Gaurico, Luca—I, II.
Geminus, Thomas—IV.
Gemma *Frisius* [Regnier]—I, II, VI.
Gesner, Konrad—III, IV.
Ghaligai, Francesco—II.
Glareanus [Heinrich Loritz]—II.
Günther, Johann—IV.
Guidi, Guido—III.
Juan de Ortega—II.
Jung, Ambrosius—III.
Köbel, Jacob—II.
Le Fèvre d'Étaples, Jacques—II, V.
Leonicenus [Nicolò da Lonigo]—III, IV.
Machiavelli, Nicolò—VI.
Manardi, Giovanni—III.
Mariani, Giovanni—II.
Massa, Nicolò—III, IV.
Mattioli, Pierandrea—III, IV.
Maurolico, Francesco—I.
Melanchthon, Philipp—I.
Mercator, Gerhard—VI.
Monte, Giovanni Battista da—III.
Nifo, Agostino—V.
Nunes, Pedro—V, VI.
Panteo, Giovanni Agostino—VI.

Paracelsus [Philippus Aureolus Theophrastus
    Bombastus Paracelsus von Hohenheim]—
    I, III, VI.
Paré, Ambroise—III.
Pedro de Medina—VI.
Perlach, Andreas—I.
Peylick, Johannes—IV.
Piccolomini, Alessandro—V.
Pistoris, Simon—III.
Pol, Nicolaus—III.
Pomponazzi, Pietro—V.
Ponzetti, Fernando—III.
Recorde, Robert—II.
Reisch, Gregor—II, IV, VI.
Rheticus, Georg Joachim—I.
Riese, Adam—II.
Rodriguez de Castello Branco, João—III, IV.
Rojas Sarmiento, Juan de—II, VI.
Roseto, Giovanni Ventura [?]—VI.
Rudolff, Christoff—II
Ruelle, Jean de la—IV
Scheubel, Johann—II
Schöner, Johann—I
Serlio, Sebastiano—VI
Servetus, Michael—I, IV
Sfortunati, Giovanni [Johannes Infortunatus]
    —II
Steber, Bartholomaeus—III
Stifel, Michael—II
Stöffler, Johann—I, VI
Tagliente, Giovanni—II
Tagliente, Girolamo—II
Tartaglia [Nicolò Fontana]—II, V, VI
Tunstall, Cuthbert—II
Turner, William—IV
Ulrich von Hutten—III
Ulstadt, Philip—III
Van der Hoecke, Giel—II
Vesalius, Andreas—III, IV
Vigo, Giovanni da—III
Vögelin, Joannes—II
Werner, Johann—II
Widmann, Johann—II, III
Ziegler, Jakob—I

Comprehensive Surveys of Authors and Periods

SARTON, G. Introduction to the history of science. Washington: Carnegie Institute, 1927–1948. f°. 3 vols. in 5. [Reprinted, 1945, 1950, 1953.]

A basic work combining bibliography and humanism and relating both to European civilization and the Orient. Arranged by periods, from antiquity through the 14th century.

CROMBIE, A. C. Augustine to Galileo. London, 1952. 8°. [Reprinted, London, 1961. Mercury Books, nos. 3–4.]

A discussion of texts and the status of science in Western civilization, from the 5th through the 17th centuries. Non-bibliographical excepting for its modern, reference material.

PALTER, R. M., ed. Toward modern science. New York, 1961. 8°. 2 vols.

Comprising 26 brief monographs, including *Exact science in antiquity* by O. E. Neugebauer; *Chemistry in Islam* by E. J. Holmyard; *Laws of motion in Medieval physics* by E. A. Moody; *Metallurgy and technology in the Middle Ages* by R. J. Forbes; *Humanism and the history of astronomy* by G. McColley; *The medical school at Padua and the renaissance of medicine* by A. Castiglioni; *etc.* Slightly bibliographical.

TATON, R., ed. Ancient and Medieval science from the beginnings to 1450 . . . Translated [from the French] . . . New York: Basic Books, 1963. 4°. [First issued by Presses Universitaires de France, 1957, as *La Science Antique et Medievale*.]

A collection of monographs by 21 scholars. A concise but comprehensive survey, including *Greek science* by P.-H. Michel; *Hellenistic and Roman science* by J. Beaujeu and others; *Arabic science* by R. Arnaldez and L. Massignon; and *Medieval science in the Christian West* by G. Beaujouan, including sections on *Western contacts with Moslem science, Science and practical achievements at the end of the Middle Ages*; together with monographs on Hindu, Chinese, Byzantine, and Jewish science; *etc.*

TATON, R., ed. The beginnings of modern science from 1450 to 1800 . . . Translated [from the French] . . . [London] New York, Basic Books, 1964. 4°. [First issued by Presses Universitaires de France, 1958, as *La Science Moderne*.]

Although the majority of the monographs included emphasize the late 16th and the 17th centuries, *The exact sciences* as treated by A. Koyré contain sections on *The revival of mathematical studies, Humanistic astronomy*, and *Physics in the 15th century*; and under *The descriptive sciences* various monographs relating to geology, chemistry, human biology, medicine, zoology, and botany contain introductory matter discussing earlier periods or refer to authors whose works were influential during the first century of printing.

B: 2   Chronological Table of
First Editions

I	Astronomy	IV	Natural Science
II	Mathematics	V	Physics
III	Medicine	VI	Technology

ABBREVIATIONS:
C   A collection of texts as in Opera, Opusculae, or a specialized compilation.
W   Issued *with* one or more other texts.

CATEGORIES AND NUMBERS:
The Roman numerals I–VI indicate, respectively, the six sections noted above. The subsidiary numbers in the designated columns refer to the numbered titles in the text.

DATE AND PLACE OF PRINTING:
The dates cited in the first column indicate the date of the first printing of a text, whether as a separate or in combination with other works. The corresponding place of printing is cited in the column following those naming author and title. The use of brackets, [ ], with place or date indicates supplied data.

Earliest Printing	Author and Title		Place	Categories and Numbers						
				I	II	III	IV	V	VI	
[1454]	Manung (Türkenkalender für 1455) [Ger.]	......	[Mainz]	76						
[1456]	Calendarium, 1457	......	[Mainz?]	35		324				
[c. 1457]	Cisioianus [Ger.]	......	[Mainz]	42						
[1458]	Planetentafel ("Calendar for 1448") [Ger.]	......	[Mainz]	90						
[1458–72]	Saliceto	De salute corporis	[Utrecht?]			510				W
1460	Balbi	Catholicon	Mainz						821	
[1461]	Almanach für Wien, 1462 [Ger.]	......	[Germany]	16		267				
[1466/67]	Gerson	De pollutione nocturna	[Cologne]			388				W
[1467]	Rabanus Maurus	Opus de universo	[Strasbourg]			491	687			
1469	Pliny the Elder	Historia naturalis	Venice			487	684	788	873	
[1469]	Strabo	De situ orbis	Rome						893	
1470	Dionysios Periegetes	De situ orbis	[Venice]				617			W
[c. 1470]	Dondis	Aggregator	[Strasbourg]			355				
[c. 1470]	Nider	De contractibus mercatorum	[Cologne]		200					
[1470–80]	Pietro da Tossignano	Consilium	[Venice]			482				

				I	II	III	IV	V	VI	
1470	Priscianus of Caesarea	Carmen de ponderibus....	[Venice]					792	875	W
[c. 1470]	Thomas Aquinas	De judiciis astrorum	[Cologne]	119						W
1471	Abū al-Kāsim (Abulcasis)	Liber servitoris ...	Venice			256				
[1471/72]	Aderlassregeln [Ger.]	......	[Basel]			259				
[1471(?)]	Bartholomaeus Anglicus	De proprietatibus rerum	[Basel]				595			
1471	Cicero	De natura deorum	Rome, [Venice]				612			
[c. 1471]	Columella	De cultu hortorum carmen	[Rome]				613		833	
1471	Crescenzi	Ruralia commoda	[Augsburg]			350	615			
[c. 1471]	Curtius Rufus	Historiae Alexandri Magni	[Venice]				616			
1471	Nicolaus Salernitanus	Antidotarium Nicolai	Venice			461				
[1471/72]	Simon of Genoa	Synonyma medicinae	[Ferrara]				697n			
1471	Tortelli	Orthographia	Venice						895a	C
[1471]	Yūhannā ibn Masawaih al-Mārdīnī (Mesuë the Younger)	Opera	[Venice]			553				
1472	Aristotle	De anima	Padua				572			
[c. 1472–75]	,,	Physica	[Padua]					736		
[c. 1472]	,,	Physiognomia	[Cologne]				581			W
[c. 1472]	,,	Secreta secretorum	[Cologne]				584			
[c. 1472–75]	Averroës	Commentarium in physicam	[Padua]					737		W
1472	Avicenna	Canon medicinae, liber III	[Italy]			288				
1472	Bagellardo	De aegritudinibus infantium	[Padua]			291				

Earliest Printing	Author and Title	Place	Categories and Numbers						
			I	II	III	IV	V	VI	
[1472]	Cato (Catone?)	De cometa anni 1472	[Naples]	40						
[1472]	De cometis	......	[Beromunster]	44						W
[1472/73]	Ferrari	Practica	[Milan]			365				W
[c. 1472]	Gerson	Triglogium astrologiae ...	[Cologne]	62						
1472	Gherardo da Sabbioneta	Theorica planetarum	Ferrara	63						
1472	Isidorus Hispalensis	Etymologiae libri XX	[Augsburg]				665		850	
1472	"	De vocabulario arithmetice discipline	[Augsburg]		180					
[1472]	Joannes de Sacro Bosco	Sphaera mundi	[Venice]	70						W
1472	Macrobius	In somnium Scipionis expositio	Venice	74						W
1472	Pietro d'Abano	Conciliator	Mantua			478				W
1472	"	De venenis	Mantua			480				W
[n.a. 1472]	Platea	Opus restitutionum, usurarum	[Italy]		209					
1472	Regimen sanitatis [Ger.]	......	Augsburg			495				W
[1472/73]	Rhasis	Liber nonus Almansoris	[Milan]			502				
1472	[A compilation]	Scriptores rei rusticae	Venice				695		889	
1472	Valturio	De arithmetica et militari geometria	[Verona]						897	C
[1473]	'Abd-al-'Azīz (Alchabitius)	Libellus ysagogicus	[Mantua]	1						
[c. 1473-74]	Aderlassbüchlein [Ger.]	......	[Alost(?)]			258				
1473	Aristotle	De caelo et mundi	Padua	25						

				I	II	III	IV	V	VI	
1473	Aristotle	Metaphysica	Padua	26						
[c. 1473]	"	Problemata	Mantua				583			
[c. 1473–74]	"	De sensu et sensato	[Padua]				580n			W
1473	Arnaldo de Villa Nova	De arte cognoscendi venena	Padua			273				W
1473	"	"	Mantua			273n				
1473	Avicenna	Canon medicinae	Milan			287	589			
[1]473	Boccaccio	De montibus, silvis . . .	Venice				603			
1473	Bonaventura de' Castelli	Ricetta dell' aqua de Porretta [Ital.]	[Padua]			315				
1473	Casini	De balneo Petriolo	[Padua]			330				W
[c. 1473/74]	Cepolla	De servitutibus urbanorum . . .	[Perugia]			332n				
1473	Galen	De virtute centaureae	Milan			376:11	643			W
1473	Gentile da Foligno	Balneae	[Padua]			380				W
1473–74	Guaineri	Opera medica	[Padua]			396				C
1473	Jābir ibn Ḥaiyān	Flos naturarum	[Rome]			428			851	
1473	Jacopo da Forlì	Expositio in Aphorismos Hippocratis	[Venice]			429				W
[1473]	Lucretius Carus	De rerum natura	[Brescia]				672	773		
[1473/74]	Manilius	Astronomicon	Nuremberg	75						
[1473]	Metlinger	Ein Regiment der jungen Kinder	[Augsburg]			452				
[1473]	Peurbach	Theoricae novae planetarum	[Nuremberg]	85						
1473	Pietro d'Abano	De lapide bezoar	Mantua			479				W

Earliest Printing	Author and Title		Place	Categories and Numbers					
				I	II	III	IV	V	VI	
1473	Simon of Genoa	Synonyma medicinae	Milan			523				
1473	Steinhöwel	Büchlein der Pestilenz [Ger.]	Ulm			530				
1473		De utilitatibus aquae balnei de Porretta	......	Padua			386				
1473	Valasco de Taranta	De epidemia et peste	Mantua, Padua			545				W
[c. 1473–74]	Vegetius	De re militari	[Utrecht]						898	
1473	Yūhannā ibn Sarābiyūn the Younger	Liber Serapionis aggregatus	Milan			556	714			W
1474	Aratos	Phaenomena	Bologna	23				730n		W
1474	Aristotle	De generatione et corruptione	Padua			576		733		
1474	„	Meteorologica	Padua				577	735		
[c. 1474]	„	Parva naturalia	[Padua]				580			
[c. 1474?]	Arnaldo de Villa Nova	Regimen sanitatis ad regem Aragonum	[France]			277				
1474	Averroës	In meteorologica	Padua					738		W
[147]4	Grassus	De oculis	[Ferrara]			392				
1474	Marliani	Quaestio de caliditate corporum	[Milan]				675	776		
1474	Modestus, pseud (?)	De re militari	[Venice]						861	W
1474	Pietro d'Abano	De physiognomia	Padua				683			
[1474]	Regiomontanus	Bücheranzeige [Ger.]	[Nuremberg]	98						

				I	II	III	IV	V	VI
[1474]	Regiomontanus	Calendarium, 1475–1515	[Nuremberg]	99					
1474	„	Ephemerides, 1475–1506	[Nuremberg]	102					
1474	Saliceto	La ciroxia [Ital.]	[Venice]			509	694		
1474	Silvatico	Liber medicinae pandectarum	Naples			522	697		
[c. 1474]	Thomas Aquinas	Commentum in octo libros Physicorum	[Genoa]					799	
[c. 1475]	Albertus Magnus, St.	Secreta mulierum et virorum	[Cologne]			262			
[c. 1475]	Algorithmus [Ger.]	......	[Trent]		127				
1475	Andalò di Negro	Tractatus astrolabii	Ferrara						808
[c. 1475]	Calendarium perpetuum	......	[Trent]	38					
[c. 1475]	Capelluti	De curatione pestiferorum	Rome			326			
1475	Cepolla	Cautelae	Milan			332			
[1475/76]	Cermisone	Consiglio [Ital.]	[Naples]			333			
[c. 1475]	„	Recollectae de urinis	[Upper Italy?]			335			
[14]75	Conrad von Megenberg	Buch der Natur [Ger.]	Augsburg			345	614		
[1475]	Gentile da Foligno	Consilium contra pestilentiam	[Padua]			382			
1475	Gregorius I	Dialogi [Ital.]	Venice			393			
1475	Hyginus	Poeticon astronomicon	[Ferrara]		67				
[c. 1475]	Jacopo da Forlì	Expositio in librum I Canonis Avicennae	[Upper Italy?]			430			
1475	„	Super I, II, III Tegni Galeni	Padua			431			

Earliest Printing	Author and Title		Place	Categories and Numbers					
				I	II	III	IV	V	VI
1475	Joannes Canonicus	Quaestiones super libros Physicorum Aristotelis	Padua					768	
[1475]	Lichtenberger	Conjunctio Saturni et Martis 1473	[Lübeck]	72					
[1475–80]	Ludolf von Suchen	Iter ad Terram Sanctam	[Strasbourg]				673		
[1475?]	Petrarca	De remediis utriusque fortunae	[Esslingen]			476			
[c. 1475]	Platina	De honesta voluptate et valetudine	[Rome]			485			872
1475	Ptolemy	Geographia	Vicenza		212				
[c. 1475]	Regiomontanus	Disputationes contra Cremonensia deliramenta	[Nuremberg]	101					
1475	Yūhannā ibn Masawaih al-Mārdīnī (Mesuë the Younger)	Il libro della consolatione delle medicine . . . [Ital.]	[Modena]			554			
1476	Albertus Magnus, St.	De mineralibus	[Padua]				567		807
[1476/77]	Albertus de Saxonia	Tractatus proportionum	[Padua]					725	
[c. 1476/78]	Algorithmus [Ital.]	. . . . . .	[Venice]		128				
[c. 1476]	'Ali ibn Ridwān	Commentaria Tegni Galeni	[Padua]			280n			W
1476	Aristotle	De animalibus	Venice				573		W
[c. 1476]	Articella	. . . . . .	[Padua]			280			W
1476	Avicenna	De viribus cordis	Padua			290			W
1476	Burley	Expositio in Aristotelis Physica	Padua					743	W

				I	II	III	IV	V	VI
1476	Cermisone	Consilia medica	Brescia			334			
[1476]	Gaetano di Thiene	Recollectae super Physica Aristotelis	[Treviso]					758	
[c. 1476]	Galen	Ars medica (Tegni)	[Padua]			376.1			W
[c. 1476]	"	In Hippocratis Aphorismos	[Padua]			376.3			W
[c. 1476]	"	In Hippocratis Prognosticam	[Padua]			376.4			W
[c. 1476]	"	In Hippocratis De victus ratione in morbis acutis	[Padua]			376.10			W
1476	Gentile da Foligno	Super prima fen quarti Canonis Avicennae	Padua			385			W
[b. 1476]	Hippocrates	Aphorismi cum commentationibus Galeni	[Padua]			408			W
[b. 1476]	"	De regimine acutorum morborum	[Padua]			420			W
[c. 1476]	Hunain ibn Ishāq (Johannitius)	Isagoge ad Tegni Galeni	[Padua]			425			W
[1476/77]	Jacopo da Forlì	De intensione et remissione formarum	[Padua]					766	
[c. 1476]	Mondino	Anatomia	[Padua]				679		
1476	Montagnana	Consilia medica	[Padua]			455			
[b. 1476]	Régime de l'épidémie [Fr.]	. . . . . .	[Lyon]			493			
1476	Regiomontanus	Calendarium, 1475–1531	Venice	100					
1476	Saliceto	Chirurgia	Piacenza			511			W
1476	"	Summa . . . curationis	Piacenza			511			W

Earliest Printing	Author and Title		Place	Categories and Numbers						
				I	II	III	IV	V	VI	
[c. 1476]	Theophilos	De pulsibus. De urinis	[Padua]				700			W
[c. 1477]	Albertus Magnus, St.	Liber aggregationis	[Ferrara]			261				
[c. 1477]	Gentile da Foligno	De febre	[Padua]			383				
[1477–87]	Guy de Chauliac	Chirurgia parva [Dutch]	[Delft]			399	651			
1477	[Odo de Meung?]	Macer floridus	Naples			442				
1477	Michael Scotus	Liber phisiognomiae	[Venice]			453	678			
1477	Ortolff von Bayrlandt	Arzneibuch [Ger.]	Nuremberg			466				
[c. 1477]	Pflaum	Calendarium, 1477–1554 [Ger.]	[Ulm]	86						
1477	Polo, Marco	Buch des edlen Ritters [Ger.]	Nuremberg				686			
[14]77	Puff von Schrick	Von den ausgebrannten Wassern [Ger.]	Augsburg				878			
[1477/78]	Robertus Anglicus	De astrolabii compositione	[Perugia]						884	W
[1477/78]	,,	De astrolabio canones	Perugia						884	W
[c. 1477]	Swineshead	Opus aureum calculationum	[Padua]					794		
[1477 or later]	Vincent de Beauvais	Speculum doctrinale	[Strasbourg]			550				
1478	Albertus Magnus, St.	De animalibus	Rome				566			
[1478]	Arnaldo de Villa Nova	Von Bewahrung ... der Weine [Ger.]	[Esslingen]			279			817	
1478	Arte dell' abbaco [Ital.]	......	Treviso		144					
1478	Bavario de Bavarii	Regimento della peste [Ital.]	Bologna			297				

				I	II	III	IV	V	VI	W
[1478–80?]	Benzi	Expositio super IV fen I Canonis Avicennae	Pavia			306				W
1478	Celsus	De medicina	Florence			331	610			
1478	Dioskorides	De materia medica	Colle			354	618			
1478	Guy de Chauliac	Chirurgia [Fr.]	Lyon			398	650			
[1478]	Manfredi	Trattato della pestilenza [Ital.]	[Bologna]			447				
[1478–80?]	Marsiglio da San Sofia	Super IV primi Avicennae	Pavia			306n				W
1478	Oppianos	Halieutica	Colle di Valdelsa				680			
[c. 1478]	Prognosticatio for 1479	......	[Lübeck]	93						
[1478]	Rhasis	Libro III dell Almansor chiamato Cibaldone [Ital.]	[Venice]			503				
1478	Soldi	Opus de peste	Bologna			524				
[n.a. 1478]	Vincent de Beauvais	Speculum naturale	[Strasbourg]				712			
1479	Calendarium, 1479–1578	......	Geneva	36						
1479	Gentile da Foligno	De proportionibus medicinarum	Pavia			384				
1479	Jacopo da Forlì	Expositio in Avicennae de generatione embryonis	Pavia				666			
[1479/80]	Lanfranchi	Chirurgia maior [Fr.]	[Lyon]			437				
1479	Regimen sanitatis parvum	......	Geneva			497				W
1479	Savonarola, Giovanni Michele	Practica medicinae	Colle di Valdelsa			514				
1479	Yūḥannā ibn Sarābiyūn the Elder (Serapion the Elder)	Breviarium medicinae	Venice			555				

Earliest Printing	Author and Title		Place	Categories and Numbers					
				I	II	III	IV	V	VI
1480	Arcolani	Expositio noni libri Almansoris	[Padua]			271			W
[n.a. 1480]	Berlinghieri	Geographia in terza rima [Ital.]	[Florence]		147				
1480	Bernardus de Gordonio	Practica	Naples			312			
[1480]	Cernisone	Ricette [Ital.]	[Milan]			336			
[c. 1480]	Ferrari	Perutilia consilia	[Pavia]			364			
[1480]	Habichtbuch [Ger.]	......	[Augsburg]				652		
[n.a. 1480]	Marsiglio da San Sofia	Expositio in particulam ... Aphorismorum Hippocratis	[Padua]			448			W
[c. 1480]	Marsilius ab Inghen	Abbreviationes libri Physicorum Aristotelis	[Pavia]					777	
1480	Pietro d'Argellata	Chirurgia	Venice			481			
[1480]	Regimen contra pestilentiam	......	[Paris]			494			
[c. 1480]	Regimen sanitatis Salernitanum	......	[Cologne]			498			W
[n.b. 1480]	Reg. san. Sal.: Noviter correctum ... anno 1480 (Montpellier)	......	[Lyon?]			499			
[1480/82]	Themo	Quaestiones Meteorologicorum Aristotelis	[Pavia]					798	
1481	Albertus de Saxonia	Quaestiones ... de caelo et mundo	Pavia	11				723	
[1481]	Arsmetrike	......	[Westminster]		143				W

				I	II	III	IV	V	VI	
1481	Benzi	De conservare la persona [Ital.]	Milan			309n				W
1481	"	Consiglio [Ital.]	Milan			309n				W
1481	"	Trattato circa la conservazione della sanità [Ital.]	Milan			309				W
[n.b. 1481]	Bradwardine	De proportionibus velocitatum in motibus	Paris					740		W
1481	Chiarini	Libro che tratta di mercanzie [Ital.]	Florence		157					
[c. 1481]	Faber von Budweis	Prognostikon für Leipzig, 1482 [Ger.]	[Leipzig]	54						
1481–84	Falcucci	Sermones medicinales	Pavia			361	633			
1481	Ficino	Consiglio contro la pestilenza [Ital.]	Florence			366				
1481	Galen	De medicinis expertis	Milan			376:6				W
[c. 1481–83]	Herbarium Apulei	. . . . . .	[Rome]			401				
1481	Heytesbury	De moto locali	[Pavia]					762		W
1481	"	Regule solvendi sophismata	[Pavia]					764		W
1481	"	Sophismata	[Pavia]					765		W
1481	Hippocrates	De aere et aqua et regionibus	Milan				658			W
1481	"	Capsula eburnea	Milan			410				W
[c. 1481]	"	De insomniis	[Rome]			413				
1481	"	De natura hominis	Milan				660			W
1481	"	De pharmaciis	Milan			417				W
1481	"	Secreta	Milan			421				W

333

Earliest Printing	Author and Title		Place	Categories and Numbers					
				I	II	III	IV	V	VI
1481	Lanfranchi	Chirurgia parva [Dutch]	Louvain			438			W
[c. 1481]	Maimonides	De regimine sanitatis	Florence			445			
[n.b. 1481]	Oresme	De proportionibus proportionum	Paris					783	
[1481]	Practica, 1482 [Ger.]	......	[Mainz]	92					
1481	Rhasis	Liber ad Almansorem, libri X	Milan			500	689		W
1481	Strode	Consequentiae	[Pavia]					764n	
1481	Yūhannā ibn Masawaih the Elder (Mesuë the Elder)	Aphorismi	Milan			552			W
1482/83	Abrāhām ben-'Ezrā	De luminaribus et diebus criticis	[Padua]	3					
[c. 1482]	Angelo da Fossombrone	De velocitate motus	[Pavia]					729	
1482	Aristotle	De coloribus	Venice				575		W
1482	,,	De motu animalium	Venice				579		W
1482	,,	De plantis [spurious]	Venice				582		W
1482	Averroës	Colliget	Ferrara			285	587		
1482	Benzi	Consilia ad diversas aegritudines	[Bologna]			300			
	,,	Cura ... morsi a serpente venenoso	[Bologna]			301			W
1482	Euclid	Elementa geometriae	Venice		163				
1482	Hypsicles of Alexandria	Interpretatio libri Euclidis	Venice		163n				

	Author	Title	Place	I	II	III	IV	V	VI	W
1482	Jacopo da Sancto Martino	De latitudinibus formarum	Padua					767		
1482	Lul, Ramòn	Arbor scientiae	Barcelona						856	
1482	Magninus Mediolanensis	Regimen sanitatis	Louvain			443				
[1482]	Marliani	Disputatio	[Pavia]					774		
1482	„	De proportione motuum in velocitate	Pavia					775		
[1482?]	Peckham, John de	Prospectiva communis	[Milan]		205					
1482	Pelacani	Questiones de latitudinibus formarum Johannis Horen [Oresme]	Padua					785		
1482	Sanct Climent	Suma de arismetica [Catalan]	Barcelona		229					
[1482]	Sherwood	Epitone de ludo arithmomachiae	[Rome]		235					
1482	Wagner	Rechenbuch [Ger.]	Bamberg		249					
1483	Alfonso X	Tabulae astronomicae	[Venice]		14					W
1483	Arnaldo de Villa Nova	Breviarium practice medicinae	Milan			274				
1483	Avicenna	Cantica de medicina	Venice		289		590			
1483	Beldamandis, Prosdocimus de	Algorithmus de integris	Padua		146					W
1483	Danck, Johann, de Saxonia	Canones in tabulas Alphonsi	[Venice]	48						W
[1483]	Engel, Johann	Almanach . . . 1484 [Ger.]	[Bamberg]	50						
[1483–90]	Frontinus	De aquaeductu urbis Romae	[Rome]						842	

335

Earliest Printing	Author and Title	Place	I	II	III	IV	V	VI	
1483	Gaetano di Thiene	Expositio regularum et sophismata Hentisberi	Venice				755		
1483	Galen	De divisione librorum Galeni	Venice			376:2			W
1483	Gilles of Corbeil	De urinis carmen	Padua			391			
1483	Heytesbury	Probationes conclusionum in regulis positarum	[Pavia]					763	
[c. 1483–90]	Hippocrates	Demonstratio quod artes sunt	[Rome]			407.1			W
1483	,,	Epidemiae libri VII	Venice			411			W
[c. 1483–90]	,,	Invectiva in obtrectatores medicinae	[Rome]			407.2			W
1483	,,	Iusiurandum	Venice			414			W
1483	,,	Medicinae lex	Venice			415			W
1483	,,	De medicorum astrologia	Padua			416			
1483	,,	De natura foetus	Venice				659		W
1483	,,	Opera parva, *so-called*	[Rome]			407			C
[c. 1483–90]	,,	De tuenda valetudine	[Rome]			407.6			W
[c. 1483–90]	,,	De victu	[Rome]			407.7			W
[1483–90]	Jābir ibn Ḥaiyān	Summa perfectionis magisterii	[Rome]					852	W
1483	Jean de Linières (Lignières)	Algorithmus	Padua		182				W
[c. 1483]	Pierre d'Ailly (Alliaco)	Imago mundi	(Louvain)	89					W

336

				I	II	III	IV	V	VI	
1483	Theophrastos	De historia et causis plantarum	Treviso			533	702			
[1483–95]	Vitruvius Pollio	De architectura	[Rome]						899	
1484	Abrāhām ben-'Ezrā	De nativitatibus	Venice	4						W
1484	Bate, Henri	Magistralis compositio astrolabii	Venice						823	W
1484	Borghi, Pietro	Arithmetica [Ital.]	Venice		151					
[1484]	Galen	Introductorium ad medicinam	[Milan]			376:5				W
1484	Gilles de Corbeil	De pulsibus carmen	Padua				648			
[14]84	*Herbarius*	......	Mainz			402				
[1484/88]	Lirer	Chronik von allen Königen . . . [Ger]	[Ulm]						855	
[1484–85]	Plato	Opera	Florence	91		486				C
1484/85	Ptolemy	Quadripartitum, sive Tetrabiblon	Venice	96						W
1484	Torni	De motu locali Hentisberi	Pisa					801		
1484	Valasco de Taranta	Philonium pharmaceuticum et chirurgicum	Barcelona			546	706			
1485	Abū-l-Hasan (Albohazen)	Liber in iudiciis astrorum	Venice	6						
1485	Alberti	De re aedificatoria	Florence						806	
[1485]	Albrecht, *Meister*	Arzneibuch der Rosse [Ger]	[Augsburg]			263				
[1485/86]	Bartolommeo *dalli Sonetti*	Isolario [Ital.]	[Venice]						822	

Earliest Printing	Author and Title		Place	I	II	III	IV	V	VI
[b. 1485]	Eaux artificielles [Fr.]	......	Vienne			359			
[1485]	Eck, Paulus	Almanac, 1486	[Leipzig]	49					
1485	Firmin de Beauval	De mutatione aëris	Venice					753	
1485	Gart der Gesundheit [Ger.]	......	Mainz			379			
[1485]	Granollachs	Sommario . . . di astrologia [Ital.]	[Naples]	64					
1485	Savonarola	De balneis et thermis	Ferrara			512			
1485	Torres	Eclipse del sol [Sp.]	Salamanca	121					
[c. 1486–88]	Arbolaire [Fr.]	......	[Besançon]			269			
1486	Barnes	The Book of hawking	St. Albans				594		
1486	Breydenbach	Peregrinatio in Terram Sanctam	Mainz				605		
1486	Bricot	In cursum totius Physices et Metaphysicorum Aristotelis	Lyon					741	W
1486	Calendarium, 1486–1504	......	Venice	37					
[1486]	Faber von Budweis	Almanach für Leipzig, 1487 [Lat.]	[Leipzig]	53					
1486	Georges de Bruxelles	Quaestiones super Physica	Lyon					759	
1486	Henri de Ferrières	De chasse [Fr.]	Chambéry				654		
1486	Rhasis	Liber dictus Elhavi continens artem medicinae	Brescia			501			
1487	Aelianus	De instruendis aciebus tractatus	Rome						804

Categories and Numbers

				I	II	III	IV	V	VI	
1487	Bernardus de Gordonio	De pulsibus	Ferrara			312n				W
1487	"	De urinis	Ferrara			312n				W
[c. 1487/88]	Computus Cracoviensis	......	[Leipzig]	45						
1487	Frontinus	Strategematicon	Rome						843	
1487	Isḥāq al Isrā'īlī	De particularibus diaetis	Padua			427				
1487	Savonarola	De febribus	Bologna			513				
1487	"	De pulsibus, urinis et egestionibus	Bologna			515				
1487	Sermoneta	Super Aphorismos Hippocratis et libros Tegni Galeni	Milan			521				
1487	Sulpicius, ed.	Scriptores rei militaris	Rome						888	C
1488	Abū-Ma'shar Ga'far (Albumasar)	Flores astrologiae	Augsburg	7						
1488/89	Albertus Magnus, St	Physica	Venice					722		
1488	Anianus	Computus manualis	Strasbourg		134					W
1488?	Aristarchos	De magnitudinibus.... solis et lunae	Venice	24						W
1488	Benzi	Quaestio de malitia complexionis diversae	Pavia			307				W
1488	Boethius	Arithmetica	Augsburg		148					
1488	Engel, Johann	Astrolabium planum	Augsburg	51						
1488	Gaetano di Thiene	Commentarium	Venice					754		W
[1488?]	Gentile da Foligno	Consilia	[Pavia]			381				

Earliest Printing	Author and Title	Place	I	II	III	IV	V	VI	
								Categories and Numbers	
1488	Joannes de Sacro Bosco	De arte numerandi	Strasbourg							W
[1488]	Lichtenberger	Prognosticatio, 1488–1567	[Ulm]	73	185					
1489	Abū-Maʿshar Gaʿfar (Albumasar)	Introductorium in astronomiam	Augsburg	8						
1489	„	De magnis conjunctionibus	Augsburg	9						
1489	Arcolani	Expositio in I fen IV Canonis Avicennae	Ferrara			270				
1489	Bavario de Bavarii	Consilia medica	Bologna			296				W
1489	Dino del Garbo	De emplastris et unguentis	Ferrara			351n				W
1489	„	Expositio super III, IV, et parte V fen IV Canonis Avicennae	Ferrara			351				W
1489	Estwood	Summa astrologiae judicialis	Venice	52		360				
1489	Leopoldus, *Dux Austriae*	Compilatio de astrorum scientia	Augsburg	71				749		
1489	„	De mutatione aeris	Augsburg					771		W
1489	Maimonides	Aphorismi	Bologna			444	674			W
[1489–94]	Marsilius ab Inghen	Quaestionum optimarum cursus	[Cologne]					778		
1489–91	Mondino	Expositio super canones universales	Venice			454				W
1489	Torrigiani	Plusquam commentum in Microtegni Galeni	Bologna			538				

340

				I	II	III	IV	V	VI
1489	Widmann	Rechnung auf allen Kaufmannschaft [Ger.]	Leipzig	253					
1489	Zerbis	Gerontocomia	Rome			558			
[c. 1490]	Alcañiz	Regiment de la pestilencia [Sp.]	[Valencia]			264			
[c. 1490/95]	Algorithmus integrorum	......	[Leipzig]		129				
[c. 1490/95]	Algorithmus minutiarum physicarum	......	[Leipzig]		131				
[c. 1490/95]	Algorithmus minutiarum vulgarium	......	[Leipzig]		132				
1490	Aristotle	Chiromantia	Ulm				574		
1490/91	Avenzohar	Antidotarium	Venice			284			W
1490/91	"	Rectificatio medicationis et regiminis	Venice			284			W
1490	Galen	Opera [73 'firsts']	Venice			375	642		C
1490	Jean de Tournemire	Clarificatorium ... super nono Almansoris	Lyon			432			
1490	Pierre d'Ailly	Concordantia astronomie cum theologia	Augsburg	88					
1490	Portolano per tutti i navichanti [Ital.]	......	Venice					874	
[c. 1490]	Regimen sanitatis parisiense	......	[Leipzig]			496			
1490	Regiomontanus	Tabella sinus recti	Augsburg		217				W
1490	"	Tabulae directionum et profectionum	Augsburg		217				W

341

Earliest Printing	Author and Title		Place	Categories and Numbers						
				I	II	III	IV	V	VI	
1491	Aristotle	De inspiratione et respiratione	Cologne				580n			W
1491	Benzi	Expositio in I [et II] fen I Canonis Avicennae	Ferrara			303				W
1491/92	Boethius, *spurious*	De geometria	Venice		149					W
1491	Bonatti	Introductio ad iudicia stellarum	Augsburg	31						
1491/92	Calandri	Pictagoras arithmetrice introductor [*Ital.*]	Florence		154					
1491	*Calendrier des bergiers* [*Fr.*]	......	Paris			325				
1491	Cittadino	Tractatus de febre	Ferrara			303n				W
1491	Gaetano di Thiene	De intensione et remissione formarum	Venice					756		W
1491	"	De reactione	Venice					757		W
[1491]	Hernsheimer	Almanach für Mainz, 1492 [*Ger.*]	[Mainz]	65						
1491	*Hortus sanitatis*	......	Mainz			424	663			
1491	Ketham	Fasciculus medicinae	Venice			436	667			W
1492	Abû Bakr al-Ḥasan (Albubather)	De nativitatibus	Venice	5						
1492–93	Barbaro	Castigationes Plinianae	Rome				592			
1492	Brant	Von dem donnerstein . . . im xcii. iar [*Ger. & Lat.*]	[Basel]	32						

				I	II	III	IV	V	VI
1492	Haly Abbas	Liber medicinae sive Liber regius	Venice			400	653		
1492	Le Fèvre d'Étaples	In Aristotelis octo Physicos libros paraphrasis	Paris					770	
1492	Leonicenus	De Plinii . . . in medicina erroribus	Ferrara			441	671		
1492	Montis, Petrus de	De dignoscendis hominibus	Milan			458			
1492	Pellos	Compendiom de lo abaco [Ital.]	Turin		206				W
1492	"	De la art arithmeticha [Ital.]	Turin		206				W
1492	Tardif	L'art de faulconnerie [Fr.]	Paris				699		
1492	Urbano of Bologna	Expositio commentarii Averrois super Physica Aristotelis	Venice					802	
1493	Aegidius Romanus (Colonna)	In Aristotelis Physica commentum	Padua					719	
1493	Al-Farghāni (Alfraganus)	Compilatio astronomica	Ferrara	13					
1493	Benedetti	De observatione in pestilentia	Venice			298			
1493	Benzi	Super Aphorismos Hippocratis et Galeni expositio	Ferrara			308			
[1493]	Collenuccio	Pliniana defensio adversus Nicolai Leoniceni accusationem	Ferrara			344			
1493/94	Cornazzano	Dell' arte militare [Ital.]	Venice						834

Earliest Printing	Author and Title	Place	Categories and Numbers						
			I	II	III	IV	V	VI	
1493	Folz	Wem der geprant Wein nutz sey . . . [Ger.]	Bamberg						840	
[1493]	Honiger	Almanach für Erfurt, 1494 [Ger.]	[Nuremberg]	66						
1493	Riedrer	Spiegel [Ger.]	Freiburg im Breisgau						883	
[1493]	Ruffo	Arte di conoscere la natura dei cavali [Ital.]	Venice			508				
1493/94	Tartaret	Quaestiones super Philosophia et Metaphysica Aristotelis	[Poitiers]					797		W
1494	Achillini	De distributionibus ac de proportione motuum	Bologna					718		
1494	Barzizza	Introductorium ad opus practicum medicinae	Pavia			295				W
1494	Brudzewo	Commentum in theoricas planetarum	Milan	33						
[n.a. 1494]	*Computus Nurembergensis*	. . . . . .	[Leipzig]	46						
[c. 1494/95]	Faber von Budweis	Tabulae solis et lunae coniunctionum [for Leipzig]	[Leipzig]	55						
1494	Ferrari	Expositiones super . . . fen XXII tertii Canonis Avicennae	Milan			363				
[c. 1494]	Grapaldi	De partibus aedium	[Parma]						846	
1494	Jung	Regimen der Pestilenz [Ger.]	Augsburg			435				

				I	II	III	IV	V	VI
1494	Ockham	Summulae in Physica Aristotelis	Bologna					782	
[1494]	Onasandros	De optimo imperatore eiusque officio	Rome						888n W
1494	Pacioli	Somma di aritmetica, geometria . . . [Ital.]	Venice		203				
1494	Simon de Lendenaria	Supra sex sophismata Hentisberi	Venice					793 W	
1494	Tiberti	Chyromantia	Bologna				703		
1494/95	Willem Gilliszoon	Super coelestium motuum indagatione sine calculo	Cremona	122					
[c. 1495]	Algorithmus linealis	. . . . . .	[Leipzig]						
1495–98	Aristotle	Opera [Grk.]	Venice		130		570		C
1495	Arnaldo de Villa Nova	Antidotarium	Valencia			272			
[c. 1495]	"	Speculum medicinae	[Leipzig]			278			
1495	Bianchini (Blanchinus)	Tabulae celestium motuum	Venice	29					
1495/96	Bradwardine	Arithmetica speculativa	Paris		152				
1495	"	Geometria speculativa	Paris		153				
1495/96	Ciruelo	Algorismus	Paris		158				
1495	Herodianos	De numeris [Grk.]	Venice		177				W
[c. 1495–1500]	Hippocrates	De insania Democriti	[Augsburg]			412			W
[c. 1495]	Ortolff von Bayrlandt	Büchlein der schwangeren Frauen [Ger.]	[Augsburg]			466n			
[1495]	Peurbach	Algorithmus	[Vienna]		207				

Earliest Printing	Author and Title		Place	Categories and Numbers					
				I	II	III	IV	V	VI
1495[96?]	Pico della Mirandola	Disputationes contra astrologos	Bologna	87					W
[1495]	Schellig	In malum de francia consilium	[Heidelberg]			518			
[c. 1495–1500]	Ulsen	Carmina	[Augsburg]			541			W
[n.b. 1495]	Zerbis	De cautelis medicorum	[Venice]			557			
1496	Aristotle	De vegetabilibus	Venice				586		W
[1496–99]	Benzi	De cura lapidis renum	Pavia			302			W
1496	„	Expositio super libros Tegni Galeni	Pavia			305			
1496	Brant	De pestilentiali scorra . . .	Basel			316			W
1496	Burley	De intensione et remissione formarum	Venice					744	
1496	Dino del Garbo	De ponderibus et mensuris	Venice			352			W
1496	Ganivet	Amicus medicorum	Lyon			378			W
[1496]	Grünpeck	De pestilentiali scorra . . .	[Augsburg]			395			
[c. 1496]	Hippocrates	Prognostica (Secreta)	[Memmingen]			420			W
1496	Jordanus de Nemore	Arithmetica	Paris		187				
1496	Le Fèvre d'Étaples	Epitoma in . . . arithmeticos Boetii	Paris		192				W
1496	„	De ludo arithmomachiae	Paris		193				W
[1496]	Le livre du faulcon [Fr.]	. . . . . .	Paris				669		

346

				I	II	III	IV	V	VI	
1496	Leonardi	Liber desideratus canonum aequatorii coelestium motuum	Venice						854	
1496	Regiomontanus *and* Peurbach	Epytoma in Almagestum Ptolemaei	Venice	103						
1496	Scillacio	Opuscula	Pavia			520				C
1496	Sommariva	Del mal franzoso [*Ital.*]	Venice			525				
[1496]	Torrella	De imaginibus astrologicis, 1496	Valencia?	120						
[1496]	Ulsen	Pharmacandi accidens	[Nuremberg]			542				W
[1496]	"	Pharmacandi substantia	[Nuremberg]			542				W
1496	"	Vaticinium in epidemicam scabiem	Nuremberg			543				
1496	Zacuto	Almanach perpetuum .... Radix est 1473	Leiria	123						
1497	Aristotle	De animalium incessu [*Grk.*]	Venice				570*n*			W
1497	"	Mechanica [*Grk.*], *spurious*	Venice					734		W
[1497/98]	*Astrolabii canones*	......	[Venice]						819	
1497	Avenzohar	De curatione lapidis	[Venice]			283				W
[1497]	Brunschwig	Anathomia ossium corporis humani [*Ger.*]	[Strasbourg]				607			
1497	"	Chirurgia [*Ger.*]	Strasbourg			320				
1497	Censorinus	De die natali	Bologna				611			W
1497	Cleomedes	De motu circulari corporum caelestium	Brescia	43						W

Earliest Printing	Author and Title	Place	I	II	III	IV	V	VI	
1497	Firmicus Maternus	De nativitatibus	Venice	56					
[n.b. 1497]	Gilino	De morbo quem gallicum nuncupant	[Ferrara]			390			
1497	Leonicenus	De epidemia quam . . . morbum Gallicum vocant	Venice			440			
[1497?]	Montesauro	De dispositionibus quas vulgares mal franzoso appellant	[Bologna]			457			
1497	Rhasis	De proprietatibus membrorum . . . animalium	[Venice]				690		W
[c. 1497]	Savonarola	Contro gli astrologi [Ital.]	[Florence]	108					
[1497–98]	Steber	A malafranczos morbo gallorum praeservatio	Vienna			529			
1497	Theophrastos	Opera [Grk.]	Venice				701		C
1497	"	De vertigine oculorum [Grk.]	Venice			534			W
1497	Thomas Aquinas, St.	Expositio Meteorologorum Aristotelis	[Cologne]					799n	W
1497	Torrella	Tractatus cum consiliis contra pudendagram	Rome			537			
[1497]	Widmann	Tractatus de pustulis	[Strasbourg]			551			
1498/99	Albertus Magnus, St.	Summa de creaturis	Venice				568		
1498	Apicius, pseud.	De re coquinaria	Milan						815
1498	Benzi	Expositio in I fen IV Canonis Avicennae	Pavia			304			W

				I	II	III	IV	V	VI	
1498	Galen	De praesagitura	Venice			376:7				W
1498	,,	Praesagium experientia confirmatum	Venice			376:8				W
1498	,,	De succedaneis	Venice			376:9				W
1498	Nicephoros Gregoras	De astrolabo	Venice						862	W
1498	Paulus Venetus	In Aristotelem De generatione et corruptione	Venice				681			W
1498	Proclos	De fabrica usque astrolabii	Venice						877	W
1498	Rhasis	De pestilentia	Venice			504				W
1498	Savonarola	De vermibus	Venice			516				W
1498	Scanaroli	Disputatio de morbo gallico	Bologna			517				
1499	Aratos	Phaenomena [Lat.-Grk.]	Venice	23n						W
1499	Dioskorides	De materia medica [Grk.]	Venice			354n				
1499	Geminos	Elementa astronomiae [Grk.]	Venice	60						W
1499	'Isā ibn ʾAli (Jesu Haly)	De cognitione infirmitatum oculorum et curatione earum	Venice			426				W
[1499–1505]	Johannes Mercurius	Contra pestem	[Rome]			434				
1499	Martianus Capella	De nuptiis Philologiae et Mercurii	Vicenza	77						
1499	Nicander	Alexipharmaca [Grk.]	Venice			460				W
1499	,,	Theriaca [Grk.]	Venice			460				W
1499	Paulus Venetus	Super Physica Aristotelis et super commento Averrois	Venice					784		

Earliest Printing	Author and Title		Place	Categories and Numbers						
				I	II	III	IV	V	VI	
1499	Peylick	De anathomia totius corporis humani	Leipzig				682			W
1499	Proclos	Sphaera [*Grk.*]	Venice		211					W
1499	Regiomontanus	In ephemerides commentarium	Ulm	104						W
1499	Stöffler *and* Pflaum	Almanach nova, 1499–1531	Ulm	115						W
1499	"	Canon de domibus fabricandis	Ulm	115						W
1499	"	Erklärung des neuen Almanach [*Ger.*]	Ulm	115						W
1499	Vergilius, Polydorus	De inventoribus rerum	Venice				707		898a	W
1500/01	Abū al-Kāsim (Abulkasis)	Cyrurgia	Venice			255				W
[*c.* 1500]	*Algorithmus novus*	......	[Cologne]		133					W
[*a.* 1500]	Arnaldo de Villa Nova	Phlebotomia	[Lyon]			276				W
[1500]	Augustone	De curatione elephantiasis	[Genève]			282				W
[1500]	"	Defensio Cornelii Celsi	[Genève]			282				W
[1500]	"	De helebori natura	[Genève]			282				W
[*c.* 1500]	Avicenna	De animalibus	[Venice]				588			
[*a.* 1500]	Barbantini	De dieta	[Lyon]			293				W
1500	Brunschwig	Kleines Distillierbuch [*Ger.*]	Strasbourg						829	
1500	"	Pestbuch [*Ger.*]	[Strasbourg]			321				
1500	Grosseteste	Super octo libris Physicorum Aristotelis	Venice					761		W

				I	II	III	IV	V	VI
[1500]	Licht	Algorithmus linealis	Leipzig		194		668		
[c. 1500?]	Le livre de la chasse [Fr.]	......	[Paris]						
[c. 1500]	Nicolaus de Cusa	De docta ignorantia	[Strasbourg]	81					W
[c. 1500]	"	Idiota	[Strasbourg]					779	W
[c. 1500]	"	Opuscula theologica et mathematica	[Strasbourg]		198				C
1500	Pferdearznei-Büchlein [Ger.]	......	Erfurt			477			
[1500]	Pistoris	Declaratio defensiva .... de malofranco	[Leipzig]			484			
1500	Torrella	Dialogus de dolore	Rome			536			
1501	Arnaldo de Villa Nova, ed.	Computus ecclesiasticus	Venice	27					
1501	Autolycos	De ortibus et occasibus	Venice	28	145				W
1501	"	De sphaera quae movetur	Venice	28	145				W
1501	Euclid	Catoptrica	Venice		162				W
1501	"	Perspectiva seu Optica	Venice		164				W
1501	Hundt, Magnus, the Elder	Antropologium	Leipzig				664		
1501	Huswirt	Enchiridion novus	Cologne		178				
1502	Benedetti	Historia corporis humani	Venice				596		
1502	Johannes de Cusa	Algorismus	Zwolle		186b				
1502	Leonardi	Speculum lapidum	Venice				670		
1502	Pollux	Onomasticon [Grk. & Lat.]	Venice				685		
1502	Zerbis	Liber anathomie corporis humani	Venice				716		

Earliest Printing	Author and Title		Place	Categories and Numbers						
				I	II	III	IV	V	VI	
1503	Achillini	De subjecto physionomiae	Bologna				560			
1503	Archimedes	Circuli dimensio	Venice		142					W
1503	"	Quadratura parabolae	Venice		142					W
1503	Gaurico, ed.	Tetragonismus, idest circuli quadratura	Venice		170					
1503	Grosseteste	De fractionibus et reflexionibus radiorum	Nuremberg		176					
[1503]	Grünpeck	Libellus de mentulagra....	[Reutlingen]			394				
1503	Pasi	Tariffa de pesi e mesure [Ital.]	Venice		204					
1503	Reisch	Margarita philosophica	Freiburg [im Breisgau]		219		688		882	
[1504]	Albertus de Saxonia	In Physica Aristotelis	[Venice]					724		W
1504	Alexander of Tralles	Practica	Lyon			265				
1504	Arnaldo de Villa Nova	Opera	Lyon			272n			816	C
1504	Māshā 'Allāh	De scientia motus orbis	Nuremberg	78						
1504	Rocca	Chyromantie et physionomie...	Bologna			505	691			
1504	Stöffler and Pflaum	Almanach nova, 1504–1531	Venice	116						W
[c. 1505]	Averroës	De tyriaca	[Lyon]			286				W
[c. 1505]	"	De venenis	[Lyon]			286				W
1505	Bergbüchlein	......	Augsburg				601		824	W

Date	Author	Title	City	I	II	III	IV	V	VI
[1505?]	Fontaine	La fontaine des amoureux de science [Fr.]	[Paris]						841
1505	Giovanni di Casali	Quaestio subtilis de velocitate....	Venice					760	
[c. 1505]	Oresme	Traicté de l'espère [Fr.]	Paris		201				
1505	Politus	Tractatus proportionum introductorius...	Venice					789	
1505	Theōn of Alexandria	Interpretatio libri Euclidis	Venice		244				W
1506	Champier	De medicinae claris scriptoribus	Lyon			340			
1506	Dullaert	Super octo libros Phisicorum Aristotelis	Paris					748	
1507	Abrāhām ben-'Ezrā	In re iudiciali opera	Venice	2					
1507	Al-Kindi	De iudiciis astrorum	Venice	15					
1507	"	De pluviis imbribus et ventis...	Venice					728	
1507	Benivieni	De abditis nonnullis ac mirandis morborum ...	Florence			299	597		
1507	Ptolemy	Planisphaerium	Rome		213				W
1507	Waldseemüller	Cosmographiae introductio	St. Dié		250				W
1508	Die maniere om te leeren cyffren [Dutch]	......	Brussels		179n				
1508	Nifo	De Physica Aristotelis	Venice					780	W

Earliest Printing	Author and Title	Place	I	II	III	IV	V	VI
1509	Bertuccio — Collectorium	Lyon			313	602		C
1509	Buridan — Super octo Phisicorum libros Aristotelis	Paris					742	
1509	Pacioli — De divina propertione	Venice		202				
1509	Ptolemy — De iudiciis ad Aristonem	Venice	95					W
[c. 1509]	*Regimento do estrolabio e do quadrante* [Port.] —	[Lisbon]						879 W
[1509]	Thome — Liber de triplici motu	Paris					800	
1510	Paulos of Aigina — Praecepta salubria	Paris			475			
1510	Strabo, Walafrid — Hortulus	Vienna				698		
[c. 1510]	Walter of Henley — Boke of husbandry	[London]				713		
1511	Arnaldo de Villa Nova — De conservanda juventute...	Leipzig			275			W
[n.b. 1511]	Coronel — Physicae perscrutationes	[Paris]					747	
[c. 1511]	Hippocrates — De victus ratione, I-IV	[Paris]			422			W
1512	Bouelles — Physicorum elementorum libri X	Paris					739	
1512	Brunschwig — Liber de arte distillandi... (Grosses Distillierbuch)	Strasbourg						828
1512	Champier — Speculum Galeni	Lyon			342			
1512	Galen — De oculis	[Lyon]			377.20			W
1512	Hippocrates — De praeparatione hominis	Tübingen			418			

Categories and Numbers

				I	II	III	IV	V	VI	W
1512	Joannes de Stobnicza	Introductio in Ptholomei Cosmographia	Cracow		186					
1512	Juan de Ortega	Tratado . . . de arismética y de geometria [Sp.]	Sevilla		188					
1512	Māshā 'Allāh	Tractatus de compositione astrolabii	Strasbourg						859	W
1512/13	Stöffler	Elucidatio fabricae ususque astrolabii	Oppenheim						892	
1513	Clichtove	De mystica numerorum	Paris		159					
1513	Röslin	Der schwangern Frauen [Ger.]	Strasbourg			507				
1513	Waldseemüller	Tabula nova	Strasbourg						900	W
1514	Dino del Garbo	Super IV fen primi Avicennae	Venice			353				
1514	Hock von Brackenau	Mentagra	[Strasbourg]			423				
1514	Joannes de Rupescissa	De consideratione quintae essentiae	Venice			433			853	W
1514	Köbel	Ein new geordnet Rechenbiechlin auf den linien . . . . [Ger.]	Augsburg		190					
1514	Lul, Ramòn	De secretis naturae	Venice						857	W
1514	Peurbach	Tabulae eclypsium	Vienna	84						W
1514	Pomponazzi	De intensione et remissione formarum	Bologna					790		

Earliest Printing	Author and Title	Place	Categories and Numbers					
			I	II	III	IV	V	VI
1514	Regiomontanus	De compositione . . . meteoroscopii	Nuremberg						880	W
1514	"	Tabula primi mobilis	Vienna	105						W
1514	Stöffler	Tabulae astronomicae	Tübingen	114					
1514	Vigo	Practica copiosa in arte chirurgica	Rome			548			
1514	Werner	De quatuor terrarum orbis in plano figurationibus	Nuremberg		252				W
[n.a. 1515]	Champier	Liber de omnibus generibus febrium	[Lyon]			341			W
[n.a. 1515]	"	Practica nova in medicina	[Lyon]			341			W
1515/16	Galen	De anatomia parva	Pavia				644:1		W
"	"	De anatomia vivorum	"				644:2		W
"	"	De compagine membrorum, sive De natura humana	"				644:12		W
"	"	De natura et ordine cuiuslibet corporis	"				644:11		W
"	"	De pulsuum usu	"				644:17		W
"	"	De subfiguratione empirica	"			377:35			W
"	"	De urinae significatione	"			377:36			W
1515	Jean de Meurs	Arithmetica communis ex . . . Boetij Arithmetice	Vienna		183				W
1515	Joannes de Gmunden	Tractatus de minucijs phisicis	Vienna		184				W

				I	II	III	IV	V	VI
[1515]	Köbel	Ein neu geordnetes Visierbuch [Ger.]	Oppenheim		189				
1515	Ptolemy	Syntaxis mathematika (Almagest)	Venice	97	215				
1515	Tagliente, jt. au.	Opera . . . de mercatia [Ital.]	Venice		240				C
1516	Barbaro	In Dioscoridem corollariorum libri V	Venice			294	593		
1516	Champier	Symphonia Platonis cum Aristotele	Paris			343n			
1516	Lockert, ed.	Quaestiones et decisiones physicales insignium virorum . . .	Paris					772	
1516	Peurbach	De quadrato geometrico	Nuremberg					881n	W
1516	Ptolemy	Inerrantium stellarum significationes	Venice	94					W
1517	Bonini	Lucidario darithmetica	Florence		150				
1517	Celaya	Expositio in octo libros Phisicorum Aristotelis	Paris					746	
1517/18	Feliciano	Libro de abaco [Ital.]	Venice		166				
1517	Gersdorff	Buch der Wundarznei [Ger.]	Strasbourg			387			
1517	Vigo	Practica in professione chirurgica	Rome			549			
1518	Berengario	Tractatus de fractura calve . . .	Bologna		311		600		

357

Earliest Printing	Author and Title		Place	Categories and Numbers						
				I	II	III	IV	V	VI	
1518	Campano da Novara	Tractatus de sphaera	Venice	39						W
1518	Fries	Spiegel der Artzny [Ger.]	Strasbourg				638			
1518	Panteo	Ars transmutationis metallicae	Venice						866	
1518	Ptolemy	De speculis	Venice		214					W
1518	Recept [Ger.]	....	Augsburg			492				
1518	Schmaus	Lucubratiuncula de morbo gallico...	Augsburg			519				
1518	Schreiber	Ein neues künstliches Buch [Ger.]	[Nuremberg]		233					
1518	Stöffler	Calendarium Romanum, 1518–1579	Oppenheim	112						
1518	Thābit ibn Qurra	De figura sectore	Venice	117	242					W
1518	Theodosios of Bithynia	Sphaera	Venice		243					W
1519	Abū al-Kāsim (Abulcasis)	Liber theoriae...	Augsburg			257				
1519	Fernández de Enciso	Suma...del arte del marear	Sevilla						837	
1519	Nicolas, Gaspar	Tratado da practica darismetyca	[Lisbon]		197					
1519	Ulrich von Hutten	De guaiaci medicina...	Mainz			540				
1520	Achillini	In Mundini anatomiam	Bologna				559			
1520	Alexander of Aphrodisias	Super nonnullis Physicis...	Basel					726		

				I	II	III	IV	V	VI
1520	François de Meyronnes	Scripta in quatuor libros Sententiarum	Venice	58					
1520	Köbel	Mit der Kryden . . . [Ger.]	Oppenheim		191				
[n.a. 1520]	Pierre de Maricourt (Petrus Peregrinus)	De virtute magnetis	Rome					787	871
1520	Roche, Estienne de la	Larithmetique . . . de la regele de la chose [Fr.]	Lyon		224				
[c. 1521]	Apianus	Isagoge in typum cosmographicum	Landshut	22					
1521	Berengario	Commentaria cum . . . additionibus super anatomia Mundini	Bologna			310	598		
1521	Ciruelo	Apotelesmata astrologiae Christianae	Alcalá	41					W
1521	Ghaligai	Summa de arithmetica [Ital.]	Florence		174				
1521	Machiavelli	Libro della arte della guerra [Ital.]	Florence						858
1521	Manardi	Epistolae medicinales	Ferrara			446			
1521	Ponzetti	Libellus de venenis	Rome			489			
1521	Schöner	Aequatorii astronomici . . . canones	Bamberg	110n					
1521	Ventallol	Practica mercantivol [Sp.]	Lyon	247					
[1522]	Apianus	Declaratio . . . typi cosmographici	Regensburg	20					

Earliest Printing	Author and Title	Place	Categories and Numbers					
			I	II	III	IV	V	VI
1522	Berengario	Isagogae breves in anatomiam . . .	Bologna				599		
1522	Galen	De musculorum motu	London				644:10		W
1522	"	Quos quibus et quando purgare oporteat	London			377:31			W
1522	Herbolario [Ital.]	. . . . . .	Venice						
1522	Riese	Rechnung auff der Linien . . . [Ger.]	Erfurt		222	403			
1522	Tunstall	De arte supputandi	London		245				
1522	Werner	Super vigintiduobus elementis conicis	Nuremberg		251				
1523	Abiosi	Vaticinium [for 1523]	Naples						803
1523	Anatomia porci	. . . . . .	Lyon				569		
[1523]	Fitzherbert	Boke of husbandry	London				637		
1524	Apianus	Cosmographicus liber	Landshut	136					
1524	Probierbüchlein [Ger.]	. . . . . .	Magdeburg						876
1525	Banckes	Herball	London			292			
1525	Brissot	Apologetica disceptatio . . .	Paris			319			
[1525?]	Champier	Le myrouel des papothiquaires [Fr.]	Lyon			339			W
[1525?]	"	Les lunectes des cirurgiens & barbiers [Fr.]	Lyon			339			W

				I	II	III	IV	V	VI	
1525	Dürer	Vnderweyssung der Messung mit dem Zirckel . . . [Ger.]	[Nuremberg]		161					
1525	Galen	Opera [Grk.]	Venice			374	641			C
1525	Hippocrates	Opera	Rome			406	657			C
1525	Pomponazzi	De reactione	Venice					791		W
1525	Riese	Rechnung auff der Linihen [Ger.]	Erfurt		223					
1525	Rudolff	Rechnung durch die Kunstreichen regeln Algebre [Ger.]	Strasbourg		226					
1526	Cellanus	In aequatorem planetarum	Paris						831	
1526/27	Feliciano	Libro di arithmetica et geometria . . . [Ital.]	Venice		167					
1526	Fernández de Oviedo y Valdés	Natural hystoria delas Indias	Toledo				634			
1526	Galen	De arteriarum . . . dissectione	Paris				644:4			W
1526	"	De nervorum dissectione	Paris				644:13			W
1526	"	Oratio suasoria ad artes	Basel, Paris			377:21				W
1526	"	Quod optimus medicus sit . . .	Basel, Paris			377:29				W
1526	Hippocrates	Opera [Grk.]	Venice			405	656			C
[1526]	"	De atrae bilis agitatione, I	Paris			409				W
1526	"	De natura muliebri	Paris				661			W

Earliest Printing	Author and Title	Place	Categories and Numbers						
			I	II	III	IV	V	VI	
1526	Hippocrates	De sterilibus	Paris				662			W
1526	Rudolff	Die künstliche Rechnung mit der Ziffer [Ger.]	Vienna		227					
1526	Ulstadt	De secretis naturae	Strasbourg			544				
1527	Apianus	Eyn Newe... Vnderweysung aller Kauffmanns Rechnung [Ger.]	Ingolstadt		137					
1527	Dürer	Etliche Vnderricht zu Befestigung der Stett... [Ger.]	Nuremberg						835	
1527	Glareanus	De geographia	Basel		175					
1528	Aristotle	De mineralibus	Lyon				578			W
1528	"	De signis aquarum, ventorum, & tempestatum	Lyon				585			W
[1528?]	Champier	Symphonia Galeni ad Hippocratem...	[Lyon?]			343				W
1528	Dürer	Vier Bücher von menschlicher Proportion [Ger.]	Nuremberg				622			W
1528	Fernel	Cosmotheoria	Paris		168					
1528	Galen	Definitiones medicae	Paris			377:7				
1528	"	De plenitudine	[Paris]			377:23				
1528	"	De propriorum animi cuiusque affectuum dignotione...	Paris			377:26				W

				I	II	III	IV	V	VI	
1528	Galen	Quaestiones in Hippocratis . . . De urinis	Strasbourg			377:28				W
1528	"	De usu partium corporis humani	Paris				644:20			
1528	Musa, Antonius, *spurious*	De herba betonica	Basel			459				W
1528	Oreibasios	De victus ratione	Basel			465				W
1528	Paulos of Aigina	Opera [*Grk.*]	Venice			472				C
1528	Ringelberg	Institutiones astronomicae	Basel		107					
1528	Soranos	In artem medendi isagoge	Basel			527				W
1528	Thorer, Alban, *ed.*	Collectio	Basel			535				C
1529	Apianus	Cosmographicus liber	Antwerp						810	
1529	*Buchsenmeisterei* [*Ger.*]	. . . . . .	Augsburg						830	
1529	Cordus, Euricius	Ein Regiment: . . . Der Englisch schweis genant . . . [*Ger.*]	Marburg			348				
1529	Galen	De anatomicis administrationibus	Bologna				644:3			W
1529	"	In Hippocratis . . . de victus ratione privatorum	Paris			377:16				W
1529	"	De sanguisugis et scarificatione	Paris			377:34				W
[*c.* 1529–30]	"	De urinis [*Grk.*]	Paris			377:37*n*				W
1529	Oreibasios	Europista	Basel			463				
1529	Paracelsus	Vom Holz guaiaco . . . [*Ger.*]	Nuremberg			468				

Earliest Printing	Author	Title	Place	I	II	III	IV	V	VI	
						Categories and Numbers				
1529	Psellus	De victus ratione	Basel			490				W
1529	Soranos	Tardarum passionum libri V	Basel			528				
1529	Tory	Champ fleury	Paris						896	
1529	Vögelin	Elementale geometricum . . .	Strasbourg		248					
1530	Agricola	Bermannus	Basel				562			W
1530	Antonius Cartaginensis	Libellus de fascinatione	Alcalà			268				W
1530	"	Liber de peste . . .	Alcalà			268				W
1530	_Artzney Büchlein_ [Ger.]	. . . . . .	Leipzig			281				
1530–36	Brunfels	Herbarum vivae eicones	Strasbourg				606			W
1530	Constantinos VII	Hippiatrici scriptores	Paris			346				
1530	Fracastoro	Syphilis	Verona			369				
1530	Fuchs	Errata recentiorum medicorum	Hagenau				639			
1530	Galen	De affectus renum dignotione et medicatione	Mainz			377:1				
1530	"	De compositione medicamentorum per genera	Paris			377:4				
1530(?)	"	De remediis facile parabilibus I [_Grk._]	Paris			374n				
1530	Gemma	De principiis . . . cosmographiae	Antwerp	61	173				845	

364

				I	II	III	IV	V	VI	W
1530	Le Fournier	La decoration . . . et aornement des dames [Fr.]	Paris			439				
1530	Panteo	Voarchadumia contra alchimiam	Venice						867	
[c. 1530]	Perlach	Ephemerides . . . M.D.xxxi	[Vienna]	83						
1530	Rudolff	Exempel Büchlin [Ger.]	Augsburg		228					
1531	Al-Bitrūjī	Alpetragii arabi planetarum theorica . . .	Venice	12						W
1531	Al-Kindī	De medicinarum compositarum gradibus . . .	Strasbourg			266		727		
1531	Apianus	Cosmographia introductio	Ingolstadt		135					
1531	Fuchs	Annotationes aliquot herbarum et simplicium a medicis . . .	Strasbourg			370				W
1531	"	Compendiaria . . . in medendi artem	Hagenau			371				W
[1531]	Galen	In Hippocratis epidemiarum lib. I	Paris			377:9				W
[1531]	"	In Hippocratis librum de natura humana	Paris			377:14	644:7			W
1531	"	De libris propriis	Basel			377:18				W
1531	"	De ordine librorum suorum	Basel			377:22				W
1531	"	Pro puero epileptico consilium	Basel			377:24				W
[1531]	Paracelsus	[A]usslegung des Commeten [Ger.]	[Zurich]	82						

Earliest Printing	Author and Title	Place	I	II	III	IV	V	VI	
						Categories and Numbers			
1532	Apianus	Quadrans astronomicus	Ingolstadt						814	
1532	Champier	Castigationes seu emendationes pharmacopolarum…	Lyon			337				
1532	Chaucer	Tretis of the astrolabie	London						832	W
1532	Fine	Protomathesis	Paris						838	
1532	Galen	De praesagatione ex pulsibus	Paris				644:15			W
1532	"	De pulsibus dignoscendis	Paris				644:16			W
1532	Novus orbis regionum	……	Basel						865	C
1532	Paulos of Aigina	Opera	Paris			473				C
1532	"	Opera	Basel			473n				
1532	Stahel und Eysen … zu machen [Ger.]	……	Mainz						891	
1532	Stifel	Ein Rechenbüchlein [Ger.]	Wittenberg		238					
1532	Theodorus Priscianus	Rerum medicarum libri IV	Strasbourg			532				
1533	Agricola	De mensuris et ponderibus	Paris					721		
1533	Apianus	Horoscopion … dignoscendis horis	Ingolstadt						811	
1533	"	Instrument Buch … new beschriben [Ger.]	Ingolstadt						812	
1533	"	Introductio geographica	Ingolstadt		138				813	W
1533	Champier	Hortus gallicus	Lyon			338				
1533	Galen	De antidotis	Paris			377:2				W

				I	II	III	IV	V	VI	
1533	Galen	De ptisana	Basel			377:27				W
1533	"	De remediis facile parabilibus I	Antwerp, Paris			377:32				W
1533	Gemma	Libellus de locorum describendorum ratione	Antwerp		172				844	W
1533	Hildegard of Bingen, *Saint*	Physica Hildegardis	Strasbourg			404	655			W
1533	Jordanus de Nemore	De ponderibus propositiones . . .	Nuremberg					769		W
1533	Nicolaus de Cusa	De quadratura circuli	Nuremberg		218n					W
1533	Oreibasios	Commentaria in Aphorismos Hippocratis	Paris			462				W
1533	"	De simplicibus	Strasbourg			464				W
1533	Paulos of Aigina	De chirurgia	Basel			474				W
1533	*Periplus* [*Grk.*]	....	Basel						870	W
1533	Proclos	In primum Euclidis . . . librum [*Grk.*]	Basel		210					W
1533	Regiomontanus	De triangulis omnimodis	Nuremberg		218					W
1533	Riese	Ein gerechent Büchlein [*Ger.*]	Leipzig		220					
1533	Soranos	Celerum passionum libri III	Paris			526				W
1533	Theodorus Priscianus	Diaeta	Strasbourg			531				W
1534	Aëtius	Opera [*Grk.*]	Venice			260				C
1534	Al-Zarqālī (Arzachel)	Canones in tabulas tholetanas	Nuremberg	17						W
1534	"	Regule super tabulas astronomie	Nuremberg	17						W

Earliest Printing	Author	Title	Place	I	II	III	IV	V	VI	
						Categories and Numbers				
1534	Apianus	Instrumentum primi mobilis	Nuremberg	21						W
[1534]	Cordus, Euricius	Botanologicon	[Cologne]			347				
1534	Fine	Quadrans astrolabicus	Paris						839	
1534	Galen	In Hippocratis Epidemiarum lib. I, III	Paris			377:10				W
1534	,,	De Hippocratis et Platonis decretis	Paris			377:8				
1534	Jābir ibn Aflah	De astronomia libri IX in quibus Ptolemaeum . . . . emendavit	Nuremberg	68	181					W
1534	Sfortunati	Libro di arithmetica [Ital.]	Venice		234					W
1534	,,	Nuovo lume [Ital.]	Venice		234					W
1535	Estienne, Ch.	De re hortensi libellus	Paris				629			
1535	Faleiro	Tratado del esphera y . . . del marear	Sevilla					752	836	
1535	Galen	De foetuum formatione	Basel				644:5			W
1535	,,	In Hippocratis praedictiones lib. I	Paris			377:15				
1535	,,	De ossibus ad tyrones	Lyon, Paris, Rome				644:14			
1535	,,	Prognostica de decubitu infirmorum	Venice			377:25				W
[1535]	,,	De urinis	Venice			377:37				W
1535	Mariani	Tariffa perpetua [Ital.]	Venice		195					W

	Author	Title	Place	I	II	III	IV	V	VI
[1535]	Paracelsus	Vonn den Bad Pfeffers... [Ger.]	[Zurich]			469			
1535	Pietro da Tossignano	De regimine sanitatis	Paris			483			
1535	Pol, Nicolaus	De cura morbi gallici...	[Venice]			488			
1535	Witelo	Perspectiva	Nuremberg		254				
1536	Amico	De motibus corporum coelestium... sine excentricis & epicyclis	Venice	18					
1536	Berossos, *spurious*	Hemicyclium	[Basel]					825	W
1536	Brasavola	Examen... simplicium medicamentorum	Rome			317			
1536	Cardano	De malo recentiorum medicorum... usu	Venice			328			W
1536	,,	De simplicium medicinarum noxa	Venice			328			W
1536	Dryander	Anatomia capitis humani	Marburg				619		
1536	Estienne, Ch.	De latinis et graecis nominibus arborum...	Paris				627		
1536		Seminarium	Paris				630		
1536	Galen	Utrum sanguis in arteriis... contineatur	Paris				644:21		W
[1536]	,,	De venae sectione adversus Erasistrataeos	Basel, Paris				644:23		W
[1536]	,,	De venae sectione adversus Erasistratum	Basel, Paris				644:24		W

Earliest Printing	Author and Title	Place	Categories and Numbers					
			I	II	III	IV	V	VI
1536	Günther	Institutionum anatomicarum secundum Galeni sententiam.... libri IV	Basel, Paris				649		
1536	Massa	Liber de morbo gallico	Venice			449			
1536	"	Liber introductorius anatomiae	Venice				676		
1536	Paracelsus	Der grossenn Wundartzney [Ger.]	Augsburg, Ulm			467			868
1536	Regiomontanus	De aequationibus XII domorum coeli	Nuremberg	110					W
1536	Rodriguez de Castello Branco	Index Dioscoridis	Antwerp			506	692		
1536	Ruelle	De natura stirpium	Paris						
1536	Schöner	Tabulae astronomicae	Nuremberg	110			693		W
1536	Ziegler	Sphaerae atque astrorum coelestium ratio. . . [Grk. & Lat.]	Basel	124					W
1537	Al-Battānī	De motu stellarum . . .	Nuremberg	10	126				W
1537	Apollōnios of Perga	Opera	Venice		139				C
1537	Dryander (Eichmann)	Anatomiae hoc est corporis humani dissectionis pars prior	Marburg				621		W
1537	"	Ein new Artznei. . . . Büchlein [Ger.]	Marburg			356			

				I	II	III	IV	V	VI	
1537	Estienne, Ch.	Vinetum	Paris				632			W
1537	Euclid	De ponderoso et levi	Basel					750		W
1537	Hippocrates	De purgatoriis medicamentis libellus	Venice			419				W
1537	An introduction for to lerne to recken	......	St. Albans		179					
1537	Nunes	Tratado em defensam da carta de marear [Port.]	Lisbon						864	W
1537	"	Tratado sobre certas duvidas da navegação [Port.]	Lisbon						864	W
1537	Serlio	Regole generali di architetura [Ital.]	Venice						890	
1537	Servetus	Syruporum universa ratio . . .	Paris				696			W
1537	"	Vera purgandi methodus	Paris				696			W
1537	Tartaglia	Nuovo scienza . . . per . . . matematico bombardiero [Ital.]	Venice					795	894	W
1537	Van der Hoecke	Een sonderlinghe boeck in . . . Arithmetica	Antwerp		246					
1537	Zerbis	Anatomia infantis . . .	Marburg				715			W
1538	Estienne, Ch.	Arbustum. Fonticulus . . .	Paris				625			
1538	"	Sylva. Frutetum . . .	Paris				631			
1538	Fracastoro	De causis criticorum dierum	Venice			367				W
1538	"	Homocentrica	Venice	57						W

| | | | Categories and Numbers | | | | | | |
Earliest Printing	Author and Title	Place	I	II	III	IV	V	VI	
1538	Galen	Utrum medicinae sit vel gymnastices hygiene	Venice			377:38				W
1538	„	Vocum obsoletarum Hippocratis explanatio	Basel			377:39				W
1538	Nicomachos	Arithmeticae libri duo [Grk.]	Paris		199					
[1538]	Servetus	Apologetica disceptatio pro astrologia	[Paris]	111						
1538	Theōn of Alexandria	In . . . Ptolemaei magnam constructionem . . . [Grk.]	Basel	118						
1538	Turner	De re herbaria novus	London				705			
1538	Vesalius	Anatomiae tabulae sex	Venice				708			
1539	Bock	New Kreutterbuch [Ger.]	Strasbourg				604			
1539	Cardano	Practica arithmetice	Milan		156					
1539	Dubois (Sylvius)	Methodus sex librorum Galeni . . .	Paris			358				
1539	Fuchs	De medendis singularum humani corporis partium . . .	Basel			373				
1539	Schöner	Opusculum astrologicum	Nuremberg	109						
1540	Apianus	Astronomicum Caesareum	Ingolstadt	19					809	
1540	Biringuccio	De la Pirotechnia	Venice						827	
1540	Galen	Utrum sit animal id quod utero contineatur	Lisbon				644:22			W

372

Date	Author	Title	Place	I	II	III	IV	V	VI
1540	Gaurico	Tractatus astrologiae iudiciariae....	Nuremberg	59					
1540	Gemma	Arithmeticae practicae methodus	Antwerp		171				
1540	Joannes de Sacro Bosco	De anni ratione....	Wittenberg	69					W
1540	Rheticus	Narratio prima	Danzig	106					
1540	Roseto	Dell' arte de' tentori [*Ital.*]	Venice						886
1541	Bacon	Speculum alchemiae	Nuremberg						820
1541	Dryander, *rev.*	Anatomia Mundini	Marburg				620		
1541/42	Galen	Contra ea quae e Juliano in Hippocratis Aphorismos dicta sunt	Venice			377:5			W
1541/42	,,	In Hippocratis .... De articulis	Venice				644:6		W
1541/42	,,	In Hippocratis Epidemiarum lib. VI	Venice			377:11			W
1541/42	,,	In Hippocratis .... De fracturis	Venice			377:12			W
1541/42	,,	In Hippocratis .... De medica officina	Venice			377:13			W
1541	,,	De instrumento odoratus	Venice			377:17	644:8		W
1541/42	,,	De melancholia ex Galeno Rufo	Venice			377:19			W
1541/42	,,	Quod qualitates incorporeae sint	Venice			377:30	644:18		W

Earliest Printing	Author and Title	Place	Categories and Numbers					
			I	II	III	IV	V	VI
1541/42	Galen	De remediis facile parabilibus III	Venice			377:33			W
1541	"	De septimestri partu	Venice				644:19		W
1541	Gesner	Historia plantarum . . .	Venice, Basel, Paris				647		W
1541	Peurbach	Super propositiones Ptolemaei de sinibus et chordis	Nuremberg		208				W
1542	Abū Ali al-Hasan (Alhazen)	De crepusculis . . .	Lisbon					717	W
1542	Bacon, Roger	De mirabile potestate artis et naturae ubi de philosophorum lapide . . . libellus	Paris				591		
1542	Copernicus	De lateribus et angulis triangulorum	Wittenberg			160			
1542	Dubois (Sylvius)	De medicamentorum simplicium delectu	Paris			357			
[1542]	Ein erschrockenliche newe Zeyttung . . . [Ger.]	. . . . . .	[Sine nota]						
1542	Fernel	De naturali parte medicinae	Paris				636		
1542	Fine	De mundi sphaera . . .	Paris		169				
1542	Fuchs	De historia stirpium . . .	Basel			372	640		
1542	Gesner	Apparatus et delectus simplicium medicamentorum	Lyon			389n			W

Year	Author	Title	City	I	II	III	IV	V	VI	
1542	Gesner	Catalogus plantarum nomina latine, graece ... proponens	Zurich				646			
[1542]	*Heuy newes of an horryble erthquake* ...	....	London				624			
1542	Nunes	De crepusculis	Lisbon					781		
1542	Recorde	The grounde of artes ... arithmetike	London		216				863	W
1542	Sagredo	Medidas d'l romanos [*Sp.*]	Lisbon						887	
1543	Archimedes	Opera	Venice		141			732		C
[1543]	Canano	Musculorum humani corporis picturata dissectio	[Ferrara]				608			
1543	Copernicus	De revolutionibus orbium coelestium	Nuremberg	47						
1543	Estienne, Ch.	Pratum. Lacus. Arundinetum	Paris				628			
1543	Gesner	Enumeratio medica- mentorum purgantium	Basel			389				
1543	Maurolico	Cosmographia	Venice	79						
1543	Vesalius	De humani corporis fabrica	Basel				710			
1543	"	De humani corporis fabrica librorum epitome	Basel				711			
1544	Archimedes	Opera [*Grk. & Lat.*]	Basel		140			731		C
1544	Biondo	Compendiosa de medicamentis	Rome			314				

Earliest Printing	Author and Title	Place	Categories and Numbers						
			I	II	III	IV	V	VI	
1544	Biondo	Tabulae annuae de anticipatione stellarum fixarum . . .	Rome	30						
1544	Caius	De medendi methodo . . . ex Cl. Galeni . . . sententia	Basel			323				W
1544	Calcagnini	Quod caelum stet, terra moveatur . . .	Basel	34						W
1544	Eutocios	In eosdem Archimedis libros . . . [Grk.]	Basel		165			751		W
1544	Guidi	Chirurgia	Paris			397				
1544	Mattioli	Di . . . Dioscoride . . . : Della historia et materia medicinale [Lat.-Ital.]	Venice			450	677			
1544	Regiomontanus	Scripta de torqueto, astrolabio armillari . . .	Nuremberg						881	W
1544	Stifel	Arithmetica integra	Nuremberg		236					
1544	Trotula	Trotulae curandarum aegritudinum muliebrium ante . . . partum, liber I	Strasbourg			539				W
1544	Turner	Avium praecipuarum . . . historia	Cologne				704			
1545	Abū Alī al-Hasan [Alhazen]	De speculis comburentibus	Louvain		125					W
1545	Ascham	. . . The schole of shootynge	London						818	
1545	Cardano	Artis magnae . . . liber I	Nuremberg		155					

				I	II	III	IV	V	VI
1545	Cardano	Contradicentium medicorum liber	Venice			327			
1545	Estienne, Ch.	De dissectione partium corporis humani	Paris				626		
1545	Fernel	De vacuandi ratione	Paris			362			
1545	Geminus	Compendiosa totius anatomiae delineatio	London				645		
1545	Paré	La methode de traicter les playes faictes par hacquebutes . . . [Fr.]	Paris			471			
1545	Pedro de Medina	Arte de navegar [Sp.]	Valladolid						869
1545	Scheubel	De numeris . . . computationum	Leipzig		232				
1545	Stifel	Deutsche Arithmetica . . . [Ger.]	Nuremberg		237				
1546	Agricola	De natura eorum quae effluunt ex terra	Basel	W			563		
1546	,,	De natura fossilium	Basel	W			564		
1546	,,	De ortu et causis subterraneorum	Basel	W			565		
1546	,,	De veteribus et novis metallis	Basel	W					805
1546	Biondo	De ventis et navigatione libellus . . .	Venice						826

Earliest Printing	Author and Title	Place	Categories and Numbers					
			I	II	III	IV	V	VI
1546	Brasavola	In libros de ratione victus in morbis acutis Hippocratis & Galeni	Venice			318			
1546	Cordus, Valerius	Dispensatorium pharmacopolarum	Nuremberg			349			
1546	Fracastoro	De contagione . . .	Venice			368			W
1546	Mercator	De ratione magnetis circa navigationem	Louvain						860
[1546]	Monte	Typus . . . Artis parvae Galeni	Venice			456			
1546	Stifel	Rechenbuch von der Welschen . . . Practick [Ger.]	Nuremberg		239				
1546	Tartaglia	Quesiti e inventioni diverse [Ital.]	Venice		241			796	895
1546	Vesalius	Epistola, rationem modumque propinandi radicis chynae . . .	Basel			547	709		
1547	Galen	Brevis denotatio dogmatum Hippocratis	Lyon			377:3			W
1547	Pastrengo	De originibus rerum libellus	Venice						868a
1547 (?)	Piccolomini	In mechanicas quaestiones Aristotelis paraphrasis . . .	Rome					786	W
1548	Fernel	De abditis rerum causis	Paris				635		

Date	Author	Title	Place	I	II	III	IV	V	VI
1548	Stöffler	Ephimeridum reliquiae … ad … 1556	[Tübingen]	113					
1549	Affaitatus	Physicae ac astronomiae considerationes	Venice					720	
1549	Agricola	De animantibus subterraneis	Basel				561		
1549	Melanchthon	Initia doctrinae physicae	Wittenberg	80					
1549	Paracelsus	Wundt vnnd Leibartznei … [Ger.]	Frankfort-a-M.			470			
1549	Scheubel	Compendium arithmeticae	Basel		231				
1550–51	Brasavola	Index … in omnes Galeni libros	Venice			318n			C
1550	Cardano	De subtilitate rerum	Paris			329	609	745	
1550	Galen	De musculorum dissectione	Lyon				644:9		W
1550	,,	De vocalium instrumentorum dissectione	Lyon				644:25		W
1550 (?)	Menelaos	Sphaericorum libri III	Messina		196				
1550	Riese	Rechenung … auff den Linihen und Feder [Ger.]	Leipzig		221				
1550	Rojas Sarmiento	Commentariorum in astrolabium … libri VI	Paris		225			885	W
1550	Scheubel	Algebrae porro regulae	Basel		230				W

INDEX

Authors and anonymous titles, as cited in the main entries; variant author-forms; subject-headings. [For special sections listing Commentators, Editors, and Translators, *see* PART II, Section A.]

In general, data given in the notes is not included. A name or title in italics and enclosed in parentheses indicates the author of a work illustrated, revised, *etc.* A name in square brackets and following an entry indicates a variant name-form. A dash included in an entry refers to the preceding author or title. In instances where an anonymous title begins with the Latin preposition "De," it is disregarded in the alphabetizing. Arabic names are listed without accent-mark.

Arabic numerals refer to numbered entries in the main text. An asterisk (*) accompanying a number in the index indicates the subject-analysis which precedes the entry thus designated. Roman numerals indicate the six categories to which the main text is devoted, as—I Astronomy. II Mathematics. III Medicine. IV Natural Science. V Physics. VI Technology. Dashes are used among the references in order to make the categories distinct from one another.

Index

Index

Fifteen hundred copies of this book have been completed in May, 1970. The text has been composed in English Monotype Bembo and printed on Curtis Colophon Text by Clarke & Way at the Thistle Press in New York. Typography and design by Bert Clarke.